PRINTED MAPS OF
SUSSEX
1575–1900

SUSSEX RECORD SOCIETY
VOLUMES ISSUED BY THE SOCIETY

Volumes marked with an asterisk can be obtained from the Hon. Secretary, Sussex
    Record Society, Barbican House, Lewes, East Sussex BN7 1YE

Most of these Volumes have been photographed in Microfiche by Messrs. Chadwyck-
Healey Ltd., 20 Newmarket Road, Cambridge, to whom enquiries should be made.

Map of Sussex by John Norden, 1595 (541 mm × 285 mm), catalogue no. 3.

PRINTED MAPS OF
SUSSEX
1575–1900

BY
DAVID KINGSLEY

WITH INTRODUCTION
BY
HELEN WALLIS

SUSSEX RECORD SOCIETY
VOLUME 72

Issued to Members of the Society for the years
1980–1981

Published in 1982
by
Sussex Record Society
Barbican House, Lewes
BN7 1YE

© Sussex Record Society

ISBN 0 85445 031 9

Produced by Alan Sutton Publishing Limited
17a Brunswick Road, Gloucester

CONTENTS

INTRODUCTION

'Oh how precious a Iewell is this, it may rightly be called a Cosmographicall Glasse, in which we may beholde the diuersitie of countries: natures of people, & innumerable formes of Beastes, Foules, Fishes, Trees, Frutes, Stremes, & Meatalles.' Such is the description of the map of England, or of any other particular region, given by William Cuningham, physician of Norwich, in his book on the principles of cosmography, geography and hydrography, published in 1559. He called the book *The Cosmographical Glasse,* and claimed that he was the first 'that euer in oure tongue haue written of this argument'. For a definition of geography he translated from the Greek Ptolemy's words 'Geographie is the imitation, and discription of the face, and picture of th' earth, with her partes knowen, and of such things as are to it connected and ioyned.' Chorography showed the parts of the earth: 'as if a painter shuld set forth the eye, or eare of a man, and not the whole body, so . . . Chorographie consisteth rather in describyng the qualitie and figure, then the bignes, and quantitie of any thinge.'[1]

Thirty years earlier the occult philosopher Henricus Cornelius Agrippa of Nettesheim had analysed the speculative cosmology of Renaissance Europe. In his treatise *De incertitudine et vanitate scientiarum,* 1530 (published in an English translation in 1569), he emphasised the imitative features of cosmography and map-making. One section dealt with 'Cosimetria', the measure of the world. Geography, he wrote, 'with a certaine imitation of paintinge, dothe according to the rules of Geometrie, and the Arte Perspectiue, expresse the whole world in a Globe, or plaine Table. Depaintinge all the worlde in a little roume'. He explained chorography in this way: that some 'searching out certaine particular places doth depainte them with a more perfecte, and as it were a full finished similitude.'[2]

Agrippa's chapter 'Of the Measure of the Worlde' is preceded by chapters on 'Geometrie', 'the Arte Opticke, or Perspectiue', 'Paintinge', 'the Arte of Grauing, and Moulding', and 'the Arte of seeing Glasses'. This was a logical sequence, for a heightening of visual awareness was one aspect of the intellectual re-awakening in the Renaissance. Optical instruments such as perspective glasses which exaggerated images and colours were devised to instruct and amuse the curious. The metaphor for a map as a mirror shows the connection between the optical sciences and cartography. The titles of maps and atlases were 'The Mariner's Mirror', 'Imago Mundi', 'Theatrum Orbis Terrarum', and 'Speculum Britanniae'.[3] Such terms were used before, and for some years after, 1595, when the name 'atlas' was first given to a specially designed collection

---

1   William Cuningham *The cosmographical glasse,* London, 1559, p. 120; sig A.vi^v; pp. 6, 7.
2   Henricus Cornelius Agrippa *Splendidæ nobilitatis viri . . . H.C. Agrippæ . . . de incertitudine & vanitate scientiarum & artium, atque excellentia verbi Dei, declamatio,* Antwerp, 1530.
    Quoted from the first English edition: James Sanford *Henrie Cornelius Agrippa, of the Vanitie and vncertaintie of Artes and Sciences, Englished by Ja. San. Gent.,* London, 1569, fol. 38^r.
3   Helen Wallis 'Maps as a medium of scientific communication', in *Études d'histoire de la geographie et de la cartographie,* Wroctaw, Imienia Ossolinskiek Wydawnictwo Poliskiej Akademii Nauk, 1973, pp. 251–2.

of maps. In the same way painters were exploiting the new techniques of landscape depiction. Inspired above all by Albrecht Dürer, they depicted the landscape as they saw it with their own eyes, in contrast with the stylised forms of the late Middle Ages. It is notable that of all the manuscripts of English origin in the British Museum and British Library, only three of the late 15th century show recognisable places.[4] Map-makers also adopted the new techniques of drawing and painting. The elaborate painted map-views of the English coasts and the large engraved plans of London which were being produced in the 1550s and 1560s were remarkable advances on the maps of the early 16th century.

Whereas map-making emerged as one of the new crafts of the Renaissance, surveying with its origins in ancient Egypt, Babylon and China was many centuries older. In mediaeval Europe various kinds of maps were made, but mainly as an adjunct to other activities. Maps were included as illustrations to mediaeval Bibles and chronicles. The first separate maps of Great Britain, *c* 1250, came from the pen of Matthew Paris, a monk of St. Albans, to illustrate his *Chronica Maiora* and his *Historia Anglorum*.[5] A masterpiece from the 14th century is the 'Gough' map, *c.* 1350, so called after its 18th century owner, the antiquary Richard Gough. Drawn on vellum and covering England, Wales and Scotland, the map shows towns, roads and rivers, and appears to have been made for some official purpose, connected perhaps with the Black Death (1348–49).[6]

In contrast with these regional maps, the earliest local plans which have survived are mainly functional, to aid the management of estates: plans of a water conduit from Wormley to Waltham Abbey *c.* 1220,[7] of the water works of Christ Church Priory, Canterbury, *c.* 1165[8] and of the Charterhouse of 15th century London.[9] The earliest known treatise on surveying written in English dates from the 14th century (BL Sloane MS. 213, ff. 123b–124).[10] It describes the use of the quadrant and plane-table in measuring first heights, then distances, then depths. Diagrams illustrate both instruments. Mediaeval land surveys normally give an area in terms of customary reckoning from its appearance, but occasionally it is 'by measure' (*per mensuram*). For this observation only a measuring rod on a chain would have been used. In the 15th century plans were made of monastic estates, such as that of Chertsey Abbey and its rich desmesne by the Thames, *c.* 1432.[11] A map of Thorne or Inclesmore in Yorkshire;

4 Edward Croft-Murray and Paul Hulton *Catalogue of British drawings* vol. 1. text, London, 1960, p. xxiii.
5 *Four Maps of Great Britain designed by Matthew Paris about A.D. 1250. Reproduced from three manuscripts in the British Museum and one at Corpus Christi College, Cambridge,* London 1928. Richard Vaughan *Matthew Paris*, Cambridge, 1958, pp. 235–41. **See plate 1.**
6 E.J.S. Parsons, *Map of Great Britain c. A.D. 1360, known as the Gough Map, preserved in the Bodleian Library, Oxford.* Oxford and London, 1958.
7 British Library, Harley MS. 391, ff.5ᵛ,6. See P.D.A. Harvey 'A 13th century plan from Waltham Abbey, Essex', in *Imago Mundi* vol. 22 (1968), pp. 10–12.
8 Trinity College, Cambridge, MS.R.17.1. f. 286.
9 Muniments of the Charterhouse, London.
10 *The Mapping of the British Isles 13th–19th centuries. An exhibition in the King's Library, British Museum . . . 1964. Catalogue,* p. 5 (typescript).
11 Cartulary of Chertsey Abbey, Public Record Office, E.164/25, m.222.

drawn in 1405–8 and illustrating an *inspeximus* of 14 January 1410, displays enclosures, rivers and bridges. A later copy, brilliantly coloured, depicts the townships in bird's eye view and the trees and flowers of the countryside.[12] One of the Isle of Thanet, *c.* 1414, in a chronicle of St. Augustine's Abbey, Canterbury, by Thomas Elmham, delineates the bounds of the Abbey's Manor of Minster, which followed, by a strange tradition, the 'run of the deer'.[13]

Printed works on surveying appeared early in the 16th century. John Fitzherbert's treatise on surveying, published in 1523, was designed as a manual for the steward of a manor. It gives information 'how a lordshyp or a maner shude be surueyed & vewed, butted & bounded.'[14] The earliest general text-book in English on geometrical survey and area-measurement was that by Richard Benese entitled *The Boke sheweth the maner of measurynge of all maner of lande,* printed in Southwark probably in 1537. Since Benese was an Augustinian canon of Merton Priory, as well as Surveyor of Works to Henry VIII, the methods he describes may indicate surveying practices on monastic estates.

Advances in the mathematical and geometrical sciences in the 16th century led to more accurate surveying techniques. Geometrical methods of land-survey were introduced into Engand from the continent of Europe, and more precise instruments such as the theodolite and cross-staff were devised. The most important book on land-survey was the treatise of the Flemish geographer Gemma Frisius, *Libellus de locorum describendorum ratione,* published as an appendix to Peter Apian's *Cosmographicus Liber* in 1533. This set out a method of triangulation which enabled the surveyor to work more rapidly, by observing horizontal angles. For the first time it was possible to measure distances between two points without walking the ground between them. The surveyor could take pride in the 'true Geometricall demonstration' of the principles of his craft. Yet the new professionalism in surveying was adopted only slowly. 'The practice hereof for surueigh of lands and tenements, is but new, and scarcely established', Ralph Agas wrote in *A Preparative to platting of Landes and Tenements for Surueigh,* London, 1596, in which he explains the use of the new instruments. He refers to 'a plaine Table man (mary he was a plumber, and had learned from a Painter)' and to 'an ancient country measurer . . . highly regarded among his neighbours'.[15] This indicates the varied background of the practitioners.

Surveying catered for the interests of a growing number of 'mathematicall Clients', as Agas called them. These included great landowners such as the Earls of Northumberland (who employed Christopher Saxton amongst others) and the Cecils (who employed John Norden). John Norden's book *The Surveyors Dialogue* (1607) explained the advantages of surveying. He described the work as 'Very profitable for

---

12 The plans belong to the Duchy of Lancaster (D.L.42/12, f. 29^v–30^r, and D.L.31/61) See *Maps and Plans in the Public Record Office 1. British Isles c. 1410–1860,* London, 1967, p. 535, nos. 3639, 3640.
13 Trinity Hall, Cambridge. MS1, f.28^v. See P.D.A. Harvey *The history of topographical maps, symbols, pictures and surveys,* London, 1980, p. 98.
14 [John Fitzherbert] *Here begynneth a ryght frutefull mater: and hath to name the boke of surueying and improumentes* London, [1523], f. xxxiii^r.
15 Ralph Agas *A Preparative to platting of Landes and Tenements for Surueigh,* London, 1596, pp. 2, 7–8.

all men to peruse, that haue to do with the reuenues of Land, or the manurance, vse, or occupation thereof, both Lords and Tenants: as also . . . for such as indeuor to be seene in the faculty of surueying of Mannors, Lands, Tenements, &c.'[16]

Surveyors, of course, were not always welcome. The defiant dog which features on various estate plans and is engraved on surveying instruments was the front line of defence for the suspicious and worried farmer. 'And oftentimes you are the cause that men lose their land', the Farmer complains in Norden's *Dialogue*. Against this and other 'pretended causes why Surueyors are condemned', Norden's surveyor gives the rather doubtful assurance, 'the faulty are afraid to be seene . . . the innocent neede not feare to be looked into'.[17] In a revised third edition of the work, 1618, Norden added a sixth book, with 'a familiar conference, between a Purchacer, and a Surueyor of Lands; of the true use of both, being very needfull for all such as are to purchase Lands.' *The Surveyors Dialogue* became a standard work, and as late as 1738 was reprinted in a 'Fourth' edition.

Just as landowners were employing surveyors for the better management of their estates and to settle disputes over lands, sovereigns and princes began to commission a wide range of mapping. In Tudor England maps were considered instruments of state-craft essential for the security and control of the kingdom. Henry VIII saw the need to obtain good surveys of English coasts and ports and to this end employed foreign military engineers and hydrographers, such as the Italian Girolamo da Treviso and Jean Rotz of Dieppe. Their military and maritime surveys were made in manuscript and were kept as secret documents. Various charts of Sussex ports are preserved in the collection of the Elizabethan antiquary Sir Robert Cotton, which came to the British Museum in 1753 and is now in the British Library. An important Elizabethan survey was that by 'S[r]. Thomas Palmere knight, and M[r]. Walter Couerte esquire Deputie lieutennts of her Ma[ties]. Countie of Sussex of all the places of descente alongste the sea coaste of the said Shire' (BL Add. MS. 57494). It was undertaken probably in 1587 in expectation of invasion from Spain.

Simultaneous with these advances in surveying was the development of the map-maker's craft. As R. A. Skelton has remarked, the early printer and the early map-maker grew up together.[18] Both trades first acquired professional status in the second half of the fifteenth century. The invention of wood-cut and copper-plate engraving made it possible to provide multiple copies of maps for the expanding market. This means of making an 'exactly repeatable pictorial statement' (as W.M. Ivins has called it) was as revolutionary an invention for map-making as was printing from movable type for the history of the book.[19] It transformed the communication of visual information. For the first time scholars and men of affairs could study and compare the same maps. The first map of the British Isles seen by educated Europeans in the later years of the 15th century was *Prima Europe tabula* in the set of ten maps of Europe in

16 John Norden *The Surveyors Dialogue,* London, 1607, title page.
17 Norden, 1607, pp. 2–3, 4, 6.
18 R.A. Skelton 'The early map printer and his problems', *The Penrose Annual. A review of the graphic arts* (ed. Herbert Spencer), vol. 57, London, 1964, p. 171.
19 W.M. Ivins *Prints and visual communication*, London, 1953, p. 23–4.

Ptolemy's *Geographia,* published with printed maps from 1477 onwards. Although the shape of the country is distorted and the information given reflects Greek knowledge of the world in about A.D. 150, the significance of the publication turned on the wide distribution of the work and the fact that a citizen of London, York, Florence or Paris was seeing the same picture of these islands when he consulted his Ptolemy.

In comparison with Italy and the Netherlands, England was backward in developing a map trade in the 16th century. There was no English counterpart to the great world atlas of Abraham Ortelius, 1570, or the world chart of Gerard Mercator, 1569. The first printed map of the British Isles was by George Lily, an English exile. It was published in Rome in 1546. The first wall-map of the British Isles, 1564, was engraved and published by Gerard Mercator at Duisburg, although based on the work of a friend in England, generally assumed to have been an Englishman.

Despite this dependence on the continent, England made a significant contribution in one distinctive field, that of regional mapping, or 'chorography'. Christopher Saxton, known as the 'father of English cartography', issued in atlas form in 1579 his county maps of England and Wales. This work, often claimed (inaccurately) as the first national atlas,[20] established a long tradition in map-making; for county atlases of the British Isles remained the outstanding feature of English map production for some two hundred years. In choosing the county as the basic region for survey and publication Saxton exploited the convenience of an administrative unit and appealed to the local patriotism of the inhabitants. The counties of England and Wales with their ancient history and traditions proved admirably suited to regional mapping. When John Speed's *Theatre of the Empire of Great Britaine* (1611–12) extended the range to Scotland and Ireland, there too the county (or shire) was the appropriate unit for mapping.

Saxton's achievement in accomplishing in the short space of seven years (c. 1572–1579) the survey of the country, the engraving of the plates and the publication of the atlas has seemed the more remarkable in view of England's late start. How England came to make such a rapid advance in national mapping, and why an apparently obscure Yorkshire estate surveyor was chosen to undertake the survey are questions which until recently remained unexplained. Research has now revealed the role, previously unsuspected, of a Yorkshire cleric, John Rudd (1498–1579), prebend of Durham Cathedral.[21] Rudd was appointed a royal chaplain to Henry VIII in 1540 and also was Clerk of the Chest. In the 1550s Rudd had 'taken some payn in makinge a platt of this our Realme.' In the early 1560s he set about making further surveys to improve the map. He received royal authority in 1561 to 'travell more diligently therein for the settinge forthe thereof bothe fayer and more p[er]fecte and truer that it hath byn hitherto. Forasmuch as for the better doing hereof it shalbe necessarye that he doe travayle by his own sight to view and consid[e]re divers parts of our sayd Realme.' For this purpose Elizabeth I requested the Dean and Chapter of Durham Cathedral to

20 Saxton's atlas is preceded by the atlas of Switzerland by Johann Strumpf, 1552, and that of the hereditary lands of the Austrian Crown by Wolfgang Lazius, 1561.
21 David Marcombe 'Saxton's Apprenticeship: John Rudd, a Yorkshire Cartographer', *Yorkshire Archaeological Journal*, vol. 50, (1978), pp. 171–5.

grant Rudd his normal stipend and other fees while he was absent for two years on the survey, and this was granted. Rudd may have been the 'distinguished friend' who sent Mercator the map of the British Isles. (Laurence Nowell, cousin of the Dean of Lichfield of the same name, is also a possible candidate).[22]

Documents in the archives of Durham Cathedral show that Saxton was apprenticed to Rudd. The earliest, of 11 April 1570, records that Saxton, then aged about 26, visited Durham Cathedral to collect £8 6s. 8d. 'for th[e] use of my M[r]. Master Rudde, for his q[uar]ter stypend dewe at th[e] Annuntyac[i]on last.' Saxton may have accompanied Rudd on his travels and also may have had access to Rudd's materials for his own survey.[23] This would help to explain the speed of its completion.

In March 1576 Thomas Seckford, Master of the Court of Requests, appears in the records as Saxton's employer in the survey. There is circumstantial evidence, though no direct evidence, that Sir William Cecil, later Lord Burghley, Lord High Treasurer to Queen Elizabeth I, was also behind the project. Burghley obtained the proof sheets of Saxton's maps which he had bound into a volume with additional manuscript maps of areas of strategic and political importance. The 'Burghley-Saxton' atlas is preserved in the manuscripts of the Old Royal Library which came in 1757 to the British Museum (now BL Royal MS 18.D.III.). The maps are endorsed with notes in Burghley's hand listing justices of the peace and notable residents in each county.[24] Burghley's possession of the atlas bears out Robert Beale's comment in *A Treatise of the office of a Councellor and Principall Secretarie to her Majestie*, 1592, on the duties of a Secretary of State: 'A Secretarie must likewise have the booke of Ortelius'[s] Mapps, a booke of the Mappes of England . . . and also a good description of the Realm of Ireland . . . and if anie other plotts or mapps come to his handes, let them be kept safelie'.[25]

Saxton's atlas was widely used by the gentry as well as by officers of the state, as the Welsh topographer George Owen of Henllys remarks in his *Description of Penbrokeshire*, 1603 (BL Harl. MS 6250): 'the printed Mappes of the sheeres made & published by Mr Christopher Saxton, which Mappes are vsuall with all Noblemen and gentlemen, and daiely pervsed by them for theire better Instruction of the estate of this Realme, especiallye touchinge the quantitie, scituacion, forme and speciall places of note of all the sheeres of this Realme.'[26]

Owen's comments on the map are also interesting in showing that Saxton's contemporaries had difficulty in understanding the cartographic principle of scale. The idea of drawing a map to a uniform scale developed in Europe in the 15th century. The first local map since Roman times drawn explicitly to scale has been identified as a plan of

22 Tyacke and Huddy *Christopher Saxton and Tudor map-making*, London, 1980, pp. 9–10.
23 Tyacke and Huddy, 1980, pp. 6, 24.
24 See R.A. Skelton and John Summerson *A Description of maps and architectural drawings in the collection made by William Cecil — First Baron Burghley, now at Hatfield House*, Oxford, 1971, pp. 26–7.
25 Quoted in Conyers Read *Mr Secretary Walsingham and the policy of Queen Elizabeth*, Oxford, 1925, vol. 1, pp. 428–9.
26 Henry Owen (ed) *The Description of Penbrokeshire by George Owen of Henllys, Lord of Kemes*, London, 1892, p. 2.

Vienna copied in the mid-15th century from one of about 1422.[27] In preparing the county surveys for publication Saxton, however, did not use a single scale. For counties each on a single page, their different sizes necessitated a variety of scales. He also grouped some counties together, drawing them on a smaller scale. Unlike most of the Welsh counties Pembrokeshire has a page to itself, a fact which had certain disadvantages, as Owen explains. Writing of Saxton's maps he says 'if they be vywed onlye superficiallie, without haueinge anye other regarde, Pembrokshere seemeth to be one of the biggest and lardgest sheres of Wales, haueinge the rome and place of a whole sheete of paper allowed to it selfe, as though it were to lardge to be ioyned with an other sheere, whereas all the rest of the xii sheres of Wales are placed, 2 at the least, and some tymes foure together in the like quantitie of paper, (Glamorgan excepted) eche of them haueinge theire proper scales of x^{en} miles . . .' In order to 'vnfold the hidden error . . . as well as to cleere Mr Saxton from anye fault', Owen explained that Saxton had passed first through the upland shires, joining them into 'three seuerall Mappes', and then coming to the 'great sheeres of Carmarthen, Cardigan, Brecknock and Radnor', he was forced 'to wringe them soe neere together thrustinge on Townredd [homestead] vpon an other, that he was forced to make the scale shorter almost by halfe of that of Pembrokshere.' As a result Pembrokeshire was regarded as 'a great riche and welthie Countrey, as though the shere were greate lardge, and well peopled, which indeed is cleene contrarye.' Saxton's generous mapping turned out to be an embarrassment, for it seemed to be one cause (Owen alleged) of 'the ouer chardginge of this shere' in the rendering of services to Queen and country.

Owen's point is relevant also to Sussex which like the various Welsh counties had to share the page with its neighbours. It is grouped with Surrey, Kent and Middlesex on a single sheet covering the whole of south-east England. In the table of scales compiled by Ifor M. Evans and Heather Lawrence this map ranks as the smallest in scale (1:313,783), compared to Monmouthshire (1:146,432), the largest.[28] Many have regretted that Saxton did not give a page to each of the counties. Why he did not is unknown, but probably relates to the nature of his source material. Whatever the reason for the varying arrangements of counties, we can doubt that the converse of Owen's argument was true, and that the south-east counties received financial gain from being crowded onto a small scale map. The main result was that others set to work to improve on Saxton. By about 1596 Middlesex, Surrey and Sussex had all been separately mapped by John Norden. Kent did best of all, for *A new description of Kent* by Philip Symonson of Rochester, drawn on a scale of nearly two miles to the inch (approximately 1:120,000), has been described as 'the most accomplished specimen of English county cartography before the eighteenth century.'

Saxton completed his work of national mapping with the publication of his wall-map of England and Wales in 1583. This was a second major landmark in the history of

27 P.D.A. Harvey, London, 1980, pp. 79–80.
28 Evans and Lawrence, *Christopher Saxton, Elizabethan map-maker,* Wakefield and London, 1979, pp. 38–9. [This assessment is derived from an analysis of 425 measurements made over Saxton's series of county maps, and differs by 1% from the calculation made in the catalogue, which is based on the distance from Chichester to Rye].

English cartography. It is the earliest known wall-map engraved and printed in England. A copy hung in the Queen's Gallery at Whitehall, and another was reported by a visitor to be in Lord Burghley's house at Theobalds, Hertfordshire. Wall-maps were especially vulnerable to damage and destruction, which probably explains why only one example printed before 1600 is known today. With the publication of Saxton's atlas and wall-map England and Wales became one of the best mapped countries of Europe. The image of the country provided by Saxton also appears as a feature in the iconography of Elizabethan art. The portrait of Elizabeth I by Marcus Gheeraerts the younger, celebrating her visit in 1592 to Ditchley Park, Oxfordshire, shows the Queen standing on a map of England (after Saxton), with her feet planted in the vicinity of the house. On the map Sussex is painted with a yellow ground, displaying rivers, woods, villages and towns.

John Norden, Saxton's successor as the leading cartographer of the day, was a 40 year old attorney practising in the law courts of Middlesex when in 1588 he began his career in mapping and survey. With Saxton's folio atlas now in the libraries and offices of scholars and statesmen, Norden sought to meet the demand for regional guidebooks. His *Speculum Britanniae* (Mirror of Britain) was planned as a series of county chorographies, the descriptive text illustrated by maps. Each was to be produced as a pocket handbook, in duodecimo. The maps were intended to remedy the omissions in Saxton, by showing roads and giving more information on settlements. Major innovations included the grid reference system and the key to conventional signs, described as 'the difference of places". The first part, a description of Middlesex, was published in 1593 at Norden's own expense. Its dedication to the Queen gained for Norden a privilege to be the sole publisher of the work, and authority 'to travel through England and Wales to make more perfect descriptions, charts and maps.' The volume for Essex was completed by 1594, but lack of response from wealthy patrons prevented its publication. In 1598 Norden (again at his own expense) published *Hartfordshire,* and this was the last of the handbooks to be printed in his lifetime.

The pamphlet which Norden published in 1596 to explain his purpose and answer the comments of friends and critics provides a rare insight into the problems of county mapping. Entitled *Nordens Preparatiue to his Speculum Britanniae*, it may be considered his *pièce justificative* as a cartographer. He described himself as 'being imployed (after the most painful & prais worthie labours of M. Christopher Saxton) in the rediscription of England.'[29] In the selection of detail he explained what he could and could not do. 'As touching the conceite of some that would haue the distinction of the limits of euery parishe, I holde it not so needefull as impossible, and I thinke the most of iudgement wil affirme the same.' To critics who thought he had included too much, he replied, 'I take it the offence can not be great to obserue the most things, for the meanest may sometime have vse in the Mappe. And can the shadow of it administer greater offence in hauing place in the plot, then the thing it selfe in the field? The more things (as I take it) are obserued, the more like is the description to the thing discribed . . . And how to moderate the worke herein, and yielde euerie man

29   John Norden *Nordens Preparatiue to his Speculum Britanniae*, London, 1596, p. 1.

his desire, is a worke of greater skill then I pretend, I would gladly please the wise. And then I hit what I ayme at.'[30]

In 1594 Norden took up the more profitable enterprise of larger scale county mapping in a decorative style. His map of Sussex was made at the expense of the London merchant William Sanderson, and displays his shield, 'Opera Mundi', which commemorated Sanderson's sponsorship of Emery Molyneux's globes, 1592, the first pair of globes to be made and published in England. Since only one impression of the Sussex map is known to have survived, the issue was presumably small.

Norden's map, however, was soon to become well-known, for John Speed, tailor and antiquary, used it as his source for Sussex in *The Theatre of the Empire of Great Britaine*, 1611–12. Norden's displayed a bird's-eye plan of Chichester, which may have inspired Speed with the idea of including inset plans of towns on all his county maps. This and the other decorative features made Speed's atlas the most popular of all early atlases of the British Isles. 'I have put my sickle into other mens corn,' Speed wrote, 'the Charts for the most part traced by others . . . were the foundations of my begun pains.' He used Saxton's and Norden's maps as his major source, choosing Norden's when available in preference to Saxton's. The atlas was revised and reissued over the years until as late as *c.* 1770. Norden's Sussex thus had a long life.

From 1612 until after the Restoration of the Monarchy in 1660 little surveying was undertaken. One notable publication was Michael Drayton's *Poly-Olbion. Or a Chorographicall Description of Tracts, Riuers, Mountaines, Forests, and other Parts of this renowned Isle of Great Britaine . . . Digested in a Poem*, 1613. Physical geography and historical and antiquarian allusions were worked into a cosmographical poem, illustrated with maps. Each song featured a county, or a group of counties, with their rivers portrayed as water nymphs. In the Seventeenth Song Drayton laments the destruction of the forests for the use of the great iron industry of the Weald: 'The Authors conceit of these Forrests being nymphs of this Great *Andredfuuda*, & their complaint for loss of Woods, in *Sussex*, so decai'd, is plain enough to every reader,' he writes, referring to the great forest 'Andredsweald', which covered 'most part of Kent, Sussex, and Surrey.'[31]

'To Sea-ward, from the seat where first our Song begun,
Exhaled to the South by the ascending sunne,
Fower stately Wood Nymphs stand on the *Sussexian* ground,
Great *Andredsweld's* sometime : who, when she did abound,
In circuit and in growth, all other quite supprest:'

The map of Sussex and Surrey shows several nymphs posing beside the rivers Lavant, Arun, and Aston, as they flow from the Downs into the sea.

Daniel Defoe criticised this poetic artifice in *A Tour . . . of Great Britain* (1724) when he wrote of the Thames 'I shall sing you no Songs here of the River in the first Person of a Water Nymph, a Goddess (and I know not what) according to the Humour of the ancient Poets. I shall talk nothing of the Marriage of old Isis, the Male River,

30 Norden, 1596, pp. 17–19.
31 Michael Drayton *Poly-Olbion*, London, 1613, pp. 281, 265.

with beautiful Thame, the Female River, a Whimsy as simple as the Subject was empty.'[32]

The Restoration in 1660 ushered in a period of renewed cartographic activity. The rapid expansion of economic activity led to demands for more accurate maps. In the 1660s and 1670s London's trades and crafts, including map-selling and publishing, grew vigorously. Several map-makers took up projects for the publication of an 'English atlas'. John Ogilby, from 1671 His Majesty's Cosmographer, planned to finance the volumes of his 'English Atlas' by subscription and lotteries. He succeeded in publishing one volume, the *Britannia*, famous as the first road-atlas of England and Wales. The second and third volumes of the *Britannia*, which were to include a 'topographical description' of the country, never materialised. Only three county maps were printed, but these do not include Sussex. John Seller, who was appointed the King's hydrographer in 1671, also planned (in 1679–80) a folio atlas, entitled *Atlas Anglicanus,* to be produced in collaboration with John Oliver and Richard Palmer. This project also failed, although Seller did publish a map of Sussex in his *Atlas Contracta* c. 1694. A third project for an 'English Atlas' was that of Moses Pitt, who chose the title presumably after John Ogilby's death in 1676. It was conceived as a work in eleven volumes on the model of the Blaeu and Jansson atlasses, and using Jansson's plates. Pitt's financial difficulties aborted the project and only four volumes were published. Those for Great Britain were never begun. Another project, that of John Adams for the geodetic survey of the kingdom, proposed in 1681, did not produce a single map. Thus progress in the re-mapping of England fell far short of the objectives set out in prospectuses and appeals for funds.

In the 18th century the development of county mapping remained slow. Maps were being printed from the copper plates of Saxton and Speed up to about 1770 when Cluer Dicey and Co issued collections of maps derived from both. Traditional methods of survey continued. William Gardiner in his *Practical Surveying Improved* (London 1737), gave directions for a county survey which involved little more than a road-traverse and filling in of topographical detail, with the help of Jonathan Sisson's theodolite. Yet some encouraging signs of change are evident. John Hammond's book *The Practical Surveyor,* published by the instrument-maker Thomas Heath, 1725, recommended Heath's new theodolite for 'measuring, mapping and adorning all sorts of lands and waters', and 'in drawing the perspective appearance of a gentleman's seat, without measuring one single length, at one setting down of the Instrument'. The need for topographical surveys of counties encouraged estate surveyors to extend their range of work. County surveyors came from varied backgrounds. Some like Benjamin Donn of Devon were mathematics teachers, whereas Peter Burdett who surveyed Cheshire and Derbyshire was an artist, Richard Davis an Oxfordshire farmer, and John Prior a clergyman and schoolmaster of Leicestershire.[33]

One of the larger scale county surveys (though years after Joel Gascoyne's mapping of Cornwall in about 1700 at one inch to a mile) was that of Sussex by Richard

---

32 Daniel Defoe *A tour thro' the whole Island of Great Britain* . . . vol. 1, London, 1724, Letter III, p. 4.
33 J.B. Harley 'The re-mapping of England, 1750–1800' *Imago Mundi* vol. 19 (1965), p. 64.

Budgen. The map was engraved by John Senex and published in 1723 at a scale of three quarters of an inch to a mile. It was severely criticized by Richard Gough as deserving 'but the name of a map at most, and even as such is neither correct nor well executed, many places of note being entirely omitted, nor does the drawing give any true ideas of the country.'[34] Gough had reason to find the map defective and to complain that 'a good Survey of the county of Sussex had long been wanted.'[35] Yet Budgen's map was innovative for its time and displayed a wealth of information on the economic resources and antiquities of the county.

The rapid improvement in county surveying in the second half of the 18th century resulted partly from the enterprise of the Society of Arts which in 1759 offered a premium of £100 for any original county survey on a scale of one inch to a mile. This encouraged the use of a standard scale, the one-inch scale which Ogilby had used in his *Britannia* (1675). Between 1759 and 1801 the Society's awards were given to 13 county maps. By 1775 nearly half of the country had been covered by one-inch to a mile mapping.[36] Standards of survey varied, as Gough remarked: 'Surveys on large scales were reserved for the labours of a Rocque, a Jefferies, and a Taylor, and a Chapman. — I invert the chronological order for the climax of merit.' He goes on to criticize those guilty of plagiaism, then widepsread. 'As to the several sets of county maps professing to be drawn from the *latest* observations, they are almost invariable copies of those that preceded them.'[37] Too many map publishers were still making a livelihood by refurbishing old copper plates. Gough's black list included Emanuel Bowen and Thomas Kitchin, authors of the *Large English Atlas,* published in 1755, and other well-known English atlases:- 'Notwithstanding the assertions of Bowen, Kitchen, and other modern makers, that their maps are framed from *actual new* surveys, there is scarce a single one which does not abound with faults: and a set of correct maps remains to be hoped for from the undertakers of surveys of counties; though it were much to be wished the abilities of some of these were more answerable to the encouragement afforded them.'[38]

Having censured the earlier surveys of Sussex, Gough heralded a new venture which was to place the county's mapping in the highest rank. He announced the forthcoming 'Great Survey' of Sussex, a two-inch to the mile map which 'will not only contain an accurate plan of every town and village, but every farmhouse, barn and garden, will have its place. Every inclosure, however small . . . will be described; every road, public or private, every bridle way and foot path will be delineated . . .' The authors of the survey were Thomas Yeakell and William Gardner, professional surveyors employed by Charles Lennox, 3rd Duke of Richmond, who was patron of the enterprise, 'It will employ them from first to last six years, and cost more than 2400 l for surveying, drawing and engraving . . . The first sheet to be delivered January 1,

34 Richard Gough *British topography* . . ., London, 1780, vol. 2, p. 297.
35 Ibid.
36 Harley, (1965), p. 56.
37 Gough (1780), vol. 1, p. xvi.
38 Gough (1780), vol. 1, p. 108.

1778 . . .'[39] The sheet was engraved in Paris, but when war broke out with France in 1779 the engraving work was 'properly withdrawn home'. In the event only four of the eight sheets were published. Covering the southern part of the county, they have been described as 'the first real map of the county, faithfully rendering every detail visible on the ground.'[40]

The role of the Duke of Richmond as employer of professional surveyors in regular salaried service had far-reaching consequences. When he took up his duties as Master-General of the Board of Ordnance in April 1782, he secured the appointment of Yeakell as chief draughtsman at the Tower of London. Gardner became 'Chief Surveying Draftsman' in 1787. The surveys undertaken by the Board of Ordnance after 1782 were fore-runners of the later official Ordnance Survey maps. The Duke also continued with the private Sussex surveys. Gardner in collaboration with Thomas Gream (for Yeakell had died in 1787), completed the one-inch map of Sussex, first published by William Faden in 1795 with a dedication to the duke. This ranks as the first map published from data derived from the official triangulation of England. It can be considered the first printed map of the Trigonmetrical Survey of England and Wales. Thus an enterprise in county surveying developed into military survey, and thence into national survey.[41]

This sequence of events was one of two lines of advance from which emerged the National Survey of Great Britain. The other followed from the military survey of Scotland after the 1745 rising. The outstanding figure here is William Roy, whose surveys from 1765 to 1781 included parts of south-east England. His 'General Map of the Southeast part of England 1765', at a scale of approximately 1:200,000 (BL K.Top. VI.97), was made as a military map, but Roy, characteristically, recorded Roman antiquities, Roman roads, names of 'Stations', and the places 'of the most memorable Battles'.

As the national survey proceeded in the 19th century, private entrepreneurs, notably the firm of C & J Greenwood, whose map of Sussex was published in 1825, and the rival firm of A. Bryant, continued to make county maps. Theirs were the last major achievements in private topographical mapping, for the Ordnance Survey maps dominated the market. Private firms continued to provide popular and thematic county maps. With the new technique of lithography available as a method of map production, they were better equipped to respond to the dynamism of economic change, adding and altering the growing network of railways and roads, and showing the expansion of towns and villages. The conservatism of copper-plate engraving no longer controlled the market. Maps were issued in many states, to keep abreast of the changing landscape.

The later years of the 18th century were thus a turning point. It was a period in which the old established practices were improved almost to perfection, before

39 Gough (1780), vol. 2, pp. 297–8.
40 Skelton, Introductory notes to *Two hundred and fifty years of map-making in the County of Sussex*, Lympne, 1970.
41 Harley and O'Donoghue *The Old Series Ordnance Survey maps of England and Wales . . .* Introduction . . . vol. 1, Lympne, 1975, pp. xxvi–xxix.

revolutionary changes affected both map-making and the face of the land to be mapped. Gough himself contributed to the process, by recording the topographical antiquities of Great Britain and Ireland. His *Anecdotes of British Topography* (1768) and his revised enlarged version, entitled *British Topography* (1780) provide the earliest comprehensive account of the maps and other geographical records of the country. The carto-bibliographies of the British Isles and of its regions have carried on into the 20th century the tradition so ably established by Gough with his passion for antiquities and his own Museum of British Topography.

David Kingsley, himself a collector and a resident of the county, has now added Sussex to the list of counties with their own carto-bibliographies. He has recorded some 200 maps in a work based on many years of devoted study. It will be welcomed by map libraries and the large public interested in maps, and, not least, by lovers of a beautiful and historic county. All will echo Gough's words of congratulation on the appearance of a new county history: 'It is with pleasure we see this branch of antiquarian knowledge increasing among us in this inquisitive age'. With the publication of this volume David Kingsley has filled in another blank patch on the map of recorded cartographic history.

Helen Wallis

PREFACE

The progress of the cartobibliography of the English and Welsh counties was reviewed by Ralph Hyde in *New Library World* in May 1972. A list of county bibliographies will be found in appendix XII. It will be seen that eighteen counties have been covered prior to the present work.

Hyde discussed the merits of the two arrangements used (A and B in appendix XII). Arrangement A was initiated by Henry George Fordham in 1901 for his bibliography of Hertfordshire maps, and was developed by Harold Whitaker. Under this arrangement every issue of every map, including lithographic transfers, is listed in chronological order. The method is cumbersome, and does not give a clear picture of the printing history of a specific map; but it has the advantage that a map can be located in the catalogue by reference to its date of publication and comparisons can be made between maps published at about the same time, even though some may be late editions of much earlier maps.

Arrangement B was again originated by Fordham in 1908 for his work on Cambridgeshire maps. It was refined by Professor Paul Harvey[1] and by Donald Hodson,[2] and has the merit that the complete printing history of each engraved plate (or set of plates) and of any lithographic transfers taken from it is presented clearly and compactly. (Lithographic transfers derived from a map of a larger area are a minor exception; the printing history of the plate(s) being restricted to alterations affecting the county.) Every group of alterations to the original plate is regarded as a new 'state' or edition of the map.[3] Every transfer is listed separately, and every group of alterations made on the stone is classified as a separate edition of the transfer. This arrangement has bibliographical correctness.

Harvey and Hodson did far more than establish arrangement B. They unearthed a vast number of additional atlases, and located many loose maps and maps originally published in books or periodicals. They listed the differences between each edition of each map in detail, thus enabling any loose map to be identified; they carefully analysed each lithographic transfer and related it to the appropriate state of the plate from which it derived. Hodson included up to three locations for every issue of every loose map, atlas or other work, and introduced notes on the cartographic derivation of each map. Referring to the work of Harvey and Hodson, Hyde concluded, 'It was a great advance, and a return to the accepted methods of the past was now unthinkable'. Walters had earlier observed[4] that 'In the related field of county carto-bibliography, through the work of Hodson, Harvey and Thorpe,[5] a tired medium is being given a new bibliographical vigour. That all this arduous work is necessary we cannot doubt.' One hopes that he is right; he is certainly right about the arduousness of the work. In the

1 Harvey, 1959 (see appendix XII for bibliography of works cited).
2 Hodson, 1974.
3 Verner, 1965, p. 10.
4 Walters, 1970, p. 87.
5 Harvey and Thorpe, *The printed maps of Warwickshire,* cited as 'Harvey, 1959'.

discussion which followed the presentation of Walters' paper, Dr Harley referred to the intricate problems encountered in analysing electrotype impressions of Ordnance Survey maps and concluded 'Whether it is all worth sorting out, I do not really know sometimes.'

In replying to people who ask me how long it takes to compile the cartobibliography of an English county, I am tempted to paraphrase an old saying, 'If you are asking how long it takes, you haven't got the time'. Hyde, in his own excellent work on maps of Victorian London published in 1975, followed arrangement B, but he took a number of short cuts. To quote his introduction, 'no attempt has been made to distinguish between editions and states according to the strictest modern bibliographical definitions' and 'no attempt has been made to distinguish between the various lithographic transfers. . . .' He also kept his account of the alterations between one edition and the next to a minimum. These considerable savings hardly detract from the value of his book; and although arrangement B is now the accepted arrangement for county map catalogues, the optimum format for such catalogues remains open for discussion.

The volume of work required to compile a county bibliography on the Harvey/Hodson basis can be assessed from an analysis of Hodson's work. He catalogued 152 different maps, including ten in the Supplement. The plates appeared in 428 different 'states' or editions, and there were 338 lithographic transfers. Some transfers, however, were found in two or more 'editions', and this increased the number of lithographic transfer 'editions' to 370. The total number of different editions to be studied was, therefore, 428 plus 370, a total of very nearly 800. Even this is not the whole story. The impression of a map in one state may appear in several different atlases or books, and may also have been issued loose. A good example is Jansson's map in state (i), see Hodson no. 12, which appears in eighteen separate editions of nine atlases. This factor increased the number of separate works or loose maps to be examined by some 400, making a total of 1,200 impressions to be checked and recorded by the compiler. Some atlases are unique, but in most cases all known copies, perhaps as many as ten, have to be examined; certainly an average of three or four impressions of each edition have to be checked. It will be seen, therefore, that at least 4,000 separate impressions have to be examined in the course of compiling a bibliography of county maps.

Harvey and Hodson recorded at least fifty per cent more atlases and works containing county maps than had been recorded by earlier bibliographers. Their investigations were so thorough that very few new series of county maps are likely to be found, and in compiling the present work no more than a dozen new atlases, or hitherto unknown editions of atlases, have been discovered. It is interesting, however, to note that between publication of Hodson's work in parts (1969–72) and its re-issue in book form in 1974, three new maps (Hodson, nos. 5a, 40A and 92a) were discovered. As recently as 1975 a hitherto unknown series of county maps (catalogue no. 85, below) came to light.

Neither the number of maps, nor the fact that the maps are distributed throughout a number of different libraries and private collections, presents the main problem to the compiler. The main problem arises from the fact that most maps are found in a number of different states or editions. The map from Cary's *New English atlas* (no. 61 in the present work) is a good example. The plate is found in eleven states, some in atlases and some loose, and in addition eleven different transfers in thirteen separate editions have been identified. The map appeared between 1801 and 1887. Every difference between each edition of the map has to be recorded before the various states of the plate and transfers can be identified and placed in chronological order. Mechanical methods for the comparison of one impression with another have been discussed,[6] but no practical solution has yet emerged. The problem is aggravated by the fact that impressions are located in different places, and comparisons can only be effected by obtaining photostatic copies of the maps, often a lengthy operation, and in the long run a major expense to the amateur. For these reasons I would recommend future compilers to weight the practical cuts adopted by Hyde against the perfectionism achieved by Harvey and Hodson.

The terminal date, 1900, adopted by recent compilers is quite arbitrary. An earlier date, say 1850, would reduce the number of atlases to be inspected by about fifty percent. The saving would not only be quantitative. It would eliminate most of the lithographic transfers, the complexities of which are so difficult to unravel, and, as Harvey has pointed out, the late nineteenth-century atlases are often the most difficult to find. From the cartographic standpoint a case can be made out for terminating the catalogue at 1850. By that date the first One Inch Ordnance Survey sheets had been published for all but the six northern counties. A termination at 1850 would also ensure the inclusion of the interesting large-scale maps based on the work of private surveyors, such as Andrew Byrant and the Greenwoods, most of which were published between 1820 and 1830. Some of these maps were superior to the earlier work of the Ordnance Survey (see Hodson no. 82). After 1850, the majority of new maps published were based on the work of the Ordnance Survey, and apart from the Ordnance maps themselves, cartographic interest centres on thematic maps, dealing with railways, roads, administration, planning, population, electoral representation, land utilisation, climate, archaeology and other subjects.

After 1850, therefore, cataloguing could reasonably be restricted to Ordnance Survey maps and selected thematic maps. On this basis, it would be practical to continue the catalogue beyond 1900. Although few county atlases have been published since 1900, the difficulty in compiling a comprehensive bibliography beyond that date arises from the fact that a vast number of county maps appeared in newspapers, magazines, journals of local and learned societies, topographical works and guide books. Most such maps are of little interest, even to the collector, and would not repay the labour involved in tracking them down. It must be remembered, however, that the primary purpose of the catalogue is to enable librarians and collectors to identify and date loose maps. For this reason, in spite of the argument above, it is hoped that future compilers will, in the interests of uniformity, adhere to 1900 as their terminal date.

Walters has observed with regret that county bibliographers do not include maps of 'the towns and smaller areas of the county'.[7] Some notes on maps of smaller areas will be found in the appendixes. Town plans are a fascinating and important study. Only one proper bibliography has been compiled for a Sussex town;[8] it is hoped that

---

6 Walters, 1970, p. 88; Margary, *Imago Mundi* vol. 29 (1977), p. 78.
7 Walters, 1970, p. 81.
8 Butler, 1972; Smail, 1949, includes several plans of Worthing; see also *MCS* no. 22.

others will soon appear.

As a result of using the Harvey and Hodson catalogues, I have made minor alterations to their format in compiling this work, and have amplified the descriptions of each map. Time will tell whether these changes are justified.

Brief biographical notes, with emphasis on any Sussex connections, are included in the catalogue, under the entry where the name is first mentioned. These notes include some hitherto unpublished information relating to Budgen, but in general they are compiled, unless otherwise stated, from published sources — *Dictionary of national biography,* Chubb (1927), Skelton (*County atlases,* 1970 and *250 years,* 1970), Tooley (1949 and 1979), Darlington and Howgego (1964), Hyde (1975), Shirley (1980) and Tyacke (1978). They are designed for Sussex users of the catalogue who may not be familiar with the cartographic literature. The exercise has been useful in bringing to light a number of minor cartographers, engravers and publishers about whom little or nothing has been published. To give but one example, Sidney Hall, who engraved a number of county and other maps (see nos. 77, 92 and 96 in the catalogue) remains but a name and an address. Gardiner[9] led the way into making good these deficiencies but much remains to be done.

Works cited (see appendix XII) are referred to by the author's name followed by year of publication. Abbreviated title is included where two works were published by the author in the same year.

The dating of undated works and maps presents many problems. All dates in square brackets in the catalogue must be accepted with caution. Some aids to dating are given in appendix X. From 1849, railways (see appendix XI) provide a useful guide, but it must be remembered that cartographers often included railways on their maps before the lines were actually opened, and sometimes they marked lines which were never built. Some untraced and unidentified maps are listed in appendix VIII.

The majority of the 155 maps noticed in the main catalogue are derived from earlier maps. Some mapmakers, such as Cary, endeavoured to keep the delineation of the road system up-to-date, and from 1840 most of them tried to keep pace with the rapid development of the railway network; but they added very little information of geographical significance. The cataloguing of all maps is, of course, essential from the bibliographical standpoint, but amidst such an accumulation of detail it may be of help to users of the catalogue to bear in mind the following key dates at which significant original work was published:

1575	Saxton no. 1	Based on an original survey.
1595	Norden no. 3	New geographical detail added.
1675	Ogilby app.V.1	Survey of the roads.
1723	Budgen no. 24	An original survey.
1778–83	Yeakell and Gardner no. 47	Original survey of coastal region.
1795	Gardner, Yeakell, Gream no. 57	Original survey based on triangulation.
1813	O.S.1" Old Series app.VI.1a	Original survey 1793 to c.1800.

9   Gardiner, 1973.

1819	Cary no. 61(vi)	Smith's geological map.
1862–8	O.S.1" Old Series app.VI.1a	Geological survey.
1872–7	O.S. 25" app.VI.2	Surveyed 1869–75. (6" maps published 1877–80).
1876–82	O.S.1" New Series app.VI.1b	Surveyed 1860–75. Revised 1893–8.

As regards the justification for a work of this nature, any reader of the *Sussex Archaeological Collections,* particularly the early volumes, will appreciate the very sketchy knowledge of map sources possessed by some contributors. As Harley[10] noted in 1968, cartobibliography is not merely an end in itself, but essential to the proper understanding and use of the maps. He has also emphasised the importance of bibliographies to students in other fields, such as the study of boundaries, communications, village morphology, place-names and family history. Only proper cataloguing can resolve the problem of dating maps. It must again be emphasised, however, that this work is designed primarily as a catalogue for the use of librarians and collectors. It should enable them to identify any loose printed map of the county, and to date it with some degree of accuracy.

Finally I wish to acknowledge with gratitude the assistance I have received from a number of librarians and archivists throughout this country and abroad. In particular, I wish to thank Donald Hodson without whose help and encouragement this catalogue would never have been completed; Dr Helen Wallis, who generously agreed to write the Introduction, Sarah Tyacke, Yolande O'Donoghue, John Huddy and all the staff at the British Library Map Library; Professor Paul Harvey who made available to me the annotated copy of his work on Warwickshire maps; Ralph Hyde and John Farrant who read the typescript and made a number of valuable suggestions; Roger Fairclough, Betty Fathers and Sylvia Mann. I also take this opportunity of thanking the Council of the Sussex Record Society for undertaking the publication of this bibliography.

Plates are reproduced by permission of the Trustees of the British Museum, plate 6(i) and (ii); British Library, plates 1, 2, 3, 4, 17, 23(iv), 24, 25; Royal Geographical Society, frontispiece; Ashburnham Christian Trust, plate 2(i); the Syndics of Cambridge University Library, plàte 31; Controller of H.M. Stationary Office, plate 34; Mr. S.H. Jollye, plate 26; and Miss Sylvia Mann, plates 6(iii), 27(i).

Thanks are also due to the East Sussex County Council for their grant of £100 towards the cost of production.

10   Harley, *Imago Mundi* vol. 22 (1968), p. 66.

GUIDE TO CATALOGUE

SCOPE

This is as complete a catalogue as possible of the printed maps of the county of Sussex from 1575, when the first printed map was published, to 1900.[1] In general, it includes any map which is described as a map of Sussex, or in which the detail outside the county boundary is only shown incidentally. Some such maps cover a larger area, eg Pickett catalogue no. 83,[2] which extends north as far as London; and some do not cover the whole county, eg Bartholomew's half-inch map no. 153, which has the title *Sussex,* but extends eastwards only to Pevensey. Maps of the diocese of Chichester, of which the boundary is virtually co-extensive with that of the county, are included. Maps which combine Sussex with more than one other county have not been included, but exceptions have been made in the case of Saxton no. 1 and of van den Keere no. 5. The catalogue includes maps which were divided arbitrarily into two or more sheets, usually because they were too large for a single sheet of paper or engraved plate. Maps of east and west Sussex are included when designed as a complementary pair, eg Davies no. 104; but not maps of smaller parts of the county, even though, when combined, they would cover the entire county. A few maps, which do not fit into the above categories, but which are predominantly 'Sussex', have been included, eg Mantell no. 84. Other maps of some interest or importance, but falling outside the scope of the catalogue, are listed in appendixes I to VII.

ARRANGEMENT[3]

To explain the form of the catalogue requires a short account of printing methods. Until 1831 all maps of the county were produced by intaglio printing. In this process the design is engraved in reverse on a metal *plate* which is then inked, wiped and passed through the press with a sheet of damp paper which takes up the ink retained in the incised lines of the metal. On the paper the design appears the right way round and each line stands up as a minute ridge of ink. An important characteristic of the process is that corrections or revisions can readily be carried out on the plate. Thus new detail can be added or, by rubbing or scraping down the surface of the plate, a part of the design can be erased and perhaps re-engraved in a new form (compare for example **plates 4 and 5,** and **30 and 31**). When an alteration, however small, has been carried out, the plate is said to be in a different *state*. All the individual maps or *impressions*, printed from a distinct state of the plate, constitute a single *edition*, although the actual

---

1 The reasons for adopting 1900 as the terminal date are discussed in the Preface.
2 Maps in the catalogue are referred to in the form 'Saxton no. 1', the word catalogue is normally omitted. Where reference is to the cartographer, rather than the map, the form 'Saxton (no. 1)' is used.
3 This description of the arrangement followed in the catalogue is taken from Donald Hodson, *The printed maps of Hertfordshire 1577–1900,* which also contains an excellent explanatory diagram, not reproduced here.

printings may have been spread over many years. There may, therefore, be more than one *issue* of a single edition.

After 1831 an increasing number of maps of Sussex were printed by lithography, the first being Lower no. 98 and Dawson no. 99. In this process the design, in reverse, is not cut; it is drawn or otherwise laid down on the specially prepared surface of a lithographic stone or (a later development) a sheet of zinc. In the catalogue the term *stone* is used to describe a lithographic printing surface, irrespective of the substance employed. After suitable treatment of the surface, the greasy ink used for printing adheres only to the lines of the design. On lithographic maps the lines are less sharp than those produced by intaglio printing and lie flat on the surface of the paper. As with an engraved plate, detail can be added or removed during the stone's period of service thus producing a succession of editions.

In the simplest form of lithography the map was drawn by hand on the stone itself or was transferred to it directly from the original drawing, eg nos. 98 and 99. Frequently, however, a transfer was taken from an existing engraved plate; thus the same map might be printed by both the intaglio and the lithographic process (see **plates 30 to 33**). Printing such a map by lithography had the advantage of eliminating plate wear with the consequent need for regular retouching of the incised lines, and increasingly maps were engraved solely as sources of lithographic transfers with no intention of using the plates for direct intaglio printing, eg no. 107. Moreover the design on the stone could be easily and extensively revised and publishers took full advantage of this scope for alteration. The position of features such as the title or scale could be changed while laying down the transfer (see **plates 24 and 25**); details might be added from another engraved plate or from type, or alterations drawn in by hand. Some of the maps so produced bear little resemblance to the design on the plate from which they were derived, and the use of lithography allowed all these revisions to be carried out without modifying the original plate in any way. This made the process particularly suitable for the production of small numbers of maps for special purposes in which selected features were emphasised, see no. 147B, or for the tentative introduction of proposed railways and other information of a possibly ephemeral nature.

Further variations of the process were introduced. Lithographic maps of the county were produced from an engraved map of the whole country by taking a transfer from the relevant portion of the plate or plates, removing extraneous detail, and adding a new border, title and scale, eg no. 129C. Or, by using a photographic process to lay down the map on the stone, it became possible to change its size. Examples of both enlarged and reduced lithographic maps are found in the catalogue, see nos. 121E and 142A. The same process, photozincography, was used to produce a succession of different lithographic maps from a single fair drawing; in the catalogue the term *lithographic transfer* is used of the photographic as well as of the direct process.

The form of the catalogue is intended to show clearly the relationships between the various editions of each map and between transfers derived from a common original. Each entry in the catalogue has a main number, representing either an engraved plate or a lithographic stone on which the map has been laid down directly from the original drawing. Where lithographic transfers have been taken from a plate, they are listed in order after the editions produced by direct intaglio printing; each of these transfers bears the main number followed by a letter. The different *states* of each plate or stone are distinguished by small Roman numerals. Thus, the complete reference for any map may consist of three parts. (1) the main or entry number; (2) a letter, if the map was printed by lithographic transfer from an engraved plate or from a drawing by photo-zincography; (3) the number of the edition, if the plate or stone has been found in more than one state. Letters, therefore, are used for lithographic maps produced by transfer from an engraved plate, eg no. 107A, or by photozincography, eg no. 146, even if the plate was never used for intaglio printing. Where a lithographic map is produced by direct transfer of an original drawing to the stone, eg no. 99, the letters are omitted, and successive editions are numbered (i), (ii), etc. It is not always possible to be certain as to which process was used, but the detail is usually rather sharper on a lithographic map produced by transfer from an engraved plate.

THE FORM OF THE ENTRIES

The maps are listed in chronological order of first appearance. Each entry gives information in the following order:

HEADING
The name of the surveyor of an original survey, if known. Otherwise the name of the draughtsman, the engraver, or the first publisher, in that order of preference.

DATE
The date appearing on the first edition of the map, or, if the map is undated, the year of its first publication. (Some notes on the dating of maps will be found in appendix X.)

MEASUREMENTS
The greatest lengths to the nearest millimetre,[4] first horizontally, then vertically, between the inmost frame lines (neat lines) of the map; followed by the width of the border in brackets. The dimensions are given in this form because loose maps are sometimes found with the borders trimmed. Some impressions of the same map will be found to vary in size by as much as $2\frac{1}{2}\%$ as a result of the shrinkage or expansion of the paper. Although most maps have north to the top, this is not invariably so, and the vertical dimension may correspond to the east/west axis of the map. The title normally indicates the position in which the map is intended to be read; but there are exceptions, eg no. 136C.

The dimensions given in the captions to the plates refer to the printed area, including border, of the map, or part of map, illustrated.

---

4 British Standards Institution, *Recommendations for bibliographical references to maps and charts. Part 1: References in accessions lists.* (BS 5195; Part 1 1975) recommends that the size be stated in centimetres (para. 4.12.1) and the scale in millimetres (para 4.4.2). The width of the border is most conveniently expressed in millimetres, and in the interests of consistency millimetres have been used as the unit of measurement throughout this catalogue. It also recommends that dimensions be stated horizontally. then vertically, but bibliographers have not been consistent in this respect.

SCALE

This has been calculated by measuring the distance on the map from Chichester to Rye, which has been taken as 66½ miles. If either of these places is not marked on the map, a major town shown towards the west or east end of the county is substituted. The scale is recorded as a representative fraction (to three significant figures). The scale thus deduced often differs from the scale bar on the map, even after the statute mile came into general use.

DERIVATION (in small print)

Where possible the sources on which each map was based are stated. In many cases this is deduced from detail on the map, including the spelling of place-names and the delineation of the coastline and rivers.

BIOGRAPHICAL and other NOTES

Reference to important features of the map, biographical notes on persons concerned with its preparation and publication, and any relevant information on the history, particularly the printing history, of the map.

EDITIONS

A full description is given for the first edition of each map in the following order: title; dedication, signature(s), imprint(s), other inscriptions, scale, compass indicator, key[5] (the explanation of conventional signs), references to rapes, hundreds or parishes, arms, views, other notes or features, longitude and latitude, graticule or grid,[6] railways, colour (other than hand colouring), and in some cases a reference to printed matter on the back of the map.

The description of the first edition is followed by a list of subsequent editions, numbered in small Roman numerals. These are not described in full, but selected alterations, erasures and additions by comparison with the preceding edition are listed.

PLACE-NAMES, etc.

Place-names, inscriptions and other wording, which appear on the map, are reproduced in *italics*, and the precise form of the wording including accents, is given as exactly as possible; except (i) a superscript letter with a punctuation mark below it is reproduced with the punctuation mark moved to the right, (ii) *a* and *e* engraved as a ligature are reproduced as separate letters (iii) the bar, used as a contraction sign, above a capital letter is omitted, and the omitted letter is added in square brackets.

Observant users of the catalogue may find errors in the transcription of punctuation marks. These are often difficult to decipher on late impressions of maps taken from worn plates, and even more difficult where the compiler has had to work from xerographic reproductions.

---

5   Other terms with similar meaning are in common use, eg *Legend* (MDTT 21.33), *Characteristic sheet* (MDTT 23.4a), *Table of conventional signs*. *Explanation* is the term most commonly used by county cartographers.

6   MDTT (322.2) defines 'graticule' as a network of lines representing meridians and parallels. A system of rectangular Cartesian co-ordinates is referred to as a 'grid' (321.1). See also Wallis 1976, pp. 23–6.

POSITION OF FEATURES ON MAPS

Where appropriate, the position of each feature on the map is given in brackets, by reference to the following grid:

Aa	Ba	Ca	Da	Ea
Ab	Bb	Cb	Db	Eb
Ac	Bc	Cc	Dc	Ec
Ad	Bd	Cd	Dd	Ed
Ae	Be	Ce	De	Ee

The position of a lengthy or large feature is taken from its centre; but a feature placed in a corner is given the reference of that corner, eg a title stretching over squares Da, Ea, Db and Eb would be recorded as (Ea). 'In border' means that the feature appears between the inner and outer lines of the border; 'OS' that it lies outside the border; otherwise the feature appears within the inner border. Where the reference is to a single sheet of a multisheet map rather than to the map as a whole, that is made clear in the text.

SCALE-BAR

The actual wording on the scale-bar is reproduced. If none, the word 'Scale' is prefixed to the length of the scale-bar, which is measured to the nearest millimetre. The number of miles marked on the bar is stated; '1 + 10' means that the bar marked a total of eleven miles, but zero is one mile from the left. The length is measured from zero.

COMPASS INDICATOR

'Compass' is used to indicate any form of compass indicator, from a simple north-pointing arrow to an elaborate compass rose.

LONGITUDE AND LATITUDE

When marked on the map, longitude and latitude are recorded in the form 'longitude 5' (2'); latitude 5' (2'),' indicating that the borders are marked for every two minutes of longitude and latitude and that the values are stated at 5' intervals.

GRATICULE AND GRID

The figures in brackets, after reference to a graticule or a grid, give the intervals to the nearest millimetre between the vertical, and then the horizontal, lines.

RAILWAYS

Railways wholly or partly in Sussex are identified by numbers; selected lines outside the county, which appear on Sussex maps, by letters. A key will be found in appendix XI; a map on page 404. There were numerous take-overs, amalgamations and changes of name during the early years; the company names in appendix XI are those of the main operating companies during the period under review. The 'date of Act' refers to the date of the main authorising Act or to the Act covering the formation of the original construction company. A list of railways authorised but never built has been included; such lines were sometimes shown on maps.

PUBLICATION

After the description of each edition is a list (indented) of the atlases, books and publications in which the map appeared. The titles, in italics, follow the spelling and punctuation of the original, but not the style of lettering or the use of capitals. Omissions are indicated by dots. Where a title is repeated, only the primary title is given. The title is followed by the place of publication, the name(s) of the publisher(s), printer or seller(s), and the year of publication. The form '1800 and 1801' means that there were two editions of the book, with title-pages substantially the same but bearing different dates; '1800 (reissued 1801)' means that the book was republished but with date unaltered. Dates in square brackets must be accepted with caution.

Where possible publication details are given for loose maps.

LOCATIONS OF ATLASES, etc.

The locations of atlases, books and loose maps are given to the far right of the publication details. No more than three locations are included for any work; the British Library is given where appropriate and a public collection in Sussex is identified when possible. Entries referring to more than one issue are separated by semi-colons. Locations of loose maps are in brackets. Where details have had to be taken from a secondary source such as Skelton's *County atlases of the British Isles,* reference to the location is replaced by reference to the source. There are all too few atlases in public collections in Sussex, but good collections of loose maps will be found at Brighton, Worthing and Hove public libraries, at the Sussex Archaeological Society at Lewes, and at the West Sussex Record Office at Chichester.

LITHOGRAPHIC TRANSFERS

The dimensions and scale are repeated for each transfer, since these can be altered by photographic processes. Information is then given for each edition on the basis described above. In some complex cases it has been found necessary to repeat a full description of the main features of a map, rather than a simple list of changes compared with the preceding edition.

The description of each transfer concludes with notes on the state of the original plate or drawing at the time the transfer was taken, and of alterations made on the transfer itself. This is a departure from the arrangement adopted by Harvey and Hodson. It is felt that many users of the catalogue will be more concerned with the development of the map as it appears on the face of the map than with its precise printing history. It is hoped that this arrangement will make such alterations easier to follow, while the printing history can still be determined from the notes on *State of the plate* and *Alterations on the transfer* that follow.

It must be remembered that alterations made on the plate recur on all subsequent transfers (unless specifically removed), whereas alterations made on the transfer are found only on maps printed from that particular stone. Where there is more than one edition of a particular transfer, a note is added, if possible, of some minor flaw which demonstrates that such editions were from the same transfer.

REPRODUCTIONS

Reference is made in the catalogue to reproductions published before 1900. An increasing number of reproductions and facsimile atlases[7] have been published in recent years, and it is hoped that this trend will continue, particularly in view of the high cost of the originals which puts them out of reach of many students and collectors. The maps reproduced in *Two hundred and fifty years of map-making in the county of Sussex*[8] are of outstanding quality. A number of useful, but not very high quality, reproductions appeared in the *Sussex county magazine.*[9]

Maps reproduced in this catalogue (see LIST OF PLATES on page xxxv) have been selected for their cartographic importance, attraction of design, rarity (in particular maps not hitherto reproduced), and as examples of the printing history of plates and lithographic transfers as described under 'Arrangement' above. Where appropriate, reference to the plate number is made in bold print following the note on derivation, and again after the description of the relevant edition or lithographic transfer.

APPENDIXES I to VII

Some interesting maps, which fall outside the defined scope of the catalogue, are listed in appendixes I to VII. The list is not comprehensive, in some instances only brief descriptions are given, and no attempt has been made to give full locations for each map. It is hoped, however, that the information may prove useful to students of Sussex maps and to researchers in other fields.

INDEX

The index covers personal names, the titles of atlases and other works, and selected subjects, eg railways, longitude. Place-names are included only in special circumstances, eg where there is an insert plan or view of the town on a map. Works listed in the Bibliography (appendix XII) are indexed under the author's names followed by abbreviated title and date of publication.

---

7 For a recent summary see A.G. Hodgkiss, 'Facsimiles of early atlases' in *Society of University Cartographers Bulletin* vol. 12 no. 2. (1978) pp. 1–12. Also list compiled by B. Noe and published by Library of Congress (stock number 030-004-00019-1, 1980).
8 Published by H. Margary, Lympne, 1970. Maps reproduced include: Saxton no. 1(ii), Norden no. 3, Speed no. 7(ii), Ogilby app. V.1 plate 81, Budgen no. 24(ii), Moll no. 25(ii), Overton no. 26, Yeakell and Gardner no. 47 sheet 1, Cary no. 49(i), Gardner, Yeakell and Gream no. 57, Ordnance Survey app. VI.1 sheets 5 and 9, and Greenwood no. 89(iii). The first three maps are also reproduced in *Sussex Life* for February 1973.
9 Maps reproduced include: in vol. II Adams app. II.4, Wagenaer app. II.1, Norden no. 6(ii), Speed no. 7(ii), Hole app. IV.1, Humble no. 8(ii), Blaeu no. 12(ii), Saxton no. 1(viii), Morden no. 20(i), Moll no. 25(ii), Blome no. 14(vii), Cary no. 49(iii or later), Bowen no. 35, Norden no. 6(iii); in vol. XII Gardner app. V.2 five plates; and in vol. XIII Bickham app. IV.2.

ANNOTATED COPY

It is proposed to deposit an annotated copy of the catalogue, giving references to the maps and sources used, at the West Sussex Record Office. There are undoubtedly errors in the catalogue, and many omissions, particularly of hitherto unknown editions of the later atlases, topographical works and guide books. It would be appreciated if anyone discovering such errors and omissions would send details to the County Archivist, West Sussex Record Office, Chichester.

LIST OF PLATES

(between pages 346–7)

(Dimensions in the captions refer to the printed area of the original map, which has been reproduced).

ABBREVIATIONS

Aa etc.	Denotes the position of a feature on a map, see page xxxi.
A	Allen Collection, Lancashire Record Office, Preston.
AD	Naval Historical Library (Admiralty).
BOD	Bodleian Library.
BL	British Library.
BRL	Birmingham Reference Library.
CJ	*Cartographic Journal*. British Cartographical Society (from 1964).
CUL	Cambridge University Library.
DNB	*Dictionary of National Biography*.
ESCL	East Sussex County Library, Lewes.
ESRO	East Sussex Record Office, Lewes.
GJ	*Geographic Journal*. Royal Geographical Society (from 1893; replacing *Journal* of the RGS, 1831–81, and the *Proceedings* 1855–92).
GL	Guildhall Library
GLC	Map and Print Collection, Greater London Council
MCS	*Map Collectors' Series,* Map Collectors' Circle (1963–75).
MDTT	*Multilingual dictionary of technical terms in cartography,* Wiesbaden, 1973.
NMM	National Maritime Museum.
P	Private collection.
PRO	Public Record Office.
RGS	Royal Geographical Society
S	R.A. Skelton, *County atlases of the British Isles 1579–1703,* London 1970. (Where quoted as a secondary source in the catalogue, the entry number is added, eg S11.)
SAC	*Sussex Archaeological Collections,* Sussex Archaeological Society, Lewes, (from 1848).
SAS	Sussex Archaeological Society, Lewes.
SCM	*Sussex County Magazine*, Eastbourne and Worthing (1926–56).
SNQ	*Sussex Notes and Queries,* SAS, Lewes (1926–71).
SRS	Publications of Sussex Record Society, Lewes (from 1902).
VCH	*Victoria history of the county of Sussex*. London, 1905 (vol. 1), 1907, (vol. 2), 1935 (vol. 3), 1937 (vol. 9), 1953 (vol. 4), 1940 (vol. 7), 1980 (vol. 6 pt. 1).
W	Whitaker Collection, University of Leeds.
WN	H. Whitaker, *A descriptive list of the maps of Northumberland,* 1949, and . . . *of Northamptonshire,* 1948.
WSCL	West Sussex County Library, Chichester.
WSRO	West Sussex Record Office, Chichester.

PRINTED MAPS
OF
SUSSEX

THE CATALOGUE

1   CHRISTOPHER SAXTON   1575

Size: 528 mm × 390 mm (8 mm)   1:301,000

An original survey. Sussex is combined with Kent, Surrey and Middlesex, but the map has been included in the main catalogue because of its outstanding importance. **See plates 4 and 5.**

Saxton[1] was born at Dunningley in Yorkshire about 1543 and died in 1610 or 1611. Between about 1571[2] and 1578, under the patronage of Sir Thomas Seckford, he surveyed and published the first maps of the English and Welsh counties. The complete atlas of thirty-five maps was published in 1579.

The maps are remarkably accurate considering the time and facilities available. Saxton did not start the survey before 1571. By 1576 he had finished the English counties and had started on the Welsh counties. All the English counties had been engraved and published by 1577, and the Welsh counties by the end of the following year.

Saxton would naturally have made use of earlier maps. Nowell's manuscript county maps (see appendix I.1. and **plate 2**) would have been available to him, and perhaps also a collection of maps made by Reyner Wolfe.[3] No further sets of regional maps are known to have existed, but there were many earlier maps of the British Isles.[4] The largest of these was Mercator's map of 1564, on a scale of about ten miles to the inch; the most recent was Humphrey Lhuyd's map of 1573 **(plate 3)**. Neither these nor the regional maps would have been of much help to Saxton. None, for example, names more than forty places in Sussex, compared with over three hundred on Saxton's map. Nor does an analysis of Sussex place-names and their spellings indicate that Saxton relied in particular on any one earlier map or set of maps. Saxton would, however, have benefited from the work of John Rudd (1498–1579) of Durham, who is thought to have made a map of the kingdom in the 1550s. Saxton is known to have been employed by Rudd in 1570. The map has not survived.

Lhuyd's map **(plate 3)** names thirty-nine places in Sussex. There are many errors. For example, the coastline from Newhaven to Fairlight (*Ferloÿ*) is almost straight, **Beachy Head being omitted and unnamed**; Selsey is shown as an island; East Grinstead (*Greenstede*) is placed on the Ouse; Shoreham is on the west bank of the Adur; Hever (*Houer*) in Kent is named twice. These and other errors were corrected by Saxton.

There is little or no direct evidence as to Saxton's methods of survey. It may be assumed that he followed the best contemporary practice and that he had studied the

1. Fordham, 1928; Lynam, 1953; Evans and Lawrence, 1979; Tyacke and Huddy, 1980. See Daly Briscoe, 1979 re Seckford.
2. Evans and Lawrence, 1979, suggest a later starting date, but the evidence (p.7) is inconclusive, and the Queen's recognition of Saxton (p.67) points to an earlier date.
3. Lynam, 1950, p. 13; Evans and Lawrence, 1979, p. xiii and p. 11.
4. Shirley, 1980; Crone, 1961.

latest available works on the subject.[5] Authorities[6] differ as to whether the basic frameworks of Saxton's maps were arrived at by compass traverse or by a form of triangulation, or by a combination of both.

A compass traverse meant that Saxton and his assistants would have proceeded along selected roads and rivers measuring the angles at each of the main bends and the distances between them. This would have enabled Saxton to fix the positions of towns and other features lying near such roads and rivers. The intervening detail would then have been plotted from suitable church towers or hills, using the plane table,[7] or by eye.

Triangulation had been described by Gemma Frisius as early as 1533,[8] and in English in Cuningham's *Cosmographical glasse* (1559). Frisius became Professor of Mathematics at Louvain, and his pupils included Mercator and John Dee. Dee was associated with Seckford,[9] and would have been in a position to pass on his knowledge to Saxton. Crone[10] describes in some detail the methods adopted by Philip Apian, another follower of Gemma Frisius, who surveyed Bavaria between 1555 and 1561, and he suggests that Saxton would have employed a similar technique. The technique described did not differ greatly from that employed by William Roy in his survey of Scotland and nearly two hundred years later,[11] except that distances would not have been measured by chain, but by pacing or riding time. Apian reckoned that one hour's riding equalled one German mile!

Apian is said to have made use of observed latitudes. Longitude and latitude are not marked on Saxton's county maps, but they appear on his general map of England and Wales in its second state (c. 1583; see Shirley, 1980, no. 138), and are accurate to within about 5', except for the south-west peninsula, which is not swung sufficiently to the south. Latitudes could have been measured from astronomical observation with some ease, but longitudes presented a major problem. Calculations of the latter from astronomical observation were complex and unreliable, while the use of time-pieces was still at the experimental stage. It is doubtful if even the observation of latitudes would have been much help to Saxton, bearing in mind the scale at which he was working and the fact that the instruments were open-sighted. Ravenhill has pointed out[12] that Norden working some twenty years later specifically rejected the use of such measurements.

Further understanding of Saxton's methods can only come from the internal evidence of the maps themselves. Ravenhill[13] has concluded from an analysis of the

5. Taylor, 1930, bibliography, pp. 170–9, and chapter 8.
6. Lynam, 1950, p. 13; Crone, 1962, pp. 106–109; Harvey, 1959, p. 2; Bagrow, 1964, p. 165; Evans and Lawrence, 1979, pp. 40–4; Tyacke and Huddy, 1980, pp. 19–23.
7. Described by Leonard Digges in *A geometrical treatis named Pantometria* (1571).
8. Crone, 1962, p. 106.
9. Ravenhill, 1972, p. 28.
10. Crone, 1962, ch. 7. Philip(p) Apian (1531–89) was the son of Peter Apian (1495–1552).
11. R.A. Gardiner, 'William Roy, surveyor and antiquary', *GJ* vol. 143, pt 3 (1977), p. 441.
12. Ravenhill, 1972, p. 31.
13. Ibid., p. 30.

map of Cornwall that triangulation, rather than the road traverse, was the basic technique employed, and has suggested that the well-established network of warning beacons would have provided a ready-made framework for his observations.

An analysis of Saxton's map of the south-east was made by the present writer by redrawing the map on a larger scale; the distance from Chichester to Dover, the major towns at opposite ends of the map, being increased from 490 mm to 600 mm. This is the distance between these two towns on the Ordnance Survey quarter inch fifth series, sheet 17 – *SOUTH-EAST ENGLAND* (1962). When the two maps were super-imposed, London (on Saxton's map), measured from the north end of London Bridge, lay only just over one mile east of its correct position. The rest[14] of the map was also reasonably accurate, except for the coastal area between Arundel and Hythe. This area, which corresponds roughly with the navigable limits of those rivers which drain southwards into the Channel, is misplaced eastwards by about four miles. The map itself gives considerable emphasis to rivers and coastline, which suggests that Saxton followed these features in the course of his survey. This is also the impression gained from reading Harrison's description of Sussex, which was based on Saxton's map and notes.[15] The extensive use of boats would not be surprising. Lythe made use of boats in his survey of Ireland[16] in 1572.

Whereas it would be wrong to draw firm conclusions from such a superficial examination of the map, the first impression gained is that triangulation, if used, was not used to lay down a framework for the whole map, but may well have been employed in the surveys of certain self-contained regions. Such regions are roughly co-terminous with the four counties, but are rather better defined by the catchment areas of the main river systems. It would appear that some difficulty was experienced when it came to fitting these regional surveys together, in particular the Sussex coastal region. The impression that no form of triangulation was used for the area as a whole is confirmed by the location, for example, of Argos Hill near Mayfield. This hill stands at the source of the Ouse, the Rother and a tributary of the Medway. Saxton's map gives it great prominence, and it is the only hill named. It stands out as a suitable station for trigonometrical observation. Nevertheless, it is badly misplaced in relation both to the Sussex coastal region and to the rest of the map.

It is hoped that a more scientific analysis of Saxton's county maps, perhaps with the aid of a computer, will elicit more information regarding his method of survey.

Saxton named 298 towns and villages, ten houses (eg *Coudrey*) and twenty other features in Sussex, of which all can be identified except *Bisshops Wood* near Hailsham and *Woking* near Lewes. The latter may refer to Offham, known as Woughton in 1545[17] and as Wogham as late as 1609.[18] It is marked as Wogham on Norden, catalogue no. 3 (1595).

14. With minor exceptions, eg Thanet, which is grossly understated.
15. Hind, 1952, p. 17. There is evidence that Saxton's notes remained available. His large map of England and Wales (1583) contains features and names which do not appear on his county maps.
16. BL, Lansdown MS, vol. 22 art. 72.
17. *SAC* vol. 23 (1871), p. 324.
18. Mawer and Stenton, 1930, p. 316.

For this map Saxton used the old English mile, equal to about ten furlongs, although it varied greatly from one region of England to another.[19] According to Saxton's own scale, the distance on the map from Chichester to Rye is 54 miles, which would be equivalent to 67½ statute miles; the distance from Brighton to East Grinstead is 16½ local or customary miles, which is equivalent to 20½ statute miles. The ratio between these two measurements is 3.3 to 1. The true distances are 66½ and 23 miles respectively; a ratio of 2.9 to 1. Saxton's representation of Sussex is, therefore, compressed along the north/south axis by about 12%, an error which persisted until the publication of Budgen's map, no. 24, in 1723.

The other most obvious error on Saxton's map is the exaggeration of the coastal features, particularly the 'bay' between *Feringe* and *New Shoreham*.[20] This error is apparent on Mercator (1564), but is not so pronounced on the Nowell and Lhuyd maps. It is not shown on the Palmer and Covert map (appendix II.2), which is probably the best representation of the coastline at that period,[21] and which compares favourably with modern charts; in spite of the fact that there have been substantial changes in the coast-line as a result of erosion and the silting of river estuaries, a subject about which there is a most extensive literature.[22]

The division of the country into shires and the sub-division into hundreds probably occurred during the Saxon period. Saxton's were the first printed maps to show county boundaries. Presumably he obtained this information from the lords lieutenant or from the sheriffs; Skelton[23] points out that Speed, who was the first cartographer to delineate sub-divisions in many counties, tells us that he obtained his information from 'the Parliament Rowles', or, where these failed him, from 'the Nomina Villarum in their Sheriffes bookes'. These would have supplied Saxton with lists of parishes, grouped by hundreds, from which the county boundary could have been determined. Hundreds are not shown on Saxton's map of Sussex; the first map to include them was Budgen no. 24 (1723).

Saxton shows *Amersham* as *Part of hampshire* within an oval enclave. In fact this should be a seven-mile strip, up to about a mile in width, stretching north to the Hampshire boundary: it is part of the parish of Steep, and was not absorbed into Sussex until 1844. It is delineated correctly on Norden no. 3 (1595).

Parish boundaries are also thought to have originated in the Saxon period,[24] although in the then less settled areas, eg the Weald, their origins must be later. They

---

19. C. Close, 'The old English mile'. *GJ* vol. 76, pt. 4(1930). Close deduces an average length for the customary mile of about 10.3 furlongs.
20. First noted by H.C.P. Smail, in *SNQ* vol. 17 (1969), p. 95; commented on in Coldwell, 1973. Corrected on Seller no. 19 (c. 1694).
21. W. Budgen (no relation to the cartographer) claims to have found a significant error in this map; see *SAC* vol. 58 (1916), p. 161.
22. For example, A. Ballard, 'The Sussex coast line', with a map by L.F. Salzman and the following two papers, *SAC* vol. 53 (1910); *SAC* vol. 79 (1938), p. 199; H. Lovegrove, 'Old shore lines near Camber Castle' *GJ* vol. 109, pp. 200–7; Steers, J.A., *The coastline of England and Wales*, Cambridge, 1969, pp. 304–33, which contains diagrams and references to Sussex maps; Brandon, 1974, map p. 117.
23. Skelton, *County atlases*, 1970, p. 33.
24. Brandon, 1978, pp. 13, 44 and 200.

are not marked by Saxton, although it seems that he set out to record all the market towns and parishes, as suggested by the notes on the map (Ee). Allowing for the fact that major towns contained two or more parishes, it is possible to reconcile this figure of 312 parishes (which includes a number of chapels) with the locations marked on the map; but comparison with contemporary records[25] throws up a number of discrepancies. Saxton, for example, omits fifteen small parishes and chapels.[26] Nevertheless, much of the information required by Saxton would have been accessible in the diocesan records at Chichester. There was a visitation of the diocese in 1569,[27] and Richard Curteys, who was appointed Bishop of Chichester in 1570, is said to have gone 'three times through this whole diocese . . .'[28] Some sort of map, or at least a written itinerary, must have been available, and would have been of considerable assistance to the cartographer.

It is contended[29] that William I divided Sussex into six rapes for the purpose of defence. Although still of administrative significance[30] at the time, they were not marked on the first edition of Saxton's map. They are delineated and named on the map in state (iv), c.1685, but not accurately; Goring, for example, is placed in Bramber rape instead of Arundel rape. Norden no. 3 (1595) was the first map to show the boundaries of the rapes.

The engraver of the map, Remigius Hogenberg, was Flemish. He is thought to have come to England shortly before 1572.[31] He engraved nine of the maps in Saxton's atlas.

A number of businesses were involved in publishing these maps. William Web was an Oxford bookseller. The title-page of the 1645 atlas in state (iii) reads *Printed for William Web at the Globe in Cornhill.* Skelton[32] suggests that this must have been the address of the printer, and that the maps were reprinted for use by the royalist armies.

Philip Lea[33] (c. 1660–1700) specialised in cartographic publications, and built up a large stock of plates which he acquired from both older and contemporary map makers. His wife, Ann (d. 1730), continued the business after 1700 with Robert Morden (see no. 17) and others. From about 1720, a number of his map-plates reappeared in the possession of Thomas Bowles (see under no. 23).

George Willdey (d. 1737) started as a spectacle maker in about 1707. He later

25. V.J.B. Torr, 'An Elizabethan return of the state of the diocese of Chichester', *SAC* vol. 61 (1920).
26. For example East Dean, Storrington and Wiston, which is marked but not named.
27. *State Papers Domestic. Elizabeth 1560–71.* Reprinted in *VCH* vol. 2, pp. 24–6.
28. Quoted from Manning, 1969, p. 63.
29. F.E. Sawyer, *Archaeological Review* vol. I, 1888; J.F.A. Mason, *SAC* vol. 102 (1964), pp. 68 et seq., which gives references to the earlier literature on this controversial subject. The most recent discussion will be found in Brandon, 1978, pp. 182, 198 et seq. The division of Sussex into administrative regions would seem to have started some time before the *Burgal Hidage* (c. 919), probably during the reign of King Alfred. The process was completed by William I.
30. See appendix I.2.
31. Evans and Lawrence, 1979, p. 35.
32. Skelton, *County atlases,* 1970, p. 244.
33. Tyacke, 1978, pp. 121–2.

became a map-seller and was for a time in association with both Charles Price and John Senex.

William Dicey of Northampton was a publisher of prints and chap-books. By 1736 his son, Cluer Dicey, had taken over the London end of his business and also that of John Cluer. The imprint C. Dicey & Co. also appears on Speed no. 7 (ix). In 1765 he was in partnership with Richard Marshall.[34] For a note of Thomas Jefferys see no. 34.

EDITIONS

(i) *CANTII, Southsexiae, Surriae, et Middelsexiae comitat, Una cum suis vndique confinibus, Oppidis, pagis, Villis, et fluminibus, in eisdem, vera descriptio* (Ea, in ornamental rectangular frame[35]). *An Dm̃ 1575 et D. Elizabethe Re:gine A°17.* (Ea, in oval frame below title.) *Remigius Hogenbergius sculpsit* (Ed, below scale). *Scala Miliarium 10 = 66 mm* (Ed). Royal Arms of Elizabeth I with motto (Ca). Arms of Thomas Seckford with notes about each of the four counties and *Londinum* (Ee); these notes were re-engraved prior to this state of the plate, traces of the original engraving remain visible. The decorated border contains the compass points *SEPTENTRIO, ORIENS, MERIDIES* and *OCCIDENTS*. **See plate 4.**

Probably proof copies not offered for sale. (BL)

(ii) Seckford's motto *PESTIS PATRIAE PIGRICIES* and new frame line above it, added (Ed, above Seckford's arms). *Christophorus Saxton descripsit* and double line above it, added (Ee, below notes). Nine new trees added near *Enfeld Chase*; the style of these trees differs from other trees on the map, the right side being formed by a continuous line with cross-hatching; others have horizontal hatching only. Capital letters have been blacked in, whereas in state (i) most capitals were engraved in outline only, e.g. *SVS* in *SVSSEX, PARTE* in *PARTE OF HERTFORDE SHIRE,* and nearly all of *SEPTENTRIO.*

Issued in an atlas containing general maps of England and Wales and county maps, all by Saxton. There is no title page, but the maps are preceded by a full-page engraving of Queen Elizabeth I enthroned. The atlas was probably first put on sale in 1579, but the definitive edition of the work was not published until about 1590. At least one early copy was printed on vellum. BL.CUL.RGS

---

34. Darlington and Howgego, 1964, no. 133.
35. The use of the term *cartouche* has been avoided where possible. The *Oxford English dictionary* defines cartouche as 'a tablet for an inscription or for ornament, representing a sheet of paper with the ends rolled up; a drawing of this'. In cartographic literature, however, the meaning of the word has been extended to cover any form of decorative framework. *MDTT* (21.23) defines cartouche 'An embellishment of a map, often in the form of a scroll.'

Issued both before and after the publication of the complete atlas as loose sheets, sold separately.

(iii)   Date (in the inscription, Ea) altered from *1575* to *1642*; but traces of the erasure remain visible at the bottom of the oval frame. Arms of Elizabeth I (Ca) replaced by those of Charles I.

> *The maps of all the shires in England and Wales. Exactly taken and trvly described by Christopher Saxton. And graven at the charges of a private gentleman for the publicke good. Now newly revised, amended, and re-printed.*
> London, William, Web, 1645. BL.CUL.BOD

(iv)   The inscription in oval frame (Ea) erased, but traces remain. The symbol for *Dertforde* moved from east side to west side of river. County boundaries are more clearly marked by heavy pecked lines; boundaries of rapes, lathes and hundreds in Sussex, Kent and Surrey are marked by dotted lines and the names added. Crosses added to indicate market towns; in Sussex at *Chechester, Midherst, Petworth, Arrūdel, Stanyng, Terringe, Bramber, New Shorehm̃, Dichinge, Brighthelmston, Lewes, E. Grinstead, Catstret, Haylshm̃, Hastinge, Winchelseye, Rye* and *Battell*. Mitres added to signify bishoprics at *CA[N]TERBVRY* and *Rochester* but not at *Chechester*. (According to the key in the front of the 1689 atlas, an archbishopric should have a mitre with a cross. CA[N]TERBVRY has the mitre without a cross, but the cross indicating a market town has two cross-bars on it. Other maps in the 1689 atlas have crowns added, which according to the key indicate parliamentary boroughs, but none has been added on the south-east map.) Form lines added to coastline and river estuaries; bolder hachuring on hill symbols; many tree symbols re-engraved, and two new tree symbols added to south of *Balco'be*; ten tree symbols reduced to seven in the enclosure east of *Balco'be*. Hill symbols added above and to the right of *E* of *SVRREY*. *Tilbury* with star-shaped (fort) symbol and *Margets Bay* added.

> No atlas has been found with the map in this state, but the known impression is from an atlas or book. Maps of Lancashire, Suffolk, Staffordshire and of Northamptonshire and Derbyshire are known to exist in this state. It has been suggested[36] that these maps were prepared for Lea's atlas c. 1689, and issued some time before that date, but after Lea commenced selling maps in 1683. (P)
> An edition was projected in 1665. Certain county maps bear that date and others are known with the date altered from 1665 to 1689. This map cannot, however, have been printed for the 1665 edition, since the watermark[37] dates it post 1680.

(v)   *SUSSEX, SURRY and KENT, by C.S. Corrected & Amended with many Additions by Phil:Lea* added (Da). *Shereness* with fort symbol, and *The Downs* (in sea off *Sandwiche*) added.

---

36.   Whitaker, 1948, p. 46; Evans and Lawrence, 1979, p. 48.
37.   Heawood, 1924, no. 117, and 1931, no. 170. The monogram is that of Pieter van der Ley. The same paper was used for Pitt's *English atlas*, 1683–5.

All the shires of England and Wales described by Christopher Saxton being the best and original mapps with many additions and corrected by Philip Lea.
London, Phillip Lea, [1689]. BL.BOD.RGS

(vi)   *Sold by P. Lea at the Atlas and Hercules in Cheap Side, London* added. (Ea, in oval frame). Roads added in four categories, those in Sussex being shown by (a) double solid lines: *Chechester* to *Arrũdel* named *Arundel Road, New Shorehm̃* to *Newhauen, Londò* to *Newhauen* named *New Haven Road*; (b) solid line and pecked line: *Chechester* to *Godalminge* named *Chichester Road*; (c) doubled pecked lines: *Chechester* to *Petersfeld* labelled *to Chichester*; and (d) single solid line: *Chechester* to *Hauant, Arrũdel* to *Guildford* (via *Petworth*), *Chechester* to *Petworth, Croydon* to *New Shorehm̃* (via *Crawley* and *Bramber*), *Arrũdel* to *New Shorehm̃, Arrũdel* to *Strethm̃* (via *Horshm̃*). Also added: five Arms of the Earls of Sussex (Ce), a river running south from *Merston* to Pagham harbour, *Wey R, Selsey Pen Insula, Peer* (at *Douer*) with engraving of mole, *Lighthouse* (at *The north Forland*) with symbol, *N* in front of *Mundhm̃*, four place-names with symbols – *S. Mundhm̃, Merston, W. Harting, E. Harting,* and many others outside Sussex. Cliffs at *The Beache* shown in perspective.

All the shires of England and Wales described by Christopher Saxton being the best and original mapps with many additions.
London, Phillip Lea, [1694][38]. BL

The shires of England and Wales described by Christopher Saxton being the best and original mapps with many additions and corrections viz: yͤ hundᵈˢ, roads. &c. by Philip Lea also the new surveis of Ogilby. Seller. &c.
London, Philip Lea, [1694]. W

(vii)   Additions include: *Storrington* with town symbol and a river running east off the Arun. *Tunbridge Wells* with symbol, *Ebbsham Wells* with symbol in addition to *Ebbeshm̃* (Epsom).

The shires of England and Wales described by Christopher Saxton being the best and original mapps with many additions and corrections viz: yͤ hundᵈˢ, roads. &c. by Philip Lea also the new surveis of Ogilby. Seller. &c.
London, Phillip Lea, [1694]. BL.CUL.NMM

Atlas anglois contenant les cartes nouvelles & tres exactes des provinces, duchés, comtes, & baronies du royaume d'Angleterre. le tout enrichi des plans des villes & des armes de la noblesse.[39]
London, P. Lea, [1694]. BLACKBURN PL

38.   Tyacke, 1978, p. xix.
39.   For collation of this atlas, see *The Map collector* no. 5, December 1978, p. 49.

(viii) *Sold by Geo Willdey at the Great Toy, Spectacle, Chinaware, and Print Shop, the Corner of Ludgate Street near S^t. Pauls London* _ added (Be). Sea stippling behind this imprint erased. **See plate 5.**

The shires of England and Wales . . .
London, George Willdey, [1731].[40]   BL.BOD
This map is included in a collection of maps (Whitaker Collection no. 3) to which a title-page from Jeffery's edition, see state (ix), has been added.

(ix) Lea imprint (Ea, in oval frame), Willdey imprint (Be) and additional sea stippling in that area erased. *CA*[N]*TERBVRY* altered to *CANTERBURY;* SVSSEX re-engraved, the first *S* is now where the *V* was previously and the south-east corner of the *Shillinghigh pke* symbol has been erased; *SVRREY* re-engraved *SURRY*.

The Shires of England and Wales . . .
London, Thomas Jefferys, [1749].   BL[41]

Issued in a set of maps without title-page, probably by C. Dicey and Co., about 1770.   W.(SAS)

40.   Tyacke, 1978, p. 122. Following the death of Philip Lea in 1700, the Saxton plates were in the possession of his widow, Anne (d. 1730), and her son-in-law Richard Glynne (1681–1755). In August 1730 they were sold at auction. They were probably acquired by Willdey, and re-published as soon as the new imprints could be added.
41.   This atlas was described by Whitaker in *Imago Mundi* vol. 3 (1939). The British Library copy, in common with all other known copies, lacks the title page; but an impression of the title page has been inserted in the copy of the Willdey edition of the atlas in the Whitaker Collection. This title page gives Jefferys's address as 'Red Lyon Street' and describes him as 'Geographer to his Royal Highness the Prince of Wales'. Jefferys had probably acquired the plates from George Willdey's brother, Thomas, who had died in 1748. Harley has pointed out (1966, p. 31) that Jefferys was appointed 'Geographer' to Frederick Prince of Wales in 1749, and that he moved from Clerkenwell (Red Lyon Street) to Charing Cross in 1750. This atlas must, therefore, have been published in or about 1749. Whether the collections of maps in the British Library (Maps C.21.c.12), at Whitaker Collection (no. 4) and at National Library of Wales were published by Jefferys or by Dicey cannot be stated with certainty since they all lack the title page. Whitaker (1949, p. 18) has suggested that the Jefferys edition may have the Willdey imprints imperfectly erased and that it will include the folding map of Yorkshire. The folding map of Yorkshire is included in the British Library copy, but is not in the other two.

2 WILLIAM BOWES   1590

Size: 39 mm × 39 mm (9 mm)   1:3,010,000

Based on Saxton's general map *Anglia*, published in 1579. **See plate 6(i).**

This is one of a set of playing cards; each card in the pack bears a map of a county, drawn on a uniform scale. On the title card of the pack is engraved *W B inuent* and *1590*. The suits are named after the points of the compass, and the choice of counties for each suit is made on a regional basis. Sussex is the tenth card of the 'South' suit.

William Bowes's full name only came to light in 1972, when another pack of cards by the same maker (no. 4 below) was found.[1] He has not been identified, but may have been related to Ralph Bowes, who held a monopoly for the importation of playing cards from 1578 until his death in 1598. Ralph was the brother of Sir Jherome (d. 1616), ambassador to Russia. Their sister, Elizabeth (b. 1534), married Sir George Hart (1533–87), the son and heir of Sir Percival Hart (1495–1580) of Lullingstone Castle, Kent.

Another family named Bowes was descended from Sir Martyn Bowes (c. 1500–66), goldsmith and Mayor of London in 1546. Sir Martyn's will mentions Sir Percevall Harte, and demonstrates a connection between the two branches of the family. Sir Martyn had a son, William (b. 1543), and a son or grandson, also William (b. 1556).[2] Either could have been the maker of the playing cards described below.

Sir Martyn's family had cartographic and Sussex connections. His third wife outlived him, and married Thomas Seckford in 1577. She died in 1586, and is described as 'Dame Elizabeth Bowes, wife of – Sackford, one of her Majestie's Maisters of her Courte of Requests and Surveyor of her Courte of Wardes, and lyeth within the tombe of her late husband, Sir Martin Bowes, Knight, diceased'.[3] This identifies 'Sackford' with Thomas Seckford, Saxton's patron (d. 1587).

Sir Martyn's daughter, Ciseley, married first Henry Harte, and secondly Richard Covert (d. 1579). Richard's children by his first wife included John (d. 1589) and Sir Walter (1543–1631), who was responsible, with Sir Thomas Palmer, for the survey of the Sussex coast in 1587 (appendix II.2). A John Covert married Charity Bowes, granddaughter of Sir Martyn, and died without issue. She then married his cousin, also a Walter Covert.

Augustine Ryther, the engraver, was an Englishman whose work included five maps in the Saxton atlas and Robert Adams's Armada charts (see appendix II.4). He was also a bookseller, and it has been suggested[4] that he took over the sales of Saxton's

---

1. Mann and Kingsley, 1972, p. 5.
2. *Transcript of the registers of the united parishes of S. Mary Woolnoth and S. Mary Woolchurch Haw, 1538 to 1760,* London, 1866. See also *Calendar of wills. Court of Hustings, London. Part III, 1358–1688.* London, 1890.
3. Ibid.
4. Skeleton, *County atlases,* 1970 p. 241.

maps when the latter's patent expired in 1587. However, by 1595 he was in prison for debt.

EDITION

SVSSEX the 10 of the South hath Miles In Quantitie supficiall 900. In Circuite, 172. In Lengthe from Hamshire vnto Kent, 68, In Bredth from Surrey to y^e Brittaine sea 23. (This title appears in the top part of the card above the map, which is placed in the centre. Below are topographical notes. The size of the whole card is 56 mm × 94 mm). Scale, 10 miles = 6 mm (Ae). Compass (Ea). Cardinal points *N, E, S* and *W* (in border). *X* (Aa and Ee). **See plate 6(i).**

> Issued in a pack of cards printed from four plates. On each plate were engraved all cards of one suit and two additional cards. The cards were arranged on the plate in three horizontal rows of five, and were not in numerical order. Sussex is the last card in the middle row of the South plate.
> BL.RGS

3 JOHN NORDEN   1595

Size: 521 mm × 265 mm (10 mm)   1:251,000

Based on Saxton no. 1, with the addition of much original material. Norden himself appears to have followed the coast route between the Kent border and Eastbourne, and to have proceeded along the Downs from Eastbourne to Chichester, or vice versa.[1] **See frontispiece.**

Norden (1548–c.1625)[2] was probably born in Somerset, the son of a yeoman. He was a BA (1569) and MA (1573) of Hart Hall, Oxford. From at least 1584 onwards he published devotional books with puritan sympathies; but by the end of the decade he was living in London and practising law.

His work in the field of cartography seems to have commenced in 1588 with a survey of monastic estates in Northamptonshire. It was about this time that he conceived and planned his *Speculum Britanniae,* which was to have been a series of county chorographies accompanied by new and improved maps, the first work to combine both text and maps. He worked on this scheme until about 1604, and he produced descriptions and maps of at least eight counties, but only two – Middlesex and Hertfordshire – were printed in his lifetime, both at his own expense. Only five of the descriptions and maps were designed as part of the *Speculum Britanniae* series,

---

1. J.H. Farrant, 'John Norden's 'Description of Sussex', 1595' *SAC* vol. 116 (1978) pp. 269–75; *Sussex Archaeological Newsletter* no. 16, July, 1975.
2. Ravenhill, 1972; Farrant, *SAC* vol. 116; A.W. Pollard, 'The unity of John Norden', *The Library* 4th ser. vol. 7 (1926–7); Lynam, 1950, p. 15; Skelton, 1952, pp. 52–3.

those for Middlesex, Essex, Hertfordshire, Northamptonshire and Cornwall. The maps of Surrey, Hampshire and Sussex were larger than the others, but could have been adapted to the series.

From 1592 to c. 1599 Norden received official support, particularly from Lord Burghley, but for the next five years he was out of favour because of his adherence to the cause of the Earl of Essex. This delayed until 1604 the completion and submission to the King of his work on Cornwall. Throughout this period, Norden was forced to make a number of appeals for assistance on behalf of his cartographic work. In 1595, for example, he presented the Queen with *A Chorographicall discription of the seuerall Shires and Islands of Middlesex, Essex, Surrey, Sussex, Hampshire, Weighte, Garnesey & Jarsey.*[3] This composite manuscript contained descriptions, some abridged or now incomplete, and maps. It has never been printed, and the maps were removed, although those of Essex and Hampshire have been reunited with it. It was accompanied by a letter describing his plans, and was designed to secure royal patronage.

After 1605 he seems to have abandoned hope of proceeding with the *Speculum Britanniae;* but in that year he was made surveyor of the lands of the Duchy of Cornwall, and from then until his death Norden practised as an estate surveyor.

His work included a number of estate surveys in Sussex.[4] He also wrote some notable books, including *The Surveyors dialogue* (1607) and *England. An intended guyde for English travailers* (1625). An updated summary of Norden's known work on English county maps will be found in appendix IX.

On the cartographic side, it is to Norden's credit that he popularised in England the use of the reference grid with marginal letters and numbers, and the key to conventional signs introduced into this country by William Smith[5] a few years earlier. The grids and borders are characteristic of Norden's maps, and he was the first to incorporate an inset town plan on a county map. All these features will be found on the Sussex map described below. He also pioneered in England the triangular distance table, which first appeared in *England. An intended guyde for English travailers* (1625). His plan of Chichester is the earliest known plan of that city,[6] and was copied by Speed (see no. 7), who omitted the figures in the streets. This is the first map of Sussex to mark the boundaries of the six rapes, but the divisions are virtually diagramatic. *Slindon,* for example, is placed in Arundel rape, whereas it should be in that of Chichester as it is part of Aldwick hundred. Rapes continued to be delineated in this imprecise manner until Budgen, no. 24. Even Lower gets Slindon wrong on his map (no. 98), although his text is correct.[7]

The delineation of the coastline shows only a marginal improvement on Saxton; Beachy Head is represented more accurately, but the 'bay' between *Fering* and *New Shorham* remains. Towns and parishes correspond well with Saxton, but Norden has added a number of *Howses of Gent,* eg *Sheffelde.* The first *f* is not crossed, an error

3. BL Add. MS 31853.
4. See Farrant, *SAC* vol. 116. Also *SAC* vol. 44 (1901) p. 147, and Steer, 1962 and 1968.
5. Campbell, 1962, p. 412; Skelton, *County atlases,* 1970, p. 21.
6. Butler, 1972.
7. Lower, 1831, p. 224.

repeated by Speed and Blaeu, which caused Jansson (no. 13) to spell it *Shesfield*.

Norden introduced a number of other features, such as distinctive palings for parkland, beacons (prominent in the county), havens, and the 'walks' of Ashdown forest. He placed *Peppleshm* to the east of *Hastings* instead of to the west,[8] an error which persisted until Budgen, no. 24. *Bisshops Wood, Argos Hill* and four other names from Saxton's map have been omitted. *Woking* has been altered to *Wogham. Frant* (Saxton) is now *Farnte,* an accepted alternative form.[9] On Norden's 1607 map (no. 6) it has been copied as *Farate,* probably as a result of a scratch on the plate. This in turn was copied by Speed (no. 7) as *Farat.* The sea is covered by zig-zag shading, which was introduced by the Dutch cartographers, and copied from Norden by van den Keere (no. 5), Speed (no. 7) and Bill (no. 9). Saxton had used stippling, to which Norden reverts for his 1607 map (no. 6). Later cartographers tended to leave the sea area plain. The coast has form lines; and cliffs, foreshore and the outflow of rivers[10] are indicated on the map. The key is not as extensive as that on some of his other sixteenth-century maps; but several conventional signs not included in the key appear on the map itself; for example, at *Pagham* there is a circle with eight radiating dashes, which is the sign used for *Mylls*[11] on his map of Essex (1594), and a circle with an arrow attached is used for the 'walks' in Ashdown Forest. Roads are marked on some of Norden's maps, but not on this map of Sussex. His Surrey map (1594) includes some place-names in the north of Sussex which do not appear on this map, eg *Forestrowe* and *Shelarstrode.*[12]

The engraving by Christopher Shwytzer is of a very high standard. Speed described Shwytzer as 'the most exquisite and curious hand of that age'.[13]

The map was published with the financial assistance of William Sanderson, and his arms appear on the map. He was a merchant adventurer who sponsored a number of overseas enterprises, including John Davis' voyages in search of the north-west passage (1585–7). He financed, at a cost of over £1,000 the production of the first English-made globes in 1592–3. They were made by Emery Molyneux, a Lambeth instrument-maker, with the help of the Cambridge mathematician Edward Wright, and were engraved by Jodocus Hondius. They were the largest printed globes yet made, having diameters of 622 mm.

Sanderson presented pairs of globes to the Universities of Oxford and Cambridge, and to the Queen, who received them at his house in Newington-Butts.[14] A globe and *Opera Mundi* appear as additions to his arms on the map of Sussex. Molyneux followed Hondius (see no. 7) to the Netherlands in 1596–7, and died in 1599.

The plates for the globes were acquired by Hondius, and taken to the Netherlands, where they were superseded by Dutch globes, which may account for the scarcity of the

8. Ray, 1936.
9. Mawer and Stenton, 1930, p. 373.
10. Skelton, 1952, p. 37 describes similar engraving on early Ptolemaic maps as 'gushing estuaries'.
11. Budgen no. 24 uses a similar symbol with six dashes, which are slightly tangential, suggesting the wheel of water-mill.
12. Shovelstrode Farm. See Mawer and Stenton 1930, p. 333.
13. Quoted from Hind, 1952.
14. H.M. Wallis, 'The first English globe', *GJ* vol. 117 (1951); 'Further light on the Molyneux globes', *GJ* vol. 121 (1955); 'Globes in England up to 1660', *Geographical Magazine* vol. 35 (1962).

Molyneux globes. A fine pair is in the possession of the Middle Temple Library, of which the terrestrial globe is the revised version, and is dated 1603. The only other terrestrial globe to survive (and the only specimen of the first edition) is at Petworth House, in West Sussex. There is a tradition that it was given to Henry Percy, ninth Earl of Northumberland, by Sir Walter Ralegh when they were both prisoners in the Tower, but there is reason to think that it was in Percy's possession rather earlier. It is probable that it was removed from the Tower to Petworth in 1622, along with Percy's other goods. Ralegh himself would probably have owned a pair of the globes. Sanderson knew him well; he had married Ralegh's niece in 1571, and had acted as his adviser for the 1595 expedition to Guiana.

EDITION

SVSSEX (Ba, in ornamental rectangular frame). *Johēs Norden deliniauit anno 1595. Christof. Shwytzer Scul:* (Ae). List of rapes (Ce). Key (Ce) with nine symbols (in addition, the six 'walks' of Ashdown forest are marked on the map by small circles with arrows attached, although this symbol is not listed). Royal arms (Aa). Arms of Thomas Sackville, Lord Buckhurst (Ea). Arms of William Sanderson (Ec). Plan of Chichester (Ee). Grid 16 mm × 16 mm, lettered *a* to *r* vertically and numbered *2* to *64* horizontally. Only even numbers are used, but the top and bottom borders have 129 divisions. There is no scale-bar, but the interval between grid lines (16 mm) represents 2 miles, and the top and bottom borders, being numbered, serve as a scale. **See frontispiece.**

Probably issued from 1595 as loose sheets sold separately.   RGS
The only known impression lacks the right border.

4   WILLIAM BOWES   circa **1605**

Size: 24 mm × 24 mm (0.5 mm)   1:6,300,000

Copied from Bowes no. 2. **See plate 6(ii).**

This map appears in a second series of playing cards (see no. 2). Sussex is the 10 of Spades. The whole card measures 52 mm × 89 mm. The map is located in a panel 25 mm × 25 mm on the lower right of the card. Within this panel is another square (12 mm × 12 mm) within which most of the county maps are placed; but the Sussex map extends well beyond the left and right edges of this inner square. The larger area, therefore, has been regarded as part of the map. There are seven other panels on the card containing a variety of information.[1] The inscriptions *W. BOWES Inventor* and *W.*

---

1. Mann and Kingsley, 1972.

16

Hole Sculp appear on two of the title cards.

William Hole was an early English engraver, known for his portraits and as the first engraver of music on copper-plates in this country. Together with William Kip, he engraved the maps for Camden's *Britannia* (see no. 6). He also engraved the title page for Drayton's *Poly-Olbion* (see appendix IV.1).

EDITIONS

SVSSEX (not on the map, but in another panel at bottom right of the card, followed by text copied from Bowes no. 2). Scale-bar, *m 10* = 4 mm (Ae). Lines marking eight points of the compass appear behind the maps, but the east-west line is not visible on the Sussex map. The cardinal points are marked and the names of neighbouring counties etc. are engraved across them as follows: *N Surrie, E Sea, S B.Sea* (ie *Brittaine Sea* from no. 2) and *W H* (ie *Hamshire*). *X*, the card number (Ee), has *Shire* engraved across it. *SC* with *900.172* across it (Aa) standing for *Quantitie Supficiall 900* and *In Circuite 172* (from no. 2). *LB* with *68.23* (Ea), standing for *Lengthe . . . 68* and *Bredth . . . 23. South*, the suit mark, is engraved across the scale (Ae). **See plate 6(ii).**

Issued c. 1605 as a pack of 52 cards plus 3 title cards and 4 'Cards of use'. BL

5   PIETER VAN DEN KEERE   circa **1605**

Size: 120 mm × 84 mm (1 mm)   1:370,000

Based on Saxton no. 1. Sussex is combined with Kent, Surrey and Middlesex, but is included here because of its early date.

Pieter van den Keere[1] (1571–c. 1646) was born at Ghent, and came to London as a protestant refugee in 1584–5. In 1593 he settled in Amsterdam, where he died. He was the brother-in-law of Jodocus Hondius, who engraved the maps for Speed's *Theatre* (no. 7), and was related to Abraham Goos (c. 1590–1643), the Amsterdam engraver, cartographer and publisher. He married the sister of Petrius Bertius, see app. III.3. The maps in the present series were engraved in Amsterdam and probably sent to London as proofs and for the preparation of the accompanying text; two sets are known with the same text in manuscript. That publication would have been the first printed atlas of the British Isles, but the maps were not in fact published as a set until some twelve years later.

The author of the work below, William Camden[2] (1551–1623) was headmaster of Westminster School. His *Britannia* was first published in 1586, without maps.

1. Wallis, 1972; Schilder and Welu, 1980.
2. Copley, 1977. The introduction deals extensively with Camden's antiquarian and topographical sources.

Subsequent editions, with maps, were published in 1607 and 1610 (Norden no. 6); in 1617 containing maps in this series and published in Amsterdam; in 1626 (Bill no. 9); c. 1659 (Jansson no. 13); 1695, 1722 [1730], 1733 and 1772 (Morden no. 20); and in 1789 and 1806 (Cary no. 50).[3]

The maps in this series were republished in England by George Humble about 1619. This map of the south-east counties, however, was then replaced by separate maps of each county (see Humble no. 8).

EDITIONS

Cantii. South-sexiae. Suriae. et Middlesexiae. cō (Ee, in rectangular frame). *Scala Miliarium 10* = 15 mm (Ea).

Probably produced between 1600 and 1610 as proofs, and found in sets of county maps, without title pages and without text on back.   RGS

Guilielmi Camdeni, viri clarissimi Britannia, sive florentissimorum regnorum Angliae, Scotiae, Hiberniae & insularum adjacentium . . . descriptio. In epitomen contracta à Regerno Vitellio Zirizaeo, & tabulis chorographicis illustrata. Amsterdam, William Jansson, 1617.   BL.CUL.RGS

Page number *196* (Eb OS, sideways) printed from type, not engraved on plate. Latin text on back.

6 JOHN NORDEN   1607

Size: 393 mm × 222 mm (single-line border)   1:333,000

Copied from Norden no. 3, with a few minor spelling differences, eg *Selscombe* (Sedlescombe) altered to *Selcombe.*

This map appears in the first edition of Camden's *Britannia* to contain maps. The first English translation was published three years later, in 1610. Six maps (Hampshire, Surrey, Sussex, Kent, Hertfordshire and Middlesex) are ascribed to Norden; most of the others are based on Saxton. William Kip, who engraved the map of Sussex and thirty-three others in this work, was active between 1598 and 1610.

The translator, Philemon Holland (1552–1637), came from Chelmsford, Essex. He graduated at Trinity College, Cambridge, obtained a medical degree in 1597, and practised in Coventry. He is mainly known as a translator, in which field he secured a good reputation, both among his contemporaries and later writers. He is said to have

---

3. For full printing history of the work, see S. Piggott, 'William Camden and the *Britannia*', *Proceedings of the British Academy*, vol. 37 (1951). See also Seller no. 19(i), *Camden's Britannia abridg'd* (1701).

received £5 for his translation of *Britannia,* and it has been suggested that he also translated Speed's *Theatre.* He was always in poor circumstances towards the latter part of his life, and survived largely on charity.

EDITIONS

(i) *SVSSEXIA Siue Southsex, olim pars REGNORVM,* (Ea). *Iohānes Norden deliniauit. Wilhel: Kip Sculpsitt.* (Ee, in ornamental frame). Scale, 10 miles = 59 mm; 10 is engraved as *01* in error (Ee, above signature). Rapes (Ce). Royal arms (Aa). *Caracters distinguishing Places* (Ce), with a list of eight symbols.

> *Britannia, sive florentissimorum regnorum Angliae, Scotiae, Hiberniae . . . chorographica descriptio . . . chartis chorographicis illustrata. Giulielmo Camdeno authore.*
> London, George Bishop and John Norton, 1607.   BL
> Latin text on back; pages 219 and 220.

> *Britain, or a chorographicall description of the most flourishing kingdomes, England, Scotland, and Ireland . . . beautified with mappes of the severall shires of England: written first in Latine by William Camden . . . Translated newly into English by Philemon Holland . . .*
> London, George Bishop and John Norton, 1610.   BOD
> Without text on back.

(ii) Compass added (Ed).

> *Britain . . .*
> London, George Bishop and John Norton, 1610.   BL

(iii) Plate number *10* added (Ae).

> *Britain . . .*
> London, George Bishop and John Norton, 1610.   MANCHESTER PL

> *Britain . . .*
> London 1637.   BL
> This edition of the book has been recorded with the imprints of the following booksellers on the title-page: William Aspley; Andrew Crooke; Andrew Heb; George Latham; Joyce Norton and Richard Whitaker.

Reissued, according to Chubb,[1] by Christopher Browne in the early 18th century.

---

1. Chubb, 1927, no. XXI.

7 JOHN SPEED

circa **1610**

Size: 498 mm × 372 mm (6 mm)   1:252,000

Based on Norden no. 3. **See plate 7.**

John Speed (1552–1629) was born in Cheshire. He followed his father in the tailoring trade, and was a member of the Worshipful Company of Merchant Taylors. His interest in antiquities brought him to the notice of Sir Fulke Greville. Greville made him an allowance which enabled him to devote the latter part of his life to historical research and to cartography. He is perhaps the best-known of English cartographers, although he did little or no original work on the county maps themselves, a fact which he readily acknowledged; however, in compiling his *Theatre* he was most careful to search out the best available sources, and many of the town plans were based on his own surveys. The title *Theatre* in this connection had first been used by Ortelius in 1570.

The main difference between Speed's map of Sussex and that of Norden (no. 3) lies in the spelling of a few place-names, eg *Farat* (*Farnte* on Norden), *Woortinge* (*Worthing*), *Selsey* (*Celsey*). It has been observed[1] that place-names were constantly revised on later editions of Speed's atlas, but this is not the case on the map of Sussex. Speed can be credited with some minor improvements. For example, Norden had *Alborne* incorrectly in Lewes rape; Speed places it on the border of Lewes and Bramber rapes, and his text on the back of the map locates it properly in the latter.[2] This text was reset many times. It comprises a list of hundreds and parishes and a short description of the county adapted from Camden. Speed introduced on his map an island or sandbank[3] off the coast near Hastings, a feature which persisted on larger maps until Budgen no. 24 (1723).

The maps were engraved by Jodocus Hondius in Amsterdam, but were printed in London.[4] Hondius (1563–1612) was the leading cartographer and map publisher of the period. After ten years exile in London (c. 1584–94) he returned to Amsterdam, and in 1604 took over the business of the great Gerhard Mercator. The firm was later continued under the supervision of his sons Jodocus and Henricus. His daughter married Jan Jansson (see no. 13), and Jansson took over the business after the death of Henricus in 1638.

John Sudbury, the publisher, came from Nottingham. He was apprenticed to Robert Hackforth, a London stationer. His imprint first appeared on a map in 1599. He went into partnership with his nephew, George Humble, and retired about 1618. He died in 1621.

George Humble was probably the son of the London bookseller, Robert Humble. He carried on after Sudbury's retirement until his death in 1640. His later output

1. Tooley, 1949, p. 69.
2. *SAC* vol. 74 (1933), p. 244.
3. Ray, 1936.
4. Skelton, *County atlases* 1970, p. 33.

included cartographic works (see for example no. 8). He was succeeded by his son, William (1612–86), who actively supported Charles II in exile, and was created a baronet in 1660. William's sister, Honor, married Sir Thomas Viner, Lord Mayor of London, in 1653.

Some of George Humble's map plates were sold to Peter Stent, but the Speed plates passed to William Humble, and from him to William Garrett in 1659. Garrett conveyed them soon afterwards to Roger Rea, father and son; and the son probably sold them to Bassett and Chiswell between 1668 and 1674. The plates may then have been acquired by Robert Walton, whose stock passed on his death in 1688 to Christopher Browne.[5] Before 1700 they came into the possession of John and Henry Overton (see no. 18), who had also acquired the stock of Peter Stent. Much later, about 1770, they turned up in the possession of C. Dicey and Co., who had also acquired the Saxton plates.[6]

Thomas Bassett (fl. 1659–93) and Richard Chiswell (1639–1711) were both London booksellers. The former specialised in law books; the latter was publisher to the Royal Society, and was held in high repute by his contemporaries. Their partnership seems to have been restricted to the publication of Speed's work. Although Chiswell left a son, also Richard, his business was taken over by Charles Rivington.

EDITIONS

(i) *SUSSEX Described and divided into Rapes with the situation of Chichester the cheife citie thereof. And the armes of such Nobles as have bene dignified with the title of Earles since the conquest and other accidents therein observed.* (Ca, across engraving of an open book). *The Scale of miles 8* = 62 mm (Ae). Royal Arms (Ea). Arms of four Earls of Sussex (Ce). Plan of *CHICHESTER* (Aa). Note on history of the county commencing *WILLIAM the Bastard* . . . (Ee).

Produced as a set of proofs. PAUL MELLON COLL

Without text on back. The description of the map in this state is based on Skelton.[7]

(ii) The following additions: *Described by IOHN NORDEN. Augmented by Iohn Speede And are to be sold in popes head Alley against the Exchange by I.S. and George Humble cum privilegio* (Cb); *Jodocus Hondius caelavit Anno Domini 1610* (Ce); sea shading and a group of trees in centre of map.

Produced as a set of proofs.[8] BL.RGS.CUL

---

5. Tyacke, 1973, p. 69; and 1978, p. 113.
6. For a summary of the printing history, see R.V. Tooley, 'John Speed: a personal view', *Map Collector* no. 1 (1977).
7. Skelton, *County atlases*, 1970, p. 211.
8. Ibid. pp. 35 and 211.

The theatre of the empire of Great Britaine: presenting an exact geography of the kingdomes of England, Scotland, Ireland and the iles adioyning: with the shires, hundreds, cities and shire-townes, within ye kingdome of England, divided and described by Iohn Speed.
London, John Sudbury and George Humble, 1611 (actually published 1612).

BL.RGS.CUL

The theatre of the empire of Great Britaine. . .
London, John Sudbury and George Humble, 1614 (actually published 1616). BL

Theatrum imperii Magnae Britanniae; exactam regnorum Angliae, Scotiae, Hiberniae et insularum adiacentium geographiā . . . Opus, nuper quidem à Iohanne Spédo cive Londinensi, Anglicè conscriptum: nunc verò, a Philemone Hollando, apud Conventrianos medicinae doctore, Latinitate donatum . . .
London, John Sudbury and George Humble, 1616.

BL.RGS.CUL

Theatrum imperii Magnae Britanniae . . .
Amsterdam, Jodocus Hondius, 1621.

S11

Theatrvm imperii Magnae Britanniae . . . A Ioanne Spedo Anglice, conscriptum & à Philemone Hollando latinitate donatum.
Amsterdam, Jan Blaeu, 1646.

BOD

The text on back of 1611 (1612) and 1614 (1616) editions is in English. The signature in the former is *CI* and the latter *I*. In the 1616, 1621 and 1646 editions the text is in Latin and has not been reset so that these issues cannot be distinguished.

(iii) *Beau Cliffe* (Dd), *VINDELLS* (Ec), *Rother flu* (Dc) and *THE REGNI* (Cc) added.

The theatre of the empire of Great Britaine . . .
London, John Sudbury and George Humble, 1614 (actually a reissue of 1623).   W

The theatre of the empire of Great Britaine . . .
London, George Humble, 1627 (reissued 1632 and 1646) and 1650 (reissued 1651, 1652, 1653, and 1654).

BL;BL;BL;W;S50;S51;S55;S57

Also issued without text in large numbers during the Civil War for military use. Sets of Speed's county maps were stitched together in such a way that they could be rolled up and strapped to a saddle.

S36

In each issue of the *Theatre* listed above, the map has a description of Sussex printed on the back. Four different type-settings are found, and the table below will assist in the identification of a loose map. It is possible, however, that some copies of the *Theatre* of 1627 (1646) and later may have been issued with old sheets of the map bearing the text in the 1627 (1632) setting.

22

	1614 (1623)	1627	1627 (1632)	1627 (1646), 1650, 1650 (1651–4)
Top right of folio 10	*Chap V*	*Chap. V.*	*Chap. 5.*	*Chap 5*
Margin of paragraph 4 on folio 9	*The soile*	*The Soyle*	*The Soyle*	*The Soile*

The map is included in a set of Speed maps accompanied by galley proofs for the text of the *Theatre* dated 1615. There is no title-page and the maps have no text on the back.

BOD

(iv)   The imprint (Cb) altered to read . . . *sold by Roger Rea the Elder and younger at the Golden Crosse in Cornhill against the Exchange.*

The theatre of the empire of Great Britaine . . .
London, Roger Rea the elder and younger, 1650 (actually issued 1665).   BL

(v)   Date altered from *1610* to *1666.*

An atlas, without title-page, published by John Overton, c. 1670 (Skelton, *County atlases,* 1970 no. 89).

AD[9]

Without text on back.

(vi)   The imprint (Cb) altered to read . . . *sold by Tho: Bassett in Fleet Street, and Ric: Chiswell in St. Paul's Churchyard. Cuckfeild* re-engraved *Cuchfeild. Leonard L. Dacres E. of Sussex* and arms added (Be). Part of border missing in bottom left corner as a result of damage to plate.

The theatre of the empire of Great Britaine . . . As also a prospect of the most famous parts of the world by Iohn Speed with many additions never before extant.
London, Thomas Bassett and Richard Chiswell, 1676.   BL.CUL.W

With English text on back.

---

9.   Also found as one of the loose maps in the collection described by R.W. Shirley, 'An unusual collection of maps in a pre-Overton atlas', *Map Collector* no. 7 (June 1979).

England fully described in a compleat sett of mapps of ye county's of England and Wales, with their islands, containing in all 58 mapps.
London, Henry Overton, [1713].   NMM
Without text on back. An earlier edition of this work (c. 1700) contains no. 18. A post-1772 edition (Gardner coll., S89) may contain this map or no. 18.

Issued in sets of Speed's county maps without title-page or text by Christopher Browne in about 1695 and by Henry Overton after 1716.   NMM;BL
The advertisement found with the British Library set (Maps C.7.e.12) reads 'A catalogue of a set of maps of the several counties of England and Wales with the islands thereto belonging; each map is printed on a sheet of good royal paper, having a plan of its respective city, or county-town on it. Printed and sold by Henry Overton, at the White Horse without Newgate, London. Sold either in complete sets, or singly.'

Issued as loose sheets, sold separately, by Henry Overton, and probably by Bassett and Chiswell and by Christopher Browne.

(vii)   *And now Sold by Henry Overton at the White Horse without Newgate – London* (De), and four roads running to the north border from *CHICHESTER, Terring, Seaford* and *Rye,* have been added.

England fully described . . .
London, Henry Overton, [1730].   BOD

(viii)   Date *1666* erased.

England fully described in a compleat sett of mapps of ye county's of England and Wales, with their islands, containing in all 58 mapps. By John Speed.
London, Henry Overton, 1743.   CUL

Issued in a set of county maps by John Speed.
London, Henry Overton, 1743.   BL
The advertisement found with the British Library set (Maps C.7.e.7) reads 'A sett of the counties of England and Wales, with their islands, containing fifty-eight maps, each on a sheet of royal paper. By John Speed. Reprinted in the year, 1743. With additions. Sold either in complete setts, bound or single, either coloured or plain, by Henry Overton, at the White Horse . . . London . . .'

Issued in 1743 by Henry Overton as loose sheets, sold separately.

(ix)   In the imprint (De) *Henry Overton . . . Newgate* erased and replaced by *C. Dicey & Co: in Aldermary Church Yard.* The bridge over the Arun river at *Houghton* has been extended as far as the town symbol. **See plate 7.**

Issued in an atlas with manuscript title-page: *The English atlas, or a complete set of maps of all the counties in England and Wales . . .*
[London, C. Dicey and Co. 1770].   CUL

Reproductions of the map in state (vii) were published by Kelly and Co. about 1874.

8 GEORGE HUMBLE

circa **1619**

Size: 121 mm × 81 mm (1 mm)

1:1,020,000

Based on Speed no. 7.

The text in the 1627 and later editions is reproduced from that in Speed's *Theatre*, and these maps are often referred to as 'miniature Speeds'.

EDITIONS

(i)   *SUSSEX* (Aa, in an ornamental frame). *The Scale of Miles 10 = 19 mm* (Ea). Plate number *3* (Be).

England, Wales, And Ireland: their seuerall counties. Abridged from. a farr. larger. vollume: By John Speed.
London, George Humble, [1619].   BL
Without text on back. Of the fifty-seven maps in this atlas, forty are reworked from van den Keere plates (see no. 5); seventeen (including Sussex) are from new plates.

(ii)   An additional plate number *4* (Ee). The original plate number is noticeably less clear on some issues.

England Wales Scotland and Ireland described and abridged with ye historie relation of things worthy memory from a farr larger volume done by John Speed.
London, George Humble, 1627 (reissued 1632 and 1646).
                                              BL.CUL;BL.CUL;BL.CUL.BOD

England Wales Scotland and Ireland described and abridged . . .
London, Robert Rea the elder and younger, 1627 (actually issued 1662) and 1662.
                                                                         P;W

A prospect of the most famous parts of the world . . .
London, Roger Rea, 1665,   S82
This includes a new edition of the preceding work without a separate title-page.

England Wales Scotland and Ireland described and abridged . . .
London, Roger Rea, 1666.   A

On the back of each map in the works listed above is a description of Sussex. The text was frequently reset and the issues may be distinguished as follows:-

25

	1627	1627 (1632)	1627 (1646) 1627 (1662) 1662	1666
heading	*SVSSEX.* (59 mm) *CHAPTER IIII.*	*SVSSEX.* (59 mm) *CHAPTER IIII.*	*SVSSEX.* (38 mm) *CHAPTER IIII*	*SVSSEX.* (33 mm) *CHAPTER IV*
line 2	*British*	*Brittish*	*British*	*British*

The measurements show the length of the county name. The text was also reset for the 1665 edition, which has not been inspected.[1]

(iii)   The plate has been retouched. The place number *4* has a horizontal bar at the bottom; vertical hatching in the crescent under the scale does not now extend as far beyond the top of the crescent.

England Wales Scotland and Ireland described and abridged . . .
[London, Roger Rea], 1666 (actually a reissue of 1668).   BL.CUL

England Wales Scotland and Ireland described and abridged . . .
[London, Thomas Bassett and Richard Chiswell], 1676.   BL.BOD.W

These two issues can be distinguished by the text on the back. In the 1666 issue the first word in line one is *SUTH-SEX*; in the 1676 issue it is *SOUTH-SEX*.
A copy of the 1676 edition in the University Library, Cambridge (7.67.1) has the Sussex map in state (ii), and the text in the same setting as the 1627 edition.

9   JOHN BILL   **1626**

Size: 82 mm × 118 mm (1 mm)   1:380,000

Based on van den Keere no. 5, but with some direct reference to Saxton no. 1. It marks a few places which do not appear on no. 5 (eg *Ardingligh*). It is the earliest Sussex map to show longitude and latitude. **See plate 8.**

Bill[1] came from Shropshire. He was apprenticed to the distinguished bookseller, John Norton (see Norden no. 6), who remained his life-long friend. He was commissioned to travel abroad and to buy books for the library of Sir Thomas Bodley. From 1604 until his death in 1630 he acted as King's Printer. His son Henry settled in Lewes, and is buried at Laughton; his grandson, also Henry, was bailiff of Seaford in 1680,[2]

1. Skelton, *County atlases*, 1970 nos. 82 and 83.

1. Chubb, 1927, p. 422.
2. *SAC* vol. 9, p. 137.

and married Letitia, daughter of Sir Thomas Colbrand, probably a relative of the James Colbrand referred to in appendix I.2.

EDITION

SUSSEX (Aa, in ornamental frame). *A Scale of miles 20* = 26 mm (Da). Longitude 5' (along bottom border); latitude 5' (along left border only). Brighton is 24°32' east, 50°50' north. Longitude is measured from the Azores. **See plate 8.**

> *The abridgement of Camden's Britañia with the maps of the seuerall shires of England and Wales.*
> [London], printed by John Bill, 1626.   BL.CUL.BOD

10   JACOB FLORENSZ VAN LANGEREN   1635

Size: 101 mm × 101 mm including table of distances (single-line border)   1:2,900,000

Based on Bowes no. 2.

   Jacob Florensz van Langeren was a member of a famous cartographic family,[1] but little is known about him. He lived in Brussels, and it is probable that the plates for this publication were engraved on the Continent. The tables of distances were copied from Norden's *England. An intended guyde for English travailers* (1625).
   Matthew Simmons, the publisher, was a bookseller and printer whose output included many of the works of John Milton. The plates for the works listed below were acquired and reused by Thomas Jenner (see no. 11) and later passed to John Garrett. Simmons is sometimes spelt Simons and it is possible that there were two publishers of similar name.
   Jacob van Langeren sculp: appears at the foot of the title-page of *A direction for the English traviller;* it is presumed that he was also responsible for the maps.
   The map has no border, but there is a ruled border to the whole sheet which measures 101 mm × 101 mm. About two-thirds of the sheet is occupied by a triangular table of distances, the map appearing in the bottom right hand corner. The dimensions of the map, measured to the wording which appears along each edge, are 42 mm × 35 mm. Towns are shown by initial letters only. Jenner no. 11 is a larger map, engraved in place of the present map, on the same plate.

1.   J. Keunig, 'The van Langeren family', *Imago Mundi* vol. 13 (1956), p. 109.

EDITIONS

(i) *Sussex* (Aa, above table of distances). Scale *10* = 6.5 mm (Ee). Compass points marked by three lines running north/south, north-west/south-east and north-east/south-west behind map. Plate number *34* (Ee OS). *Surrey & Kent North* (along top of map, *the Narrow sea. E* (along right side of map), *the Britt: sea South.* (along the bottom) and *Hant shire West:* (along left side).

> *A direction for the English traviller by which he shal be inabled to coast about all*
> *England and Wales* . . .
> London, Matthew Simmons, 1635 and 1636.   BL.CUL;BL

(ii) An additional line of figures has been engraved along the diagonal of the distance table, giving the distance of each town from London, eg *Lewes . . . 40.*

> *A direction for the English traviller* . . .
> London, Matthew Simmons, 1636.   BL

11   THOMAS JENNER   1643

Size: 101 mm × 101 mm including table of distances (single line border) 1:1,620,000

Based on the *Kingdome of England* in Speed's *Theatre.* **See plate 9.**

Jenner (d. 1673) was a Puritan and parliamentarian, with a long and successful career (1618–73) as a print-seller, during which he exploited prints as a medium of propaganda.[1]

This is a fresh map engraved on the same plate as no. 10, from which the earlier map has been erased. The table of distances remains, but the border in the bottom right corner has been erased to accommodate a larger map, which now gives town names in full and marks a number of towns outside Sussex, eg *Winchester.* The old scale and plate number have also been erased. North is now to the top left corner. The works below and the Quartermaster's map (appendix III.6) were probably issued for use by the parliamentary armies. Copies of *A direction for the English traviller* have been found with an assortment of plates in the original state (no. 10 above) and in this state, suggesting a rushed publication.[2]

John Garrett took over the business on Jenner's death. He was active as a print and map-seller from 1676 to about 1718.[3]

1. Rostenberg, 1963, pp. 26–7.
2. E.G. Box, 'Two sixteenth-century maps of Kent', in *Archaeologia Cantiana* vol. 45 (1933).
3. Tyacke, 1978, pp. 114–15. He was one of a number of John Garretts recorded during the period.

EDITIONS

(i) *Sussex* (Aa, above table of distances). Scale, *10* = 12 mm (Ee).

A direction for the English traviller by which he shal be inabled to coast about all England and Wales . . .
London, Thomas Jenner, 1643.   BL.BOD.W

A booke of the names of all the hundreds contained in the shires of the kingdom of England together with the number of towns parishes villages and places of every hundred . . .
London, Thomas Jenner, 164[4].   S26

A book of the names of all parishes, market towns, villages, hamlets, and smallest places, in England and Wales . . .
London, Thomas Jenner, 1657, 1662 and 1668.   BL.CUL.BOD;BL.BOD.RGS;W

In the first two books listed above, the page bearing the map has no text and the back is plain. In all three issues of the third book there is a heading *Sussex* and a page number *162* printed from type at the top of the page. Below the table of distances and map is a list of place-names. In each issue the list is printed from a different setting and may be identified from the third name in column 3 as follows: 1657 *Eborne chich;* 1662 *Eborne, Chich;* 1668, *Eborn, chich.*

(ii)   The table of distances has been retouched, and is most easily identified by the addition of a vertical bar to the top of most number 7s. This addition is noticeable on all maps except *Bark-shire* and *Somerset-shire.* **See plate 9.**

A direction for the English traviller . . .
London, Thomas Jenner, 1643 (actually issued 1668).   BOD.W

A book of the names of all parishes . . .
London, Thomas Jenner, 1668.   BL.RGS

A direction for the English traviller . . .
London, John Garrett, [1677], [1680].   A;BL.BOD

A book of the names of all parishes . . .
London, John Garrett, 1677.   BL.BOD.CUL

In all three issues of *A direction* . . . the page bearing the map has no text and the back is plain. In both issues of *A book of the names* . . . there is a heading, page number and list of place names, as in edition (i). In the 1668 issue the rape following *Eridge* on p. 162 is written *Peven;* in most copies of the 1677 issue the text has been reset and it is written *Pev en.*

12   JAN BLAEU   1645

Size: 504 mm × 364 mm (8 mm)   1:253,000

Based on Speed no. 7 (iii), (iv) or (v). **See plate 10.**

The famous Dutch cartographer firm of Blaeu was founded by William Janszoon Blaeu (1571–1638). On his death the business passed to his son Joan or Jan[1] (1595–1673). Their first world atlas, *Theatrum orbis terrarum,* appeared in two volumes in 1635, and eventually expanded to twelve volumes. The maps of England and Wales first appeared in the 1645 edition, and they usually appear in volume IV or V. The printing-house was damaged by fire in 1672, but loose maps from some plates continued to be printed after that date. They are beautifully engraved, and the Sussex map, together with that produced by Jansson (no. 13) is superior in clarity and decorative quality to any Sussex map published before or since.

The map described below was issued in Blaeu's atlases, with the text, taken from Camden's *Britannia,* on the back in Latin, French, German, Dutch and Spanish. Impressions of the map were also issued without text, both separately and bound in atlases.

The engraved title-page of the first (Latin) edition was used in all subsequent editions of the volume which included England, with the date in the imprint altered as required and with the title (in the appropriate language) printed from type on a label pasted over the central panel. Since the date in the imprint was not always altered for each reissue, the imprint date is not necessarily the date of actual issue. The list below gives the titles and imprints of the volumes in which the map appeared, without conjectural dates for the reissues except where the text has been reset.

EDITIONS

(i)   *SVTHSEXIA; Vernacule Sussex.* (Ca, on a rectangular banner). *Milliaria Anglica quorum quatuor constituunt unum Milliare Germanicum. 10* = 75 mm (Ae). Royal arms (Aa and Ea). Arms of four Earls of Sussex (Ba and Da). **See plate 10.**

> *Guil. et Ioannis Blaeu theatrum orbis terrarum, sive atlas novus.* Part 4.
> Amsterdam, Jan Blaeu, 1645 and 1646.   BL;S30

> *Le theatre du monde, ou nouvel atlas, mise en lumiere par Guillaume & Jean Blaeu.* Part 4.
> Amsterdam, Jan Blaeu, 1645 and 1646.   S29;S31

---

1.   Stevenson, 1914.

Novus atlas, das ist Welt-beschreibung mit schönen newen aussführlichen Land-Taffeln in Kupffer gestochen und an den Tag gegeben durch Wilhelm und Joan Blaeu. Part 4.
Amsterdam, Jan Blaeu, 1645 (actually issued 1646) and 1646.   S32;S33

(ii) *Occidens* (Ac) *Septentrio* (Ca) *Oriens* (Ec) *Meridies* (Ce) added. Guide lines scribed by the engraver under certain place names have been erased, eg under *Weembrug Belgis, LEWES RAPE.*

Guil. et Ioannis Blaeu Theatrum . . .
Amsterdam, Jan Blaeu, 1648.   BL.BOD.W

Le theatre du monde . . .
Amsterdam, Jan Blaeu, 1648.   S43

Novus atlas das ist Welt-beschreibung . . .
Amsterdam, Jan Blaeu, 1648.   W

Toonneel des aerdrycks oft nieuwe atlas uytgegeven door Willhelm en Joan Blaeu. Part 4.
Amsterdam, Jan Blaeu, 1646 (actually issued 1647).   UNIV.UTRECHT

Vierde stuck der aerdrycks-beschryving, welck vervat Engelandt.
Amsterdam, Jan Blaeu, 1648 (reissued 1664).   BL;BL

Nuevo atlas del reyno de Ingalaterra.
Amsterdam, Jan Blaeu, 1648 (actually issued 1659 or later), and 1659.
          MITCHELL LIBRARY, GLASGOW;W

Geographiae Blavianae, volumen quintum, quo Anglia . . . continetur.
Amsterdam, Jan Blaeu, 1662.   BL.CUL.NMM

Cinquiéme volume de la geographie Blaviane, contenant l'Angelterre . . .
Amsterdam, Jan Blaeu, 1662, 1663 and 1667.   NMM;BL;S84

Nuevo atlas del reyno de Inglaterra.
Amsterdam, *En la Officina Blaviana,* 1662.   BL

Printed on the back of the map in the above atlases are two pages of Camden's description of Sussex in the appropriate language; these pages are numbered and bear a signature. The table below will assist in identifying a loose map.

Atlas	Skelton[2]	Date	State	Language	Pages	Sig.
Guil.et Ioannis	28	1645	(i)	Latin	173–4	Ddd
Guil.et Ioannis	30	1646	(i)*	Latin	173–4	Ddd
Guil.et Ioannis	42	1648	(ii)	Latin	145–6	Yy
Geographiae	71	1662	(ii)	Latin	145–6	Yy
Le theatre	29	1645	(i)	French	151–2	Yy
Le theatre	31	1646	(i)*	French	151–2	Yy
Le theatre	43	1648	(ii)	French	151–2	Yy
Cinquiéme volume	72	1662	(ii)	French	125–6	Ss
Cinquiéme volume	75	1663	(ii)	French	125–6	Ss
Cinquiéme volume	84	1667	(ii)	French	125–6	Ss
Novus atlas	32	[1646]	(i)*	German	169–70	Ddd
Novus atlas	33	1646	(i)*	German	169–70	Ddd
Novus atlas	44	1648	(ii)	German	169–70	Ddd
Toonneel	38	[1647]	(ii)	Dutch	161–2	Ccc
Vierde stuck	45	1848	(ii)	Dutch	137–8	Tt
Vierde stuck	77	[1664]	(ii)	Dutch	137–8	Tt
Nuevo atlas	64	[1659]	(ii)	Spanish	157–8	Ccc
Nuevo atlas	64	1659	(ii)	Spanish	157–8	Ccc
Nuevo atlas	73	1662	(ii)	Spanish	157–8	Ccc

The Latin issues of 1648 *(S42)* and 1662 *(S71)* are from different settings; the 1662 issue can be distinguished by the addition of *NOMEN* top left on page 145.

Issues marked (i)* in the list above have been catalogued as state (i) on the basis of information from Skelton (29–33). However, he also indicates (see 38) that the Dutch issue (1647) is in state (i) whereas the impression in the atlas at the University Library, Utrecht, is in state (ii).

13   JAN JANSSON   1646

Size: 488 mm × 361 mm (9 mm)   1:259,000

Based on Speed no. 7(ii). *Bognor Rocks* appear as *Rognor Rocks*.

Jan Jansson married the daughter of Jodocus Hondius (see no. 7), and in 1638 on the death of his brother-in-law, Henricus, he took over the business; thus becoming the successor to the great Gerard Mercator (1512–94). Mercator's atlas, first published by his son Rumold in 1595, contained sixteen maps relating to the British Isles. Sussex, together with fifteen other counties, made up one plate covering the whole of south-east England (appendix III.I). Maps of selected English counties were included in the

2.   Skelton, *County atlases,* 1970 (entry numbers).

1636 and 1644 editions of the atlas, but Sussex did not appear as a separate plate until the publication of *Novus Atlas* in 1646. The volume containing the British Isles shows signs of rushed production; probably in an attempt to get it ready before the publication of the 1645 edition of Blaeu's atlas. Jansson's atlas eventually extended to eleven volumes.

After Jansson's death in 1664 the business was carried on by his son-in-law, Joanes van Waesberghe, (d. 1681). He published an *Atlas Contractus*, which contained some county maps, but omitted Sussex (Chubb no. LXXVIII).

In 1694 the plates of Jansson's British maps were bought at auction by Gerard Valk (c. 1650–1720) and Pieter Schenk (1645–1715) of Amsterdam, and loose impressions were sold. Sheets in the original state from old stock were incorporated in an atlas published by Karel Allard (1648–1706) of Amsterdam in about 1705, and sheets in state (ii) were included in later atlases published by David Mortier and Joseph Smith in London.

Jan Jansson was not related to Willem Janzoon Blaeu, who used the form 'Guiliemus Janssonius' prior to 1619.

David Mortier (b. 1673) was the brother of Amsterdam bookseller Pieter Mortier. He first came to England in about 1696, and died or retired in 1728 or soon afterwards.

The map described below was issued in Jansson's atlases, with the text of Camden's *Britannia* on the back in Latin, French, German and Dutch. After Jansson's death in 1664, the map was included in Dutch atlases with a Latin text. The map was also printed, probably very frequently from 1646, without text. English booksellers such as John Overton included the map in sets of county maps without title-pages.

The engraved title-pages of Jansson's first (Latin) edition of the British Isles volume was normally used in subsequent editions of this volume, the date in the imprint being altered as required and the title (in the appropriate language) printed from type on a label which was pasted over the panel bearing the Latin title. Since the date was not always revised in the imprint at each reissue, the printed date is not necessarily the date of actual issue. Until 1658, Jansson's atlas was issued in four or five volumes, and the British maps constituted volume IV; but later expanded editions in six, nine, ten or eleven volumes appeared and the British maps are found variously in volumes IV, V, VI, VII and VIII. Listed below are the titles and imprints of the volumes in which the map appeared, without conjectural dates for the reissues; volume numbers are not given.

EDITIONS

(i) *SUTHEXIA: vernacule SUSSEX*. (Ea, in illustrated frame; with oxen, sheep and two rustic figures). *Amstelodami Apud Joannem Janssonium* (Ce). *Milliaria Anglica. 8 = 61 mm, Milliaria Germanica 2 = 61 mm* (Ee). Compasses (Ed and Be). Royal arms (Ca). Four arms of Earls of Sussex and one blank shield (Aa).

Ioannis Ianssonii novus atlas, sive theatrum orbis terrarum: in quo Magna Britannia, seu Angliae & Scotiae nec non Hiberniae, regna exhibentur.
Amsterdam, Jan Jansson, 1646 and 1659. BL.CUL;BL

33

Le nouvel atlas ou theatre du monde, auquel est representée la Grande Bretagne, contenant les royaumes d'Angleterre, d'Ecosse & d'Irelande. Par Jean Jansson.
Amsterdam, Jan Jansson, 1646, 1647, 1652 and 1656.   S35;W;S52;S61

Novus atlas, oder Welt-Beschreibung, in welcher aussführlich abgebildet die Königreiche Engelland, Schotland, vnd Irland.
Amsterdam, Jan Jansson, 1647 and 1652 (actually issued 1658).   S40;S53

Niewen atlas, ofte Werelt-Beschrijvinghe, vertoonende Groot Britannien, vervattende de Koninghrijcken van Engelandt, Schotlandt ende Yrlandt.
Amsterdam, Jan Jansson, 1647, 1649, 1652, 1653 and 1659.   S41;S47;AD;S56;S57

Novus atlas, das ist: Weltβeschreibung mit schönen neuen geographischen figuren. Inhaltende Gross-Britannien und Irland.
Amsterdam, Jan Jansson, 1649.   BL

Novus atlas absolutissimus. Das ist, generale Welt-Beschreibung mit aller-ley schönen und neuen land-carten gezieret . . .
Amsterdam, Jan Jansson, 1647 (actually issued 1659).   NMM

Guilielmi Cambdeni Brittannia Magna illustrata.
Amsterdam, Jan Jansson, [1659].   P

Joannis Janssonii atlas contractus, sive atlantis majoris compendium: in quo totum universum velut in theatro . . .
Amsterdam, Jan Jansson 'p.m. Haeredes,' 1666.   BL

Atlas Anglicanus et Cambria, or a booke of mapps of all the countyes in the Kingdom of England.
London, John Seller, [1694[1]].   P

Atlas major, ex novissimis, selectissimisque, a quovis auctore editis cum generalibus ominium totius orbis terrarum regnorum, rerumpublicarum et insularum . . . tabulis geographicis . . . consistens . . . Ex collectione Caroli Allard, Amstelo-Batavi.
Amsterdam, Karel Allard, [1705].   BL

Printed on the back of the map in most of the above atlases are two pages of Camden's description of Sussex in the appropriate language. These pages are normally numbered and bear a signature. The table below will assist in the identification of a loose map.

---

1. Skelton, *County atlases,* 1970 pp. 217–8.

Atlas	Date	Language	Pages	Sig.
Ioannis Ianssonii novus	1646, 1659	Latin	89–90	Cc
Guilielmi Cambdeni	[1659]	Latin	89–90	Cc
Joannis Jansonii atlas	1666	Latin	none	none
Le nouvel atlas	all	French	101–2	Gg
Novus atlas, oder	all	German	119–20	Rr
Novus atlas, das ist	1649	German	119–20	Rr
Novus atlas absolutissimus	[1659]	German	119–20	Rr
Nieuwen atlas	all	Dutch	101–2	Ii
Atlas Anglicanus	[1694]	none	–	–
Atlas major	[1710]	none	–	–

Although the 1646 and 1659 issues of *Ioannis Ianssonii novus* have the same page number and signature, the text is from different type-settings. In the 1646 issue the last word in line 2 on page 89 is *In*; in the 1659 issue it is *infederunt*.

(ii)   Imprint (Ce) altered to *Amstelodami Apud Geriardium Valk, et Petrum Schenk*. Plate number 9 added (Ee, in border). Longitude 10' (2½'); latitude 10' (2½'); graticule at 10' intervals added. Town symbol for *CHICHESTER* replaced by minature town plan not related to the actual layout. Pecked lines marking county boundaries strengthened and extended. Maps in this state are without text on back.

Issued after 1681 by Pieter Schenk and Gerard Valk as loose sheets, sold separately.

Atlas anglois, ou description generale de l'Angleterre, contenant une description geographique de chaque province, avec les cartes . . .
London, David Mortier, 1714 and 1715.   W;WN
Each of these issues formed part of *Nouveau theatre de la Grande Bretagne . . . Auquel on a ajoûté un atlas de l'Angleterre . . .* Vol. 3. London, David Mortier, 1715.

Atlas anglois, ou description generale de l'Angleterre, contenant les cartes geographiques de chaque province . . .
London, Joseph Smith, 1724.   BL

14   RICHARD BLOME

Size: 210 mm × 135 mm (2 mm)   1:648,000

Based on Speed no. 7.

Blome published maps and books from about 1660 until his death in 1705. The map described below forms part of a series which started in 1667 and seems to have been completed within about five years; but publication in atlas form was delayed until 1681. In the meantime Blome's *Britannia* containing his series of larger maps (no. 15) was published in 1673. After Blome's death the plates of the smaller maps came into the possession of the London booksellers Thomas Taylor and Thomas Bakewell, who republished from them.

When first published in atlas form the dedication of the Sussex map is to Thomas Lennard, 15th Baron Dacre (1662) and 1st Earl of Sussex (1674). The baronetcy of Gillesland (usually so spelt) was held by the Dacres of the North and became extinct in 1634. It was claimed, unsuccessfully, by Francis Lennard, the father of Thomas.[1] There is, therefore, some doubt as to Thomas Lennard's right to use the title. He was a Gentleman of the Bedchamber from 1680 to 1685, which perhaps accounts for the dedication to him of this map. He married Lady Ann Fitzroy, the natural daughter of Charles II. His extravagance and gambling compelled him to sell Herstmonceux in 1708,[2] and to retire to Chevening in Kent, where he died in 1715.

The 1685 edition is dedicated to Henry Brouncker in place of Lord Dacre. Brouncker had no particular Sussex connections. In 1684 he had become a Viscount in the Irish peerage on the death of his brother William. William had been the first president of the Royal Society, and in 1668 had sat on a committee to consider Blome's plans for the reissue of Sanson's maps.[3] This accounts for Blome's connection with the family. Henry was another notorious gambler. He died in 1688.

The 1693 and later editions are dedicated to William Benge, a member of an old Wadhurst family. Wace[4] traces their history from 1653, but they were established in the area at least a hundred years earlier. A William Benge was born about 1622 and died in 1689. The man to whom this map is dedicated was probably his son, and in 1692 this William Benge purchased the Faircrouch estate near Wadhurst, which is marked on Budgen no. 24. He rebuilt the Gloucester furnace[5] at Lamberhurst to make it the most extensive in the county; but the enterprise failed very soon afterwards.[6] He died in 1714, and is buried at Southwark.[7]

---

1. *DNB*.
2. Barrett-Lennard, 1908. Herstmonceux castle was sold for £38,215 to 'Counceller' Naylor and passed in 1775 to his nephew, Francis Hare Naylor, an ancestor of Augustus J.C. Hare (see no. 150).
3. E.G.R. Taylor 'Robert Hooke and cartographical projects of the late seventeenth century (1666–1696)', *GJ* vol. 90 (1937).
4. Wace, 1923, pp. 77–8.
5. According to local tradition, the rails for St Paul's Cathedral were cast there. See Lower, 1854, p. 132.
6. *SAC* vol. 56 (1914), pp. 155, 160.
7. *SNQ* vol. 5 (1934), p. 105.

The engraver Wenceslaus Hollar[8] (1607–77) was born in Prague. He was trained as an engraver and worked in Germany from 1627. In 1636 he met Thomas Howard, Earl of Arundel (1604–46), who brought him to England. His engravings during this period, included a number of views of Sussex.[9] After the Earl left England in 1642, Hollar joined the retinue of the Duke of York, although he continued to work independently, and was from time to time employed by members of the parliamentary faction. He was at Oxford in 1642 and engraved the 1643 map of that city. He also engraved, in 1644, the famous 'Quartermaster's map' (see appendix III.6). Nevertheless in 1644 his association with the Stuart cause made it advisable for him to move to Antwerp.[10] About 1650 he was back in England and undertaking a variety of work, particularly for the antiquarian William Dugdale. Hollar survived the plague, in which his son died. Following the great fire he executed a plan of the City of London.[11] Pepys wrote (22 Nov. 1666) 'My Lord Brouncker [William] did show me Hollar's new print of the City . . . and tells me that he [Hollar] was yesterday sworn the King's Servant, and that the King hath commanded him to go on with his great map of the City'. He received the title *Royal Scenographer and designer of prospects*. He died a poor man in 1677. A major collection of his work is housed in the Royal Library at Windsor.

EDITIONS

(i)   *A Mapp of the County of SUSSEX with its divisions. by Richard Blome, by his Maies^ties. especiall Command.* (Aa, in decorative frame). *London Printed for Rich: Blome A. 1668.* (Ee). *W. Hollar fecit* (Ae). *Scale of Miles 10 = 30 mm* (Eb). *The Names of the Rapes . . .* (Ea). The last two features are enclosed in the same rectangular frame.

Found only as a loose sheet.   ROYAL LIB.WINDSOR

(ii)   In the title (Aa) by *Richard Blome . . . Command* erased and replaced by a straight line. The imprint (Ee) erased and replaced by arms and *To y^e. R^t. Honourable Thomas Earle of Sussex Baron Dacres of Gilesland This Mapp is D.D. by R.B.* To make space for this alteration, *or NARROW SEA* and two ships have been erased and replaced by *SEA*. The border has been expanded by some decorative crosses, which are most noticeable between the top border and the plate mark.

Speed's maps epitomiz'd: or the maps of the counties of England, alphabetically placed.
London, 1681.   BL

---

8. Van Eerde, 1970.
9. *SAC* vol. 5, p. 40.
10. Van Eerde has shown that the traditional story that Hollar was taken prisoner at Basing House (see *SAC* vol. 5) cannot be true (Van Eerde, 1970, p. 33).
11. Darlington and Howgego, 1964, no. 19.

(iii)   Dedication (Ee) altered to *To Henry Brouncker of Rownbold Esqr Cofferer to his Ma^tys K: Ch^r ye 2 this Map is DD by RB*, and the arms changed.

> *Speed's maps epitomiz'd:* . . .
> London, Samuel Lownes, 1685.   W

(iv)   Dedication (Ee) altered to *To William Benge of Coselywood in Wadherst in this County Gentleman this Mapp is humbly Dedicated by Richard Blome.* Arms changed. *ey* in *Pemsey hauen* erased.

> *Cosmography and geography, in two parts: the first . . . being a translation from that eminent and much esteemed geographer, Varenius . . . The second part . . . taken from the notes and works of the famous Monsieur Sanson . . . The third impression, illustrated with maps. To which is added the county-maps of England, drawn from those of Speed.*
> London, Richard Blome, 1693.   W

> *England exactly described or a guide to travellers in a compleat sett of mapps of all the county's of England being a map; for each county* . . .
> London, Thoms Taylor, [1718].   CUL

(v)   Plate number *37* added (Ea).

> *England exactly described* . . .
> London, Thomas Taylor, [1715].   BL.CUL.BOD

(vi)   Seven roads added, together with distances between towns, eg *10* on road from *CHICHESTER* to *Arondel*.

> *England exactly described or a guide to travellers in a compleat sett of maps of all the counties of England; being a map for each county . . . with . . . the roads and distances in measured miles according to Mr Ogilby's survey* . . .
> London, Thomas Taylor, [1716].   BL.RGS.GL

(vii)   *Richard Blome* in the dedication (Ee) blacked out. *ey* added to *Pemsey hauen*. The plate has been retouched, most noticeably in the form lines along the coast, and at *Old Shoram*, which was partially erased in earlier editions.

> *England exactly described* . . .
> London, Thomas Taylor, [1718].   W

> *England exactly described or a guide to travellers in a compleat sett of mapps for each county* . . .
> London, Thomas Taylor (actually published by Thomas Bakewell in about 1750).
>   CUL

38

England exactly described or a guide to travellers in a compleat sett of most correct mapps of counties of England; being a map for each county . . . with . . . the roads and distances in measured miles according to Mr Ogilby's survey.
London, Thomas Bakewell, [1750].   W

15 RICHARD BLOME   1673

Size: 309 mm × 205 mm (single-line border)   1:393,000

Based on Speed no. 7. (ii) or (iii).

Blome's cartographic work (see also no. 14) is poorly contrived and unoriginal. Anthony à Wood described his *Britannia* in which this map appeared as 'Scribbled and transcribed from Cambden's *Britannia* and Speed's Maps'.[1] Rawlinson referred to it as 'one of the most notorious instances of plagiarism, that ever was committed'.[2] This work, like many of his others, was financed by soliciting subscriptions (20s, of which 10s had to be paid in advance), which entitled the subscriber to have his 'Coat of Arms affixed to the Mapp of the County . . .' The arms in fact appear on separate plates. In the prospectus he seeks the help of local dignitaries and others in 'rectifying the many errors frequently committed in Books and Maps yet extant'. The Sussex map, however, shows no improvement compared with its immediate predecessors such as Speed. The book contains a useful list of the nobility and gentry of the county.[3]

Lord Buckhurst, to whom the Sussex map is dedicated, and his father Richard, Earl of Dorset, were Lords Lieutenant of Sussex from 1670 to 1677.

The engraver of the Sussex map is not known.

Maps of other counties, eg Warwickshire,[4] in this series have been found in more than one state. Although Sussex has been found in only one state, there are signs of re-engraving.

EDITION

A MAPP OF THE COUNTY. OF SVSSEX WITH ITS RAPES BY RIC BLOME BY HIS MA^{ty} ESPECY'ALL COMAND (Ae, in circular floral frame). To y^e. R^t. Honble Charles Lord Buckhurst one of ye Gentlemen of his Ma^{tys} Bedchamber & son & heire of ye R^t Hon^{ebl} Ric. Earle of Dorset Baron Buckhurst Lord Leiutenant of this County. This

1. Quoted from Chubb, 1927, p. 423.
2. Rawlinson, 1720, p. XIX.
3. *SAC* vol. 32, p. 223.
4. Harvey, 1959, no. 14.

Mapp is humbly dedicated by Ric Blome (Ea, or a cartouche with arms of Lord Buckhurst). *A Scale of 8 Miles* = 41 mm (Ee). *A TABLE OF THE RAPES IN SVSSEX* (Ee). *North* (Ca), *East* (Ec), *South* (Ce).

Britannia: or, a geographical description of the kingdoms of England, Scotland and Ireland . . . Illustrated with a map of each county of England, besides several general ones . . .
London, Richrad Blome, 1673.   BL.CUL.BOD

Britannia . . .
London, John Wright, 1677.   P

16 WILLIAM REDMAYNE   **1676**

Size: 51 mm × 23 mm (1 mm)   [1:3,120,000]

Possibly derived from *The Kingdom of England* in Speed's *Theatre* The coastline and rivers bear some resemblance to Jenner no. 11. **See plate 6(iii).**

The *Term Catalogue* for 12 June 1676 refers to 'Recreative pastime by Card-play; Geographical, and Historiographical, of England and Wales; shewing the commodities and Rarities of each County . . . By a long Student in the Mathematicks'. The cards have been attributed to Redmayne in this and other catalogues because he is the first-named seller of the first edition and the sole seller of the second edition. The 'long student' has not been identified.

The *Term Catalogue* for 26 November 1677 includes the entry 'Geographical, Chronological, and Historiographical, Cards of England and Wales. Sold formerly for 1s.; now newly done, and sold at 6d. a Pack. By W. Redmayne at the Crown on Addle Hill.' It has been assumed[1] that this second entry referred to the cards in state (ii). However, an incomplete pack in state (ii) has recently come to light with a 6d tax stamp on the two of spades. The stamp is of design C below, and indicates that the cards were not issued before 1712.

Stamp duty on playing-cards was imposed from 11 June 1711. Stocks held at that date were charged ½d only, provided they were brought in for stamping by 1 August 1712. They were marked with a special stamp bearing the letters *SH*. Packs printed after 11 June 1711, and up to 1759, were subject to a duty of 6d. Hand-drawn stamps were used up to 17 July 1711, after which embossed stamps became available. These are known in three designs:

1. Skelton, *County atlases*, 1970, no. 97.

A. 31 mm × 41 mm, inscribed *VI PENCE DUTY.*
B. 15 mm × 19 mm, inscribed *VI PENCE.*
C. 13 mm × 16 mm, inscribed *VI PENCE.*

It was thought[2] that design A was used only until 1 August 1712, but it now appears that it continued in use after that date, concurrently with designs B and C. There is, however, reason to believe that design A preceeded both B and C, and that the latter were not used before 1 August 1712. There is also some indication that design B was not used after 1718.

It is possible, therefore, that the 1677 entry in the *Term Catalogue* refers not to the Redmayne cards in state (ii), but to a reissue of the cards in state (i), and that the words 'now newly done' should not be taken to imply alterations to the engraved plates. Possibly state (ii) did not appear until after 1712. If, however, the 1677 entry is taken to refer to state (ii), then it is clear, from evidence of the tax stamp, that the cards in state (ii) were reissued in or after 1712, and probably before 1714. From 1714 the mark was usually placed on the ace of spades, although this did not become a legal requirement until 1722.

The cards in state (iii) have borders, which are characteristic of John Lenthall (see no. 22). Lenthall had advertised geographical cards as early as 1709, and again in 1714 and 1716.[3] The 1709 advertisement refers to 'Geographical Cards of England, and part of Scotland and Ireland with adjacent Coasts of France and Flanders . . .' The later advertisements refer to 'the whole Territories of Great Britain'. The term 'Great Britain' would not have been used incorrectly so soon after the Union of 1707. None of these advertisements can, therefore, refer to the Redmayne cards, which only cover England and Wales.

In 1717 Lenthall published an advertisement in the *St. James's Evening Post,*[4] which listed twenty packs. He also published a broadside,[5] which has now been dated 1723 or later,[6] listing no less than forty packs available for sale. Both these lists included county maps, which can be identified with the re-engraved version of the Morden cards (no. 17) and which are catalogued below (Lenthall no. 22). Both lists also included 'Historiographical Cards', which have been identified with the Redmayne pack.[7] Since Lenthall omitted this pack from earlier advertisements, it is reasonable to assume that it was first issued by him in or about 1717.

Redmayne was active from 1674 to 1719, when he was imprisoned in Newgate for a libel on the government. He died of fever in the same year. These dates are consistent with his reissue of the cards about 1712, and the transference of the plates to Lenthall by 1717.

The size of a whole card is 51 mm × 89 mm. Sussex is the ace of spades. The title appears at the top of the card; topographical information is given above and below the

2. Mann and Kingsley, 1972, p. 19. Sylvia Mann has contributed much of the information relating to tax stamps.
3. V. Wayland, in *The Journal of the Playing-Card Society* vol. 5, no. 1. (August 1976), p. 7. Based on information provided by Donald Hodson.
4. Hodson, 1974, p. 40.
5. For details, see Mann, 1966, pp. 134–50.
6. Information from Donald Hodson.
7. Mann, 1966, p. 140.

map, and is separated from it by horizontal frame lines. *Chechester* is the only town named; the scale, therefore, is estimated.

EDITIONS

(i) *SVSSEX* (Ca OS, above the topographical notes). The spade suit-mark is engraved in outline in the centre of the map.

> Issued in a pack of cards, sold by W. Redmayne, Henry Mortlock, Robert Turner, H. Cox and B. Billingsley. London, 1676. W
>
> Perhaps reissued by Redmayne in this state in 1677.

(ii) The outline suit-marks filled in with engraved cross-hatching.

> Issued in a pack of cards, sold by W. Redmaync. London 1677. BL
>
> With suit-mark stencilled over in black. **See plate 6(iii).**

> Issued in a pack of cards, sold by W. Redmayne. London, [1712]. P⁸
>
> With suit-mark not stencilled over.

(iii) Plain border replaced by decorated border (3 mm).

> Issued in a pack of cards, sold by J. Lenthall. London, [1717]. GL
>
> With suit-mark not stencilled over.

17 ROBERT MORDEN   1676

Size: 56 mm × 57 mm (1 mm)   1:2,230,000

Based on Blome no. 15. The spelling of place-names follows both Speed and Blome. The map shows *Arondel Haven,* which is not named on earlier maps, except for *Portvs Arvndi* on Norden no. 6 and *Arundel Hauen* on Blome. **See plate 6(iv).**

Morden was a London bookseller from 1669[1] until his death in 1703. He specialised in the geographical field, and was himself something of a cartographer (see no. 20) and a publisher (see no. 21). Throughout the seventeenth and most of the eighteenth centuries there was little distinction between the activity of book or print-selling and that of publishing: many booksellers were also printers or engravers. They undertook

8. One of a set of forty-one cards in the possession of the Stanley Gibbons group. The British Library has one card (Surrey) in this state.
1. Tyacke, 1978, p. 123. Earlier authorities have suggested that he was active from about 1650.

the sale of each other's works, and often combined to meet the high cost of publishing a new map or the reissue of an old atlas, even if the original plates were still available.

This is the first map of Sussex to show roads: that from Chichester to Petworth is marked by a plain double line, and the others by single lines. Those marked by single lines are taken from Ogilby's *Britannia* (appendix V.I), published in 1675; but the road from Chichester to Petworth is not in Ogilby. The Philip Lea edition of Saxton no. 1 (vi), published about 1694, was the next map to mark roads – in four categories, the first three being the roads delineated by Ogilby, and the fourth consisting of roads not in Ogilby and including the road from Chichester to Petworth.

The statistics below this Morden map give the length of the county as 53 miles. This is consistent with the small scale-bar on the map, but it is a gross understatement by comparison with the true length of about 80 statute miles. Assuming that Morden was using the old English mile of about 10 furlongs,[2] the length should appear as approximately 64 miles. The length of the county based on the scale-bars of earlier maps works out as follows: Saxton no. 1, 62 miles; Bowes no. 2, 68 miles; Norden no. 6, 68 miles; Speed no. 7, 65 miles; and Blome no. 14, 63 miles.

The latitude of Chichester is given as 50°48', which is consistent with a reading from the general map in Ogilby's *Britannia*. On Bill no. 9, the only earlier map of Sussex to mark latitude, it lies at 50°52', compared with a true latitude of 50°50'.

The card is one of a set of playing cards each bearing a county map. The size of the whole card is 56 mm × 92 mm, excluding the 1 mm border. Sussex is the four of diamonds. The map occupies the centre portion of the card. The suit-mark, title and number appear in the panel above the map; statistics relating to Sussex in the panel below the map. Lenthall no. 22 is very similar.

Each suit was probably engraved on a single plate in the same way as Bowes no. 2. Certainly each card was cut from a larger sheet after printing. When the maps were later issued in the form of a pocket atlas, the cards were not printed directly on the pages of the book, but were cut out and stuck down on the blank leaves.

EDITIONS

(i) *Sussex*. (Ca OS). *Miles 10* = 10 mm (Be). Compass (Aa). *4* (Aa OS). *IIII* (Ea OS). **See plate 6(iv).**

Issued in a pack of cards, with diamond suit-mark stencilled in red (Aa OS, above number *4*). Sold by Robert Morden, William Berry, Robert Green and George Minikin, London.[3]   BL.GL.W

---

2. C. Close, 'The old English mile', *GJ* vol. 76 (1930), comes to the conclusion that between 1544 and 1695 'customary' miles averaged about 10.4 furlongs. On this basis the actual length of 80 statute miles should be stated as 61½ miles (compared with 64 miles for a ten furlong mile). This does not make Morden's statistic look much better, but it says much for Saxton's accuracy.
3. *Term Catalogue*, 5 May 1676.

Issued, without suit-mark, in a set of county maps without title page.   W

(ii)   County boundaries marked by dotted lines and names of adjoining counties added, eg *Pᵗ. of Hant.*

Issued in a pack of cards, with stencilled suit-mark. *The Second Edition* . . . sold by Robert Morden, W. Berry, Robert Green, and G. Minikin, London.[4]   BL

(iii)   *Brighthemston* erased and replaced by *Helington*. Most town symbols elaborated.

Issued in a pack of cards, with stencilled suit-marks.[5]   S102

A pocket book of all the counties of England and Wales . . .
London, Robert Morden and Joseph Pask, [1680].   BL
Without suit-mark.

A brief description of England and Wales; . . .
London, H. Turpin, [1773].   BL.W.
Without suit-mark.

18   JOHN OVERTON   circa **1685**

Size: 475 mm × 311 mm (single-line border)   1:266,000

Based on Speed no. 7 (iii), (iv) or (v). A slavish copy, even to the extent that Surrey is still written *SUR REY,* although the reason for the separation on the Speed version no longer applies. The scale is smaller. Decorative detail has been copied from Blaeu no. 12, but the coats of arms have been enlarged. **See plate 11**.

John Overton[1] (1640–1713) was the son of Thomas Overton, a tailor of Covent Garden. In 1665 he acquired the stock of Pieter Stent, which included a number of early county maps and in particular the William Smith maps.[2] Some time before 1700 he acquired also the plates of Speed's maps, which Christopher Browne had in turn acquired from Bassett and Chiswell in about 1688.

John Overton was twice married, his second wife being Sara, the sister of John Garrett (see no. 11). He had four sons: Thomas went to America and probably died before 1713; Henry (d. 1751) took over his father's stock in 1707: Philip (d. 1745) went

4.   *Term Catalogue,* 22 November 1676.
5.   Cowling, 1959, nos. 144 and 145.
1.   Tyacke, 1978 pp. 130–135. Also Skelton, *County atlases,* 1970, pp. 129–33, 245.
2.   Skelton, *County atlases,* 1970 no. 3.

into the trade and published a map of Sussex (no. 26 below); and James. James's son Henry took over the business from his uncle Henry, and continued in business until 1764.

Between 1670 and 1755 the family published 'Overton' atlases, which included Speed maps after 1700, together with maps from other sources. From about 1713 Speed atlases were also reissued by Henry Overton. Skelton[3] gives a valuable chronology of these atlases and a summary of the composition of the Overton atlases. Some of the latter are collections of maps without title-pages, but Skelton argues in favour of their classification as atlases.

The first Overton atlas, published about 1670 (S89) contains Speed's map of Sussex no. 7(v); in the second (S91) the Sussex map is missing; the third (S107) contains the map described below. The 'post-1772 Speed (Overton) atlas' (Skelton, p. 131) may contain the same map, or Speed no. 7(vii).

The date of this entry in the catalogue (c. 1685) has been taken from the earliest atlas in which the map has been found. If the second Overton atlas, which Skelton dates as c. 1675, contained the map described below, the date would have to be reconsidered. Skelton (p. 130) refers to a catalogue listing a map of Sussex described as 'a new plate, after Speed, engraved for Overton c. 1672'. This may well refer to the map described below, and would suggest a date earlier than 1672. Skelton (pp. 132, 202), mistakenly suggests that the Sussex map in the second and subsequent Overton atlases was copied from Blaeu, an error which may have arisen from the inclusion on the map of the Blaeu coats of arms.

EDITION

A NEW Map of SVSSEX CORRECTED and Amended With all the Hundered Parkes and Other Places There unto Belonging With the armes of Such Nobels that haue bin Dignified With the title of Earles (Ea, in illustrated framework, with arms and two angels). *Sould With all other Countey and Contrer Maps by Iohn Ouerton at the white Horse without Newgate neere the fountaine tauern* (De). *The Scale of miles 8 = 60 mm* (Ee). Royal arms (Aa), and arms of four Earls (Ba to Da). **See plate 11.**

An atlas without title-page.
[London, John Overton, c. 1685].   S107[4]

An atlas without title-page.
[London, John Overton, c. 1690].   BL

3. Skelton, *County atlases*, 1970, pp. 131, 132, 201, 202.
4. The copy of this unique atlas catalogued by Skelton. *(AD, Vb.10)* cannot now be found.

An atlas without title-page (s121).
[London, John Overton, c. 1700].

P

England fully described in a compleat sett of mapps of yᵉ county's of England and
Wales, with their islands, containing in all 58 mapps.
London, Henry Overton [1720].

W

An atlas without title-page.
[London, Henry Overton, c. 1740].

P

An atlas without title-page.
[London, Henry Overton, c. 1755].

BL

19   JOHN SELLER   circa **1694**

Size: 141 mm × 111 mm (4 mm)   1:907,000

Probably based on Speed no. 7 and Greenvile Collins' chart of the English Channel in *Great Britain's coasting pilot,* 1693.

The first Sussex map to use London as the prime meridian, probably measured from St Paul's Cathedral.[1]

Seller ran his business as instrument maker and map-seller from a shop in Wapping and from various addresses in London. He first appears about 1660; in 1671 he was appointed Hydrographer to the King. After his death in 1697 the Wapping shop was managed by his widow, Elizabeth, (d. 1711), and by his second son, Jeremiah, who for a short period (1703–5) was in partnership with Charles Price (see no. 28), a former apprentice of his father. Jeremiah seems to have left the map trade about 1705, but lived at least until 1720. John Seller's elder son, also John (c. 1667–98) was also a map-seller.[2]

In 1679 Seller, in partnership with John Oliver and Richard Palmer, planned to make an 'actual survey of all the counties' to be published in an *Atlas Anglicanus.* Only six maps were produced (not including Sussex), and the scheme collapsed, as did other schemes for the publication of county atlases during that period.[3]

The maps in *Anglia contracta* (see below) have no special merit and are unoriginal. The delineation of the Sussex coastline shows a marginal improvement, being based on

1. Lynam, 1944, p. 31.
2. Tyacke, 1978, pp. 139–142.
3. Skelton, *County atlases,* 1970, pp. 184–7.

the Collins chart published by Richard Mount in 1693. The 'bay' at *Fering* has at last been eliminated; but the northerly trend of the coastline from both *Selsey* and *Newhaven* towards *Shoram* is over-stated.

Francis Grose (c. 1731–91), the author of the works listed in state (ii) below, was born in Middlesex. He was Richmond Herald from 1755 to 1763, adjutant of the Hampshire militia from 1763, and of the Surrey militia from 1778. He was an artist and keen antiquarian. It is said that he started collecting pictorial material for the *Antiquities* (see also no. 36) as early as 1760.

EDITIONS

(i) *SUSSEX by I. Seller* (Ea, in laurel wreath). *Miles 10* = 22 mm (Ce, along border). Compass (Ce). Grid at 10-mile intervals. The vertical lines are marked *10, 20* and *30* outwards from the centre line, which is marked *0* and *Merid of (London)s.Lati.* The horizontal lines are marked *10, 20, 30, 40* and *50*, from top to bottom. The middle line *(30)* also has the value *51*.

> *Anglia contracta. or a description of the kingdom of England & principality of Wales. in several new mapps of all the countyes therein contained by John Seller . . .* [1694].   BL.BOD.W

> *The history of England . . . with exact maps of each county, by John Seller . . .* London, John Gwillim, 1696 and 1697.   BL.CUL;P

> *The history of England . . . together with a particular description of the rarities in the several counties of England and Wales. By John Seller. . .* London, H. Newman, 1697.   S120

> *Camden's Britannia abridg'd; with improvements, and continuations, to this present time . . . The whole carefully perform'd, and illustrated with above sixty maps exactly engraven.* vol. 1. London, Joseph Wild, 1701.   BL.CUL

> *The history of England . . . With the maps of all the counties and islands belonging to England . . . By John Seller . . . 3rd edn.* London, J. Marshall, 1703.   BL.RGS

(ii) Title and laurel wreath erased. *SUSSEX* re-engraved (Ea, in rectangular panel with plain double-line border).

> *The antiquities of England and Wales by Francis Grose Esq. F.A.S. 'New Edition.'* vol. 5. London, Hooper and Wigstead [1785].   BL.CUL

47

The antiquities of England and Wales, By Francis Grose Esq[r], F.A.S. vol. 3.
London, S. Hooper, 1775. (actually a re-issue of 1787).   BL

Supplement to the antiquities of England and Wales. By Francis Grose Esq[r]. F.A.S.
vol. 2.
London, S. Hooper, 1787.   BL.BOD

The antiquities of England and Wales by Francis Grose Esq. F.A.S. 'New Edition'.
vol. 5.
London, S. Hooper, [1787].   CUL.W

The antiquities of England and Wales, by Francis Grose Esq[r]. F.A.S. 'New Edition'.
vol. 6.
London, S. Hooper [1787].   BL

In each of the above works the map is printed at the top of the page. Below and on the reverse are
notes relating to the county printed from type, found in several different settings. However, identifi
cation of a loose map cannot be made, since not all copies of an issue of the work have the same setting
of text.

Eastbourne; being a descriptive account of that village . . .
London, Hooper and four others, 1787.   BL

Eastbourne; . . . second edition . . .
London, Hookham and Wigstead, 1799.   BL

20   ROBERT MORDEN   1695

Size: 394 mm × 325 mm (9 mm)   1:318,000

Based on Speed no. 7.

Morden also published the playing-card maps (no. 17) and a series of small maps
(no 21). In the preface to his edition of Camden, Edmund Gibson wrote about this
series of maps in excessively glowing terms: 'The Maps are all new engrav'd, either
according to Surveys never before publish'd, or according to such as have been made
and printed since Saxton and Speed. Where actual Surveys could be had, they were
purchas'd at any rate; and for the rest, one of the best Copies extant was sent to some
of the most knowing Gentlemen in each County, with a request to supply the defects,
rectifie the positions, and correct the false spellings. And that nothing might be wanting
to render them as complete and accurate as might be, this whole business was committed to Mr. Robert Morden, a person of known abilities in these matters . . . Upon
the whole, we need not scruple to affirm, that they are by much the fairest and most
correct of any that have yet appear'd. . .'[1] Skelton[2] has pointed out that the Churchills

1.   Quoted from Chubb, 1927, p. 94.
2.   Skelton, *County atlases* 1970, p. 192.

were substantial publishers, of whom it was said, 'They never starve an undertaking to save charges.' That Morden took some advtantage of this situation, in order to seek out the best available sources, cannot be doubted.[3] Skelton[4] also observed that maps of the coastal counties were improved by the incorporation of detail from the sea charts of Greenvile Collins, and that the modernisation of place-names began with the efforts of Gibson and Morden.

Practically none of the above encomium is borne out by a study of the map of Sussex. It is crudely drawn, decoratively uninteresting, and the delineation of the coast-line is a slavish copy from Speed's map of the county. One is more inclined to agree with Gough's judgement that the maps are 'very faulty'. There is, however, some modernisation in the spelling of place-names compared with earlier maps, eg *New Shoreham* (formerly New Shoram) and *Pevensey* (formerly Pemsey).[5] Furthermore, this is the first map of Sussex to indicate (in the top margin) the difference in local time.

According to most authorities[6] the longitudes on the maps in this series are based on the meridian of St Paul's, which had been introduced by Seller on his map of Hertfordshire[7] in 1676, and marked on four of his county maps in *Anglia contracta*[8] (see no 19). That Morden used St Paul's as the prime meridian for most of the maps in this series is clear from an examination of the maps of the home counties which show London; some other maps, eg Hertfordshire, actually have *from London* in the bottom border. Longitudes on the map of Sussex, however, are based on Greenwich. The true Greenwich meridian passes about a quarter-mile east of East Grinstead, half a mile west of Lewes, two miles west of Newhaven and three miles east of Brighton; the meridian of St Paul's would lie about four miles to the west of this line. The zero meridian on the map described below passes through *East Grinstead* and *Lewes*, and just west of *Mitching* (Newhaven). Confirmation that this is intended to refer to Greenwich rather than London may be had from an examination of the map of Surrey in the same series, which also markes *Grinstead* some five miles to the east of the zero meridian, which passes through London Bridge. Sussex is not the only map in the series to have its origin based on Greenwich;[9] nor is its adoption so surprising, since the Royal Observatory had been founded in 1675. Morden used the same origin for his smaller map of Sussex (no. 21); but later cartographers, including Budgen (no. 24), reverted to the meridian of London, until the appearance of the Yeakell and Gardner map (no. 47) in 1778. Fordham dates the general acceptance of the Greenwich meridian from 1794,[10] and the first county atlas to use it throughout was Smith's *New*

3. For example, Hertfordshire (Hodson, 1974, no. 19); Cheshire (see Harley, 1972, p. 74).
4. Skelton, *County atlases*, 1970, p. 195.
5. The pronounciation 'Pemsey' seems to have come into fashion in the fourteenth century; but 'Pevensey' was always favoured when referring to the rape. Thus, in *A book of the names* (see no. 11) the list below the map includes *Pemsey. Peven.* referring to the town and to the rape respectively.
6. Fordham, 1969, p. 15; Lynam, 1944, p. 31; Skelton, *County atlases*, 1970, p. 194.
7. Hodson, 1974 no. 16.
8. Skelton, *County atlases*, 1970, p. 182.
9. For example, Yorkshire, see Raistrick 1969 p. 26.
10. Fordham, 1969, p. 15.

English atlas (no. 60) in 1804. Morden was, therefore, well ahead of his time in adopting it for this map of Sussex in 1695.

The publisher, Awnsham Churchill, acquired an estate in Dorset, and was MP for Dorchester from 1705 to 1710.

Edmund Gibson (1669–1748), the editor, was only twenty-six when this edition of *Britannia* was published. The problems which he encountered in editing the material and bringing it up to date are well documented.[11] He later became librarian at Lambeth Palace and subsequently Bishop of London.

Chubb[12] records a 1715 edition of these maps without title-page.

EDITIONS

(i)   *SUSSEX By Robt*. Morden (Aa, in decorative framework). *Sold by Abel Swale Awnsham and John Churchill*. (Ee). *Scales of Miles 10 = 61* mm; *10 = 57* mm; *10 = 53* mm (Eb).[13] Longitude 10' (1'); latitude 5' (1'). Longitude is marked along the bottom border only; the top being graduated to show *Minutes of Time. Brighthemston* is 0°9'W, 50°48'N. Unexplained obelisks are attached to a number of places, eg *CHICHESTER, St Lukes Ch., Stening, Hoo, Hastings.*

> *Camden's Britannia, newly translated into English:* . . . *Publish'd by Edmund Gibson* . . .
> London, A. Swalle and A. and J. Churchill, 1695.   BL.CUL

(ii)   A number of place-names re-engraved and some spellings amended, eg *Worthing* (formerly *Worting*), *Sheffield* (*Shasfield*), *Gravely* (*Gravetye*).

> *Britannia: or a chorographical description of Great Britain and Ireland* . . . *by William Camden* . . . *translated into English, with additions and improvements* . . . *by Edmund Gibson, D.D.* . . . 2nd edition, vol. 1.
> London, Awnsham Churchill, 1722.   BL.CUL

> *Britannia* . . . 2nd edition, vol. 1.
> London, James and John Knapton and ten others, [1730].   BRL

(iii)   The plate has been retouched. This is most noticeable in the framework round the title (Aa). Vertical strokes have been added to the shading on both sides of *Robt. Morden.*

---

11.   G. Walters, and F. Emery, 'Edward Lhuyd, Edmund Gibson and the printing of Camden's *Britannia*', *The Library*, 5th series, vol. 2 (June 1977). S. Piggott, 'William Camden and the *Britannia*', *Proc. Brit. Acad.*, vol. 37 (1951), pp. 199–217.
12.   Chubb, 1927, no. CXIV.
13.   Equivalent to 9½, 9 and 8¼ furlongs. Presumably the first two refer to the 'customary' or local miles in use in the county at that time.

Britannia . . . 3rd edition, vol. 1.
London, R. Ware and twelve others, 1753.   BL.W

Britannia . . . 4th edition, vol. 1.
London, W. Bowyer and twenty-six others, 1772.   BL

21 ROBERT MORDEN   1701

Size: 200 mm × 160 mm (4 mm)   1:582,000

Based on Speed no. 7.

A prospectus published in 1693 for Camden's *Britannia* (see no. 20) included the following: 'The Maps mentioned in the former Proposals . . . were not thought Large and Comprehensive enough, by some Judicious and Ingenious Gentlemen that assist in the Work, Who think it Proper and Necessary to have the Maps of every County full as Large as this Sheet will admit . . .'.[1] It is probable that the map described below was one of the smaller maps referred to in the prospectus, and that it was engraved, or at least drawn, before 1693. This view is supported by the fact that some of the spelling has not been modernised as it has been on no. 20, eg *New Shoram* and *Pemsey* (in one place) remain as on Speed no. 7; on no. 20 they have been amended to *New Shoreham* and *Pevensey*.

Magna Britannia et Hibernia . . . was conceived by John Nutt as an extension of his *Atlas geographus*, published in monthly parts from 1708, with maps (but not county maps) by Moll. Under the title *Britannia et Hibernia antiqua et nova* it was listed by Bernard Lintot (see no. 24) as early as 1714, but it seems to have been first published somewhat later. The six volumes were published in 1720 (vols. 1, 2), 1724 (3), in 1727 (4), in 1730 (5) and in 1731 (6). The text is attributed to the Rev. Thomas Cox, vicar of Broomfield in Essex (not to be confused with T. Cox the publisher) and the Rev. Anthony Hall, fellow of Queen's College, Oxford.[2]

This is the first map of Sussex to indicate parliamentary representation by asterisks. At this period Sussex returned twenty-eight members (see appendix X.vi).

EDITIONS

(i) *SUSSEX By Robt. Morden* (Ca, in wreath). *A Scale of Miles 10* = 34 mm, 10 = 32 mm, *10* = 30 mm (Ea). The Rapes and key to five places in Sussex (Aa). Longitude 10'; latitude 10'. Longitude is marked along bottom border only; the top border shows *Minutes of Time*.

---

1. Quoted from Skelton, *County atlases*, 1970, p. 193.
2. Wiles, 1957, p. 86.

The new description and state of England, containing mapps of the counties of England and Wales, in fifty three copper-plates, newly design'd, exactly drawn and engraven by the best artists . . .
London, Robert Morden, Thomas Cockerill and Ralph Smith, 1701.   BL.RGS

The new description and state of England, containing the maps of the counties of England and Wales, in fifty three copper-plates, newly design'd by Mr. Robert Morden, exactly drawn and engraven by the best artists . . . 2nd edn.
London, S. and J. Sprint, J. Nicholson, S. Burroughs, A. Bell and R. Smith, 1704.
BL.CUL

The new description and state of England . . . exactly drawn and engraven by Mr. Hermann Moll and the best artists . . . 2nd edn.
London, Ralph Smith, 1704.   WN

(ii)   *Pearmarsh* erased. *Isling* re-engraved. Coastline and rivers in the *Rye* area re-engraved and the county boundary extended into the border. Compass added (Ee). Other additions include *New Haven, East Lavant, Eastborne* (near *Mydhurst*), *Houghton, Ebeny, Rye, Rother R., Ch* (north of *Rye*) and a cross at *CHICHESTER*. Asterisks have been added at *CHICHESTER, Mydhurst, Arondel, Horsham, Stening, Bramber, New Shoram, Lewes, East Grinsted, Hastings, Winchelsea, Rye* and *Seaforde*. The county boundary has been completed from *Tratton* to the coast. Roads added and extended, eg *Rye* to *Lamberhurst* and on into Kent. Other roads re-routed, eg *East Grinsted* to *New Haven* via *Lewes* moved to the west in two places. Six road directions added, eg *to London* in three places.

Fifty six new and accurate maps of Great Britain, Ireland and Wales . . . Begun by Mr. Morden: perfected, corrected and enlarg'd by Mr. Moll . . .
London, John Nicholson, John Sprint, Andrew Bell and Ralph Smith, 1708.
BL.CUL.RGS

Magna Britannia et Hibernia, antiqua & nova. Or, a new survey of Great Britain, wherein to the topographical account given by Mr. Cambden, and the late editors of his Britannia, is added a more large history . . . collected and composed by an impartial hand (attributed to Thomas Cox). vol. 5.
London, M. Nutt and J. Morphew, 1730.   BL.CUL.BOD

Magna Britannia et Hibernia . . . Printed by E. and R. Nutt; . . .
London, T. Cox, 1730.   BL.SAS

A compleat history of Sussex. Containing . . . 7. A map of the county . . . Printed by E. and R. Nutt; . . .
London, T. Cox, 1730.   BRIGHTON PL
This is the Sussex section of the preceding work with a separate title-page. The work is said[3] to have

3.   *SAC* vol. 23, (1871), p. 319.

inspired the famous Burrell collection at the British Library, which includes a disbound copy (MS.5708) with extensive notes in manuscript. Another copy with marginal notes by Sir William Burrell (EASTBOURNE PL) has a printed label stuck over the original imprints on the title-page, and reading *Printed for C. Ward and R. Chandler, Booksellers, at the Ship without Temple Bar; and Sold at their Shops in Coney-Street, York, and at Scarborouh Spaw, where may be had any single County.*

Magna Britannia antiqua & nova: or, a new, exact, and comprehensive survey of the ancient and present state of Great-Britain . . . And illustrated not only with general mapps, but also particular ones of each county . . . vol. 5.
London, Caesar Ward and Richard Chandler, 1738.   P
A note on the title-page states that particular counties may be had separately; presumably, therefore, the Sussex section was also issued with a separate title-page, as in 1730. This is confirmed by an entry in *SAC* vol. 36 (1888) p. 233 which refers to *Sussex, History of the County, with Map. By Marden (Robert); a portion of a larger work, in Five Vols., 4to., entitled 'Atlas Geographicus', part vol.V 1738.*

Genuine sheets of the Sussex section, with the map, but with spurious title-pages, were issued, probably in the late 18th century. Two such title-pages are known:

A topographical, ecclesiastical, and natural history of [blank] *. . . by Thomas Cox. In the Savoy: sold by M. Nutt in Exeter-Exchange, 1700.*   P

Magna Britannia; or topographical, historical, ecclesiastical, and natural history of Sussex . . . By the Rev. Thomas Cox. In the Savoy: Printed by Eliz. Nutt; and sold by M. Nutt, in Exeter-Exchange in the Strand, and J. Morphew near Stationers-Hall. MDCCXX.   BRIGHTON PL

22 JOHN LENTHALL   [1717]

Size: 56 mm × 60 mm (2 mm)   1:2,180,000

Copied from Morden no. 17. **See plate 27(i).**

John Lenthall,[1] son of Thomas Lenthall of Hornchurch, Essex, was apprenticed to William Warter in 1699. He was made a freeman of the Stationers Company in 1706, and in 1708 became Warter's partner. Warter retired in 1709. Lenthall issued a large number of playing cards, mostly copied from the work of others. His broadside, in the possession of the British Library and now thought to have been issued in about 1723, lists no less than forty packs.[2] His advertisements continued to appear until about 1737.[3]

The pack containing the card described below was first advertised by Lenthall in

1. H. and V. Wayland, in *Journal of the playing-card society* vol. 1, no. 1 (August 1972).
2. Mann, 1966, pp. 134–50.
3. Information from Donald Hodson; see no. 16 for references to other advertisements.

1717. Although the cards in state (i) do not have the decorative border typical of Lenthall cards, the only known cards in this state[4] are found with two 'explanation cards'[5] which carry the Lenthall imprint. It is probable, therefore, that they were originally published by Lenthall, but with plain borders.

This was the fifth series of county maps to be published as a pack of cards (see nos. 2, 4, 16 and 17); the fact that there were exactly fifty-two English and Welsh counties proved irresistable to the makers of playing cards. It is sometimes thought that these cards were designed for instructional use rather than actual play. The introduction to the Lenthall broadside reads 'For the Improvement of Gentlemen, Ladies, and others, in several Arts and Sciences, as well as the agreeable Diversion of CARD-PLAYING, . . .' This could be taken to mean that some packs were for 'improvement' and others for 'card-playing'; but Rostenberg[6] reproduces an advertisement, from the London Gazette of 24–7 January 1675, which reads 'Geographical Cards, designed and fitted to all our known English Games of Cards . . . Sold by Henry Broome at the Gun. General publisher, & George Smith, Milliner'. The advertisement goes on to state that the packs may be had 'plain at 1/-, gilt & embelisht at 2/6, or bound in Book, and so serving for Geographical Tables at 2/-'. The implication is that one pack[7] at least was intended both for instruction and for play.

Sussex is the four of diamonds. The map forms the centre portion of the whole card, which measures 60 mm × 94 mm. Below the map is the same information as appeared on the Morden playing-card (no. 17), but *Breadth* is now spelt with an *a*, and *Latitude* without the double *t*.

EDITIONS

(i) *Sussex* (Ca OS). Diamond suit-mark with vertical hatching (Aa OS). *Miles 10 = 10 mm* (Be). Compass (Aa). Place-names as no. 17(i), but some spelling differences, eg *Winchelsea* in place of *Winchelsey*. The boundaries of the neighbouring counties are marked and the counties named.

Issued c. 1717 as a pack of cards.   BOD
The card number, IIII (Ea OS), appears to have been overprinted, not engraved on the plate.

(ii) Plain double-line border replaced by decorated border, typical of Lenthall cards.
See plate 27(i).

Issued c. 1717 as a pack of cards.   P

4. Bodleian Library; the diamond suit and king, queen, knave of hearts.
5. Mann and Kingsley, 1972, plate XIII.
6. Rostenberg, 1963. See also Tyacke, 1978, nos. 50a and 52.
7. No. VI in the Lenthall broadside. See also H. and V. Wayland, in *Journal of the Playing-Card Society* vol. 2, no. 4 (May 1974); Mann, 1966, p. 137. The designs on these cards did not include maps. It has been suggested that the original designer of this family of cards was Sir Peter Wyche (1628–99) (see *DNB* and J. Dallaway *Inquiries into the origin and progress of the science of heraldry in England . . .* 1793, appendix p. xxxii).

23 EMANUEL BOWEN   1720

Size: 107 mm × 80 mm (4 mm, top and sides; 27 mm, bottom)   1:1,240,000

Based on Morden no. 21. **See plate 14.**

Emanuel Bowen was a map- and print-seller, engraver and publisher. *Britannia depicta* was probably his first publication, and he must have been gratified at its success. He continued in business until his death in 1767, and at one time held the appointments of engraver to both George II and Louis XV. Nevertheless he died in reduced circumstances. His son Thomas carried on the business until about 1790, when he died in the Clerkenwell workhouse. (See also nos. 35, 37 and 45).

Thomas Bowles II published the work below in conjunction with Bowen. The Bowles family[1] flourished as print- and map-sellers and publishers for over a hundred years. Thomas Bowles I (d. 1721) was active from about 1683, and at some stage acquired parts of the stocks of Morden, Lea and Seller. His son, Thomas Bowles II (b. before 1695, d. 1767) was trained as an engraver, but probably took over the business on his father's retirement about 1714; he himself retired in 1762–4. John Bowles (1701–79) was the youngest son of Thomas I; he set up in business on his own, but collaborated on many occasions with his brother. John's son, Carington (d. 1793), first worked with his father, but in 1762–4 he took over from Thomas II the business originally founded by his grandfather, Thomas I. On Carington's death in 1793 the firm continued under the name Bowles and Carver. John Bowles's business, however, passed into the hands of Robert Wilkinson. Thomas II had a daughter, Bethia, and sons, William and Thomas III. The latter may be the Thomas Bowles whose death is recorded in 1788.[2] In contrast to the Bowens, the Bowles family seems to have prospered and to have died in comfortable circumstances. See nos. 34, 35, 43–6 for other atlases published by the family.

A short note by R.W. Blencowe on the 1731 edition of *Britannia depicta* appears in *SAC* vol. 16 (1864), p. 305. A facsimile of the first edition was published in 1970,[3] with an introduction by J.B. Harley.

The map forms the bottom part of page 8, which is headed *THE ROAD FROM LONDON TO ARUNDEL IN SUSSEX . . .*

EDITIONS

(i) *A MAP OF SUSSEX* (Aa, in rectangular frame). *English Miles 16* = 26 mm (Ca). Key to *The Rapes* numbered 1 to 6 (Ea, in plain rectangular panel). Topographical

1. These notes are based on Tyacke, 1978, pp. 111–3; Chubb, 1927, pp. 424–5; Darlington and Howgego, 1964; and Fordham, 1914 (the supplement includes a family tree). Some of the information given by the earlier authorities is contradictory.
2. Nichols, 1812–15, vol. 8, p. 479.
3. *Britannia depicta; or, Ogilby improved, by Emanuel Bowen 1720 Facsimile reprint.* Newcastle-upon-Tyne, 1970. See also *MCS* no. 34, in which the prospectus for the original work is reproduced.

notes starting *The County of SUSSEX is 158 Miles in Circumference* . . . (in bottom border). The back of the map (page 7) shows the road from *Aberistwith* to *Riadergowy*. **See plate 14.**

> *Britannia depicta or Ogilby improv'd; being a correct coppy of M^r: Ogilby's actual survey of all ye direct & principal cross roads in England and Wales . . . And to render this work universally usefull & agreeable . . . are added . . . a full & particular description & account of all the cities . . . &^c . . . by In^o. Owen of the Midd: Temple gent . . . lastly particular & correct maps of all ye counties of south Britain . . . by Eman: Bowen engraver.*
> London, Thomas Bowles and Emanuel ('Em') Bowen, 1720.   BL

(ii)   Numbers *1* to *6*, identifying the rapes, have been added on the map. In the first edition the numbers appear in the key, but not on the map itself.

> *Britannia depicta . . .*
> London, Thomas Bowles and Emanuel ('Em') Bowen, 1720.   BL

> *Britannia depicta . . .*
> London, Thomas Bowles and E. Bowen, 1720 (actually reissues made in 1721 and 1723).   BL;BL

> *Britannia depicta . . . 4th edn.*
> London, Thomas Bowles and I. Bowles, 1724.   BL

> *Britannia depicta . . . 4th edn.*
> London, Thomas Bowles, 1730, 1731, 1734, 1736, 1749, 1751, 1753 and 1759
> A;BL;WN;BL;WN;BL;BL;BL
> In the 1759 edition changes have been made on the back of the map. Nine lines of text starting with an obelisk and *The Point of bearing* . . . have been added and an obelisk added at the top of the third column. In *THE IRISH SEA* the lower of the two ships has been erased together with a pennant on the bow of the upper ship. *See Pl. 244* has been added under to *Llanbeder.*

(iii)   The map is unchanged, but in the panel above, the *Meas^d Miles* to *Arundel* has been altered from *55* to *55½*. Similar changes have been made in the list below, eg *Towting 6'7* altered to *6'6.*

> *Britannia depicta: or, Ogilby improved. Being an actual survey of all the direct and principal cross-roads of England and Wales . . . Engraved by Emanuel Bowen, geographer. To which is added, an accurate historical and topographical description of all the cities . . . and other places of note . . . by John Owen, gent. The whole illustrated with maps of all the counties of south Britain . . .*
> London, Carington Bowles, 1764.   BL.CUL
> Further revisions have been made on the back of the map, eg [*at 199*] has been added to the end of the note headed *Aberistwith,* and [*at 170½*] to the end of the note headed *Riadergowy.* Many mileages have been increased by one; some new mileages have been added, and others erased.

24 RICHARD BUDGEN   1723

Size: 1500 mm × 660 mm (10 mm)   1:86,500

Based on original surveys by Budgen. **See plates 12 and 13.**

The first large-scale map of Sussex, and one of the first large-scale county surveys.[1] It incorporates a great deal of information not previously published, in particular the location of many iron furnaces and forges, a theme represented in the framework of the title panel. Gough's[2] judgement that it 'deserves but the name of a map at most, and even as such is neither correct nor well executed' has been qualified by Skelton,[3] who points out that Gough was writing in 1780, only two years after the publication of the first sheet of the Yeakell and Gardner map (no. 47), with which it cannot be compared. It is significant that Gough does not make the same criticism in *Anecdotes of British topography* (1768). Nevertheless, Harley,[4] writing about pre-1750 county surveys, notes that they '. . . were justly censored by their users, as was that of Richard Budgen.' A balanced assessment is that of William Roy, who wrote in 1766: 'There are already good surveys made by different people, of the undermentioned counties. viz. Middlesex, Hertfordshire, Berkshire, Hampshire, Dorsetshire, Devonshire, Herefordshire and Shropshire; there is also *a tolerable map of Sussex* and another of Cornwall . . .'[5] Lower[6] refers to it as 'a very useful document'.

With all its failings, Budgen's map is a great improvement on its predecessors, and is clearly based on painstaking research and some original fieldwork, which justify the claims made for it in the title. The coastline is more accurately delineated than in earlier maps and compares well with the Gardner, Yeakell and Gream map of 1795 (no. 57). The EW:NS ratio (Chichester to Rye: Brighton to East Grinstead) is almost correct at 2.8. It is the first map of the county to be oriented to true north and to indicate magnetic variation, the first to have parallels and meridians drawn across the map, and the first to have a scale-bar in statute miles. The parallels and meridians form a reference graticule, which is used to locate the seats of the gentry whose arms are engraved below the map. Each seat on the map is numbered to correspond with the arms but there are some minor mistakes, eg *Monk . . . of Buckingham house in old Shoram* in state (ii) has the reference *I d 26,* but *26* does not appear on the map; *Board John of Peckhill* is *Packhill* on the map.

The nautical information in the area of *Selsey Bill* is copied from an undated chart in the British Library (Maps 189.b.24) with the title: *An exact draught [being an actual survey] of the sea coast from Arundel in Sussex to St Albans in Dorset . . . Jos. Avery. Eman Bowen Sculpt., and sold by Willm Mount & Thomas Page on Tower Hill.* It was published in 1721. A later edition of this chart is inserted in *Collins's British coasting*

---

1. Laxton, 1976, appendix I.
2. Gough, 1780 vol. 2, p. 297.
3. Skelton, introduction to *Two hundred and fifty years of map-making,* 1970.
4. Harley, 1965, p. 56.
5. Quoted from Harley and O'Donoghue, 1975, p. xiii.
6. Lower, 1854, p. 133.

pilot (BL Maps 31.e.7) and has the imprint altered to *Sold by R.Mount & Comp̄. on Tower Hill, 1731*. The chart marks *East Burrow Head,* but Budgen uses the earlier form *Borrow*. (Overton no. 26 also has *Borrow*. It is omitted on other derivatives, but reappears on Kitchin no. 46, which reverts to the spelling *Burrow,* as on the chart). Longitudes on the chart are measured east and west of Southampton.

We do not know the method used by Budgen to determine longitude. He may have used a time-piece – they had been used with varying success since 1583 – but this is unlikely; Harrison's chronometer did not come into use until later in the century. He probably worked from tables based on observation of the satellites of Jupiter or of the moon. A great deal has been written about the determination of longitude at sea;[7] very little about the measurement of longitude on land.

Budgen's *EXPLANATION* (**see plate 12**) introduced a number of new conventional signs, including *Mineral Waters* (not found on the map), *Stonequarrys,* and a rowing boat which *Shews how far yᵉ Rivers are Navig*. Churches – *Drawn According to their Several Forms* – and houses are shown in elevation; but major towns are in plan. Mileages on major routes are indicated by dots.[8]

Little is known about the life or work of Richard Budgen[9] (1695–1731). His grandfather was Thomas Budgen of Clarks, Frant, who died about 1660. His father, Edward (1643–1713) was the fifth of six children, and Richard was the seventh in a family of eight. He married Elizabeth Carpenter in 1727. His only child, Richard II, was born in 1730. His wife re-married a John Cooper in 1746.

There is no record of his work prior to the publication of the Sussex map, but several of his estate plans from the period 1724 to 1728 have survived. In 1730 he wrote a pamphlet entitled *The Passage of the Hurricane from the Sea-side at Bexhill in Sussex to Newingden-level. The Twentieth day of May, 1729 . . .,* dedicated to Sir Hans Sloane and printed for John Senex. It is accompanied by *An Exact Plan,* which is reproduced in *SAC* vol. 36 (1888), and in an article by Arthur Beckett in the *Sussex County Magazine* for May 1934. The latter concludes: 'Of Richard Budgen himself . . . I know next to nothing. That he was interested in meteorological phenomena[10] is evident, for in the course of his account of the tornado he states that he kept a journal in which he recorded the state of the weather'. The pamphlet implies that he lived in Frant, and perhaps worked in Tunbridge Wells. Much might have been achieved had he lived longer. The inventory[11] of his estate was valued at £223. 0s. 6d., and included two globes, a number of books, seventy-two maps and prints, two theodolites and other surveying and meteorological instruments.

Richard Budgen II (1730–89), whose name appears on the 1779 edition of the

---

7. Taylor, 1956, for example, tells the story clearly and concisely.
8. I.D. Margary, 'Traffiic routes in Sussex, 1724', *SAC* vol. 109 (1971), pp. 20–3.
9. A family tree covering the period 1660 to 1800 can be pieced together from manuscript notes at SAS made by Rev. Walter Budgen (probably no relation) in 1888; from Eeles, 1947; and from references to the family in *SAC* and SRS publications. Thomas Budgen (d. 1660) had two sons, Thomas (1633–94) and Edward (1643–1713), and eight grandsons named: Thomas (2), Edward (2), Richard (2), John and William. The repetition of these five first names makes the rest of the pedigree difficult to unravel, and the conclusions somewhat speculative.
10. As was his contemporary, Henry Beighton, surveyor of Warwickshire (see Harvey, 1959, pp. 20, 34).
11. ESRO, W/INV 2365, dated 30 Oct. 1731.

map, was the son of the original cartographer,[12] and also lived at Frant. He was an estate surveyor, and plans by him are known dated between 1757 and 1783.[13] In 1774 his map, *A scetch of the roads within fourteen miles of Tunbridge Wells*, at a scale of four miles to 75 mm was published by Jasper Sprange.[14] He could not have learnt his trade from his father, who died in the year following his son's birth. His father's surviving brothers are both described as butchers, but there may have been a cousin who practised as a surveyor. In any event, the family continued the surveying tradition in the area.

Thomas Budgen (1766–1832) practised at Lewes, and produced a large number of estate plans between 1788 and 1826. He was the son of Richard II, and was living in Brighton when he died. In 1791 he was employed on a survey of the Ouse.[15] His plan of Brighthelmstone, engraved by Neele, was published in 1788, and a Brighton terrier of c. 1792 (*SAS*) was probably his work. Charles Budgen (1769–1838) was also the son of Richard Budgen II, and worked for the Ordnance Survey between 1798 and 1824.[16] William Budgen (b.1790) was a grandson of Richard II, and was active from 1809 to about 1830, often in collaboration with his brother, Lieut John Budgen, of whom rather more is known.[17] A great-grandson of the original cartographer, Richard I, he was born at Frant in 1794, and served in the navy, as did his brothers Richard and William, from 1803 to 1816. He described himself as *Secretary to Queen Caroline,* and as *Surveyor & Assistant Commissioner to the Reform Bill.* He was active as a surveyor from 1826–1840,[18] probably in the Tunbridge Wells area, where a John Budgen is known to have been in practice in 1839.[19]

Bernard and Henry Lintot, who were concerned with publication of the map, were members of a family long established in the Horsham area.[20] There are a number of references to them, sometimes with the spelling 'Lintott', in the *Sussex Archaeological Collections,* mainly as tradesmen and persons of yeoman stock. One branch of Lintots, from the Bolney and Cowfold district, obtained a grant of arms in 1723, which appeared on the map as the arms (no. 143) of *Lintot Thos. of Walhurst.*

A Joshua Lintott was *Printer of the Votes* from 1708 to 1710. Bernard Lintot (1675–1736) was probably his nephew, and held the same appointment from the Hon Spencer Compton from 1717 to 1727. He started life as Barnaby Lintott of Southwater, near Horsham, but later called himself Bernard Lintot. He was a considerable literary figure, and published a number of poetical works, including those of Pope, with whom he quarrelled. Pope refers to him in the *Dunciad* as 'lofty Lintot.' Size seems to have

12. Gough, 1780, vol. 2, p. 297.
13. BL, Add.MS 41176; Steer, 1962, 1968; Dickins, 1981 pp. 47, 50, 59; Eden, 1975, states that he was active between 1757 and 1781. It is possible that some of the later surveys may have been the work of his son, Richard III, born 1760.
14. Reissued, 1802, 1809 and 1811, and in 1820 by J. Clifford.
15. J.H. Farrant, 'The Lower Ouse Navigation' *Sussex Ind. Arch. Soc. Newsletter* no. 3 (June 1974).
16. *CJ*, Dec. 1971, p. 96; Harley and O'Donoghue, 1977, pp. xvii, xxi; Hodson, 1978, p. 135.
17. BL, Add.MS 38040, f.368; O'Byrne, 1849.
18. Eden, 1975.
19. *Pigot and Co's royal national and commercial directory and topography of the counties of Bedford . . . and Sussex.* London, 1839.
20. Information regarding the family comes from *DNB*; Nichols, 1812 vol. 8, pp. 161–76, 293–304; *SAC* vol. 8 (1856), pp. 275–7; Lower, 1865, p. 274.

been a characteristic of the family; it is recorded[21] that in 1732 'Henry Lintott died, aged 32, at Bolney . . . He was the largest man that ever was seen.' This was not the 'H. Lintot', whose imprint appears on the map in state (ii), but presumably some relation. Bernard is among the booksellers listed in the 1712 edition of *The Traveller's guide*,[22] and was the publisher of *Charters of the Cinque Ports*, by Samuel Jeake, in 1728. He was nominated High Sheriff of Sussex, but died before he could take office.[23]

The day-to-day running of Lintot's business was taken over by his son, Henry (1703[24]–58), in about 1738, when his name first appeared in advertisements. Humfrey Wanley, the antiquarian, records that 'Young Mr. Lintot, the bookseller, came inquiring after arms, as belonging to his father, mother and other relations, who now, it seems, want to turn gentlefolks. I could find none of their names.' Nevertheless, on the map in state (ii), the arms of *Henry Lintot of Southwater* have been added (no. 147) alongside those of Thomas Lintot.[25] The arms thus 'acquired' by Henry Lintot bear a resemblance to those of the Honywood family from the same district.[26] He took his father's place as sheriff of the county in 1736. He married Elizabeth, daughter of Sir John Aubrey of Borstal. He is one of thirteen booksellers named in the 1753 edition of Camden's *Britannia*. His daughter, Catherine, built up a successful business as a law printer in partnership with Samuel Richardson, the novelist, and amassed a fortune of £45,000. She married Sir Henry Fletcher of Ashley Park, Surrey, and died in 1816.

John Senex, the engraver of the map, came from Shropshire. He started as a bookseller in London in about 1702, but later he concentrated on mapmaking and engraving. He became a fellow of the Royal Society in 1728, and died in 1740. He traded from the 'Globe' in Salisbury Court, Fleet Street, at least until 1721.[27] This was 200 or 300 yards from S[t]. Dunstan's-in-the-West, the address given for him on the map in state (i) (1723). His output included a map of Surrey on a scale of one inch to one mile on four sheets in 1729, and a map of south-east England on a scale of three miles to one inch published by his widow in 1746 (see appendix III.8).

Jasper Sprange, see state (iii) below, was the publisher of the *Tunbridge Wells Guide* from 1780 to 1817. The 1786 edition, published in conjunction with Rivingtons of London, carried this advertisement: 'Map of the County of Sussex, by the late Richard Budgen . . . This map is worked off the original plates, which have been kept in excellent preservation; having continued in the possession of Mr. Richard Budgen, son of the late Richard Budgen, Land Surveyor of Frant in Sussex.'

The background to the publication of the map described below is obscure. How and under whose auspices Richard Budgen I came to undertake the work has not been

---

21. *SAC* vol. 18 (1866), p. 158.
22. A version of Ogilby's *Britannia*, without the strip maps.
23. Albery, 1927, p. 82, refers to another Barnard Lintott living in 1739.
24. Nichols, 1812, gives 1709 as his date of birth, but this seems unlikely.
25. On Kitchin no. 43 (c.1763) *Sedgewich Park Lintot Esq[r].* is listed among only fourteen *Seats of Nobility and Gentry in Sussex.*
26. W.S. Ellis, *SAC* vol. 25 (1873), pp. 85–100, deals in detail with the heraldic aspects of Budgen's map. Ellis describes the Honywood arms (no. 68 on the map) as 'eagle's heads', and those of Henry Lintot as 'hawk's heads'. Horsfield (Lewes, 1824) and Berry in his *Sussex genealogies* describe the Honywood arms as 'falcon's heads'.
27. Darlington and Howgego, 1964, no. 65; and Senex's *New general atlas of the world.*

established by any direct evidence, nor has the original prospectus been found. It was financed by subscription in accordance with the custom at that time.

The problems connected with the publication of Budgen's map were probably similar to those encountered by Beighton, whose map of Warwickshire on a scale of one inch to the mile was published in 1725, and with which Senex was also involved. Thorpe gives the story of that map in some detail.[28] Of the 160 shields on Budgen's map, 143 were completed in edition (i), 148 in edition (ii). Beighton was not so fortunate; his map has only 131 coats of arms depicted in full.

The following advertisements[29] appeared in the *Weekly Journal or Saturday's Post*. On 25 May 1723 'MR. Bugden's (sic) Map of Sussex being now finish'd, the Subscribers who are to have their Arms engraved thereon are desired to send them to Bernard Lintot, Bookseller, at the Cross-Keys between the Temple Gates, forthwith, and that the said Map may be immediately published. N.B. Those who have not subscribed may, for the present, subscribe, and send in their Arms to the Place as aforesaid'. And on 21 December 1723 'Ready to be delivered to Subscribers, An actual Survey of the County of Sussex, divided into Rapes, Hundreds, and Deanries; in which the exact Longitude and Latitude of all the remarkable Places, are determined from Observation; also an accurate Delineation by Admeasurement of the Sea Coast, the Roads, and the Rivers, as far as Navigable, &c. By Richard Budgen, at Frant, near Tunbridge Wells, and by Bernard Lintot, at the Cross-Keys between the Temple Gates, Mr. Webb at Colchester, Mr Norman at Lewes, and Mr Smith at Battell.' It will be seen that the wording of the second advertisement follows in part the wording in the title on the map. The word 'sold' seems to have been omitted before the words 'by Bernard Lintot'. 'Colchester' is an error for 'Chichester'.

Bernard Lintot is mentioned in both advertisements, but there is no reference to Senex. It is therefore probable that Lintot was the initiator of the scheme, particularly in view of his connection with Spencer Compton, to whom the map is dedicated. Spencer Compton (1673–1743), later Earl of Wilmington, purchased the manor of Eastbourne. He died unmarried, and his estate passed to his brother, later to Lady Elizabeth Compton, and then by marriage to the Dukes of Devonshire, whose association with Eastbourne has continued to the present day.

The second advertisement implies that by the end of 1723 the map was ready for delivery to the 143 original subscribers. It would be natural to assume that this refers to the map in state (i), which according to the inscription was sold by Senex, in conjunction with Webb and Norman, but which does not refer to Bernard Lintot. Why he handed over publication to Senex is not explained. Nor is it easy to understand why the map is undated, and why only one impression has survived, compared with at least a dozen impressions of the map in state (ii). It is tempting, therefore, to assume that this sole surviving and undated impression was a proof copy, and to accept the map in state (ii) as the first corrected edition. But such an assumption raises other problems. The map in state (ii) cannot have been issued before 1725 (see note 32). Furthermore, the reference to Senex, Webb and Norman has been replaced in state (ii) by *Printed for H.*

28. Harvey, 1959, pp. 19–27.
29. I am indebted to Donald Hodson for bringing these and other advertisements to my attention.

Lintot. This must be Bernard's son Henry, who would have been aged only 21 in 1724, and who would not appear, from the evidence of other advertisements, to have taken over from his father until nearly ten years later.

It is possible that there was an intermediate edition of the map between states (i) and (ii), with the date added and with perhaps some minor additions, and that the map in this intermediate state was issued to the original subscribers. This would account for the retention of the 1724 date when the map was reissued, perhaps some years later, by Henry Lintot. But this hypothesis still presents two problems. Firstly, why did Bernard Lintot hand over to Senex, and how did the publication rights subsequently come back into the hands of his son, Henry? In this connection it is worth noting that Henry's device (Cross Keys) is the same as his father's, and that his address is the same as Senex's. Secondly, why have no impressions of such an intermediate edition survived? If it had been issued to the 143 original subscribers, it would almost certainly have been the largest single edition. For this reason, it seems very probable that the map issued to the original subscribers was in state (ii) below, that it was issued in 1725 or after, and probably (in view of the Henry Lintot imprint) some years after.

Any explanation of such a sequence of events can only be tentative. Perhaps Bernard Lintot got into financial trouble, and, despite the December 1723 advertisement, was unable to go though with the printing and distribution of the map to the original subscribers. Senex may have taken over, and run off a few proof impressions in state (i), of which only one is known to have survived. Then perhaps some years later Henry Lintot revived the project – possibly in conjunction with Senex – and published the map in state (ii) for the benefit of all 148 subscribers.

The map itself is printed from three plates.[30] The title dedication, town plans and views, which appear above the map, are printed from three further plates.

EDITIONS

(i)   *AN ACTUAL SURVEY OF THE County of Sussex Divided into Rapes Hundreds and Deanryes. In which the EXACT LONGITUDE AND LATITUDE Of all the Remarkable Places, are Determin'd from Observation. ALSO AN ACCURATE DELINIATION By Admeasurement of the SEA-COAST, ROADS and the RIVERS so far as NAVIGABLE etc. By Rich. Budgen.* (Aa OS, in illustrated framework, including Royal Arms, Britannia, Vulcan, Venus and Cyclops). *TO THE R^T. HON^BLE. Spencer Compton Esqr Speaker of the Honble. House of Commons Paymaster General of HIS MAJESTIES FORCES One of His Maties. most Honble. Privy Council. TREASURER TO THE PRINCE. KNIGHT OF THE SHIRE FOR THE COUNTY OF SUSSEX &c. This Survey thereof is Dedicated By His most humble & most Obedient Servant Rich. Budgen.* (Ea OS). *Engrav'd by I: Senex* (Ae). *Sold by M^r. Senex at the Globe*

---

30.   Each sheet measures 560 mm × 720 mm (22" × 28¼") which was near to the maximum size of paper then available. It is usually found in six sheets, but the sale catalogue of the collection of Michael Lort (1791) included 'Budgeon's Map of Sussex. 24 sheets' (see G. Walters, 'Two Welsh map collectors of the 18th century' in *The Map collector* no. 6, March 1979). It must have been cut to quarto size, and perhaps bound.

ag^st. St. Dunstans Church in fleetstreet. London, M^r. Webb at Chichester, and Mr Norman at Lewes in Sussex (Ae OS). *A Scale of Geometrical Miles 1+4* = 77 mm (Ee). Compass (Aa). *EXPLANATION* (Ea, in elaborate cartouche). Longitude 5' (1'); latitude 5' (1'), with graticule at 5' intervals and reference letters *a* to *f* and *A* to *X*. *Brighthelmston* is 0°3'40"W, 50°53'50"N, longitudes being based on S^t. Paul's. Latitudes are overstated by about six minutes. The minutes of longitude west of London in the bottom border are marked incorrectly, running from 10' to 55' from left to right instead of right to left. Only three values – 40', 45' and 50' E – are marked on the top border. In the centre panel above the map are *THE ICHNOGRAPHY OF CHICHESTER, THE ICHNOGRAPHY OF LEWES, THE SOUTH PROSPECT OF LEWES, NORTH PROSPECT OF CHICHESTER* and coats of arms of the peers and bishops of Sussex. Across the bottom of the map inside the border are numerous coats of arms of the gentlemen of Sussex with references enabling their seats to be located on the map.

Issued in 1723 as loose sheets. (CUL)

(ii)   The date *1724* added at end of title (Aa OS). The beginning of imprint (Ae OS) is re-engraved, and now reads *Printed for H. Lintot at ye Cross Keys ag^st. S^t. Dunstans Church in fleetstreet. London,* the rest erased. Rhumb lines from the compass (Aa) extended into the title panel. Minor additions to the map, eg *Cliff* added at *S. Malling*. In top centre panel (Ca OS) *LORD IRWIN* now reads *LORD V. IRWIN*, presumably for Viscount.[31] A number of additions to the coats of arms below map, eg *Monk . . . of Buckingham house in old Shoram; Courthope Alex Esqr. . .; Kirril John Esqr. . .; Lade John Esqr. . .; Lintot. Henry of Southwater,* with reference number *147* added on map (the arms of *Lintot Thos. of Walhurst* already appear on the map in state (i)). Also a number of alterations, *Blackmore Raymond,* formerly *Blackmore Raymon; Mad^m. Martha* erased from *Luxford Mad^m. Martha of Nes-sington; Fermer Sr Hen.Bart . . .* formerly *Fermer Hen, Esqr of Welshes.* Some arms have also been amended, eg *Conyers John Esqr.* **See plates 12 and 13.**

Issued after 1725[32] as loose sheets. (BL).(BOD).(ESRO)

(iii)   *Republish'd with the tunrpike Roads, corrected from a Survey of them lately taken throughout the County, by I. Sprange, Bookseller Tunbridge Wells, and R. Budgen of Frant, Sussex, June 1st. 1779.* added (Ae OS). There are no additions to the map, and no roads have been added.

Issued from 1779 as loose sheets. (BL).(WSRO)

---

31. Albery, 1927. This work includes a history of the family of Richard Ingram, the fifth viscount, who died in 1721 and was succeeded by his brother, Arthur.
32. Possibly much later; Henry Fermor was created a baronet in 1725. Henry Lintot's advertisements do not appear before 1733.

25 HERMAN MOLL   1724

Size: 241 mm × 180 mm (5 mm)   1:535,000

Based on Budgen no. 24; the coastline incorporates many of the improvements made by him. The EW:NS ratio has been over-corrected, and is 2.6 to 1 (see Saxton no. 1 and Budgen no. 24). The map includes a number of coastal features not seen on maps prior to Budgen, eg *Sluce Haven, Brickelsöme (Brackelsome Bay* on Budgen), and *Seven Cliffs,* placed to the east of *Beachy Head,* but shown correctly by Budgen to the west thereof. This last feature does not appear on earlier maps of Sussex, but it is marked on sea charts, starting with the 1583 chart in Waghenaer's *Spieghel der Zeevaert* (appendix II.1). Moll's spelling tends to follow Budgen rather than Morden, eg *Middleton (Midleton* in Morden*)* and *Echingham (Etchingham).*

Moll (c.1654[1]–1732) was probably German,[2] He started as an engraver, but after he came to London in or before 1678, he worked as a cartographer, publisher and bookseller until his death. He would have been over seventy when the works below were published.

Sussex, and other maps in the series, are untidily engraved and the decoration is uninteresting. Nevertheless, Moll must be given credit for seeking out the latest and best surveys available.[3] He went to the trouble of making a reduction from Budgen, a map drawn on three sheets and on six times the scale. The roads are from Ogilby's *Britannia* (appendix V.1).

The map of Hertfordshire in this series has been found in a fifth state, later than (iv) below, and with an additional plate number.[4]

Charles Rivington (1688–1742) was the founder of a distinguished line of publishers.[5] In 1711 he took over the business of Richard Chiswell (see no. 7). His sons, John and James, are included in the list of booksellers on Camden's *Britannia* 1753 and 1772 (see no. 20). The printer Alexander Rivington, of 64 High Street, Lewes, whose imprint appears on the *Sussex Archaeological Collections* for 1879–80 (vols. 29–30) does not seem to have been a member of the same family.

EDITIONS

(i) *SUSSEX by Herman Moll Geographer.* (Ca, in rectangular frame). *English Miles 10* = 36 mm (Ee). Compass (Ee, above scale). Key to rapes (Ea). Longitude 15' (5'); latitude 15' (5'). Outside the border on the left are illustrations of two Sussex antiquities, and on the right six *Roman Coins.* There is no plate number.

> *A new description of England and Wales, with the adjacent islands . . . To which is added, a new and correct set of maps of each county . . . and, to render 'em the*

---

1. J.N.L. Baker, 'The earliest maps of H. Moll'. *Imago Mundi* vol. 2 (1937).
2. Tyacke, 1978, p. 123.
3. In the absence of any better source, the maps in this series were based on Morden's large maps (no. 20). See Harvey, 1959, p. 18.
4. Hodson, 1974, no. 27.
5. Rivington, 1919; Maxted, 1977, p. xxxv.

more acceptable to the curious, their margins are adorn'd with great variety of very remarkable antiquities, &c. By Herman Moll, geographer.
London, H. Moll, T. Bowles, C. Rivington and J. Bowles, 1724.   CUL

A set of fifty new and correct maps of England and Wales, &c. . . All, except two, composed and done by Herman Moll, geographer. . .
London, H. Moll, Thomas Bowles and J. Bowles, 1724.   CUL

(ii)   Plate number *(12)* added (Aa, in border).

A new description of England and Wales . . .
London, H. Moll, T. Bowles, C. Rivington and J. Bowles, 1724 and 1728.   A;WN

A set of fifty new and correct maps of England and Wales . . .
London, H. Moll, Thomas Bowles and J. Bowles, 1724.   BL,RGS

A new description of England and Wales . . .
London, J. Wilford, T. Bowles, C. Rivington and J. Bowles, 1733.   WN

A set of fifty new and correct maps of the counties of England and Wales, &c. . . . All, except two, composed and done by Herman Moll, geographer . . .
London, Thomas Bowles and J. Bowles, 1739.   BL.CUL.WORTHING PL

In all copies of the above books seen by the compiler, the back of the map is blank, but the map may also have been included in an untraced issue of one of these works with the map of another county printed on the back.[6]

(iii)   Plate number (Aa) altered to *(39)*.

The geography of England and Wales; or, a set of maps of all the counties in England and Wales. . . all, except two, composed and done by Herman Moll, geographer. . .
London, Thomas Bowles and J. Bowles, 1747.   CUL

(iv)   The plate has been cut down so that the engraving outside the border on the left and right no longer appears. Many place-names added, eg *or Selsey Harbour, Lippock, Lamberhurst, Pier Rocks* (at *Hastings*). *e* has been added at end of *Tunbridge*. Roads added from *CHICHESTER* to *Havant*, and from *Midhurst* to the west border.

H. Moll's British atlas: or, pocket maps of all the counties in England and Wales . . . Composed and engraved by Herman Moll, geographer; and lately revised and improved, with the addition of many hundred places, by Emanuel Bowen,

6.   Hodson, 1974, p. 43. The compiler has also seen a loose map of Warwickshire with Worcestershire on the back.

26 PHILIP OVERTON   circa **1726**

Size: 964 mm × 563 mm (10 mm)   1:130,000

A reduced version of Budgen no. 24. Overton adds *Tikeredg,* just two miles west of *E.GRINSTEAD.* Budgen has a house symbol at this spot, but no place-name. This is, in fact, the site of Gulledge Farm; Tickeridge lies about one and a half miles further south.

Earlier sources, eg the British Library map catalogue, have dated this map c.1740. The date adopted here is based on the fact that Philip Overton and Thomas Bowles published a map of Essex, Middlesex and Hertfordshire in 1726, similar in size to this Sussex map, and with the same style of border. Furthermore, Overton probably moved from his address near St Dunstan's Church prior to 1728.[1]

Neither draughtsman nor engraver of this map is known. It has been catalogued under the name of Philip Overton, whose name appears first on the imprint. Overton, the son of John Overton (see no. 18), died in 1745.

EDITION

An *ACTUAL SURVEY OF THE COUNTY OF SUSSEX. Divided into RAPES HUNDREDS and DEANRIES. In which the EXACT LONGITUDE AND LATITUDE of all ye Remarkable Places are Determin'd from Observation. also AN ACCURATE DELINIATION by Admeasurement of The Sea-Coast, Roads and the Rivers so far as Navigable.* (Aa, in decorative framework copied from that which surrounds the *EXPLANATION* on Budgen's map). *Printed and Sold by Philip Overton near S^t. Dunstans Church Fleetstreet And Thomas Bowles next y^e Chapter house in St Pauls Church yard.* (Ee). *A Scale of Geometrical Miles* 1 + 4 = 50 mm (Eb). Compass (Ee). *EXPLANATION.* (Ea, in decorative framework). Longitude 10' (1'), latitude 10' (1'), with graticule at 10' intervals. *THE SOUTH PROSPECT OF LEWES* (Ba). *NORTH PROSPECT OF CHICHESTER* (Da).

Issued as loose maps, sold separately, c.1726.   (BL).(BOD)

Atlas nouveau . . . vol. 3.
Amsterdam, J. Covens and C. Mortier, [1761].   LIB OF CONGRESS
This atlas is in nine volumes. Individual maps are dated from 1683 to 1761. Publication dates are not given for any of the nine volumes.

1. Tyacke, 1978, p. 135.

27 RICHARD WILLIAM SEALE

circa **1730**

Size: 240 mm × 178 mm (6 mm)   1:549,000

Copied from Moll no. 25; the geographical detail is almost the same on both maps. This version omits *Ouse R* and the road distance *12* near *Bright Helmston*. **See plate 15.**

Seale (d. 1785) was primarily an engraver. His signature has been found on maps between 1731[1] and 1775. Overton and Hoole, the publishers, were in partnership from about 1724 to 1731.[2] It seems probable that this map was published towards the end of their association.

EDITION

SUSSEX (Ca, in rectangular frame). *English Miles 10* = 35 mm (Ee). Compass (Ee, above scale). Longitude 15' (5'); latitude 15' (5'). Nine shields with arms of Sussex towns and one blank shield are engraved to left and right outside the border. **See plate 15.**

A collection of nine similar maps.   BL

The maps are engraved on two sheets in three rows of three. Sussex is in the middle of the bottom row. It is therefore printed from part of two separate plates and is joined down the centre. Across the top of the nine maps is the title and imprint *NINE NEW & ACCURATE MAPS OF THE SOUTHERN COUNTIES OF ENGLAND viz; CORNWALL, DEVON, SOMERSET, WILTS. DORSET, HANTS, SURREY, SUSSEX & WIGHT-ISLE . . . Printed and Sold by Henry Overton & I. Hoole at yᵉ White Horse without Newgate, LONDON.* The signature *R. Seale*[3] appears on the right sheet (Ee OS).

28 CHARLES PRICE

1730

Size: 583 mm × 230 mm (2 mm)   1:225,000

Based on Budgen no. 24. The layout is similar, but on Price's scale-bar the mile is equivalent to nearly ten furlongs. Price also adds *Tickeredge,* just over two miles west of *E. GRINSTEAD* (see Overton, no. 26). **See plate 16.**

Charles Price was known as the 'geographical engraver'. He was apprenticed to John Seller in 1693, and from 1697 he was in partnership with Jeremiah Seller. Subsequently he worked with John Senex, and later (1710–12) with George Willdey. He died in 1733.

---

1. Darlington and Howgego, 1964, no. 75: *A Pocket MAP of LONDON,* also *Printed and Sold by H. Overton & J. Hoole.*
2. From an analysis of advertisements by Donald Hodson. See also Tooley, 1979, p. 572.
3. This is the only map found with the signature *R. Seale.* All others are signed *R.W. Seale* or *R.W.S.*

Richard Mount (1654–1722), see (ii) below, was a man of Kent from Chislet.[1] He was apprenticed to William Fisher in 1670, married his daughter, and became a partner in the firm. Fisher died in 1691. In 1701 Mount was joined by his own apprentice Thomas Page (d. 1733), thus founding the famous firm of chart makers and publishers. About 1707 Mount and Page took over most of the stock of Seller and Price, who were in financial difficulties.[2]

Advertisements in the *Country Journal: or, the Craftsman* in November 1729 and January 1730 show that Price intended to produce a county atlas as part of an 'atlas for sea and land'. The booksellers named on the map in state (i) also appear in the advertisements.[3] Some charts appeared, but Sussex was the only county map to be produced.

Gough[4] refers to this map as being by Charles *Pine*, an error repeated by subsequent bibliographers.

The map proper occupies the lower half of the sheet, which measures 587 mm × 461 mm. The top part includes title, imprints and the following plans and views: *NORTH PROSPECT OF CHICHESTER, SOUTH PROSPECT OF LEWES, THE ICHNOGRAPHY OF CHICHESTER, THE ICHNOGRAPHY OF LEWES.*

EDITIONS

(i) *A Correct MAP of the County of SUSSEX Humbly Dedicated to   by Cha: Price. 1730* (Ca OS, in decorative framework). *London Sold by M^{rs}. Chilcot in Westminster Hall, M^{r}. Heath next to the Fountain Tavarn in the Strand, Mr Clark Bookseller at the Royal Exchange, Mrs Penn Bookseller in Bristoll.* (Da OS, below and to the right of title). *A Scale of Miles 10* = 87 mm (Ee). Compass (Be). Longitude not shown; latitude 5'. Parallels at 5' intervals. **See plate 16.**

Issued as loose maps, sold separately.   (BL).(BOD).(SAS)

(ii) Date *1730* erased from title. Booksellers' imprints (Da OS) erased and replaced by *Sold by Willm. Mount & Thos. Page on Tower Hill. London.*

Issued as loose maps, sold separately.   (RGS)

1. Tyacke, 1978, p. 126.
2. Verner, 1973, pp. 14, 44. Wilson, [1937], traces a business connection between Mount and Page and two other firms – Imray & Son and Norie & Wilson. These two firms amalgamated in 1899. In 1903 they further malgamated with R.H. Laurie (See no. 56) to form Imray, Laurie, Norie & Wilson Ltd. See also diagram in Robinson, 1962.
3. Information from Donald Hodson.
4. Gough, 1780, vol. 2, p. 297.

29 THOMAS BADESLADE

1741

Size: 148 mm × 139 mm (2 mm)   1:973,000

Based on Budgen no. 24.

Thomas Badeslade,[1] who drew the maps in this series, was active as a surveyor and engineer between 1712 and 1745. William Henry Toms, the engraver, was a print-seller at various London addresses between 1723 and 1758. He engraved a map of Ashdown Forest in 1747, which is reproduced in *SAC* vol. 81, p. 130.

North on the map is to the left. The map occupied a panel, 99 mm × 139 mm, on the right side of the sheet.

EDITIONS

(i)   *The COUNTY of SUSSEX. South from London.* (Ca OS). *T. Badeslade delin.* (Ae OS). *Publish'd by the Proprietors T. Badeslade & WHToms Sept*[r]*. 29*[th] *1741.* (Ce OS). *WHToms Sculpt.* (Ee OS). *A Scale of Miles 15 = 29* mm (Ce). Compass (Ea). Plate number *39* (Ea OS). List of towns with notes on Parliamentary representation, markets and fairs in panel, 47 mm × 139 mm, to left of map.

> *Chorographia Britanniae. Or a set of maps of all the counties in England and Wales . . . This collection . . . was first drawn . . . by order and for the use of his late Majesty King George I. By Thomas Badeslade surveyor and engineer, and now neatly engrav'd by Will: Henry Toms.*
> London, W.H. Toms, 1742.   BL.CUL.RGS
> Some copies of this work have a note engraved at the foot of the title-page: 'Price in Sheets 5[s]. Bound 6[s].' These were probably a slightly later reissue.   CUL

(ii) Much of the information on the left of the map has been amended: *East Grinstead . . . Fairs* now reads *July 2. Nov 30.,* formerly *Apr 16. July 16.; East Born* erased; *Saturday* added after *Haylsham.* Over fifty place-names added on map in italics, eg *Marden, Black Rock, Breade.* Roads added *Crawley* to *Cuckfield, Horsham* to *Steyning, Petersfield* to *Pulborough.*

> *Chorographia Britanniae . . .*
> London, W.H. Toms, 1742.   BL.CUL.RGS

> *Chorographia Britanniae. Or a new set of maps of all the counties in England and Wales . . . This collection . . . was first drawn, . . . by order and for the use of his*

---

1. P. Eden, 'Land surveyors in Norfolk 1550–1850', *Norfolk Archaeology* vol. 35, part 4 (1973). He was working in Kent in 1712.

late Majesty King George I. For his intended tour thro' England and & Wales . . .
2nd edn.
London, C. Hitch and W.H.Toms, 1745.   CUL.BRIGHTON PL

(iii)   Imprint (Ce, OS) erased and replaced by *Publish'd by the Proprietor WHToms Sept. 29. 1742.*

> *Chorographia Britanniae. Or a set of maps of all the counties in England and Wales*
> *. . . This collection . . . was first drawn, . . . by order and for the use of his late*
> *Majesty King George I. By Thomas Badeslude surveyor and engineer, and now*
> *neatly engrav'd by Will: Henry Toms.*
> London, W.H.Toms, 1742.   CUL

> *Chorographia Britanniae. Or a new set of maps of all the counties in England and*
> *Wales . . . This collection . . . was first drawn, . . . by order and for the use of his*
> *late Majesty King George I. For his intended tour thro' England & Wales . . .*
> London, J. Clark, C. Hitch and W.H.Toms, [1743].   BL.BOD.W

> *Chorographia Britanniae . . . 2nd edn.*
> London, C. Hitch and W.H.Toms, 1745.   BL.CUL.RGS

> *Chorographia Britanniae . . .*
> London, C. Hitch, W. Johnston and W.H.Toms, [1749]. BL.BOD.CUL

The compiler has seen a loose impression in this state, on which the plate number *39* appears to have been erased.

30   JOHN COWLEY   1744

Size: 170 mm × 118 mm (5 mm)   1:723,000

Based on Morden no. 21; the coastline, for example, includes the 'pre-Budgen' errors.

   John Cowley, a political writer and geographer, prepared this series of county maps for publication by Robert Dodsley.
   Dodsley was born in Nottinghamshire in 1703. His varied experiences as a youth included working for a time as a footman. He wrote poems and plays, and in 1735 he set up as a bookseller in Pall Mall with help from Alexander Pope. He was a friend of Samuel Johnson, who referred to him as 'Doddy', and he was among those who suggested to Johnson the idea for an English dictionary. He published the weekly *Publick Register,* which contained *An historical & geographiacal description of all the counties in England* by Cowley.[1] He died in 1764. His brother James continued the business (see no. 42).

1.   Wiles, 1957, p. 59.

An Improved MAP of the COUNTY of SUSSEX containing the Borough and Market Towns with those adjoining; also its Principal Roads and Rivers by I. Cowley Geographer to his MAJESTY (Aa). *English Miles 10 = 26* mm (Ee). *Explanation* (Ea). Longitude 10'; latitude 5'.

The geography of England: done in the manner of Gordon's geographical grammar . . . To each county is prefix'd a compleat mapp from the latest and best observations, shewing the chief towns, parks, rivers and roads, both direct and across . . .
London, R. Dodsley, 1744.   BL.BOD.RGS
A later edition of this work, published as *The geography and history of England . . .* (London, J. Dodsley, 1765) does not contain county maps.

A new sett of pocket mapps of all the counties of England and Wales . . .
London, R. Dodsley and M. Cooper, 1745.   CUL.GL.

31 THOMAS READ   [1746]

Size: 195 mm × 157 mm (single-line border)   1:665,000

Based on Moll no. 25. The county outline is badly distorted. The EW:NS ratio is 2 to 1, compared with a correct ratio of 2.9 to 1. In fact, one mile on the north-south axis is equivalent to about 3.48 mm, compared with 2.42 mm on the east-west axis.

Read was a printer who operated in the Fleet Street area between 1726 and 1753. See no. 41 on John Rocque, the publisher.
For reasons given below, it is possible that this map was not issued before 1753.

EDITIONS

(i) *SUSSEX.* (Ca OS). *English Miles 10 = 28* mm (Ea). Compass (Ee).

The English traveller: giving a description of those parts of Great-Britain called England and Wales. Containing . . . a map of every county, from the best and latest observations . . . after the designs of Herman Moll, vol. 4.
London, T. Read, 1746.   BL
The description of this map is deduced from that of other county maps in the work; all known copies lack vol. 4. It is possible that this volume never appeared, and that the Sussex map does not exist in this state; Chubb[1] refers to the work as having three volumes only.

(ii) Plate number added (Ea OS). No impression of the map in this state has been

1. Chubb, 1927, no. CLXXXV.

found, but those for other counties are known, eg Hertfordshire[2] with plate number *24*. The Sussex map in state (iii) shows signs of an erased earlier plate number, indicating that the plate was engraved in this state, even if the map was never issued.

(iii)   Signs of erased plate number (Ea).

The small British atlas: being a new set of maps of all the counties of England and Wales.
London, John Rocque and Robert Sayer, 1753.   BL.RGS.W.

(iv)   Plate number *35* added (Ea OS).

The small British atlas . . .
London, John Rocque, 1762.   BL.A

(v)   Plate number (Ea OS) altered to *34*.

The small British atlas . . .
London, John Rocque, 1764.   BOD.CUL.W

(vi)   Plate number erased.

England displayed. Being a new, complete, and accurate survey and description of the kingdom of England, and principality of Wales . . . By a society of gentlemen . . . revised, corrected and improved, by P. Russell, Esq; and . . . Mr. Owen Price, vol. 1.
London, S. Bladon, T. Evans, J. Coote, W. Domville and F. Blythe, 1769.
                                                                         BL.BOD.CUL

Daniell and Nield[3] refer to an untraced edition of *England displayed . . . .* c. 1780.

Signs of the erased plate number in state (vi) remain visible, and suggest a *4*. State (vi) can, however, be distinguished from state (iii) by a scratch running south-east from the south-east point of the compass.

2. Hodson, 1974, no. 31 (iii).
3. Daniell and Nield, 1909.

32   ROBERT WALKER   1746

Size: 195 mm × 155 mm (single-line border)   1:673,000

A re-engraved version of Read no. 31.

Walker was a prolific publisher of part-works, which included an edition of
Shakespeare's plays. He also published the *London and County Journal* from 1739 to
1743. He was notorious for literary piracy; J. Tonson (see appendix V.2) secured an
injunction against him for infringement of the former's copyright in Milton's *Paradise
Lost.*[1]

EDITION

SUSSEX. (Ca OS). *English Miles 10* = 28 mm (Ba). Compass (Ee). *The Arms of
Sussex* (Ea).

> *The agreeable historian, or the compleat English traveller: giving a geographical
> description of every county in that part of Great-Britain, call'd England . . . With a
> map of every county prefix'd to each, from the best and latest observations, after the
> designs of Herman Moll, and others . . . By Samuel Simpson, gent.* vol. 3.
> London, printed by R. Walker, 1746.   BL

33   THOMAS HUTCHINSON   1748

Size: 162 mm × 136 mm (4 mm)   1:709,000

Based on Budgen no. 24.

T.Hutchinson sculp. appears on the maps of Gloucestershire and of England and
Wales in the same series; Sussex was probably the work of the same engraver. The
title-page, dated 1748, is inscribed *S.Wale inv*[t]*. & fec.*

EDITION

A Correct MAP of SUSSEX. (Aa, in broad frame). *Miles 10* = 31 mm (Ce). Plate
number *36* (Ea OS). Compass (Da). Longitude 10' (5'); latitude 5'.

---

1. Wiles, 1957, pp. 188–9.

Geographia Magnae Britanniae. Or, correct maps of all the counties in England, Scotland, and Wales . . .
[London], S. Birt, T. Osborne, D. Browne, I. Hodges, I. Osborne, A. Millar and I. Robinson, 1748.   GL.RGS.W

Geographia Magnae Britanniae . . .
[London], T. Osborne, D. Browne, J. Hodges, A. Miller, J. Robinson, W. Johnston, P. Davey and B. Law, 1748, (actually issued in 1756).   A.BRIGHTON PL

34   THOMAS JEFFERYS AND THOMAS KITCHIN   1749

Size: 124 mm × 111 mm (5 mm)   1:1,000,000

Based on Morden no. 20, with which latitudes correspond; but some detail seems to have been taken from Budgen no. 24, eg *Hanover Hall,* north of *Buxtead.*

Thomas Jefferys[1] was a prolific engraver and map publisher who flourished between 1732 and 1771. In 1746 he was appointed *Geographer* to Frederick, Prince of Wales, and in 1757 to his son, the future George III. Jefferys began his career, as did most of his contemporaries, by publishing copies of earlier maps, and he specialised for a period in maps of North America. About 1760, however, perhaps as a result of the £100 award offered by the Society of Arts for accurate county surveys, he adopted a more enterprising approach. He engraved Donn's map of Devonshire, the first to win the above award, and financed surveys of a number of counties, including Yorkshire, which he published in twenty sheets. His bankruptcy in 1766 has been attributed to his enthusiasm for such original work.[2] Subsequently he was helped by his friends, who published in association with him. Those who came to his rescue included Robert Sayer, who eventually acquired many of his map plates.

Thomas Kitchin, an engraver and publisher from about 1738 to 1776, held the appointment of *Hydrographer to the King.* Like Jefferys, his output was prolific, but his work was less original. He engraved the map of the British and French dominions in North America by John Mitchell (1755), which was used at the peace council at the end of the revolutionary war. In his later years he worked with his son, hence *sen[r]* after his name in the c.1775 edition of the *Small English atlas.* He died in 1784. (See nos. 36, 42, 43 and 46). His name is sometimes spelt Kitchen.

The Small English atlas was apparently first published in twelve parts issued at intervals of about a week, commencing in November 1748. The publishers were M. Payne, T. Glass and M. Sheepey, H. Whitridge, J. King, S. Lyne, P. Griffin, M. Amey and J. Brindley, all of London. No copy of the atlas has been found, and it is possible

1. R.A. Gardiner, review of *Thomas Jefferys' American atlas, 1776* in *GJ* July 1976; Raistrick, 1969, p. 51.
2. Harley, 1966, p. 27.

that Kitchin and Jefferys took over the work at an early stage, perhaps even before the initial publication in parts was complete.

EDITIONS

(i) *A Map of SUSSEX* (Ca OS). *English Miles 12* = 21 mm (Ae). Compass (Ed). Longitude 20' (5'); latitude 20' (5'). Below the map is a note, *Sussex Contains . . .,* followed by a list of towns. On the map there are traces of a graticule.

> *The small English atlas being a new and accurate sett of maps of all the counties in England and Wales.*
> London, Kitchin and Jefferys, 1749.   BL.CUL.RGS

(ii) Road distance *25* near *Nordid* (Northiam) altered to *34.* Road distances added, *7* between *Brighthelmstone* and *New Shoreham,* and *9* between *Brighthelmstone* and *New Haven.* The road running north from *Amburley* now joins the main road north of *Pulborough;* additional road between *Chailey* and *E.Grinstead.* Town symbol at *New Haven* altered to a circle.

> *The small English atlas. . .*
> London, Kitchin and Jefferys, 1749 and 1751.   A;CUL.RGS

(iii) Plate number *39* added (Ae OS).

> *The small English atlas . . .*
> London, Kitchin and Jefferys, 1751.   W

(iv) Pecked lines added to mark boundaries of rapes. Several roads added, eg *Arundel* to *Brightelmstone* via *Bamber.* Note below map re-engraved, now begins *This County contains . . .* The towns are now in alphabetical order, except *Storrington* which has been added at the end.

> *The small English atlas being a new and accurate sett of maps of all the counties in England and Wales by T Jefferys, geo: to the king, and Tho⁵. Kitchin senʳ.*
> London, Robert Sayer and John Bennett, John Bowles, and Carington Bowles, [1775].   BOD.CUL.RGS

> *The small English atlas . . .*
> London, Robert Sayer, [1785].   CHUBB³

> *An English atlas or a concise view of England and Wales; divided into counties . . . On fifty two copper plates.*
> London, Robert Sayer, 1787 (reissue by Laurie and Whittle in 1794).   CUL;W

---

3. Chubb, 1927 no. CXCIV.

35   EMANUEL BOWEN   1749

Size: 665 mm × 487 mm (9 mm)   1:195,000

Based on Budgen no. 24; the framework to the *EXPLANATION* is copied from Budgen's map. *Tickeredge* (see no. 26) not shown.

Most of the maps on this atlas, including that of Sussex, were drawn by Emanuel Bowen (see no. 23); the remainder are by Thomas Kitchin (see no. 34).

The ever-changing combination of names, in the imprints and on the title-pages of *The large English atlas,* illustrates both the publishing history of the work and the extent to which booksellers were obliged to co-operate, primarily to reduce the risk involved in bringing out a new edition of a major atlas, even when the original plates were available.

Sussex was the first map in this series to be published. The original intention had been to bring out one map each month. This, however, proved over-optimistic. In 1752 Hinton got into financial difficulties, and he was bought out by Tinney. When a collection of maps was made up in about 1755, see state (iv) below, only thirty-seven maps had been completed; the remaining eleven were finished between 1755 and 1760.[1]

John Hinton (d. 1781), whose imprint appears on the Sussex map in state (ii), was a bookseller and publisher; John Tinney (d. 1761) was an engraver and publisher. Robert Sayer was active as a publisher and map-seller from 1751 to 1794, in partnership with John Bennett from 1775 to 1784. Sayer, successor to Philip Overton (see no. 26), was himself succeeded by Laurie and Whittle (see nos. 56 and 63).

The scale on the map of Sussex is labelled *English Statute Miles 69 to a Degree.* This refers to one degree of latitude, and compares with an actual value of 69.15 miles to a degree. This is the first Sussex map to adopt this formula, but as early as 1676 Seller's map of Hertfordshire[2] carried the legend *On the east Side of the Mapp is Placed ye Meridian line each Degree of Latitude Containing 69½ of Common or Statute Miles and 14 Pole . . .* A reasonably accurate value for the statute mile has been established since at least 1637, when Richard Norwood arrived at a value of just over 69 miles to the degree,[3] and the statute mile itself had been officially recognised since 1593. Cartographers, however, continued to use various customary, or vulgar, miles even after the publication in 1675 of Ogilby's *Britannia,* which recommended adoption of the statute mile. Morden (no. 20, 1695), for example, exhibits three different scale-bars on his map, all larger than the statute mile. His middle mile is nine furlongs,[4] or sixty miles to a degree, which is equivalent to the present nautical mile, sometimes referred to as the 'geographical' mile. This simple measurement, in which one minute of latitude equals one mile, had an obvious appeal to mariners, and was adopted by early cartographers and followers of Ptolemy. Bowen (no. 23, 1720) and Moll (no. 25, 1724) use

---

1. Weinreb and Douwma, *Catalogue 17* (1977), item 16.
2. Hodson, 1974, no. 16.
3. Taylor, 1956, p. 230.
4. On the map of Warwickshire the small mile is nine furlongs, see Harvey, 1959, p. 18.

the words *English Miles*, but these are not statute miles, being equivalent to 10.0 and 9.6 furlongs respectively. Budgen no. 24 was the first Sussex map to use the statute mile, and he labels his scale-bar *Geometrical Miles*. On the map, his mile works out at about 67 miles to a degree. Those later maps which were based on Budgen used the statute mile; but others continued to use a mile of nine or more furlongs. After 1749 the labelling of scale-bars *Statute Miles,* with or without reference to the number equivalent to one degree, became the general rule, although there were exceptions.

The descriptions of towns surrounding the map are condensed from *Magna Britannia et Hibernia* (see no. 21) and other secondary sources.[5]

As well as appearing in the various editions of *The large English atlas* listed below, the map was probably sold loose until at least 1795.

EDITIONS

(i) *AN ACCURATE MAP of the COUNTY of SUSSEX. Divided into its RAPES, Deanries and HUNDREDS. DRAWN from SURVEYS. Shewing (amongst various Improvements, not extant in any other Map) what Parishes are Rectories, and what Vicarages; where Charity Schools have been erected &c. By Eman Bowen Geographer to His MAJESTY.* (Aa, in illustrated framework showing a boy using a theodolite and a surveyor with a measuring wheel). *To His Grace Algernon Duke of Somerset, Lord Lieutenant & Custos Rotulorum of the COUNTY of SUSSEX. This MAP is humbly Dedicated by his Grace's most Obed^t. and most devoted serv^t. Eman: Bowen* (Ea, in floral framework surmounted by arms of the Duke). *English Statute Miles 69 to a Degree 15* = 125 mm (Ed). Compass (Ed). *EXPLANATION.* (Ce, in illustrated framework). Longitude 10' (1'); latitude 10' (1'). Graticule at 10' intervals. *THE ICHNOGRAPHY OF LEWES* (Ba). *The ICHNOGRAPHY of CHICHESTER* (Da). *THE NORTH PROSPECT OF CHICHESTER.* (Be). *THE SOUTH PROSPECT OF LEWES.* (Ee). The map is surrounded by topographical and other information. A note (Ae) reads: *We find upon comparing M^r. Budgens Geometrical Survey of this County with the Trigonometrical Survey of the British Channel made by M^r. Renshaw under the directions of M^r. Whiston in the years 1741 & 1742,[6] that there is a difference both of Latitude and Longitude with regard to the Situation of some Towns . . . The latter makeing Rye in Lat: 50:56 Long: 0:56E. which is about 4 min: more Southerly and 9 minutes more Easterly than Budgens . . . but as M^r. Budgens Scale is much the largest. We have principally followed his Map . . .* There are also descriptions of Chichester (Be), Lewes (Ee) and Winchelsey (Eb), and a note regarding Heene (Bd).

Maps of other counties[7] were issued in this state (without imprint and without *West Longitude from London* in lower border), probably as proofs or advance copies. Sussex may or may not have been issued in this state.

5. Harley and Hodson, 1971, p. 11.
6. *BL*, maps 1068(11).
7. Hodson, 1974, no. 36 (1).

(ii)   *Sold by I. Hinton at the Kings Arms in S^t. Pauls Church yard London 1749* added (Ae OS). *West Longitude from London* added (Be, in border).

One of a series of maps issued loose and sold separately, commencing in 1749. (BOD)

(iii)   Note reading *Earls of Sussex 1155 William of Albiny . . . 1717 Talbot Yelverton Vicount Longville then his Son George 1731.* added (Ea).

Issued as loose maps, sold separately, [1750].   (BL)

(iv)   Hinton imprint (Ae OS) erased and replaced by *Sold by I. Tinney at the Golden Lyon on Fleetstreet London 1753.*

A collection of thirty-seven maps without title-page [1755].   P^x

The large English atlas: or, a new set of maps of all the counties in England and Wales, drawn from the several surveys which have been hitherto published; . . . By Emanuel Bowen, geographer to His Majesty, Thomas Kitchen, and others.
London, T. Bowles, John Bowles and Son, John Tinney and Robert Sayer, [1760].
BL

(v)   Tinney imprint (Ae OS) erased, but traces remain. New imprint added *Printed for John Tinney in Fleet Street, T. Bowles in S^t. Pauls Church Yard, John Bowles and Son in Cornhill & Robt. Sayer in Fleet Street.* (Ce OS).

A set of maps without title-page, [1760].   W

(vi)   Imprint (Ce OS) erased and replaced by *Printed for Robt. Sayer in Fleet Street, T. Bowles in St Pauls Church Yard, John Bowles & Son in Cornhill.* Plate number *12* added (Ea OS and Ee OS).

The large English atlas . . .
London, T. Bowles, John Bowles and Son, John Tinney and Robert Sayer, [1760].   P

The large English atlas . . .
London, John Bowles, Carington Bowles and Robert Sayer, [1764].   BL
1764 is the provisional date assigned to this atlas by Hodson.[9] Harvey[10] suggests a date about three years later. The Sussex map in this atlas is an earlier state than that in the *RGS* (c.1763) atlas, which is in stage (vii). The Hertfordshire map, however, is in the same state in both this atlas and in the *RGS* atlas. On the evidence of the Sussex map alone, therefore, an even earlier date, perhaps 1760–2, would seem more probable.
    In the copy at the British Library the plate number on the Sussex map has been altered by hand to *35*; the words *& Son* in the imprint show no sign of erasure.

8.   See Weinreb and Douwna, *Catalogue 17* (1977), item 16.
9.   Hodson, 1974, no. 36(iv).
10.   Harvey, 1959, no. 33(iv).

(vii) *& Son* in imprint (Ce OS) partially erased. Plate number (Ea OS) altered to *35*. Plate number (Ee OS) erased.

The large English atlas . . .
London, T. Bowles, John Bowles and Son and Robert Sayer, [1762].   WN

It is possible that this atlas recorded by Whitaker contains the Sussex map in state (vi).

The large English atlas . . .
London, T. Bowles, John Bowles and Robert Sayer, [1763].   RGS

(viii) Imprint (Ce OS) altered to *Printed for Robt. Sayer in Fleet Street, John Bowles in Cornhil, & Carington Bowles in St Pauls Church-Yard.*

The large English atlas . . .
London, T. Bowles, John Bowles and Robert Sayer, [1765].   CUL

The large English atlas . . .
London, John Bowles, Carington Bowles and Robert Sayer, [1765].   A

The large English atlas . . .
London, Carington Bowles, 1767 (reissued 1780).   WN;W.NMM

The large English atlas . . .
London, Robert Sayer, [1780].   BRL

In all the above works the plate number, *35* (Ea OS), is very faint, and on some impressions, eg 1767 in Whitaker collection, almost undetectable.

(ix) Imprint (Ce OS) altered to *Printed for Robt. Sayer in Fleet Street, Robt. Wilkinson in Cornhil, & Carington Bowles in S^t. Pauls Church Yard.*

The large English atlas . . .
London, Robert Wilkinson successor to John Bowles, [1785].   BL

The large English atlas . . . The whole engraved on 50 copper plates . . . By Emanuel Bowen, Thomas Kitchen, Captain Andrew Armstrong, and others.
London, Robert Sayer, 1787.   BL

In the above works the plate number is only partly visible, and in some impressions cannot be seen at all. The detail, particularly in the area of the title, is very faint.

(x) Imprint (Ce OS) altered to *London. Printed for R.Wilkinson 58 Cornhill, Laurie & Whittle 53 Fleet Street, and Bowles & Carver 69 S^t. Pauls Church Yard.*

The large English atlas: or, a new set of maps of all the counties in England and Wales, drawn from the several surveys which have been hitherto published: . . . By Emanuel Bowen, geographer to His Majesty, Thomas Kitchen, and others.

London, Carington Bowles, 1767 (actually issued not before 1794).   BL

The large English atlas . . . The whole engraved on 50 copper plates . . . By Emanuel Bowen, Thomas Kitchin, Captain Andrew Armstrong, and others.
London, Robert Sayer, 1787 (actually issued not before 1794).   RGS

(xi)   Imprint (Ce OS) altered to *London. Printed for Laurie & Whittle 53 Fleet Street, R.Wilkinson 58 Cornhill, and Bowles & Carver 69 S^t. Pauls Church Yard.*

From an issue of *The large English atlas* c.1794.   (BRIGHTON PL)

36   THOMAS KITCHIN   1750

Size: 219 mm × 129 mm (5 mm)   1:626,000

Based on Budgen no. 24

Robert Baldwin, the publisher of the *London Magazine,* was a bookseller in Paternoster Row and was active as a publisher between 1749 and 1810. He succeeded his uncle, R. Baldwin, and was succeeded by another Robert Baldwin.[1] Chubb,[2] however, gives his name as Richard Baldwin, and suggests that he was the son of 'R. Baldwin'. The *London Magazine* was published from 1732 to 1785.

Alexander Hogg, a bookseller and publisher of works containing this series of maps, also of Paternoster Row, was active from about 1778 to 1805. He issued a number of widely advertised part-works, then referred to as 'Paternoster Row numbers'. An advertisement for *Boswell's Picturesque Views of the Antiquities of England and Wales* in the *Sussex Weekly Advertiser* of 14 May 1792, makes it clear that the work had originally been published in parts. He was also the publisher of no. 48.

For a note on Francis Grose, the writer, see no. 19.

EDITIONS

(i)   *SUSSEX Drawn from an ACTUAL SURVEY and Regulated by ASTRONOM^L. OBSERVAT^S. By T.Kitchin Geog^r.* (Ea, on scroll with *The Arms of Chichester* above). *Printed for R. Baldwin Junr. at the Rose in Paternoster Row* (Ce OS). *For the London Magazine.* (Ca OS). *Statute British Miles 16* = 40 mm (Ca). Compass (Ce). *Explanation* (Aa). Longitude 15' (5'); latitude 15' (5').

The London magazine: or, gentleman's monthly intelligencer . . . vol. 19.
London, R. Baldwin. Issue for January 1750.   BL

1. Plomer, 1932, p. 14.
2. Chubb, 1927, p. 420.

(ii) *Jan*. *1750. Page. 8.* added (Ea OS). Baldwin imprint (Ce OS) erased.

The London magazine: . . . vol 19.
Dublin, S. and I. Exshaw. Issue for January 1750. TRINITY COLL. DUBLIN

The antiquities of England and Wales displayed . . . By Henry Boswell, Esq. F.A.S. Assisted by many antiquarians, and other ingenious gentlemen . . . A new edition, with alterations and improvements.
London, Alexander Hogg, 1795. BOD

A new and complete abridgement or selection of the most interesting and important subjects in the antiquities of England and Wales . . . By Francis Grose, Esq. F.A.S. To which will be added . . . a complete set of county maps, by the best artists . . .
London, H.D. Symonds and Alexander Hogg, 1798. W

(iii) *For the London Magazine* (Ca OS) erased. Fourteen place-names added, eg *Goodwood, Parham, Eridge* and four rivers named *Adur R., Ouse R., R. Rother, Arun R.*

Historical descriptions of new and elegant picturesque views of the antiquities of England and Wales . . . published under the inspection of Henry Boswell, Esq. F.A.R.S. assisted by Robert Hamilton, L.L.D. and other ingenious gentlemen . . .
London, Alexander Hogg, [1786]. BL.W.WORTHING PL

Complete historical descriptions of a new and elegant collection of picturesque views and representations of the antiquities of England and Wales . . . containing . . . a complete set of the county maps . . . accurately executed by the best artists . . . By Henry Boswell, Esq., F.A.S., assisted by many antiquarians, and other ingenious gentlemen . . .
London, Alexander Hogg [1790]. WARWICK COUNTY RECORDS OFFICE

37 EMANUEL BOWEN   1756

Size: 187 mm × 163 mm (6 mm)   1:669,000

Based on Budgen no. 24 or Bowen no. 35.

The work in which this series of maps appeared was published by William Owen, a distinguished publisher and bookseller, who was active from 1748 until his death in 1793. He was Master of the Stationers Company in 1781. He published a number of political pamphlets.

Benjamin Martin (1704/5–82), the author of *The natural history*, started work as a plough-boy in Surrey, and became a teacher at Guildford. A legacy of £500 enabled him to take up writing, and he published books on a variety of subjects, including globes and the determination of longitude. About 1734 he settled in Chichester, where he kept a school, made optical instruments and compiled *Bibliotheca Technologica*. In 1740 he set up as an instrument maker in London and retired in 1781, but lacking his control the business quickly declined. He attempted suicide and died in the following year.

EDITION

SUSSEX Divided into its RAPES Containing the City Burough & Market Towns, with the principal Roads and Distances &c. By Eman. Bowen Geographer to His Majesty (Ea, in decorative framework). *Engrav'd for the General Magazine of Arts & Sciences for W.Owen at Temple Bar 1756.* (Ce OS). *British Statute Miles 15 = 37 mm* (Ca). Compass (Ca, below and right of scale). *Rapes* (Aa). *Explanation* (Ee). Longitude 10' (2'); latitude 10' (2').

> *The natural history of England; or, a description of each particular county . . . By Benjamin Martin.* vol 1.
> London, W. Owen and 'the AUTHOR', 1759.   BL.CUL.W
> This formed part of *The general magazine of arts and sciences,* 1755–65.[1]

38 JOHN GIBSON   1759

Size: 105 mm × 56 mm (4 mm)   1:305,000

Possibly based on Kitchin no. 36, but may have been compiled from several sources.

John Gibson was a prolific engraver of maps and charts between 1750 and 1792.[1]

William Carnan, the publisher, was proprietor of *The Reading Mercury and Oxford Gazette,* one of the earliest provincial newspapers. He died in 1737, and his widow married John Newbery in 1740. Newbery's publications covered a wide field; in addition to geographical works, he was the first publisher of a juvenile library, of which the first title was *Goody Two Shoes.* He was associated with most of the great literary figures of the age.

Thomas Carnan was the son of William Carnan. He published in association with John Newbery, and later with Newbery's son, Francis. Carnan's imprint appears on several editions of *Paterson's Roads.* He is best remembered for his successful challenge of the Stationers Company's monopoly of the publication of almanacs. He died in 1788.

EDITION

Sussex (Ea in foliar framework). *English Miles 20 = 21 mm* (Bd). Compass (Ee). Plate number *36* (Ee OS, sideways). Longitude 15' (3'); latitude 15' (3'). A topographical note

---

1. J.R. Millburn, 'Martin's magazine . . .', *The Library* 5th ser, no. 28 (1973).

1. Jervis, 1936, p. 95, seems to confuse Gibson with Thomas Jefferys.

commencing *Sussex is in the Diocese of Chichester* . . . fills space above the county boundary.

New and accurate maps of the counties of England and Wales drawn from the latest surveys by J. Gibson.
London, J. Newbery, [1759].   BL.BOD.CUL

New and accurate maps . . .
London, T. Carnan, [1770].   W.A

Chubb[2] refers to a 1779 edition of this atlas by Carnan and Newbery in the Bodleian Library. This is almost certainly an error. The atlas cannot be traced, but the Bodleian does have a copy of Gibson's *Atlas minimus* of 1779, published by Carnan and Newbery.

39   PIETER MEIJER   1759

Size: 187 mm × 162 mm (6 mm)   1:673,000

Copied from Bowen no. 37. **See plate 17.**

Pieter Meijer was an Amsterdam publisher. In 1760 he published a map of London,[1] and in 1768 his *Kliene atlas,* in which the maps were again taken from Bowen.

EDITION

SUSSEX, Verdeeld in zyne Rapes of Hoofdverdeelingen, bevattende alle de Steden, Burgen Markvlekken, met de Wegen Afstanden, enz. Opgesteld door Eman Bowen, Landbeschryver van zyn Britsche Mejesteit. Te Amsteldam by Pieter Meijer, Uytgegeven 1759 (Ea). *L. Schenk J. Soon, sculp, 1759.* (Ae OS). *Engelsche Mylen 15* = 37 mm. *Duitsche Mylen 3* = 35 mm (Ab). Compass (Da). Longitude 10' (2'); latitude 10' (2'). *Rapes of Hoofdverdeelingen* (Aa). *Verklaaring* (explanation) (Ee). A note commencing *NB. Het Graafschap SUSSEX* . . . (Ba). **See plate 17.**

Algemeene Oefenschoole van Konsten en Weetenschappen . . . (Second section, first part).
Amsterdam, Pieter Meijer, 1763.   BL

2. Chubb, 1927, no.CCXIVa.

1. Darlington and Howgego, 1964, no. 113.

40 RICHARD WILLIAM SEALE   1760

Size: 217 mm × 173 mm (5 mm)   1:598,000

Based on Bowen no. 35.

The *Universal Magazine* was published monthly from 1747 to 1803, and as the *New Universal Magazine* until 1814.

EDITION

SUSSEX, Drawn from an actual SURVEY by R.W. Seale. Universal Mag. J. Hinton, Newgate Street. (Aa, in decorative framework). *English Statute Miles 12 = 34 mm* (Cb). Compass (Ee). *Explanation* (Bd). *This County is divided into six Rapes, which . . .* (Ca). Longitude 10' (2'); along top border only; latitude 10' (2'). The bottom border is marked in minutes of time. *ARMS OF CHICHESTER* (Ea). Note commencing *SUSSEX sends 28 Members . . .* (along bottom of map, inside border).

> *The universal magazine of knowledge and pleasure . . .*, vol 26.
> London, John Hinton. Issue for May 1760.   BL
> A later edition of this work, published by W. Bent in 1795, contains no. 56(i).

41 JOHN ROCQUE   1761

Size: 680 mm × 420 mm (1 mm)   1:190,000

Based on Bowen no. 35. **See plate 18.**

It is probable that Rocque's parents were Huguenots, that they had settled in Geneva, and that John was born there in about 1705. Some time in the early 1730s[1] John moved to London, together with his sister and two brothers. One brother, Bartholomew, is known to have set up as a market gardener in Walham Green; John started as an estate surveyor. His outstanding achievements, the large-scale plans of London[2] in twenty-four and sixteen sheets, were published in 1746 and 1747. In 1750 his premises were destroyed by fire, but he managed to continue in business. His output included *A Topographical Map of the County of Surrey* in nine sheets, which was completed and engraved by Peter Andrews and published by Rocque's widow after his death in 1762. Rocque achieved some recognition in his lifetime, and held the

---

1. The earliest work attributed to him is *Plan of House, Gardens, Park and Hermitage of their Majesties at Richmond . . . J.R. 1734* (BL,K Top XIL. 16. f).
2. Reproductions, with introduction by J. Howgego, published by Harry Margary, Lympne Castle, Kent, 1971.

appointment of 'Topographer' to the Prince of Wales; nevertheless, he died a poor man.

The map of Sussex must have been one of his last works. The duplication of the title in English and French may reflect his origins, although it was quite common for topographical prints at that time to carry a title in both languages. It is not included in Varley's list of Rocque's maps.[3]

The hills on this map are shown in plan, and resemble 'hairy caterpillars'. It was the first Sussex map to abandon completely the 'molehill' method.

EDITION

A New MAP. of the COUNTY of SUSSEX, Drawn from the latest and best Surveys, and Improved by John Rocque, Topographer to his MAJESTY 1761. (Ae, in a decorative framework, which stretches across the bottom of the map and embraces the title, plans of Chichester and Lewes, and the scale-bars). *CARTE DE LA PROVINCE DE SUSSEX reduite d'apres les derniers Arpentages qui en ont eté faits & Augmentée par I. Rocque Topographe de sa Majesté Britannique dans le Strand 1761.* (Ce OS). *A Scale of Measured Miles 20* = 167 mm, and *Echelle de 7 Lieues de 25 au Degre 7* = 159 mm (Ee). Compass (Da). Longitude 5' (1'), along bottom border only; latitude 5' (1'); top border has *Minutes and Seconds of Time from the Meridian of London. Explanation* (Ea). *THE PLANS of CHICHESTER*[4] *and LEWES* (Ce). **See plate 18.**

Probably issued as loose maps, sold separately. (BOD)

42   THOMAS KITCHIN   1763

Size: 238 mm × 183 mm (6 mm)   1:527,000

Based on Bowen no. 35.

EDITION

A New MAP of SUSSEX Drawn from the best Authorities By Tho[s]. Kitchin Geog[r]. Engraver to H.R.H. the Duke of York. (Ea, in decorative frame with view of harbour on left). *British Statute Miles 69 to a Degree 14* = 43 mm (Ca). Compass (Cd). *Remarks* (Aa). Longitude 10' (2'); latitude 10' (2').

3. Varley, 1948.
4. The names *South Street* and *East Street* are transposed in this plan. The error was corrected in a re-engraved version of the plan published a few years later by A. Dury in *A collection of the plans of the principal cities . . . by the late M[r]. J. Rocque.* It is reproduced in Butler, 1972.

England illustrated, or, a compendium of the natural history, geography, topography, and antiquities ecclesiastical and civil, of England and Wales. With maps of the several counties . . ., vol 2.
London, R. and J. Dodsley, 1764.   BL.BOD.W
This work was first published on 1 December 1763, but no copy bearing that date has been found; it is possible that this first issue was published with the date 1764 on the title-page.

Kitchen's English atlas: or, a compleat set of maps of all the counties of England and Wales . . . The whole engraved . . . from drawings after actual surveys and other the best authorities. By Thomas Kitchen, geographer to His Royal Highness the Duke of York.
London, J. Dodsley, [1765].   BL.CUL

43 THOMAS KITCHIN   circa **1763**

Size: 484 mm × 394 mm (8 mm)   1:262,000

Based on Bowen no. 35.

As well as appearing in the atlases listed below, the map was probably issued loose until at least 1795. WORTHING PL has loose impressions in all three states.

EDITIONS

(i) *An ACCURATE MAP of SUSSEX Drawn from the Best SURVEYS & INTELLIGENCES Divided into its HUNDREDS SHEWING the Several ROADS & Measured Distances between Town and Town ALSO THE Rectories, Vicarages & Curacies, the Parks & Seats of the Nobility & Gentry with other useful Particulars by Thos. Kitchin GEOGR.* (De, on the representation of a monumental stone and surrounded by picturesque drawings of the county and its produce). *Printed for Thos. Kitchin at the Star Holborn Hill, R. Sayer & J. Ryall in Fleet St., H. Overton without Newgate, T. Bowles in St. Pauls Church Yard, J. Bowles & Son, & Messrs. Bakewell & Parker in Cornhill* (Ea). *British Statute Miles 69 to a Degree* 10 = 63 mm (Dd). Compass (Cd). *Remarks* (Aa). Longitude 10' (1'); latitude 10' (1'). Graticule at 10' intervals. *The Cathedral Church of CHICHESTER* (De). Topographical and historical notes fill the area outside the county boundary, and are similar to those on Bowen no. 35, including the note referring to Budgen. The descriptions have been condensed, but additions have been made, eg reference to the manufacture of needles at Chichester, and *Here are frequent Horse Races* at Lewes. Descriptions of Horsham, Selsey, Rye, Seaford and the diocese of Chichester have been added. *Middleton Church is in danger of being washed away by the sea, which approaches very near it.* added (Ad). Some maps in the series have plate numbers; Sussex does not.

The royal English atlas: being a new and accurate set of maps of all the counties of

south Britain, drawn from surveys, and the best authorities . . . By Emanuel Bowen,
geographer to His late Majesty, Thomas Kitchin, geographer, and others. The whole
comprised in forty-four sheet maps.
London, Thomas Kitchin, Robert Sayer, Carington Bowles, Henry Overton,
Henry Parker, John Bowles and John Ryall. [1763].[1]   BL.CUL.W
The order of the publishers' names on the title-page varies.

The royal English atlas: being a new and accurate set of maps of all the counties in
England and Wales, drawn from the several surveys which have been hitherto
published . . .
London, C. Bowles, [1781].   P

(ii) Imprint (Ea) erased and replaced by *London Printed for Rob[t]. Sayer & John*
Bennett, N[o]53 Fleet Street. John Bowles, N[o].13, Cornhill, & Carington Bowles, N[o]69,
S[t]. Pauls Church Yard. as the Act directs 1st. of June 1777.

The royal English atlas: . . . of all the counties in England and Wales . . .
London, C. Bowles, [1778].   SAS

The royal English atlas: . . . of all the counties of south Britain . . .
London, R. Wilkinson, [1779].   CUL

The royal English, atlas; being accurate maps of all the counties in England and
Wales: from numerous surveys . . . The whole comprized in fifty sheet maps. By
Thomas Kitchen, geographer, and others.
London, R. Sayer and J. Bennett, [1780].   BOD.BRL

(iii) Imprint (Ea) erased, and replaced by *London. Printed for Laurie & Whittle 53*
Fleet Street, Robert Wilkinson 58 Cornhill, & Bowles & Carver 69 S[t]Paul's Church
Yard.

The English atlas: or, a set of maps of all the counties in England and Wales, drawn
from the best authorities. . .
London, R. Martin, [1828].[2]   BL.RGS

1. Facsimile edition, with introduction by J.B. Harley and D. Hodson, David and Charlles Ltd, Newton
    Abbot, 1971.
2. Date from Harley and Hodson, 1971. The Sussex map in the BL copy has a 1792 watermark.

44 JOSEPH ELLIS

1765

Size: 235 mm × 180 mm (6 mm)

1:535,000

Copied from Kitchin no. 42. The general layout, *Remarks,* scale and compass are exact copies.

The name *Joseph* Ellis is first recorded by Hodson[1] on the authority of an advertisement by Bowles and Carver in 1795. Earlier authorities[2] and some later writers[3] refer to him as *John* Ellis. Ellis is known primarily as an engraver, working between 1750 and 1796, and he may well have been related to Thomas Joseph Ellis, the surveyor of Huntingdonshire and Nottinghamshire.[4] Although unoriginal, this atlas appears from the number of reissues to have been very popular.

EDITION

A Modern MAP of SUSSEX, Drawn from the latest Surveys; Corrected & Improved by the best Authorities. J.Ellis sculpt. (Ea, with rural scene in background). *Printed for Carington Bowles in S^t. pauls Church yard, & Robt. Sayer in Fleet Street.* (Ce OS). *British Statute Miles 69 to a Degree 14 = 42 mm* (Ca). Compass (Cd). Plate number *42* (Ea OS). *Remarks.* (Aa). Longitude 10' (2'); latitude 10' (2').

> *The new English atlas; being the completest sett of modern maps of England and Wales . . . ever yet published: accurately drawn from actual surveys . . . and engrav'd in the best manner, by J. Ellis, and others, on fifty-four copper-plates.*
> London, Robert Sayer and Carington Bowles, 1765.   BL

> *Ellis's English atlas: or, a compleat chorography of England and Wales: in fifty maps . . . From the latest surveys of the several counties; engraved by, and under the direction of, J. Ellis.*
> London, Robert Sayer and Carington Bowles, 1766.   BL

> *Ellis's English atlas . . . in fifty maps . . .*
> London, Carington Bowles and Robert Sayer, 1766.   RGS

> *Ellis's English atlas . . . in fifty-four maps . . .*
> London, Carington Bowles and Robert Sayer, 1766.   BL*.W*

> *Ellis's English atlas . . . in fifty-four maps . . .*
> London, Robert Sayer and Carington Bowles, 1766 (two issues).   CUL.BOD*

1. Hodson, 1974, p. 54. (First published in *Map Collectors Series* no. 53, 1969).
2. Gough, 1780; Tooley, 1979.
3. Rawnsley, 1970. This book includes useful biographical notes based mainly on Chubb. Maxted, 1977, refers to a *Joseph* and a *John* Ellis, both of Islington.
4. Rodger, 1972.

Atlas britannique, ou chorographie complette de l'Angleterre et de la principauté de Galles . . .
London, R. Sayer, 1766.   LIB OF CONGRESS[5]

Ellis's English atlas . . . in fifty-four maps . . .
London, Carington Bowles, 1768 (two issues).   W.WN*

Ellis's English atlas . . . in fifty maps . . .
London, Robert Sayer, Thomas Jeffery's and A. Dury, 1768.   BL.CUL.

Ellis's English atlas . . . in fifty maps . . .
London, Robert Sayer, 1773.   BL.CUL.BOD

Ellis's English atlas . . . in fifty maps . . .
London, R. Sayer and J. Bennett, 1777.   BL.CUL.RGS

Ellis's English atlas . . . in fifty-four maps . . .
London, Carington Bowles, [1785].   BL*

Ellis's English atlas . . . in fifty maps . . .
London, Carington Bowles, [1786].   RGS

Ellis's English atlas: being accurate maps of all the counties in England and Wales, according the latest surveys . . . engraved by, and under the direction of J. Ellis: in fifty maps.
London, Robert Sayer (actually issued by Laurie and Whittle in 1796).   RGS

* The map of Surrey is printed on the back of the map of Sussex in those atlases marked with an asterisk.

45 EMANUEL BOWEN   circa **1767**

Size: 314 mm × 212 mm (7 mm)   1:413,000

Based on Bowen no. 35.

EDITIONS

(i) *SUSSEX, Divided into its RAPES, DEANRIES & HUNDREDS; Exhibiting the City, Borough, Market Towns &c. with concise Historical Extracts, relative to its Trade, Manufactures & Natural Produce. Distinguishing also the Church Livings; with*

5. Phillips, 1914, no. 4013.

Improvements not Inserted in any other Half Sheet County Map Extant. By Eman: Bowen, Geographer to His late Majesty, & Thoˢ. Bowen. (Ee, in decorative framework). *British Statute Miles 69 to a Degree 20 = 80 mm* (De). Compass (Be). Longitude 10' (1'); latitude 10' (1'). Graticule at 10' intervals. *Explanation.* (Bd). The space outside the county boundary is filled with topographical and historical notes, which are copied, with minor alterations, from Kitchin no. 43.

> *Atlas Anglicanus, or a complete sett of maps of the counties of south Britain . . . By the late Emanuel Bowen, geographer to His Majesty George IIᵈ. and Thomas Bowen.*
> London, T. Kitchin, [1767].   BOD.CUL.W

> *Atlas Anglicanus . . .*
> London, T. Kitchin [1770].   BL.RGS

(ii)   *Printed for Thomas Kitchin at Nᵒ.59 Holborn Hill, London.* added (Ce OS).

> *Atlas Anglicanus . . .*
> London, T.Kitchin and Andrew Dury, 1777.   BL.CUL.BRIGHTON PL

(iii)   Title and framework (Ee) and imprint (Ce OS) erased and replaced by *BOWLES's NEW MEDIUM MAP OF SUSSEX, DIVIDED into its RAPES, DEANRIES and HUNDREDS; exhibiting the Roads, Towns and Villages; with their Distance from London, Church Livings, Seats of the Nobility, and Historical Remarks. LONDON: Printed for the Proprietor Carington Bowles, Nᵒ.69 in Sᵗ. Pauls Church Yard.* (Ee, in plain circular frame); and *Published as the Act directs, 3 Jan. 1785* (Ce OS). Plate number *35* added (Ea OS). Compass (Be) elaborated. Penultimate line in *Explanation* erased and replaced by *61 Measured Distances from London,* and a number of such distances added on the map, eg *56* at *New Shoram.* Distances between towns erased, eg *10* on road from *Rye* to *Sedlescomb.* In the description of Rye, the words *Its Port is now choaked up with Sands* erased and replaced by *Its old Port is choaked up with Sands, but a new and commodious one is now made.*

> *Bowles's new medium English atlas; or, complete set of maps of the counties of England and Wales . . . Compiled and laid down from the latest and most approved authorities.*
> London, Carington Bowles, 1785.   BL.CUL.W

(iv)   In the title (Ee) the imprint has been erased and replaced by *LONDON: Printed for the Proprietors Bowles & Carver, Nᵒ.69 in Sᵗ Paul's Church Yard.* Imprint (Ce OS) erased.

The firm of Bowles and Carver was in business from 1793 to c.1832. A catalogue issued by firm in 1795 lists *Bowles's new medium English atlas,* and the individual county maps from this atlas were offered for sale separately. A complete set of the maps in this state is known, but this atlas is without a title-page. The Folio Fine

Art Ltd. catalogue for June 1969 listed a number of maps, including Sussex (item 300), from a Bowles and Carver atlas of 1794.

46 THOMAS KITCHIN   1769

Size: 300 mm × 143 mm (6 mm)   1:433,000

Based on Budgen no. 24, perhaps with direct reference to Avery's chart.

EDITIONS

(i) Without title. *Scale of British Statute Miles 16 = 56 mm* (Bd). Compass (Ea). *Remarks* (Ed). Longitude 10' (1'); latitude 10' (1'). Graticule at 1° intervals, ie at 51°N and at 0° and 1°E.

Kitchin's pocket atlass, of the counties of south Britain or England and Wales, drawn to one scale . . . Being the first set of counties, ever published on this plan. London, T. Kitchin and J. Gapper, 1769.   BL.CUL.W

(ii) *BOWLES's REDUCED MAP OF SUSSEX.* added (Ca OS). Plate number *48* added (Ea OS).

Bowles's pocket atlas of the counties of south Britain or England and Wales, drawn to one scale . . . London, Carington Bowles, [1785].   P

47 THOMAS YEAKELL AND WILLIAM GARDNER
1778–83

Sizes: **sheet 1:** 900 mm × 727 mm (8 mm, bottom and left); **sheet 2:** 905 mm × 730 mm (8 mm, bottom only); **sheet 3:** 955 mm × 727 mm (8 mm, bottom only); **sheet 4:** 960 mm × 725 mm (8 mm, bottom and right).   1:32,000

Based on an original survey. Longitudes measured from the meridian of Greenwich. **See plate 19.**

This map, together with no. 57 by the same cartographers, is the most important of all Sussex maps.[1] It marks the start of the new era of scientific trigonometrical survey.

1. Skelton, 1962, contains valuable biographical information and an assessment of the map. See Harley and O'Donoghue, 1975, and Seymour, 1980, for the early history of the Ordnance Survey, including the contributions of Yeakell and Gardner. *SAC* vol. 95 (1957) includes a paper by T.R. Holland on the

In fact, there is no direct evidence that triangulation was used in the survey for this map, as there is for no. 57, though the accuracy of the work suggests that it was.

The map was a forerunner, both as to style and method, of the early Ordnance Survey maps. Surveying draftsmen of the Board of Ordnance were later instructed to follow the style of William Gardner's map of the Plymouth area, executed by him in 1784–6.

The map described below was based on the Greenwich meridian. It includes detail, such as field boundaries, not found on any earlier map of Sussex. The accuracy of the field boundaries could only be assessed by an extensive comparison between this map and a number of surviving estate plans of the period, or with the tithe award maps drawn up some fifty to sixty years later. A very limited sample check along these lines indicates that boundaries on this map are intended to represent actual field boundaries, whereas on Yeakell and Gardner's later map of the whole county (no. 57, 1795) they appear to be diagramatic, even in areas covered by this earlier map. **Plate 23** illustrates this point. It shows Lattendens Farm, near Ashburnham, from four maps (i) estate plan by W. Pearce, 1793–4 (ESRO, Ashburnham MS 2364; Steer, 1962 p. 79), scale 17.6 inches = 1 mile, (ii) Yeakell and Gardner no. 47, sheet four, published in 1783, scale 2 inches = 1 mile (iii) Gardner, Yeakell and Gream no. 57, published in 1795, scale 1 inch = 1 mile. Unfortunately the farm lies on the join between sheets 3 and 4. The two black dots on the right edge of the left sheet are the farm buildings, but the road running south is omitted, (iv) original drawings for Ordnance Survey One Inch Old Series, surveyed c.1795; the scale of both the survey and the drawings was 2 inches = 1 mile. One would expect the large scale estate plan to be the most accurate of the four, and this is confirmed by comparison with the Ordnance Survey Six Inch map (sheet 42), surveyed some seventy-five years later.

There is considerable correlation between the estate plan (i) and the 1783 map (ii). It will be observed that field numbers on the estate plan do not run consecutively, and that the number *15* is engraved on the 1783 map in what is part of field 15 on the estate plan. This suggests that both surveyors had access to some earlier plan of the area, and that Yeakell and Gardner made good use of existing estate plans when available. The field boundaries on the 1795 map (iii) and on the Ordnance Survey drawing (iv) do not correspond with those on the estate plan or with each other. They are diagramatic, and cannot have been intended to represent actual field boundaries. On the Ordnance Survey drawing, however, the woodland is delineated with some accuracy.

The map described below was a great achievement, and much of the credit is due to Charles Lennox, third Duke of Richmond (1736–1806), a great patron of the arts and sciences and himself a mathematician. He employed both Yeakell and Gardner in making plans of his Goodwood estates, and is said to have been the only man of his period to have employed salaried surveyors. He was Master-General of the Ordnance between 1782 and 1795, and was a prime mover in setting up the land survey operations, with which both Yeakell and Gardner were associated as a result of his influence.

Thomas Yeakell the elder was of Dutch or German origin, and was originally an

Yeakell and Gardner maps. Reference should also be made to *SNQ* vol. 4, p. 184; *WSRO Miscellaneous Papers* nos. 17 and 103; and to Harley, *CJ* Dec. 1968.

engraver. From 1758 to 1782 he was employed by the Duke of Richmond as a surveyor, and from 1770 was concurrently in private practice with William Gardner. In 1782 he joined the Board of Ordnance as *Chief Draftsman at the Tower.* He died in 1787.

William Gardner (c. 1739–1800) was probably a Sussex man. He was married at Boxgrove in 1770, when he was described as of Westhampnett, where he had lived for only ten months; his wife, Mary Nunn, had lived in Boxgrove for six months. Thomas Yeakell, also 'of Westhampnett' was a witness.[2] From 1767 Gardner was in private practice as a surveyor (from 1770 in partnership with Yeakell), and for much of the time he worked for the Duke of Richmond. In 1784 he joined the Board of Ordnance and in 1787 was appointed *Chief Surveying Draftsman.*

Yeakell's son, also Thomas, was born in 1762 or 1763, at Westhampnett, where his father lived, and was also a surveyor. He did much valuable work for the Board of Ordnance between 1787 and 1883.[3]

Besides this map, no. 57, and a large number of estate surveys, Yeakell and Gardner produced fine plans of Chichester (1769), and of Brighton, engraved by Whitchurch (1779).[4] Gardner was also responsible for the survey of the Plymouth area on a scale of six inches to a mile, for surveys of Guernsey and Jersey on the same scale in 1787, and other important work for the Board of Ordnance, in much of which he was assisted by Thomas Yeakell junior and Thomas Gream.

The 1778–83 map of Sussex described below was known as the Great (or Large) Survey. It was intended to cover the whole county on eight sheets. A prospectus[5] dated 11 June 1778 included the following: 'The First Sheet of an Actual Topographical SURVEY of the County of Sussex, on a Scale of two Inches to a Mile; containing CHICHESTER, ARUNDEL, and Sixty Parishes: In which is not only laid down an accurate Plan of every Town and Village, but every Farm-House, Barn, and Garden has its Place. Every Inclosure, however small, is described; every Road, public and private, every Bridle-way and Foot-path; the Rivers, with their Bends, Fords, and Bridges; each Rivulet is traced; the Hills and Valleys clearly distinguished from the Low Lands, their Shape and even Height are expressed sensible to the Eye. . . . It will employ us, from first to last, six Years, and cost more than 2400 l. for Surveying, Drawing, and Engraving. . . . Many Gentlemen are apprehensive that from the infinite Detail and Precision of our Work it can never be finished; . . .' This advertisement, which was printed by W. Lee of Lewes, concluded by stating that subscriptions would be taken by Mr. Lee in Lewes, Mr. Thomas at Brighthelmston, Mr. Hogben at Rye, Mr. Watts at Petworth, Mrs. Jaques at Midhurst, Mr. Weire at East-Grinstead, Mr. Jaques at Chichester, Mr. Peadle at Arundel, Mr. Breadhower at Portsmouth, Mrs. Dury in St. Martin's Lane, and Mr. Faden at the Corner of St. Martin's Lane, Strand, London.

The apprehensions of the 'Many Gentlemen' proved justified. Only 250 of the 400 subscriptions required were forthcoming, and only four of the intended eight sheets were ever published. Some years later an unsuccessful attempt was made to complete

2. SRS vol. 32, p. 243.
3. Harley & O'Donoghue, 1977, pp. xxiii, xxvi.
4. Steer, 1962, 1968; Hodson, 1978 no. 95; Butler, 1972, p. 15.
5. Annotated copy of Gough's *British Topography* p. 475 (Bodleian Library).

the work. In advertisements for the 1795 map (no. 57) in *The Sussex Weekly Advertiser; or, Lewes Journal* for 30 May and 13 June 1791, Gardner reported that twenty-six of the original subscriptions for the *Great Survey* had been lost by death, and that he was over-spent by £400. He undertook to complete the *Great Survey* if a further 176 subscriptions were received.

A letter from Yeakell and Gardner dated 17 October 1778,[6] probably addressed to Richard Gough, reads: 'We receiv'd your favour of the 10th Ins:-& we have wrote a person in London, who will carry to Mr. Nichols's (according to your order) a Plan of Chichester, & our first Sheet of the Survey of the County. We are not possessed of a Plan of the Environs of Tunbridge Wells, but will endeavor to get One & send as soon as possible. We have finish'd the Survey of the Second Sheet, & it is Engraving & we are going on with the remainder of the Survey as expeditiously as possible. We immagine Sir, you mean to become a Subscriber, & we have therefore inserted your Name in the list, you will see in the border we insert the Names of the principal owners of Land. should be glad if you have Property in the County to know where that your Name may appear if you approve of it.' The border of the map includes *Sir Henry Gough of Bramber*, but not Richard Gough. This Sir Henry is described in *SAC* as 'of Edgbaston' and was MP for Bramber from 1774 to 1790. He was probably a cousin of Richard Gough.

Sheet 1 is said to have been engraved in Paris;[7] sheets 2 and 3 carry Yeakell's signature; the engraver of sheet 4 is not known. Sheets 1 and 4 may have been engraved by Glot who worked on plans of the Goodwood estates and has been linked with C.B. Glot, the engraver of a plan of Geneva in 1777.

Since it was never completed, this is not strictly a map of Sussex. It extends only to 50°56'30" North, and covers less than half the county; but it has been included in this catalogue because of its far-reaching importance. The sheets were published, starting from the west, in 1778 (sheet 1), in 1780 (sheet 2), and in 1783 (sheets 3 and 4). The 8 mm border extends to three sides of the map when mounted. There are additional borders, 80 mm wide, which were designed to cover all four sides of each sheet, and which were printed from four separate plates. Included in each border is a dedication. The borders also included 419 medallions with the names of Sussex landowners, and 149 blank medallions. When the sheets are mounted to form a single map, some of the additional borders have to be omitted.

According to Skelton[8] the hydrography is based on a manuscript chart by Sir Piercy Brett (1759).

EDITION

Sheet 1
THE FIRST SHEET OF AN ACTUAL TOPOGRAPHICAL SURVEY OF THE COUNTY OF SUSSEX; by T. Yeakell & W. Gardner, SURVEYORS. (Ca, outside

6.   ibid. p. 477.
7.   Gough, 1780, vol. 2 p. 298.
8.   Skelton, *250 years of map-making,* 1970.

border and covered by additional border when mounted). *Published according to Act of Parliament, March 31st. 1778.* (Ce, outside border and covered by additional border when mounted). *SCALE of Three Statute MILES. 3* = 149 mm (De). Compasses (Ae and Ee). *NOTE.* (De, under scale). Longitude 5' (1'), bottom border only; latitude 5' (1'), left border only. **See plate 19.**

To his GRACE CHARLES HOWARD, Duke of Norfolk; Earl of Arundel; Hereditary Earl Marshall; Premier Duke, Earl, and Baron of England; &c. This First Plate of the County of SUSSEX is respectfully dedicated, by HIS GRACE's most obedient and humble Servants; T. Yeakell & W. Gardner. (bottom centre of additional border). *Publish'd as the Act directs; March 31, 1778* (outside additional border, bottom centre).

Sheet 2
THE SECOND SHEET . . . (as sheet 1). *Publish'd according to Act of Parliament, July the 21st. 1780.* (Ce, outside border and covered by additional border when mounted). *Engrav'd by Thos. Yeakell.* (Be). *SCALE of Three Statute MILES. 3* = 149 mm (Ce). Compasses (Ae and Ee). *NOTE* (Ce, under scale). Longitude 5' (1'), bottom border only.

To SIR CECIL BISHOP, of Parham Park in this County, Bart. This Second Plate of the County of SUSSEX, is respectfully dedicated, by his most Obedt. & Humble Servants, T. Yeakell & W. Gardner. (bottom centre of additional border). *Publish'd as the Act directs; July 21, 1780* (outside additional border, bottom centre).

Sheet 3
THE THIRD SHEET . . . (as sheet 1). *Publish'd as the Act directs, 1783.* (Ce, outside border and covered by additional border when mounted). *Engraved by T. Yeakell* (De). *SCALE of Three Statute MILES 3* = 150 mm (Ce). Compasses (Ae and Ee). *NOTE* (Ce, under scale). Longitude 5' (1'), bottom border only.

To the Right Honble. THOMAS PELHAM, Baron Pelham, of Stanmer in this County. This Third Plate of the County of SUSSEX is respectfully dedicated, by HIS LORDSHIPS most obedient & humble Servants; T. Yeakell & W. Gardner. (bottom centre of additional border). *Publish'd as the Act directs; 1783* (outside additional border, bottom centre).

Sheet 4
THE FOURTH SHEET . . . (as sheet 1). *SCALE of Three Statute MILES. 3* = 150 mm (Ce). Compasses (Ae and Ee). *NOTE* (Ce, under scale). Longitude 5' (1'), bottom border only; latitude 5' (1'), right border only. That part of the county lying to the east of *East Guilford* is shown as an insert (Ec).

To the Right HONble. JOHN ASHBURNHAM, EARL ASHBURNHAM, VISCOUNT ST. ASAPH and Baron Ashburnham, This Fourth Plate of the County of SUSSEX is respectfully dedicated, by HIS LORDSHIPS most obedient & humble Servants: T. Yeakell & W. Gardner. (bottom centre of additional border). *Publish'd as the Act directs; 1783* (outside additional border, bottom centre).

Issued as loose sheets, sold separately, 1778 to 1783.

(BL)

48   THOMAS CONDER   1784

Size: 166 mm × 96 mm (6 mm)   1:754,000

This map appears to be based on Kitchen no. 42 or on Ellis no. 44; but the 51° parallel is now correctly placed, whereas on nos. 42 and 44, as on other maps derived from Budgen no. 24, it is some seven miles south of its true position.

Thomas Conder is known as an engraver of maps and plans between 1775 and 1801; he may also have drawn this map.

Alexander Hogg is referred to[1] as one of the 'Paternoster Row' publishers – that is to say, he issued part works in weekly numbers and used somewhat forceful selling techniques for the period. An advertisement in the *Sussex Weekly Advertiser* for 30 January 1792 refers to 'Walpoole's New and Complete British Traveller, just published in sixty numbers'. According to Timperley, 'when the sale of a book began to slacken, this gentleman (Hogg), like old Bernard Lintot (see no. 24), immediately employed some scribe to make for him *a taking title,* and the work, though not a line was altered, was brought out in a new edition.

EDITIONS

(i)   *A New MAP of SUSSEX Drawn from the Latest Authorities* (Ee, on square tablet with ship to the left). *British Statute Miles* 25 = 56 mm (Ce). Compass (Aa). *Remarks* (Ae). Longitude 10' (2'); latitude 10' (2'). Arms of Chichester (Ea).

> *The new British traveller; or, a complete modern universal display of Great-Britain and Ireland. . . . And including a valuable collection of landscapes, views, county-maps, &c . . . The whole published under the immediate inspection of George Augustus Walpoole, Esq. assisted . . . by David Wynne Evans, F.R.S. . . . Alexander Burnet, L.L.D. . . . Robert Conway, A.M. and others . . .*
> London, Alexander Hogg, 1784.   BL
> This map is engraved on the same plate as the maps of Middlesex, Surrey and Dorset. Sussex occupies the bottom right quarter. At top centre of the plate is *Engraved for WALPOOLEs New & Complete BRITISH TRAVELLER;* and at bottom centre Published by ALEX[R]. HOGG, at the Kings Arms, *N°.16 PATERNOSTER ROW.*

1.   Timperley, 1842.

(ii) T. Conder Sculp^t. added (Ee OS).

The new British traveller . . .
London, Alexander Hogg, 1784 and [1790].   W;GL.BRIGHTON PL

The new and complete English traveller: or, a new historical survey and modern description of England and Wales . . . Written and compiled from the best author- ities, by a society of gentlemen . . . Revised, corrected, and improved, by William Hugh Dalton, Esq . . . with . . . correct maps . . .
London, Alexander Hogg, [1794].   BL
In these works the inscription at top centre of the plate has been erased.

49 JOHN CARY   1787

Size: 250 mm × 197 mm (7 mm)   1:535,000

Based on Budgen no. 24, with some reference to Yeakell and Gardner no. 47. Longitude is measured from the meridian of St Paul's; *Brighthelmstone* being almost on the zero meridian.

John Cary (c. 1754–1835) was apprenticed to the engraver William Palmer in 1770. His signature appears on maps from about 1780. In 1783 he went into business on his own, and became a successful and prolific publisher of maps, plans and road-books. He also advertised as a surveyor, and undertook for the Postmaster-General a new survey of the turnpike roads, which had not been resurveyed since Ogilby (see appendix V.1).

Clear and up-to-date road classification is a feature of Cary's maps. He maintained a high standard of accuracy,[1] neatness and clarity in all his work, together with an absence of irrelevant decorative detail. According to his great admirer, Fordham,[2] 'Cary introduced a character and method of delineation which has dominated our cartographers . . . to the present time'. Fordham refers to him as the founder of the modern English school.

Cary's business acumen is confirmed not only by the volume of his output (see nos. 50, 51, 61, 65, 68 and 82), but by the large number of editions to which many of his publications extended. In 1804 he received a gold medal from the Society of Arts for the map of Cardiganshire.

In 1802 his premises were destroyed by fire, but the map plates seem to have been saved. He then took his brother George (d. 1830) into partnership. The firm continued after the death of the two brother, probably under the management of John's sons, George and John. About 1850 the stock of plates was sold to G.F. Cruchley, and some plates were still in use at the end of the century (see nos. 61 and 145).

In 1800–1 Cary won an action in the King's Bench against Longman and Rees

1. G.D. Johnston, 'Roads from Arundel to the north'. *SNQ* 17 (1968), p. 58, includes comments relevant to the general accuracy of Cary maps.
2. Fordham, 1969, p. 86. See also Fordham, 1925.

97

concerning the publication of Paterson's *A new and accurate description* . . . (see appendix II.10), into which matter from *Cary's new itinerary* (appendix II.9) had been incorporated. Fordham[3] gives an interesting summary of the case. Surprisingly, James Bell in the introduction to *A new and comprehensive gazetteer* . . ., 1837 page IXX (see no. 102), takes a less complimentary view of Cary's work: 'About the year 1796, Mr. Cary . . . was employed by the general post-office to measure the mail-coaches routes, and in 1798 he published . . . *Cary's new itinerary &c*. In this, besides the mail-coach routes – which only occupy about a fourth part of the work, and had been mostly measured before – he introduced the other roads of the Kingdom from Paterson's work'.

The map described below was replaced about 1809 by a re-engraved version (no. 68). On no. 49, the scale-bar is numbered in even miles only from 2 to 10; on no. 68, it is numbered in one mile intervals from 1 to 10.

To the right of the map is a page of descriptive text headed *SUSSEX*, which has been reset at least once. The statistics include *342 parishes*, probably a misprint for 312, the accepted figure in all earlier publications including Camden.[4] The 1787 edition lists fifteen market towns; increased to sixteen in the 1793 edition by the inclusion of *Chiddingfold*. The text includes details of titles conferred by the county and a list of *The principal Gentlemens' Seats*.

EDITIONS

(i) *SUSSEX* (Cd, in hatched frame). *By JOHN CARY, Engraver*. (Cd, below title and compass). *London: Publish'd as the Act directs September 1st. 1787 by J. Cary, Engraver, Map & Printseller the corner of Arundel Street Strand*. (Ce OS). *Statute Miles 69½ to a Degree 10* = 31 mm (Ce). Compass (Cd, behind title). Longitude 10' (2'); latitude 10' (2').

> *Cary's new and correct English atlas: being a new set of county maps from actual surveys* . . .
> London, John Cary, 1787.   BL.CUL.BOD

(ii) The *BATTEL* to *HASTINGS* road has been down-graded; new road from *BATTEL* to *Fairlight* and a new loop road from *BATTEL* to *Hollington* added. *HAILSHAM* to *E. Bourne* road down-graded and new main road added further east; also small new road at *HorseBr..Maresfield* to *Newick* road up-graded and part of old road erased. Road from *HORSHAM* through *St. Leonards Forest* up-graded.

> *Cary's new and correct English atlas* . . .
> London, John Cary, 1787.   BL.W
> Also found as a travelling atlas printed on thin paper and bound in soft leather (P).

---

3. Fordham, 1925, pp. xvi–xviii.
4. Lower, 1831 p. 26 gives the total as 318.

(iii)   Imprint (Ce OS) altered to *London: Publish'd Jany. 1st. 1793 by J. Cary. Engraver & Mapseller Strand. Kingsfold* erased. *Awfold* and two house symbols, *Sheffield Par, Halland Par, Hayling I* and *New Chap. Green* with two house symbols added. A number of parks added or extended, eg two north of *Findon* and one round the *Findon* town symbol. Pecked line 12 mm long to mark Kent/Surrey border added. Road directions along county boundary added or amended at eight places, eg *to Guildford* now *to Guildford & Kingston the London R^d.; to Guildford* now *to Godalming Guildford & Epsom the London R^d.* in two places; *to Croydon* erased to two places, the roads extended and joined and *to Croydon the London R^d.* added. Reference letters *a* and *b*, *a* to *h*, and *a* to *f* added to roads along county boundary. Roads from *Findon* to *Patching* erased; road from *Petworth* to *Billingshurst* down-graded; road from *Henfield* to *Twineham* up-graded.

Cary's new and correct English atlas . . .
London, John Cary, 1793.   (P)

(iv)   *Handcrop* and road from *Midlavant* to *W. Dean* added.

Cary's new and correct English atlas . . .
London, John Cary, 1793 (reissued 1795).   A.BOD.BRL;RGS.W.BRL

(v)   *Worthing* added.

Cary's new and correct English atlas . . .
London, John Cary, 1793 (actually issued 1808).   CUL

50   JOHN CARY   **1789**

Size: 487 mm × 355 mm (8 mm)   1:261,000

Based on Budgen no. 24.

Richard Gough (1735–1809), the translator of these editions of Camden's *Britannia,* was an eminent antiquarian and collector, and author of *Anecdotes of British topography* (1768) and *British topography* (1780), which are often the only authority for facts relating to early cartographers. The famous Gough map of Great Britain (c. 1335) at the Bodleian Library[1] was discovered by him. His father, Henry Gough (1681–1751) was MP for Bramber from 1734–47.

John Stockdale (c. 1749–1814), the publisher, came from Cumberland, and after pursuing various careers – for a time he was a blacksmith – he set up as a publisher in London. In 1788 he was acquitted for allegedly bringing a charge of corruption against

1.   R.A. Pelham, 'Studies in the historical geography of medieval Sussex'. *SAC* 72 (1931). The southeast part of this map is reproduced and discussed.

the House of Commons; later he lost a libel action brought against him by Nightingale (see no. 66). His unscrupulous behaviour was evidenced in 1794 by the support he gave to Charles Laurent, who rushed out a very inferior map of Manchester in anticipation of the far better work about to be published by William Green.[2] His son, John Joseph Stockdale (d. 1847), seems to have been equally litigious, and fought a lengthy legal action against the publishers of Hansard. Stockdale acquired the rights to Camden's *Britannia* at the sale of the Robinsons' assets. This is said[3] to have annoyed Gough, and he refused to continue work after the publication of the first volume. Stockdale is thought to have completed the work with Sir W. Betham.

Thomas Payne (1719–99) , the first publisher, came from Northamptonshire. He established himself as a bookseller in S[t] Martin's Lane. On his retirement in 1790, his son, also Thomas, succeeded him, and became Master of the Stationers Company in 1817. They were both successful, and were among the first booksellers to issue regular annual catalogues.

EDITIONS

(i) *A MAP of SUSSEX, from the best AUTHORITIES.* (Ed). *Engraved by J. Cary* (Ee). *Statute Mile 69½ to a Degree of Latitude 12 = 75* mm (De). Compass (Ea). *REFERENCES to the HUNDREDS.* (De). Longitude 5' (1'); latitude 5' (').

> *Britannia: or, a chorographical description of the flourishing kingdoms of England, Scotland, and Ireland . . . By William Camden. Translated from the edition published by the author in MDCVII . . . By Richard Gough, F.A.&R.S.S. . . . Illustrated with maps . . .* vol. 1.
> London, T. Payne and Son and G.G.J. and J. Robinson, 1789.   BL.CUL.SAS

(ii) *Published by John Stockdate Piccadilly, 26th. March 1805,* added (Ee, below title, above signature). A number of additional roads, eg *Hurstperpoint* to *BRIGHTHELMSTONE* via *Pitchling* and via *Poynings; Maresfield* to *Hartfield* and to *Withyham.*

> *New British atlas, being a complete set of county maps . . .*
> London, John Stockdale, 1805 (reissued 1809).   CUL.BOD;BL.RGS

> *Britannia: . . . By Richard Gough . . . Illustrated with maps . . .* 2nd edn, vol. 1.
> London, John Stockdale, 1806.   BL.WORTHING PL

2. C. Roeder, 'William Green, the lake artist', in *Transactions of the Lancashire and Cheshire antiquarian society* vol. 14, (1896).
3. Nichols, 1817–58 vol. 8, p. 482.

51   JOHN CARY   1789

Size: 91 mm × 123 mm (1 mm)   1:1,140,000

Based on Budgen no. 24 or on Cary no. 50. **See plate 20.**

Re-engraved versions of this map were issued in 1806 (no. 65) and in 1822 (no. 82); these later versions have a number of place-names added, eg *Newhaven. Cary's traveller's companion* is often found bound with *Cary's new itinerary,* see appendix II.9.

EDITIONS

(i)   *SUSSEX* (Ca, in rectangular hatched frame. The border is expanded to 8 mm to make space for the title). *London Published Sepr. 1 1789 by J. Cary Engraver N°.188 Strand.* (Ce OS). *By J. Cary* (Aa OS) . . . *Engraver* (Ea OS). *Scale of Miles 10* = 14 mm (Ae). Compass (Ca OS); north is to the left. Below map, and inside bottom border, is a list of towns with distances from London.

> *Cary's traveller's companion, or, a delineation of the turnpike roads of England and Wales . . .*
> London, John Cary, 1790.
> With map of Warwickshire printed on back.   CUL.BOD.W
> With plain back.   BL.CUL

(ii)   A number of place-names and other names added eg *Ouse R., Rye Harbour, Beachy Head, Worthing, Ockley, Rowhook* with extension of road, and road direction *from Dorking.*

> *Cary's traveller's companion . . .*
> London, John Cary, 1791.
> With map of Warwickshire on back.   CUL.A
> With plain back.   A

(iii)   Date and street number in imprint (Ce OS) changed to *1792* and *N°. 181.* Several place-names added, eg *Eastergate, Lit.Hampton.* Roads added *CHICHESTER* to *ARUNDEL* with branch to *Lit.Hampton.*

> *Cary's traveller's companion. . .*
> London, John Cary, 1791 (not issued before 1792).
> With map of Warwickshire on back.   A

(iv)   Road from *Maresfield* to *Chailey* added. **See plate 20.**

> *Cary's traveller's companion . . .*
> London, John Cary, 1791 (not issued before 1792).
> With map of Warwickshire on back.   BL.CUL.W
> With plain back   BL.CUL.W

52   JOHN LODGE

1790

Size: 302 mm × 243 mm (7 mm)   1:413,000

Copied from Ellis no. 44.

Lodge was an engraver in Charlotte Street, London. His name is found on a number of maps in books and magazines between 1764 and 1794.

EDITIONS

(i)   *A NEW MAP OF SUSSEX FROM THE LATEST AUTHORITIES* (Ea). *J.Lodge Sculp.* (Ee OS). *London. Published as the Act directs. July 31st. 1790. by R.Butters No79 Fleet Street* (Ce OS). *British Statute Miles 69 to a Degree 14 = 56* mm (Ca). Compass (Bd). *Remarks* (Aa). Longitude 10' (2'); latitude 10' (2'). *Meridian of London* and 51° parallel are marked. (The top border appears to be marked in minutes of longitude, but the values west from the *Meridian of London* have been reversed in error).

The political magazine, and parliamentary, naval, military and literary journal . . . vol. 19.
London, R. Butters, Issue for July 1790.   BL

(ii)   Signature (Ee OS) and imprint (Ce OS) erased.

Issued in a set of county maps, without title-page, about 1795. Some copies have a label on front cover with printed title: *Atlas of Great Britain and Ireland.*

BL.A.W

53   JOSEPH JOHNSON

1790

Size: 131 mm × 54 mm (the engraved area excluding title; no border)   1:1,070,000

Based on Cary no. 49.

John Aikin (1747–1822), see below, was son of John Aikin (1713–80), tutor at Warrington Academy. He studied medicine at Edinburgh and practised from 1784 at Great Yarmouth and from 1792 in London, having been forced to move because of his dissenting opinions. A stroke forced him to give up medicine and to devote himself to writing. His daughter, Lucy, also achieved distinction as a writer.
Joseph Johnson (1738–1809)[1] was a bookseller and publisher, originating from

---

1.   Nichols, 1817–53 p. 475; Nichols, 1812–5 p. 461–4.

Liverpool. He specialised in medical works and was Dr. Priestley's first publisher. He was well respected and known as 'father of the book trade'; but in 1792 he was imprisoned for selling a pamphlet by Gilbert Wakefield.

The dimensions of the Sussex map refer to the printed area; the sheet measures about 203 mm × 122 mm.

Both Harvey[2] and Hodson[3] have observed that the plate was retouched for the 1803 edition. The retouching of the Sussex map does not warrant treatment as a separate 'state'. If a difference must be found, it would appear that the vertical stroke to the left side of the *F* in *Ashdown Forest* has been erased.

EDITION

SUSSEX. (Db, of the sheet). Plate number *33* (Ea, of the sheet, 30 mm above and right of the full-stop in the title).

England delineated; or, a geographical description of every county in England and Wales . . . [by John Aikin]. 2nd edn.
London, J. Johnson, 1790.   BL
The first edition of this work, published in 1788, does not contain county maps.

England delineated . . . With outline maps of all the counties. 3rd, 4th, 5th and 6th edns.
London, J. Johnson, 1795, 1800, 1803 and 1809.   BL.W;BL;BL.RGS;BL.RGS
A later edition of the work, published in 1818, does not contain county maps.

54   JOHN HARRISON   1791

Size: 427 mm × 318 mm (7 mm)   1:293,000

Based on Bowen no. 35.

Hodson[1] has suggested that an advertisement in *The Morning Herald* of 2 May 1787 may refer to this series of maps. He has also found the map of Hertfordshire in an earlier state than (i) below, and suggests that this may have been issued in *The History of England . . . by M. Rapin de Thoyras . . . continued . . . by N. Tindal, M.A. . . .*, published in 1784–9 by John Harrison. Sussex has not been found in this earlier state and may never have been issued; the Hertfordshire map carries an 1788 date which remains unaltered in the 1791 atlas, whereas the Sussex map is dated *March 1. 1791*.

2. Harvey, 1959, no. 48 (ii).
3. Hodson, 1974, no. 54 (ii).

1. Hodson, 1974, no. 50. See also Phillips, 1909 p. 1089 and 1920, p. 457.

Other maps are dated from *Sept 1. 1787* (Middlesex) to *Feb 26. 1791* (North Wales).[2] Sussex was, therefore, the last map issued. Most maps carry the signature *J. Haywood* and Sussex was probably by the same hand. As regards engraver, several maps have *Sudlow Sc.;* North Wales has *G.S. Allen Sculpt.*; but there is nothing to indicate the engraver of the Sussex map.

EDITIONS

(i)   *A MAP OF SUSSEX Drawn & Engraved from AN ACTUAL SURVEY with Improvements* (Aa, in plain panel). *Drawn and Engraved for J. Harrison № 115 Newgate Street March 1 1791.* (Ce OS). *British Statute Miles 69 to a Degree 12* = 66 mm (Ae). Compass (Ea). *Reference to the Hundreds* (Ee). Longitude 10' (1'); latitude 10' (1'). Graticule at 10' intervals.

> *Maps of the English counties, with the subdivisions of hundreds, wapontakes, lathes, wards, divisions &c. to which are added two folio pages of letter-press, to face each map . . .*
> London, John Harrison, 1791.   BL.CUL

> *Maps of the English counties; with the subdivisions of the hundreds, wappintakes, wards &c.&c. which are curious and valuable. Drawn upon the most approved scales, exhibiting everything interesting, clear & distinct.*
> London, John Harrison, 1792.   RGS.A

(ii)   *General and county atlas, containing forty-seven maps.* London, [1815], which is recorded by Hodson,[3] has now been broken up. The Hertfordshire map was in a third state, with the last two figures in the imprint erased. The Sussex map may also have been in a different state.

55   SAMUEL JOHN NEELE   1793

Size: 303 mm × 123 mm (2 mm)   1:416,000

The detail is insufficient for the derivation of this map to be determined. It includes several errors, eg *Sexhill* (Bexhill), *Peringdean* (Ovingdean).

Samuel John Neele (1758–1824) and his sons James and Josiah were well-known London engravers. (For other Sussex maps engraved by them see nos. 74, 79 and 84). They engraved Thomas Budgen's plan of *Brighthelmstone* (1788), Marchant's plan of

2.   Chubb, 1927, no. CCXCI.
3.   Hodson, 1974, no. 50(iii).

the same town for Atree's *Topography of Brighton* (1809), and a plan of Tunbridge Wells (1828).[1]

The Reverend Arthur Young (b. 1769), author of the work recorded below, was the son of the agriculturist Arthur Young (1741–1810), secretary to the Board of Agriculture. This work was not well regarded. The son did not have his father's abilities, and suggestions of nepotism were raised.[2]

John Nichols (1745–1825), the publisher, was a distinguished antiquarian, editor of the *Gentleman's Magazine* for many years, Master of the Stationers Company in 1804, and compiler of important bibliographical works, including *Literary anecdotes of the 18th century* and *Bibliotecha topographica Britannia.* He was the father of John Bowyer Nichols (see no. 100).

William Sherwood (1776–1837), publisher of the 1813 edition, was born in Bristol. He worked for a Mr. Symonds in Paternoster Row, who died or retired in 1806. Sherwood continued the business in partnership with Neely and Jones, and when they retired, he took Gilbert and Piper into partnership.

EDITION

A SKETCH of the SOIL of SUSSEX. (Ca OS). *Neele sc. Strand* (Ee OS). Soil types are named, eg *RICH AND STIFF LOAM,* and are delineated by continuous or dotted lines.

General view of the agirculture of the county of Sussex . . . By the Rev. Arthur Young.
London, J.Nichols, 1793 and 1793.   BL.SAS;SAS
The second version of this work is on larger paper, and to the right of the text there is a column headed *For remarks and additional obsevations.*

General view of the agriculture. . .
London, Richard Phillips, 1808.   BL.BRIGHTON PL

General view of the agriculture. . .
London, Sherwood, Neely and Jones, 1813.   BRIGHTON PL. EASTBOURNE PL

---

1. Tunbridge Wells Library. *Signed Ja^s. & Josi^h. Neele 352 Strand.*
2. *SAC* vol. 90 (1952), p. 84.

56 BENJAMIN BAKER

1795

Size: 213 mm × 167 mm (7 mm)

1:622,000

Based on Cary no. 49, which also emphasises the lower reaches of the river Brede. This map shows *Winchelsea Castle* on an island; reference may have been made to Yeakell and Gardner no. 47.

Benjamin Baker of Islington, London, is known as an engraver between 1780 and 1824. He engraved the Lindley and Crosley map of Surrey (1793), but is best remembered for his work on the Ordnance Survey One Inch Old Series; both the main Sussex sheets (V and IX) carry the legend *Engraved at the Drawing Room at the Tower by Benjn. Baker and Assistants.*

William Darton (1755–1819) and Joseph[1] Harvey (1764–1841) were print-sellers and publishers in Gracechurch Street, London, from 1787. The firm's imprint changed from time to time.[2] After 1834 it was under the control of Robert Harvey or Thomas Gates Darton until about 1850. William Darton's son, William junior, set up on his own in 1804 at Holborn Hill House, and again used a variety of imprints. His son, John Maw Darton, joined him in 1830, and he later continued the business in partnership with Sam Clark and Robert Hodge until about 1867 (see also nos. 66B, 75, 81 and 112).

Robert Laurie, or Lowry (1755–1836), see (ii) and (iii) below, achieved a considerable reputation as a mezzotint engraver. He first published through Robert Sayer, but in 1779 he seems to have set up on his own. In 1794 he took over the business of Sayer and Bennett (see no. 35) in partnership with James Whittle. The firm's early connection with the maritime side of the trade is evidenced by the publication in 1798 of the *East India pilot*. Laurie retired in 1812. His son, Richard Holmes Laurie, joined the firm in 1814 and took over on the death of Whittle in 1818. They became chart sellers to the Admiralty. The business was carried on by others after the death of Richard Holmes Laurie in 1858, and was amalgamated with Imray, Norie and Wilson in 1903 (see no. 28, note 2).

William Bent, see (i) below, was a bookseller in Paternoster Row. From about 1792 he published regular lists of new books,[2] and in 1802 he started *Bent's literary advertiser,* which was edited by his son, Robert.[3]

EDITIONS

(i) *SUSSEX* (Cd, in hatched oval frame). *Engraved by B.Baker, Islington.* (Cd, under title). *Scale of Miles 10 = 26 mm* (Ce). Longitude 10' (2'); latitude 10' (2').

1. Hannas, 1972, p. 144. Other authorities refer to him as *Josiah* (see Tooley, 1979, p. 148; Darlington and Howgego, 1964, p. 250).
2. Hannas, 1972.
3. Timperley, 1842, p. 812.
4. Boase, 1965.

The universal magazine of knowledge and pleasure . . . vol. 96.
London, W. Bent. Issue for February 1795.   BOD
An earlier volume, no. 26 for May 1760, contains Seale no. 40. Other issues contained road maps (see appendix V.6).

Maps of the several counties and shires in England . . .
London, Darton and Harvey, 1804.   WN

(ii)   A number of additions: *Published October, 12ᵗʰ. 1806, by LAURIE & WHITTLE, Nᵒ.53, Fleet Street, London.* (Ce OS); compass (Cd); many place-names added, eg *Hayling I., Great Bognor or Hothampton, South Bourne, Brede, Breake R., Oxney Isle;* six road directions, eg *to Croydon, to Maidstone*; the roads lettered *bafedcbaabcdefg* along the county boundary, and roads extended. Parks with names also added, eg *Lady Holt Park*. Many place-names re-engraved, eg *West Tarring* (formerly *W.Tarring*). Some parks enlarged, eg *Stanmer*. Many distances from London reduced by one mile in west Sussex, eg *Petersfield 54* (formerly *55*), *CHICHESTER 62* (formerly *63*). A number of roads upgraded, eg *Heathfield* to *Burwash*, *Berwick* to *Wilmington*. Certain park symbols erased, eg at *Marden* and *Singleton*.

Laurie and Whittle's new and improved English atlas, divided into counties . . . with turnpike and principal roads. . .
London, Robert Laurie and James Whittle, 1807.   BL.CUL.RGS

A new and improved English atlas, divided into counties . . .
London, James Whittle and Richard Holmes Laurie, 1816.   BOD

(iii)   Imprint (Ce OS) amended to *Published, by R.H. LAURIE, Nᵒ. 53, Fleet Street, London.* Key to RAPES added (Ea) with numbers *1* to *6* on map. *& Park* (at *Herstmonceux*), two park symbols near *Crowhurst*, new road *Ryegate* to *Cruckfield* to the east of the existing road and a cross-road joining the two, have been added. Some roads upgraded, eg *Petersfield* to *CHICHESTER*, *Heathfield* to *BATTEL*.

A new and improved English atlas, divided into counties . . .
London, James Whittle and Richard Holmes Laurie, 1846.   P
The title page from the 1816 edition seems to have been re-used with one digit in the date altered.

57 WILLIAM GARDNER, THOMAS YEAKELL AND THOMAS GREAM 1795

Size: 1914 mm × 742 mm (15 mm)   1:64,800

Based on Yeakell and Gardner no. 47 and original survey, in which surveyors of the Board of Ordnance assisted.[1] **See plate 22.**

An advertisement in the *Sussex Weekly Advertiser; or, Lewes Journal* for May 30 and June 13 1791 reads: 'Survey of the County of Sussex. Proposals for publishing a new plan of the county of Sussex. . . William Gardner and Thomas Gream, who undertake this work, and hope for the encouragement of the Public, particularly the subscribers to the *LARGE SURVEY;* humbly beg leave to state the reasons why that work has not hitherto been completed, and the grounds on which the present proposals are founded.' An explanation follows as to why only four of the eight sheets of the large or *GREAT SURVEY* (no. 47) had been completed. That map would have measured 14' × 5'; the new map on half the scale and on three sheets, would measure 7'6" × 2'6", and '. . . except expressing the enclosures will contain every other particular in the same manner as in the Large Survey . . .'. Delivery was promised for 1792 at a cost of 1½ guineas,[2] or one guinea to subscribers to the *GREAT SURVEY.* Those interested were asked to write to Mr. Faden (London), Mr. Charles Jaques (Chichester), Mr. W. Lee (Lewes). Mr. Lambert (Lewes), Mr. Gream's Office, (No. 7, Clifford's Inn, Fleet-street, London), Mr. Crawford (Brighton) or to Mr. Campion (Horsham).

Yeakell had died in 1787. In the same year Gardner had been appointed *Chief Surveying Draftsman* to the Board of Ordnance, but he seems to have carried on his private practice at the same time. Thomas Gream was also a surveyor with the Board of Ordnance, often working with Gardner. He went into private practice in 1791,[3] but continued to do work for the Board. William Mudge, who had started on the great trigonometrical survey in 1791, was instructed by the Duke of Richmond to make his information available to Gardner so that this map could be corrected. This is, therefore, the first map based on the official trigonometrical survey to be published.[4] Gardner, Yeakell junior and Gream also worked on the Kent map, which was published by Faden in 1801.

Thomas Foot was a freelance engraver. He worked for William Faden and the the Board of Ordnance, and engraved a number of large-scale county maps.[5] He was active between 1790 and 1827.

William Faden (1750–1836) succeeded Thomas Jefferys (see no. 34) who had died

---

1. Skelton, 1962, p. 422.
2. A later advertisement in the *Gentleman's Magazine* reads '. . . on four sheets of Columbian paper. Price to subscribers £1.11.6 in sheets; to non-subscribers £1.16.0.' Gream's address is *Villiers S[rs]. Strand.*
3. Steer, 1962, p. 81, notices a 'Plan of Rose Hill Park, Brightling', 1979 by Mess[rs] Russell and Gream. Steer, 1968, p. 163 includes two plans, 1791 and 1792, by Gream.
4. Harley and O'Donoghue, 1975, p. xxvii.
5. See index to Rodger, 1972.

in 1771, and continued in business as a publisher until his retirement in 1823, when his business was taken over by James Wyld. He was a cartographer and engraver, but is best known for his prolific publishing activities, which included the issuing of a large number of county maps.[6] He seems to have been adept at securing awards offered by the Society of Arts between 1762 and 1809 for accurate county surveys on the scale of one inch to a mile.[7] This map secured him a gold medal, although one feels that the recognition might more appropriately have gone to Gardner or Gream.[8] Faden took a keen interest in the work of the Ordnance Survey and secured non-exclusive publication rights to some of the early maps.

For a note on James Wyld, see no. 58.

The map is, in fact, printed from four plates. The engraving on each sheet measures 742 mm (772 mm including borders) in the vertical dimension. The engraving on sheet 1 (west) and on sheet 4 (east) measure 472 mm horizontally, but each has one border (to left and right respectively), bringing the printed dimension on each sheet to 487 mm. Sheets 2 and 3 do not have left or right borders and measure 485 mm horizontally. The borders are in the style later adopted by the Ordnance Survey. This is the first map covering the whole of Sussex since Morden nos. 20 and 21 to have longitudes measured from Greenwich.

EDITIONS

(i)   Without title, dedication or scale. *Published by W.Faden, Charing Cross, June 4th. 1795* (on sheet 1, Ec OS; sheet 2, Ec OS; sheet 3, Ac OS; sheet 4, omitted). Compass (sheet 2, Ee). Longitude 5' (1'), along left border of sheet 1 only; latitude 5' (1'), along top and bottom of sheet 1 only.

Proof copies, probably not offered for sale.   (P)

(ii)   *A Topographical Map of the COUNTY of SUSSEX, divided into Rapes, Deanries and Hundreds, Planned from an actual Survey by a Scale of one Inch to a Statute Mile; begun by W. GARDNER and the late T.YEAKELL, COMPLETED BY Tho*[s]*. Gream, Land Surveyor, Villiers Street, Strand. Engraved by THO*[s]*. FOOT, Weston Place, Battle Bridge. LONDON Published by W. FADEN, GEOGRAPHER to HIS MAJESTY and to HIS R.H. the PRINCE of WALES. Charing Cross, June 4*[th]*.1795* added (sheet 4, Ea). *To His Grace Charles Lenox, Duke OF Richmond, Lenox AND Aubigny, EARL of MARCH, Lord Lieutenant and Custos Rotulorum of the County of Sussex; &c. &c. &c. This Map is, with Permission, dedicated by the Proprietor William Faden, Charing Cross June 4*[th]*. 1795.* added (sheet 4, Ee). *SCALE OF STATUTE MILES. 1 + 4 = 100* mm (sheet 4, Be). Extension added to top of compass (sheet 2, Ee). Longitude 5' (1') and latitude 5' (1') extended to three sides of sheets 1 and 4, to top and bottom of

6.   See index to Rodger, 1972.
7.   Harley, 1964, p. 273.
8.   Rodger, 1972, p. vii says that Gream received an award, but no other reference to it has been found, see *Journal of the Royal Society of Arts* vol. 10 (1912).

sheets 2 and 3. On sheet 1, 55'W which was lightly engraved on the proof, has now been strengthened to match the other values. Other additions include:– on sheet 1, *Canal* in two places; on sheet 2, none; on sheet 3, *Tide Mill, Court H. Compton Place,* and in the neighbourhood of *Chittingly, Upp. Vert. W, Low Vert W, Deanland Wood* and *Bentley W.;* on sheet 4, *Rose Hill* and *Turn P,* west of *Battle.* Also added are the names of many landowners, eg on sheet 3, *Rev^d. M^r. Hare* (near *Herstmonceux*): The imprints outside the border on sheets 1, 2 and 3 remain as in state (i), but are not visible when the sheets are pasted together. **See plate 22.**

Issued as loose sheets, sold separately, [1795].   (BL).(WSRO). (BRIGHTON PL).

(iii)   A large number of additions including: on sheet 1, *Vicarage* (south-east of *Climping*), *Sir Richard Hotham* (at *Felpham*); on sheet 2, *Barracks* with appropriate symbol (north of *BRIGHTHELMSTONE*); on sheet 3, *Pevensey Haven, Langley Point, New Pier, Chin Gap, Beenside, Saltdean Gap, Glynd River, Proposed Canal (Laughton* to *Hellingley). canal symbols on the Ouse north of Piddinghoe* and at several places up river, a canal from *GLYND RIVER* to *Ripe,* two pier symbols at *Newhaven;*[9] on sheet 4, *Ruins of Northly Chaple, Hook Point, Goldbury Point.*

Issued as loose sheets, sold separately, [1795].   (RGS).(PRO).(WORTHING PL).

(iv)   On sheet 3, *Chittingly* erased and replaced by *Chiddingly.* On sheet 4, *Brightling Park* erased; *Brightling* erased and re-engraved further east; *Rose Hill* erased and *Park* substituted.

Issued as loose sheets, sold separately, [1795].   (BL).(CUL).(WSRO).

(v)   *Second Edition 1815* added (sheet 4, Ea under title). Other alterations include:– on sheet 1, *R.Arun* added, and river extended north of county boundary; *Sidney Mill, Durfold Farm, Tingley Farm, Gosted Farm, Ramnest Comm^n. Leeth Hill,* and *Sturt F^m.* added along north boundary; *Arun & Wey Junction Canal to Stone Bridge Bar near Guildford* added and named. On sheet 2, the engraving of the *Roman Road* through *Billingshurst* and of the road running east and west through *Pulborough* has been strengthened; road from *Storrington* to *Amberley* and *Houghton* (partly on sheet 1), part of road from *Worthing* to *Lancing,* and road from *HORSHAM* to road-sign *from Guildford* have all been upgraded and parts have been added; *Arun & Wey Junction Canal* added and named; *Lower Lancing* re-engraved *South Lancing; Ouse Navigation* added and canal extended south of *Ardingly; Heath Common* erased and replaced by *Inclos'd,* east of *Storrington.* On sheet 3, *Buckhurst Park* added in place of *Stoneland Park* and *Duke of Dorset* erased; east of *Withyham,* parks re-engraved and road added; road from *Heathfield* to north of *Dallington* upgraded; new main road from *Ditchling* to

9.   Canals and navigations on the Ouse and works at Newhaven harbour have been documented by John Farrant. For references see appendix X (iii) (e), note 12.

Hamsey (partly on sheet 2) added. On sheet 4, *Royal Military Canal* added and course marked by heavy line.

Issued as loose sheets, sold separately, 1815. (RGS)

(vi)   In the title (sheet 4, Ea) *GEOGRAPHER TO HIS MAJESTY and to HIS R.H. the PRINCE OF WALES,* erased and replaced by *GEOGRAPHER TO HIS MAJESTY. Second Edition 1815* erased and replaced by *Third Edition 1820.* The imprints (outside borders on sheets 1, 2 and 3) altered to *Published by W. Faden Charing Cross. Third Edition Augt. 12th 1820.* A large number of other changes include:– on sheet 1, place-names and roads added, eg *Mapsoms, Barn Signal Ho, West Shops, Ferry* (at *Ford*), *Summers Town, Chalwood Com* and new road, *Hayland* and new road, and a road from *Liphook* to *Lakehouse F.*; road from just east of *PETWORTH* running north-east to *Idehurst* upgraded; *Intended Arundel and Portsmouth Canal* added and marked. On sheet 2, at *NEW SHOREHAM* the harbour has been re-engraved, and *Old Entrace, New Entrance, Egypt, Alexandria* and *Lights* have been added; *Rocks* altered to *Rocks Ho.*, *Bridger Esq* to *Henry Bridges esq.*, *John Norton Esqr* to *Goring Esqr*; on the east side of *BRIGHTHELMSTONE*, houses have been added, the windmill moved 10 mm westward, house added on old site of windmill, three small roads added and pecked line on south side of coast road strengthened, the farm about 30 mm east of the town has been erased; at *Rowfant, Rev^d. D^r. Bethune,* altered to *H.Hunt esq.*; the road from *HORSHAM* to *Little Haven* marked by continuous line, a minor road and *Inclos'd* added; road added from *Billingshurst* to *New Bridge.* On sheet 3, at *Pevensey, Barracks* added and three roads running west to the main Eastbourne road upgraded; the road from *Rottingdean* to *East Bourne* via *Newhaven* and *SEAFORD* upgraded; *Rev^d. M^r. Hare* altered to *Rev^d. T.R. Kemp* (at *Herstmonceux*); *Inclosed* added at *EAST GRINSTEAD.* On sheet 4, the county boundary from *Turnpike Road to Hawkhurst* to a point 85 mm north-west has been redrawn, reducing the area of the county (apparently in error; the boundary in edition (v) conforms with the Ordnance Survey One Inch Old and New Series); *Rose Hill* and *Hollingrove Gr.* added at *Brightling. Barehurst* and *Brookmarle* added north of *Burwash;* road from *Playdon* running north to county boundary upgraded; road added from *RYE* to *Scots flat* and eastwards to boundary.

Issued as loose sheets, sold separately, 1820. (WSRO)

The imprints (outside borders) are not visible on the impression at *WSRO,* which has been pasted together, but have been found on a set in a private collection.

(vii)   In the title (sheet 4, Ea), *W.FADEN* altered to *JAMES WYLD; June 4th. 1795* altered to *Jany. 1. 1829; 1820* (after *Third Edition*) erased. In the dedication (sheet 4, Ee) *William Faden, Charing Cross June 4th. 1795* erased. On sheet 3, a new park and *Alex. Donovan esq^r.* added. *Frantfield* re-engraved *Framfield.* The imprints on sheets 1, 2 and 3 outside the border are not visible on the only copy inspected.

Issued as a folding map.
London, James Wyld, 1829. (BRIGHTON PL)

58 THOMAS GREAM   1799

Size: 758 mm × 336 mm (11 mm)   1:166,000

Based on Gardner no. 57. Longitudes are measured from the meridian of Greenwich.

For notes on Gream and Faden see no. 57.

Little is known about I. Palmer,[1] the engraver of this map. He is probably the John Palmer whom William Mudge sought to employ in 1808.[2] He may have been related to William Palmer, a well-known engraver, who assisted with *Ellis's English atlas* (no. 44) and engraved *A PLAN of the CITIES OF LONDON* . . . published by Faden in 1785.[3]

James Wyld (1790–1836) was a cartographic publisher and is reputed to have introduced lithography to this country.[4] He liked to call himself *Geographer Royal* and did some work for the Quartermaster-General's office. In 1823 he acquired the business of William Faden. The map described below under state (ii) cannot, therefore, have been published before that date. His son, James Wyld II (1812–87) was intended for the army, but decided to follow his father into the map trade, probably about 1830, when he became a member of the Royal Geographical Society. Between 1851 and 1861 he exhibited a *Great Globe* in Leicester Square, which attracted much comment.[5] He was MP for Bodmin from 1847 to 1852 and from 1857 to 1868. He led a vigorous campaign, both inside and outside parliament, against the surveying of London by the Ordnance Survey, which he thought should be the province of civilian surveyors. He was, however, a vigorous supporter of the British Museum Library.

EDITIONS

(i) *A TOPOGRAPHICAL MAP of the COUNTY OF SUSSEX; Reduced from the LARGE SURVEY in four Sheets, by Thomas Gream.* (Ea). *LONDON: Published by W.FADEN, Geographer to His Majesty and to His Royal Highness the Prince of Wales. Charing Cross, August 12th. 1799.* (Eb). *Engraved by I. Palmer, Store Street, Bedford Square.* (Ee OS). *SCALE OF STATUTE MILES* 1 + 6 = 60 mm (Ee). Compass (Ed). *Note* (Ee, under scale). Longitude 5' (1'); latitude 5' (1').

Issued as loose sheets, sold separately, [1799].   (BL).(BOD).(CUL)

(ii) In the imprint (Eb) *the Prince of Wales* altered to *the Prince Regent,* and 1799 altered to *1819.* A number of place-names erased. eg *Finden Park, Plashet Park,*

---

1. Tooley, 1979, p. 486 states that he worked for Dalrymple in 1805. William Palmer was also associated with Dalrymple.
2. Harley and O'Donoghue, 1977, p. xxvi.
3. Darlington and Howgego, 1964, no. 180.
4. *DNB.* This claim is not confirmed by other authorities.
5. R. Hyde, 'Mr. Wyld's monster globe' in *History today* vol. 20 (1970).

Halland Park. At *Shoreham,* the harbour re-engraved and *New Entrance* and *Old Entrance* added. The county boundary re-engraved to exclude an area north-east of *Ticehurst,* see no. 57 (vi). *Surry & Sussex Canal* added and marked from under *U* of *SURREY* to *Wisborough Green,* and from thereon the river has been re-engraved and parts of the canal added. *Intended Arun and Portsmouth Canal* added and marked by pecked line. *Royal Mil^y. Canal* added and marked from *Fairlight* to county boundary. Other additions include *Barn Rocks, Ratton Park, F* after *Rodmill,* additional house symbols (eg on road east of *Pulborough*), *New Road to Merstham* and many other roads (eg *Billingshurst* to *PETWORTH*).

Issued after 1823 as a folding map in slip-case, sometimes with printed title: *Sussex.* London, James Wyld (successor to Mr Faden).   (BL).(BRIGHTON PL)

(iii)   Imprint (Eb) erased and replaced by *London: Published by JA^s. WYLD, Geographer to Her Majesty Charing Cross, East 1844.* Palmer signature (Ee OS) erased. *Barracks* and *Kemp Town* added at *BRIGHTHELMSTONE.* Also added *Hassock Gate, St Leonards, Ditchling, Ansty Cross* and *Ansty F* (south of *CUCKFIELD*), new road from *Ansty Cross* to *Billingshurst,* additional houses at *BRIGHTHELMSTONE,* which now extend to 15 mm. Railway 2 added and named *LONDON AND BRIGHTON RAILWAY. RAILWAY DEPOT,* 3 *Bridges, STATION* (at *Balcombe*) and *ST^N.* (at several places) added.

Issued about 1844 as a folding map in slip-case with printed title: *Sussex.* London, Ja^s. Wyld (successor to Mr Faden).   (BRIGHTON PL)

(iv)   In the imprint (Eb) the date *1844* erased. Notes relating to parliamentary representation and polling places added (Ce). *Intended Arun and Portsmouth Canal* now marked by continuous line, but pecked line remains. Many place-names added, eg *Suspension Br.* (at *N.SHOREHAM*), *Fort* (at *Arundel Haven*), *Barracks* (at *CHICHESTER, Selsea* and *East Bourne*), *Steyne, Chain Pier, Black Rock* and *Park* (at *BRIGHTHELMSTONE*), *Signal Ho.* (at *Selsea*), *Langley Point, Jews Gut, Steep Down* (near *Sompting*), *Somers T^n.* (at *CHICHESTER*), additional house symbols at *Worthing.* Railways, 1,3 to 5, 7 (part), 8, 9, 13 and 19 (part) added; many lines named, eg *BRIGHTON AND CHICHESTER RAILWAY;* and *STA.* added.

Issued between 1850 and 1860 as loose sheets, sold separately.   (HOVE PL)

59   NATHANIEL COLTMAN   1799

Size: 662 mm × 500 mm (14 mm)   1:189,000

Based on Gardner, Yeakell and Gream no. 57.

Nathaniel Coltman was active as a cartographer between 1797 and 1833. He worked with Laurie and Whittle over a long period, his name being associated with their Welsh atlas (1805) and with their map of London (1831).

George Allen, the engraver, worked on other maps for Laurie & Whittle about this time, eg Dorset (1799) and Isle of Wight (1800). He also undertook engraving for Faden and for Arrowsmith.

EDITIONS

(i) *A NEW MAP of the COUNTY OF SUSSEX. Divided into RAPES AND HUNDREDS, by Nathl. Coltman. LONDON: Published by LAURIE & WHITTLE N°. 53 Fleet Street May 20th. 1799.* (Ea, in circular frame). *George Allen, Engraver, N°. 19 Shoe Lane. Fleet Street.* (Ce, below compass). *Scale of 10 Miles* = 87 mm (De). Compass (Cd). *REFERENCES to the HUNDREDS* (Ae). *EXPLANATIONS.* (Ee). Longitude 5' (1'); latitude 5' (1').

> Sold loose and as a folding map in slip-case with printed title: *A new map of the county of Sussex . . . by Nathaniel Coltman.*
> London, Laurie and Whittle, 1799.   (BL).(RGS).(A)

(ii) The map has been revised to include the whole of Surrey. It now measures 662 mm × 527 mm with a 14 mm border all round. The bottom border has been raised by 108 mm and now lies 50 mm below the coast at *BEACHY HEAD,* and all detail below the border is omitted. The top border has been raised by 135 mm and now lies 247 mm north of *Tonbridge Wells.* This has been achieved as follows:- the original top border of 14 mm has been erased; the distance from the top of the original border to the edge of the plate was 11 mm; the south part of Surrey has been engraved on this section (662 mm × 25 mm) of the original plate from which all the original detail has been erased. The north part of Surrey from *Walton* to *Maldon* north to *LONDON,* together with a new top border and extensions to right and left borders, has been engraved on a new plate, the printed surface measuring 110 mm (plus border of 14 mm) vertically, and 662 mm (plus two borders of 14 mm each) horizontally.

The George Allen imprint (Ce) erased. Title erased and replaced by *LAURIE AND WHITTLE'S NEW MAP of the COUNTIES of SURREY & SUSSEX with their Subdivisions Exhibiting The Direct Roads from LONDON to Tonbridge Wells Rye Winchelsea Hastings East and South Bourne Newhaven Brighthelmstone Worthing Little Hampton Bognor, Chichester, and the whole Coast of Sussex with the principal Cross Roads Gentlemens Seats Navigable Canals Rivers &c. &c. Carefully delineated from the best Surveys and Authorities Regulated by Astronomical Observations by Nathl. Coltman 1807.* (Eb, in circular frame. This is in the same position on the original plate as the title on the map in state (i)). *Published Septr 14th 1807, by LAURIE & WHITTLE N° 53 Fleet Str^t. London.* (Eb, below circular frame). Scale, compass, *REFERENCE to the HUNDREDS* and *EXPLANATIONS* erased. New *Scale 1 + 6 Miles* = 52 mm added (Be). Fleur de Lys in place of compass (Ce). *HUNDREDS in SURREY* (Da) and *HUNDREDS in SUSSEX* (Ea) added, both being on the new plate. *Explanation* added (Ee). Longitude 5' (1'); latitude 5' (1'); new borders added at top and bottom and the values, which in state (i) were engraved to the right of the vertical lines marking each 5' of longitude, are now split by the lines; left and right borders are also included on the new plate, but the value 51° 20'N is omitted on both sides. On the map the number *47* marking the Hundred of Tarring has been moved from near *Westham* to below *Hailsham*. A number of place-names have been added, mainly along the coast east of *Cuckmere Haven*, eg *Barling Gap, Martello Towers, or Fairleigh, Hook Point. Canal* and *New Military Road* added and marked north-east from *Hook Point*. Distances from *LONDON* added to market towns, eg *62½* at *CHICHESTER*. Several roads added or upgraded, eg *Westham* to HASTINGS.

Issued as a folding map, probably in slip-case with printed title, 1807. (SAS)

(iii) In the title (Eb) commas have been added after the name of each town and a semi-colon after *Sussex*, the date (*1807*) erased and replaced by three horizontal lines. *An Improved edition. 1815* added (Ec, below title and imprint). The canal near *Hook Point* now stops short of the coastline, about 5 mm of it having been erased. Some roads added and upgraded, eg *Slaugham* to *Piecomb*, HORSHAM to *County Oak*. Canal from *GUILDFORD* to *GODALMING* erased and added to east of road, and named *Godalm Nav. Arun & Wey Junction* canal added and named.

Issued as a folding map in slip-case with printed title: *A new map of the counties of Surrey and Sussex . . . by Nathaniel Coltman.*
London, Laurie and Whittle, [1815]. (BL)

(iv) Imprint (Eb, under title) erased and replaced by *Published Septr. 14th. 1821 by RICHARD H. LAURIE N°. 53 Fleet Str^t. London*. In the title (Eb) *LAURIE & WHITTLE'S* erased and replaced by *LAURIE'S*.

Issued as a folding map in slip-case with printed title: *A new map of the counties of Surrey and Sussex . . . by Nathaniel Coltman.*
London, Laurie and Whittle, [1821]. (SAS)

(v) In the imprint (Eb, under title) the date altered to *March 14th. 1827*. A number of additions on the map, eg *Pier* and symbol and additional house symbols at *BRIGHTHELMSTONE, Kemp Town, Arun & Portsmouth Canal.*

Issued as a folding map in slip-case with printed title: *A new map of the counties of Surrey and Sussex . . . by Nathaniel Coltman.*
London, Laurie & Whittle, [1827]. (P)

Size: 480 mm × 423 mm (13 mm)   1:261,000

Based on Gardner, Yeakell and Gream, no. 57.

Jones and Smith were a firm of engravers, first in Pentonville Road and later in the Strand. There is no evidence to link this Smith with Charles Smith, the publisher of the atlas; but the two men again worked together on *Smith's actual survey of the roads from London to Brighthelmstone . . .* (appendix V.14).

Charles Smith was a stationer and mapseller in the Strand from about 1800. His *New English atlas* is a very competent work, comparable in many ways with Cary's atlas (no. 61). Both made full use of large-scale county surveys published during the previous fifty years, and both were successful; Smith's atlas being reprinted up to 1864, and Cary's plates until near the end of the century. See also no. 83 and appendix V.17, which were engraved for Smith by Pickett.

As well as appearing in *Smith's new English atlas* many of the editions of the map listed below have been found as folding maps sold separately, and the map may have been issued continuously in this form from 1801 to about 1864.

EDITIONS

(i)   *A NEW MAP of the COUNTY of SUSSEX Divided into Rapes & Hundreds. LONDON Printed for C.SMITH N°. 172 Strand. January 6th. 1801.* (Aa). *Jones & Smith sculp. Pentonville.* (Ca. below compass). *Scale* 1 + 13 *Miles* = 82 mm (Ce). Compass (Ca). *REFERENCE to the RAPES and HUNDREDS* (Ce, above scale). *EXPLANATION* (Da). Longitude 5' (1'); latitude 5' (1').

> *Smith's new English atlas being a complete set of county maps . . .*
> London, C. Smith, 1804   BL

(ii)   *Haslington Bridge* (at *Petworth*), *Arundel Nav., Newhaven Bridge, Lewes Nav.* and three house symbols at *Liphook* added.

> *Smith's new English atlas . . .*
> London, C. Smith, 1804.   CUL.W

(iii)   *Bodiham Cas.* added.

> *Smith's new English atlas . . .*
> London, C. Smith, 1804.   BL

(iv)   Date below title (Aa) altered to *January 6th. 1804.* A large number of place-names etc. added eg, *Turwick, Rake, County Gate, Tillington, Maudlin, Tortington, Birchen Bri., and place* at *Woodmanscote* and at *Alborn, Adur Riv., Tinsley Green, Medway*

River, *Horsted Place*, *Glynd Bourn*, *Terrible Down*, *Cuckmere Riv.*, *Chilley Bridge*, *Twist River*, *Burwash Wheel*, *The Abbey* at *Robertsbridge*. House symbols added, eg five at *W.Ashing*. Single line to indicate road from *PETERSFIELD* to *South Harting* added; road behind *East Harting* erased. Mileages *1,2,3,4,5,6¼,8,9½,11,12¼* added on road from *ARUNDEL* to *Old Shoreham*. Under road direction *from Horsham to Dorking, d* replaced by *c, e* added near *Copthorn Common*, and *29 M^s* replaced by *19 M^s* in the road direction *East Grinstead to Croydon*.

Smith's new English atlas . . .
London, C. Smith, 1804.   CUL.RGS.W

(v)   The title, imprint and date (Aa) unchanged, but below is added *2nd. Edition Corrected to 1808*. In the *EXPLANATION* (Da), *Mail Roads* added above the symbol, and *Turnpike Roads* with new symbol added. *To Tenterden* erased and road completed from *Seacocks Heath* to *Newenden*. From *Rye to Cranbrook 19½ miles* erased and replaced by *from Rye to Tenterden 15 miles*. *to Westerham* now reads *From Lewes to Westerham 30 Miles*. *From Haslemere to Godalming 8½ M^s*. and *From Battle to Cranbrook 16¼ M^s*. added. Also added, *Brinkhurst* and *42* under *HASLEMERE*. Hill hachures lightened throughout.

Smith's new English atlas . . . 2nd edn.
London, C. Smith, 1808.   BL.CUL.WORTHING PL

(vi)   Note below title (Aa) altered to *3rd. Edition Corrected to 1818*. In the *EXPLANATION* (Da), *Turnpike Roads* altered to *Great Roads*. Road direction *to Guildford* added at *Alford, 8½ M^s*. altered to *7 M^s*. in road direction *from Haslemere* . . . Many place-names added, eg *Badworth Park*. *Corslea Hall, Chilgrove* and *Ho., Stoke Ho., Five Oaks, Flaxham Park, Friday S^t* under *Rusper, Pevensey Level*. Place-names altered, eg *Stoneland Park* now *Buckhurst Park, Plashet Park* now *Mote Park*. *Friday Street* erased. Many park symbols added, eg at *Corslea Hall*, at *Little Green*, near *M* of *Michelgrove*, three to the west of *Horsham Common*, two near *Balcomb*. Trees erased, eg in *Stanmer Park*. Distances added, *64½* under *Littlehampton, 59½* under *Worthing*, and *16* near *Mote Park* altered to *6*. New roads added, eg *Storrington* to *North Stoke* and *Yapton*, and others upgraded, eg *PETWORTH* to *Wisborough Green, South Harting* to *PETERSFIELD;* the single line road to the south of *PETERSFIELD* has been erased.

Smith's new English atlas . . .
London, C. Smith, 1818.   CUL

(vii)   Road directions added, *to Guildford* at *Rudgwick, to Dorking, to Croydon*. Roads upgraded, eg *Buck Green* to the north-east, *CUCKFIELD* northwards to *to Croydon*.

Smith's new English atlas . . .
London, C. Smith, 1820.   BL

117

(viii)   Below title (Aa), *3ʳᵈ Edition Corrected to 1818* erased and replaced by *Corrected to 1821. Arundel and Portsmouth Canal* marked and named, and extended by pecked line from *Birdham* to north of *Thorney Iᵈ*. To make space for canal, *Merston* re--engraved on two lines, *Elbridge* re-engraved to the south, *Lidsey* re-engraved to south of the town symbol.

> *Smith's new English atlas* . . .
> London, C. Smith, 1821.   CUL

(ix)   Date below title (Aa) altered to *1825*. The road from *Wadhurst* to *Rotherfield* upgraded to 'Great Road'. New 'Great Road' from *Beeding* to *Old Shoreham* along *Adur Riv.*. The two roads running south-east from *Beeding* downgraded to 'Cross Roads', and mileages *2,3* and *4* erased.

> Issued as loose sheets, sold separately, 1825.   (P)

(x)   Date below title (Aa) altered to *1827*.

> Issued as loose sheets, sold separately, 1827.   (BRIGHTON PL)

(xi)   Date below title (Aa) altered to *1829. Jones & Smith sculp. Pentonville* (Ca, under compass) erased. Additional roads upgraded to 'Great Roads', eg *Rudgwick* to *Five Oaks, HORSHAM* to *Handcross* direct (not via *Nuthurst*).

> *Smith's new English atlas* . . .
> London, C. Smith, 1827 (actually issued 1830).   P

(xii)   In title (Aa) *and the Parliamentary Divisions* added after *& Hundreds;* date below altered to *1832. Explanation continued.* added (Ee) with six items and note relating to *Borough of New Shoreham.* Twenty one symbols added on map to denote parliamentary information, ie two squares, four stars, four circles, two triangles and nine Maltese crosses. Boundaries of parliamentary boroughs marked by pecked lines. *Sᵗ Leonards, WEST DIVISION* and *EAST DIVISION* in black capitals, and *BOROUGH OF NEW SHOREHAM* added.

> *Smith's new English atlas* . . .
> London, C. Smith, 1832.   CUL

(xiii)   Date under title (Aa) altered to *1834*.

> *Smith's new English atlas* . . .
> London, C. Smith, 1834 (actually issued 1835).   RGS

(xiv)   Date under title (Aa) altered to *1838*. The parliamentary symbols on map and in *Explanation continued,* originally engraved in outline only, filled in.

Smith's new English atlas . . .
London, C. Smith, [1839].   BRISTOL PL

(xv)   Date under title altered to *1840*. Railways 1 and 2 marked; *London & Brighton Railway* named.

Smith's new English atlas. . .
London, C. Smith, [1841].   P.(ESRO)

(xvi)   Date under title altered to *1844* In *EXPLANATION* (Da) *Mail Roads* and symbol erased and replaced by *Rail Roads* with new symbol. Railway 3 and 4 added.

[Smith's new English atlas . . .]
London, C. Smith [1844].   (P)
A loose impression of this map seen by the compiler is not a folding map; it is on a guard and is clearly taken from a later edition of *Smith's new English atlas,* or from some other atlas or collection of maps.

60 A.   FIRST LITHOGRAPHIC TRANSFER

Size: 488 mm × 430 mm (13 mm)   1:255,000

Title, imprint and date (Aa) erased and replaced by *SUSSEX SHEWING ALL THE RAILWAYS & STATIONS and the parliamentary Divisions LONDON SMITH & SON, 172 STRAND. London.   Published by Smith & Son 172 Strand 1864.* added (Ce OS). *EXPLANATION* (Da) completly re-engraved, eg *ARUNDEL 60* in place of *HORSHAM 35½, Railways & Stations* and *Dº in Construction* now included. List of *POLLING PLACES* added (Ea, to right of *EXPLANATION*). *Explanation continued* (Ee) altered to *Explanation of Signs*; the last two items erased and replaced by *4 Members are returned . .* Maltese crosses and triangles omitted on map; note relating to *New Shoreham* retained. *BRIGHTHELMSTONE* and the four road distances erased and replaced by *BRIGHTON 54. Kemp Tⁿ.* added. *Hastings 64¼* erased and re-engraved in the sea. Road directions along north boundary simplified to *to . . .* followed by the destination. Railways 1 to 14, 16 to 23, and 25 marked by continuous lines; 24, 26 to 30 shown *in Construction;* stations marked and numbered, eg *STA 73* at *Sᵗ Leonards.* Clear traces of the original railways, shown by cross-hatched lines, remain visible, eg from *Keymer* to *Seaford* via *Lewes.*

Issued about 1864 as a folding map with printed title: *Smith & Son's new series of county maps . . . Sussex.*
London, Smith & Son.   (BOD).(CUL).(SCL)

State of the plate: Later than no. 60 (xvi). Most of the changes listed above were probably made on the plate.
Alterations on the transfer: The list of polling places and the *EXPLANATION* were probably transferred from type or from separately engraved plates. Railway lines added.

60 B. SECOND LITHOGRAPHIC TRANSFER

Size: 488 mm × 430 mm (13 mm)   1:255,000

Railway 26, which was opened to traffic in 1865, is now marked by a continuous black line.

Issued about 1865 as loose maps sold separately.   (BL)

State of the plate: as no. 60A.
Alterations on the transfer: As no. 60A and railway 26 added.

61   JOHN CARY   1801

Size: 513 mm × 457 mm (12 mm)   1:250,000

Based on Gardner, Yeakell and Gream no. 57. **See plates 24 and 25.**

This fine atlas had a deservedly long life; the plates continued in use for many years after being taken over by Cruchley about 1850.

William Smith (1769–1839),[1] see state (vi) below, has been called 'the father of English geology'. He trained as a civil engineer and mineral surveyor. He is best known for his pioneer work in identifying strata by means of their fossils, and for his geological maps. His *New geological atlas of England and Wales* commenced publication in 1819 with *Part I,* which contained Norfolk, Kent, Wiltshire and Sussex. Six parts, containing twenty-one county maps, had been published by 1824 when publication ceased. Cary's maps were used in all cases. An advertisement in *Cary's New Itinerary* shows that, in addition to publication in 'parts', the maps were sold separately at 5/6 each.[2] From about 1808 to 1812, Smith worked in Sussex, being employed by 'The Company of Proprietors of the River Ouse Navigation', formed under the Upper Ouse Navigation Act of 1790.[3]

George Frederick Cruchley (1796–1880), see lithographic transfers below, trained with the firm of Arrowsmith (see no. 109). He set up on his own in 1823 and issued some attractive maps, mainly of London. After taking over the Cary plates about 1850, his publications covered a more general field, and he cashed in on the demand for railway maps by up-dating older plates and altering the titles. In 1877 his whole stock was sold at auction, the Cary plates and many others being acquired by Gall and Inglis. Cruchley died at his home, 65 Grand Parade, Brighton in 1880.

1. Sheppard, 1920; Davies, 1952; and many others. There is an extensive literature on Smith and his works.
2. Davies, 1952. References to Cary's *New and Correct English atlas* should be read as Cary's *New English atlas.*
3. D.F. Gibb, and J.H. Farrant, 'The Upper Ouse navigation 1790–1808', in *Sussex Industrial History* no. 1 (1970–1) p. 29; Hadfield, C. 1969, p. 32.

Gall and Inglis were originally an Edinburgh firm. They continued the publication of some of Cary's plates into the present century.

As well as appearing in the atlases listed below, the map in its various editions were probably issued continuously from 1801 to about 1890 as folding maps sold separately.

Although no impression has been found, it is probable, from reference to Harvey[4] and Hodson,[5] that at least one edition of *Cruchley's railway and telegraphic county map of Sussex* was issued between the fourth and fifth lithographic transfers listed below. Loose intaglio printed maps have also been found with dates later than no. 61 (xi) below, eg Warwickshire 1840[6] and Hertfordshire 1843.[7] It is probable that intaglio maps of Sussex were also issued after 1834.

EDITIONS

(i) *A NEW MAP OF SUSSEX, DIVIDED INTO HUNDREDS, EXHIBITING Its Roads, Rivers, Parks &c. By JOHN CARY, Engraver 1801.* (Aa, in oval frame). *London. Published by J. Cary Engraver & Mapseller N⁰. 181 Strand Sepʳ. 28. 1801.* (Ce OS). *SCALE 15* miles = 98 mm (Ea, in hatched frame). Compass (Ea, above scale). *REFERENCE to the HUNDREDS* (Ce). Longitude 5' (1'); latitude 5' (1'). *THE ENGLISH CHANNEL* in outline lettering (Cd, 103 mm from bottom border).

Issued from 1801, as loose sheets, sold separately.

Cary's new English atlas; being a complete set of county maps, from actual surveys . . . on which are particularly delineated those roads which were measured by order of the Right Honourable the Postmaster-General, by John Cary . . .
London, J. Cary 1809 and 1811.   BL.CUL;CARDIFF PL

(ii) *Woodmans* (near *Farnhurst*) erased. *Wˢᵗ Marden* re-engraved on one line. *Up Marden* altered to *E. Marden*. Church symbol added above *ll* of *Tillington*. Road direction *To Guildford* added. Roads from *W. Grinsted* to *Finden*, and from *Loxwood* to *Hodfoldherns* (via *Wisborough Green*) upgraded. Road from *Southwater* to *Dialpost* (near *W.Grinsted*) downgraded.

Cary's new English atlas . . .
London, J. Cary, 1809.   RGS.A.BRIGHTON PL

(iii) *Woodmans* (below *Farnhurst*) added in larger lettering than in state (i).

---

4. Harvey, 1959, nos. 57D and E.
5. Hodson, 1974, nos. 60D to F.
6. Harvey, 1959, no. 57 (x).
7. Hodson, 1974, no. 60 (x).

Cary's new English atlas . . .
London, J. Cary [1811].   (BRIGHTON PL)

(iv)   Date in title (Aa) altered from *1801* to *1811.* Date in imprint (Ce OS) altered from *Sepr 28. 1801* to *Apr 28. 1811.* Road from south of *Hurst Green* to *Northiam* upgraded.

Cary's new English atlas . . .
London, J. Cary, 1811.   CUL.RGS.A

(v)   Date in title (Aa) altered to *1818.* Date in imprint (Ce OS) altered to *Jany. 1818.* Road from *CUCKFIELD* to north boundary added and named *The New Brighton R^d.* Road from *Pyecombe* to Hurstpierpoint added. Extensive shading to indicate marsh or low-lying land added at *RYE,* Pevensey and along river valleys.

Cary's new English atlas . . .
London, J. Cary, 1818.   CUL.RGS

(vi)   Additional title *GEOLOGICAL MAP OF SUSSEX, by W. SMITH, Mineral Surveyor.* (Ca OS). Date in title (Aa) altered to *1819.* Date in imprint (Ce OS) altered to *Jany 1819.* Two notes of two and a half lines each relating to geological data have been added commencing . . . *Note. The numbers* . . . (Be OS), and *Smith's Geological Section* . . . (De OS). Pecked lines have been added to the map to mark the limits of six geological strata and the colour key is indicated by six rectangles, 14 mm × 4 mm, with legends commencing as follows: *2, 3 and 4. Brick Earth and Sand* . . . (Bd), *5. Chalk* . . . (Ac, across border), *6. and 7. Green Sand and Golt Brick Earth* . . .(Ac, across border), *8 and 10. Sand* . . . (Ac, across border), *11. Oaktree Clay* . . . (Bb), and *13. Sand and Sandstone* . . . (Cb, near Cowden). The colouring is by hand. The left border has been erased from latitude 50°55' to 50°59' and from 51°2'N to 51°3'N. Road direction *to Croydon from E. Grinstead 19m. London R^d.* erased. *HAMPSHIRE* erased and replaced by *HANTS.* All these alterations are required to make space for the geological legends.

New geological atlas of England and Wales . . . Part I, by William Smith.
London, . . . 1819.   (P)[8]
In blue wrappers.

Issued from 1819 as loose sheets, sold separately.   (P)
In one impression examined (CUL) the additional title (Ca OS) is omitted; but it was not erased on the plate. It seems probable that it was 'blanked out' during printing, as in edition (vii) below.[9]

8.   Davies, 1952, p. 389. In possession of Mr. and Mrs. V.A. Eyles. There is a bound set of these maps without title-page in the library of the Royal Geological Society. Twenty-one counties are represented; eight are dated 1819, four 1820, five 1821 and four 1824.
9.   Davies, 1952, p. 391, first drew attention to this unusual technique.

(vii)   Date in title (Aa) altered to *1821*. Date in imprint (Ce OS) altered to *Jany. 1821*.

Cary's new English atlas . . .
London, J. Cary, 1818 (re-issued 1821).   RGS.(BRIGHTON PL); RGS
The impression at BRIGHTON PL has the additional title (Ca OS). It is omitted in the RGS atlas
(1818), but it was not erased from the plate. Embossed, but uninked, traces remain visible. There is
also a rough plate-mark surrounding the area. It seems probable that a strip of paper was inserted in
the press to blank out the additonal title. The same process can be detected on other maps in the atlas,
eg Wiltshire.

(viii)   Date in title (Aa) altered to *1824*. Imprint (Ce OS) altered to *London Published
by J. Cary Engraver & Mapseller N°. 86 S^t.James's Str. April 1st. 1824*. In the note (De
OS) the address is altered from N°. 181 Strand, London to *N°. 86 S^t. James's Str.*
Embossed traces of the additional title (Ca OS) remain visible.

Cary's new English atlas . . .
London, J. Cary, 1824.   WSRO

Sold as a loose map in slip-case with printed title: *Cary's new map of the county of
Sussex. . .*
London, J. & G. Cary, [1824].   (ESCL)

(ix)   Date in title (Aa) altered to *1828*. Date in imprint (Ce OS) altered to *April 1st.
1828*. Uninked traces of additional title (Ca OS).

Cary's new English atlas. . .
London, J. Cary, 1828.   BL

(x)   Date in title (Aa) altered to *1831*. Date in imprint (Ce OS) altered to *April 1st.
1831*. Portsmouth/Arun canal marked. Road from *Northiam* to *Ewhurst* down-graded.
A number of roads up-graded, eg *PETERSFIELD* to *MIDHURST, Egdean* to
STEYNING (via *Pulborough*), and from *RYE* both north and east to the county
boundary.

Issued as a folding map in slip-case with printed title: *Cary's new map of Sussex.*
London, G. & J. Cary, 1831.   (BRIGHTON PL)

(xi)   *EXPLANATION* added (Ca) comprising the following items of parliamentary
information, – *Chief Places of County Election* marked by Maltese cross with arrow and
added on map at *CHICHESTER* and *LEWES; Polling Places* marked by Maltese cross
added on map at a number of places; eg at *PETWORTH; Boroughs returning Two
Members* marked by two stars, eg *BRIGHTHELMSTON; Boroughs returning One
Member* marked by one star, eg *RYE; Boundaries of Boroughs; Divisions of Counties.*
Uninked traces of addtional title (Ca OS).

Cary's new English atlas . . .
London, J. Cary, 1834.   BL

61 A. FIRST LITHOGRAPHIC TRANSFER

Size: 520 mm × 458 mm (12 mm)   1:250,000

Title (Aa) erased and replaced by *CRUCHLEY'S RAILWAY MAP OF SUSSEX, showing all the RAILWAYS & NAMES OF STATIONS, ALSO THE TELE-GRAPHIC LINES & STATIONS, Improved from the ORDNANCE SURVEYS. THIS MAP MAY BE HAD GEOLOGICALLY COLOURED. PRICE 3/6 IN SHEET. LONDON. PUBLISHED BY G.F. CRUCHLEY, MAP SELLER & GLOBE MAKER, 81, FLEET STREET.* (Aa). *January 1st. 1855* added (Ae OS). Imprint (Ce OS) and geological notes (Be OS and De OS) erased. In *EXPLANATION* (Ca) the last two items are now each on one line; *RAILWAYS & NAMES OF STATIONS* and *TELEGRAPH LINES & STATIONS* added with example which includes *3 BRIDGES STA., TUNNEL* and *HAYWARD HEA STA..* The geological legends commencing *5. Chalk* . . . and *6. and 7. Green Sand* . . . (Ac, across border) erased and border redrawn. *Rd. from Salisbury Romsey &c, Emsworth, Ratford, Tensley Gr., The New Brighton Rd, To Reygate from Crawley 9 M. – the London Rd, To London by Tunbridge Seven Oaks Bromley &c., Tunbridge Wells* and mileage *1* on the road to *Groombridge, Compton Pl.* and *63, Southwick, Hove or Hooe, Filcham, Swines Hill* and *11, 12,* and *59, BRIGHTHELMSTON* and *Worthing* have all been erased, mainly to allow space for the addition of railways. *BRIGHTON, Worthing* and *Southwick* are now engraved in the sea. *Tonbridge Wells* and a triangle of new roads added. Fine transverse lines engraved across outer borders at 50°44½'N, 51°7'N, 45'W, 26'W, 6'W, 13½'E and 33'E. These lines, and the additional lines added on no.61G, are at approximately equal intervals from the centre of the map, and were probably concerned with the registration of the information added to or relocated on the transfers. Railways 1 to 14, 16, A, C, E and F added. Stations named, eg *ST LEONARDS STA., HOVE STA.*

Sold as a folding map with printed cover: *Cruchley's railway map of the county of Sussex . . .*
London, G.F. Cruchley, [1855].   (BOD)

Sold as a folding map with printed cover: *Cruchley's modern railway and telegraphic county map.*
London, G.F. Cruchley, [1855].   (CUL)

State of the plate: Later than no. 61(xi). All the alterations listed above except title (Aa), imprint (Ce OS), and date (Ae OS) have been made on the plate.
Alterations on the transfer: Title and imprint erased, and new title and imprint added from separate engraved plates. Date added.

61 B. SECOND LITHOGRAPHIC TRANSFER

Size: 520 mm × 458 mm (12 mm)   1:250,000

In the title (Aa) *AND TELEGRAPHIC* added after *RAILWAY*. The date (Ae OS) altered *1856*. *Hove* and *Kempt^n.* added. *Sta.* added at *Southwick. JUN* added to *S^T. LEONARDS. STA.* to read S^T. LEONARDS JUN STA.; S^T. LEONARDS added east of *S^t. Leonards.* **See plate 24.**

> Sold as a folding map with printed cover: *Cruchley's modern railway and telegraphic county map.*
> London, G.F. Cruchley, [1856].   (BL)

State of the plate: Later than no. 61A. Place-names and stations added.
Alterations on the transfer: Title, imprint (Aa) and date (Ae OS) added.

61 C   THIRD LITHOGRAPHIC TRANSFER

Size: 514 mm × 460 mm (12 mm)   1:250,000

Compass (Ea) erased. Date (Ae OS) omitted. Scale moved (from Ea to Ca). *REFERENCE to the HUNDREDS* moved (from Ce to Ae). *EXPLANATION* moved (from Ca to Ea); part of *TUNNEL* and *EA* in *HAYWARD HEA* omitted. *THE ENGLISH CHANNEL* erased and *ENGLISH CHANNEL* in outline capitals added lower (42 mm from bottom border) and to the right. Geological legend commencing *2.3 and 4 Brick Earth . . .* moved (from Bd to Cd), but the pecked line to *Selsea Bill* remains. Legend commencing *5. Chalk . . .* erased. Of the legend commencing *6. and 7. Green Sand . . .* only the rectangle and *. . .ck Earth, at . . .* remain unerased. Railway 17 added; 18 and 20 added as projected lines, but in some impressions 18 has been 'blacked in' by hand and appears to be 'in use'. Plate number *35* (Ea OS) does not appear on the impression of the map in the British Library atlas; but it has been found on loose maps, and, since other maps in that atlas have plate numbers, it may have been cut off in binding.

> *Cruchley's railway and telegraphic county atlas of England and Wales . . .*
> London, G.F. Cruchley, [1858].   BL

> Sold about 1858 as a folding map with printed cover: *Cruchley's railway and telegraphic county map of Sussex . . .*
> London, G.F. Cruchley.   (BOD)

State of the plate: Compass and *THE ENGLISH CHANNEL* erased. Railways added.
Alterations on the transfer: Title, imprint and *ENGLISH CHANNEL* added. Scale, *REFERENCE to the HUNDREDS* and geological legends moved, but appear to be as originally engraved, perhaps by making a second transfer to the stone from the relevant parts of the plate.

61 D.   FOURTH LITHOGRAPHIC TRANSFER

Size: 521 mm × 460 mm (12 mm)   1:250,000

In *EXPLANATION* (Ea), *TUNNEL* and *HAYWARD HEA* appear in full. *To Guildford 13M. – the London R^d.* erased. *Clifton Ville* (near *BRIGHTON*) added. *or Hollington* (at *Bognor*) erased. The geological legend commencing *5. Chalk . . .* remains wholly erased; in the legend commencing *6. and 7. Green Sand . . .* all except the rectangle and *. . . Earth, at . . .* has been erased; in the legend commencing *8 and 10 Sand . . ., 8 and 10.* erased. Railways 1 to 22 now shown as in use; 23 to 30 as projected. **See plate 25.**

> Issued about 1863 as a folding map with printed cover: *Cruchley's railway and telegraphic county map of Sussex.*
> London, G.F. Cruchley.   (BL)

State of the plate: Later than no. 61C. Place-name etc. changes as above. Railways added. Plate number added, probably on no. 61C.
Alterations on the transfer: As for no. 61C.

61 E.   FIFTH LITHOGRAPHIC TRANSFER

Size: 521 mm × 459 mm (12 mm)   1:246,000

Title now reads *CRUCHLEY'S RAILWAY AND STATION MAP OF SUSSEX, showing all the RAILWAYS & NAMES OF STATIONS, ALSO THE TURNPIKE ROADS, GENTLEMENS SEATS &c. &c. Improved from . . .* (then as no. 61A). Scale moved (to Ee) and hatched frame erased. *EXPLANATION* moved (to Da) and *RAILWAYS IN PROGRESS* added. Plate number *35* (Ea OS, as 61C). *REFERENCE to the HUNDREDS* moved (to Ce). *ENGLISH CHANNEL* (De) erased; *ENGLISH CHANNEL* in plain black capitals added (Cd, 97 mm from bottom border). *To Dorking from Horsham 13M – the London R^d.* erased. *WEST PIER* and *EAST PIER* added at *BRIGHTON.* Maltese crosses added at *Worthing, MIDHURST, BRIGHTON, HAILSHAM, HASTINGS* and *RYE.* Geological legends as originally engraved. The bottom border raised by 1'; it now lies at 50°26'30'', but it has not been re-engraved. Railways 23 to 30 now shown as in use; 31 added as in use; 29 and 30 named; 34, 35 and *MIDHURST* to *HASLEMERE, Pulborough* to *STEYNING, Naldry* to *Uckfield, West Grinstead* to *Haywards Heath,* and *HAILSHAM* to *Bexhill* marked by double lines with pecked marks between them; *Uckfield* to *HAILSHAM* by plain double lines.

> Issued about 1875 as a folding map with printed title on cover: *Cruchley's railway and telegraphic county map of Sussex.*
> London, G.F. Cruchley.   (BL)

State of the plate: Later than no. 61D. Place-names, *ENGLISH CHANNEL,* road direction, Maltese crosses and railways added, including plain double lines for all projected routes.
Alterations on the transfer: Scale, *EXPLANATION* and bottom border added in new positions. Heavy pecked marks added to some projected railways.

61 F. SIXTH LITHOGRAPHIC TRANSFER

Size: 525 mm × 458 mm (12 mm)   1:246,000

Title as no. 61E, but raised to allow space for scale and now only 10 mm from top border. *SCALE* (Ab, below title). Plate number *35* (Ea OS). *EXPLANATION* (Ea). *REFERENCE to the HUNDREDS* omitted. Geological legends as originally engraved. *Groom Bridge* re-engraved *Groombridge* on one line. Railways 1 to 14, 16 to 31, 39 and 40 marked by continuous black lines; 34, 35, *Pulborough* to *STEYNING, Naldry* to *Uckfield, Uckfield* to *HAILSHAM* by pecked double lines; W^st *GRINSTEAD STA* to *HAYWARD HEATH STA* and part of railway 42 by plain double lines; *MIDHURST* to HASLEMERE by heavy pecked line; *HAILSHAM* to *Bexhill* omitted.

> Issued about 1876 as a folding map with printed title on cover; *Cruchley's railway and station map of the county of Sussex.*
> London, G.F. Cruchley.   (ESCL)

State of the plate: Later than no. 61E. *Groombridge* re-engraved. Railways 39, 40 and part of 42 added; double lines between *MIDHURST* and *HASLEMERE* erased.
Alterations on the transfer: Title, scale, *EXPLANATION* and bottom border added. Pecked marks added to some railway lines. *REFERENCE to the HUNDREDS* erased.

61 G. SEVENTH LITHOGRAPHIC TRANSFER

Size 524 mm × 456 mm (12 mm)   1:246,000

EDITIONS

(i) New title *CRUCHLEY'S COUNTY MAP OF SUSSEX Showing all the RAIL-WAYS & NAMES OF STATIONS, ALSO THE VILLAGES, TURNPIKE ROADS, GENTLEMENS SEATS &c. &c. Improved from the ORDNANCE SURVEYS LONDON: PUBLISHED BY GALL & INGLIS, 25 PATERNOSTER SQUARE. EDINBURGH: 6 GEORGE STREET.* (Ea). Hatched frame added to *SCALE* (Ee). Plate number *35* (Ea OS), *REFERENCE to the HUNDREDS* (Ce), and *ENGLISH CHANNEL* (Cd) all as no. 61F. *EXPLANATION* moved (from Ea to Aa). *Goreing* re-engraved *Goring. Guildford* with town symbol, *West Worthing, WORTHING* and houses, *Pier,* and *Signal Ho.* added. *Worthing* altered to *East Worthing.* Geological legends commencing *2.3. and 4 . . ., 11 . . .,* and *13 . . .* as originally engraved; legends commencing *5* . . ., and *6. and 7.* . . moved (to Ab) and border completed, but those parts of the original engraving, which fell inside the border, remain unerased; *8. and 10.* added above the legend. Additional fine transverse lines added across outer border at 50°39'N, 50°56'N, 51°12'N, 49'W, 32'W, 14½'W, 2½'E, 20½'E and 36½'E. Railway 32 added; 1 to 14, 16 to 32, 39 and 40 now marked by continuous black lines; 34, 35 and line from *Naldry* to *Uckfield* by pecked double lines; *Pulborough* to *STEYNING*, *W^st GRINSTEAD* to *HAYWARD HEA STA, Uckfield* to *HAILSHAM* and part of 42 by plain double lines.

> *Cruchley's railway and telegraphic county atlas of England and Wales.*
> London, G.F. Cruchley, [1878]. LEEDS PL

(ii)   At end of title (Ea) *6 GEORGE STREET* erased and replaced by *BERNARD TERRACE*.[10] Additional plate number *20* added (Ee OS).

> Issued about 1879 as a folding map with printed label: *Cruchley's railway and station map of the county of Sussex.*
> Edinburgh and London, Gall and Inglis. (WSRO)

State of the plate: Later than no.61F. Place-name alterations as above. Railway 32 added.
Alterations on the transfer: Title, scale, *EXPLANATION* and bottom border added. Pecked marks added on two railways. Geological legends moved. *20* added (Ee OS) on edition (ii).

61 H.   EIGHTH LITHOGRAPHIC TRANSFER

Size: 525 mm × 463 mm (12 mm) 1:246,000

WEST DIVISION and *EAST DIVISION* added. Geological legends commencing *2, 3 and 4* . . ., *11* . . . and *13* . . . as originally engraved; *5* . . . and *6. and 7.* . . . erased; *8 and 10.* (but not the legend itself) erased; left border completed as permitted by these erasures. *Kingston by Sea* erased. ENGLISH CHANNEL now 105 mm from bottom border, which has reverted to its original position at 50°25'30''. Railways 15, 33 and 34 added; 40 erased; other lines shown on no. 61F as projected are marked by plain double lines. Plate number *20* (Ee OS) omitted.

> Issued about 1880 as a folding map with printed title on cover: *Cruchley's railway and station map of the county of Sussex.*
> Edinburgh and London, Gall and Inglis. (P)

10.   Gall and Inglis moved to 20 Bernard Terrace in 1878 (see Hannas, 1972).

State of the plate: Later than no. 61G. *Kingston by Sea* erased. Railways added and erased.
Alterations on the transfer: Title, scale and *EXPLANATION* added. Divisions added.

61 I. NINTH LITHOGRAPHIC TRANSFER

Size: 523 mm × 465 mm (12 mm)   1:246,000

New title, *HARRISON'S BICYCLE ROAD MAP OF SUSSEX Showing all the RAILWAYS & NAMES OF STATIONS, ALSO THE VILLAGES, TURNPIKE ROADS, GENTLEMANS SEATS &c. &c. Improved from the ORDNANCE SURVEYS E. HARRISON & Co. THE. WEST. END. ATHLETIC. OUTFITTERS 259 OXFORD STREET, LONDON.* (Ea). No plate number. Geological legends as originally engraved, except *5. Chalk* . . . erased; *6. and 7. Green Sand* . . . erased except for part of rectangle and *at* . . .; *8 and 10.* (but not the legend itself) erased. Advertisements appear outside the border and on the back of the map. Railways 35 to 38 added (1 to 39 now shown as in use); lines in progress, except 35, as on no.61H.

Harrison's "Finger Post" bicycle road guide and county map of Sussex . . .
London, E. Harrison and Co., [1883].   BL
This title appears on the cover. There is an additional title-page, *The "Finger Post" bicycle road guide, . . . accompanied with road map* . . . The date is taken from the British Museum acceptance stamp.

State of the plate: Later than no.61H. Railways added.
Alterations on the transfer: Title, scale and *EXPLANATION* added. Plate number erased. Geological legends amended. Advertisements added.

61 J. TENTH LITHOGRAPHIC TRANSFER

Size: 526 mm × 465 mm (12 mm)   1:246,000

New title *DEACON'S MAP of SUSSEX Improved from the ORDNANCE SURVEYS. (Prepared expressly for this work).* (Ea). *C.W. DEACON & Cº., CHARING CROSS CHAMBERS, LONDON, W.C.* added. *SCALE 15* = 99 mm (Ee, in hatched frame). Plate number *35* (Ea OS). *EXPLANATION* (Aa). *REFERENCE to the HUNDREDS* (Ce). Geological legends as originally engraved, except *6. and 7.* . . and *5* . . . moved (to Ab); *8 and 10.* erased. Advertisements on back of map.

Deacon's court guide, gazetteer and county blue book: . . . *with a coloured map of the county. First edition.*
London, C.W. Deacon and Co., [1881].   GL
The Sussex court guide . . ., *1894.* by the same publisher contained no. 147.

State of the plate: As no. 61I.

Alterations on the transfer: Title, scale and *EXPLANATION* added. Geological legends amended. Divisions added.

61 K. ELEVENTH LITHOGRAPHIC TRANSFER

Size: 525 mm × 464 mm (12 mm)   1:246,000

EDITIONS

(i)   New title *CRUCHLEY'S ROAD AND RAILWAY MAP OF THE COUNTY OF SUSSEX Showing all the RAILWAYS AND NAMES OF STATIONS ALSO THE TURNPIKE ROADS, VILLAGES, GENTLEMENS SEATS &c. &c. Improved from the ORDNANCE SURVEYS LONDON: PUBLISHED BY GALL & INGLIS, 25, PATERNOSTER SQUARE. EDINBURGH: BERNARD TERRACE.* (Ea). *SCALE (Ee).* Plate number *35* (Ea OS). *EXPLANATION* (Aa). *REFERENCE to the HUNDREDS* (Ce). Geological legends *5 . . ., 6. and 7 . . .,* and *8 and 10 . . .* erased; *2, 3 and 4 . . ., 11 . . .* and *13 . . .* as originally engraved. *WEST DIVISION* and *EAST DIVISION* omitted. The six parliamentary divisions marked by chain dot lines (alternate dots and dashes) and named on a map, eg *N.W. OR HORSHAM.* Railway 41 and *STA* at *DEVILS DYKE* added. Printers mark *F7* (Ee OS).

> Issued about 1887 as a folding map with printed title: *Cruchley's new map of Sussex . . . based on the Ordnance Survey.*
> Edinburgh and London, Gall and Inglis.   (RGS)

(ii)   Printers mark (Ee OS) altered to *G7ˣ*.

> *Cruchley's railway and telegraphic county atlas of England and Wales . . .*
> London, G.F. Cruchley, (actually issued by Gall and Inglis in about 1887).   P.

State of the plate: Later than no. 61J. Railway 41 added.
Alterations on the transfer: Title, scale and *EXPLANATION* added. Parliamentary divisions added and named. Geological legends erased. Printer's marks added.

130

62 JOHN LUFFMAN

1803

Size: a circle of 43 mm diameter (9 mm)   1:3,200,000

The detail is insufficient for the derivation of this map to be determined. **See plate 27 (ii).**

     Luffman was a versatile character. He described himself as a geographer, justified primarily by his map of Antiqua,[1] which he visited in 1786, and about which his letters were published in 1789. He also published a certain number of works from various London addresses, but seems to have worked mostly as an engraver; not only for his own publications, but also for other publishers. The atlas mentioned below was intended for children.

     The Sussex map is printed at the top of the page; below it are notes regarding the county, which are printed from type. The reference to parliamentary representation omits the Cinque ports (see appendix X.vi).

EDITIONS

(i)   *SUSSEX* (Ca, in border). *Sold by Luffman, 28, Little Bell Alley, Coleman Street, London.* (Ce OS). *Scale of 20 miles =* 10 mm (Ce, in border). Compass (Ce). Plate number *35* (Ca OS, 10 mm above top border). *Sends 20 Members to Parl^{mt}.* (Ac, in border). Distances from London (Ec, in border).

A new pocket atlas and geography of England and Wales, illustrated with fifty-five copper plates . . . By John Luffman, Geog^r.
London, J. Luffman, 1803.   BL

(ii)   Plate number *35* (Ca OS) re-engraved immediately above outer edge of border. **See plate 27(ii).**

A new pocket atlas. . .
London, J. Luffman, 1803.   RGS

A new pocket atlas . . .
London, Lackington, Allen and Co., 1806.   BL.CUL

1. R.V. Tooley, *The printed maps of Antiqua, 1689–1899,* nos. 45 to 49 and 60. *MCS* no. 55 (1969).

63   LAURIE AND WHITTLE   1803

Size: a circle of 46 mm diameter (0.3 mm)   1:3,100,000

The detail is insufficient for the derivation of this map to be determined. **See plate 28 (i).**

The British Library catalogue suggests that this is a road map produced to illustrate a work in sextodecimo. It is printed on thin paper; the page measures 97 mm × 120 mm and the plate mark 65 mm × 77 mm.

EDITION

A NEW MAP of SUSSEX Publish'd Mar. 21, 1803. by LAURIE & WHITTLE. 53, Fleet Street. London. (Ce OS). Compass (Ce). The map contains errors, eg *Bangor* (Bognor) and *Newfield* (probably Ninfield); the Surrey/Kent border is inaccurately delineated. **See plate 28(i).**

Found only as loose sheets.   (BL)

64   R. BUTTERS   circa **1803**

Size: 87 mm × 118 mm (1 mm)   1:1,150,000

Based on Cary no. 51.

The only map of Sussex with north to the right; title and place-names are designed to be read from the 'east'. In this atlas, the map of *England and Wales* has south to the top; title and place-names are designed to be read from the north.

EDITION

SUSSEX (Ce OS) *Scale of Miles 10* = 13 mm (Ea). Compass (De).

An atlas of England . . .
London, R. Butters [1803].   BL.CUL

The picture of England illustrated with correct colour'd maps of the several counties . . . by William Green, A.B. . . ., vol 2.
London, J. Hatchard, 1804.   BL.RGS.W

65 JOHN CARY

1806

Size: 90 mm × 122 mm (1 mm)

1:1,140,000

A re-engraved version of Cary no. 51. **See plate 21.**

Earlier editions of *Cary's travellers companion* contain no. 51; later editions contained no. 82. This version, compared with no. 51, has a number of place-names added, eg *Newhaven*. It is most easily distinguished from no. 82 by alterations in the table of distances, *Chichester 63* in this version is amended to *Chichester 62* in the later version.

EDITIONS

(i)   *SUSSEX* (Ca, in border which has been expanded to 9 mm to accommodate the title). *London Published July 1806 by J. Cary, Engraver No. 181 Strand.* (Ce OS). *By J. Cary* (Aa OS) . . . *Engraver.* (Ea OS). *Scale of Miles 10 =* 13 mm (Ae). Compass (Ca OS), north is to the left. Below map, and inside bottom border, is a list of towns with distances from London.

> *Cary's traveller's companion, or, a delineation of the turnpike roads of England and Wales . . .*
> London, John Cary, 1806.

BL.CUL.BOD

(ii)   Date in imprint (Ce OS) altered to . . . *May 1. 1810* . . . **see plate 21.**

> *Carry's traveller's companion . . .*
> London, John Cary, 1810.

BL.BOD.GL

(iii)   Date in imprint (Ce OS) altered to . . . *May 1. 1812* . . .

> *Cary's traveller's companion . . .*
> London, John Cary, 1812.

BOD.CUL.W

(iv)   Date in imprint (Ce OS) altered to . . . *May 1. 1814.* . .

> *Cary's traveller's companion . . .*
> London, John Cary, 1814.

BL.CUL.RGS

(v)   Date in imprint (Ce OS) altered to . . . *Jan 1. 1817* . . . Road added from *Crawley* direct to *Patcham,* and another running northwards from *Cuckfield.*

> *Cary's traveller's companion . . .*
> London, John Cary, 1817.

BL.CUL.GL.

(vi)   Date in imprint (Ce OS) altered to . . . *Jan 1. 1819* . . .

Cary's traveller's companion . . .
London, John Cary, 1819.

CUL

(vii) Date in imprint (Ce OS) altered to . . . *Jan 1. 1821* . . .

Cary's traveller's companion . . .
London, John Cary, 1821.

BL.A

66 G. COLE

1808

Size: 218 mm × 162 mm (7 mm)

1:572,000

Based on Jones and Smith no. 60.

No biographical information about G. Cole has been found, in spite of the fact that he drew nearly all the county maps and most of the town plans in this series, and that his work was copied by others (see nos. 70, 73, and 106).

John Roper also engraved Wilkinson's *Atlas classica*.

Baldwin, Cradock and Joy were succeeded by Charles Cradock and Co. and also published maps for the Society for the Diffusion of Useful Knowledge. They went out of business in 1857, following a fire in Paternoster Row. At this period fires seem to have been a recurring hazard in the book trade.

Henry George Collins (see lithographic transfer below; also no. 119) ceased trading in 1858, when his stock was auctioned off, probably as a result of financial failure.

Joseph Nightingale (1775–1824), the author, was born at Chowbent in Lancashire. He came to London in 1805, and worked on a number of publications, including *The beauties of England and Wales* and *English topography*. He was an active Methodist. In 1809 he was awarded £200 in a libel suit against John Stockdale, see no. 50 (ii).

Thomas Dugdale, the author of *Curiosities of Great Britain,* is not mentioned in any of the reference works consulted.

The first John Tallis was a Birmingham book-seller, who moved to London in 1820. His son, also John (1818–76), is said[1] to have joined him by 1836, and it was due to him that they went into publishing. The imprint 'Tallis and Co.' appeared in 1835, see (iii) below, which suggests that the son was active in the business before 1836. By about 1843 the imprint is 'John Tallis', indicating that the father had died or retired by that date. Tallis was a successful publisher until his bankruptcy in 1861, his chief claim to fame being his *London street views*. According to Boase[2] he was in partnership with Frederick Tallis from 1842 to 1849, see no 114(ii) and (iii). John Tallis went back into business after his bankruptcy, but he never again achieved the same degree of success.

1. *CJ* December 1977 p. 136.
2. Boase, 1965.

The family relationship between John Tallis, Frederick Tallis and L. Tallis, see no. 114 (i), (iv) and (v), has not been established.

Despite the note on this and other maps in the same series, the full edition of *The beauties of England and Wales* by J. Britton, E.W. Brayley and others, published in eighteen volumes between 1801 and 1815 does not normally contain maps. The Sussex section is volume 14 published in 1813. The maps, together with town plans, were published in parts and sold as a separate series between 1804 and 1810. A prospectus of 1804 states that although the maps were designed to correspond in size and could be bound with *The beauties of England and Wales*, it was recommended that the maps be bound to form a separate quarto atlas.

EDITIONS

(i) *SUSSEX* (Ca, in border). *London; Published for the Proprietors by Vernor, Hood & Sharpe, Poultry. Mar. 1ˢᵗ. 1808.* (Ce OS). *Engraved by J. Roper, from a Drawing by G. Cole.* (Ae OS). *to accompany the Beauties of England and Wales.* (Ee OS). *SCALE – 10 Miles = 28mm* (Ce). *RAPES* (Aa). *EXPLANATION* (Ea). Longitude 5'; latitude 5'.

The British atlas; comprising a complete series of county maps . . . intended to illustrate and accompany The beauties of England and Wales: published under the direction and superintendence of the authors of that work. Part 19.
London, 'Printed for the Proprietors', 1808.   P

The British atlas; comprising a complete set of county maps, of England and Wales . . .
London, Vernor, Hood and Sharpe and nine other publishers, 1810.
                                                        BL.CUL.BRIGHTON PL

English topography: or a series of historical and statistical descriptions of the several counties of England and Wales . . .
London, Baldwin, Cradock and Joy, 1816.   BL.CUL

(ii) The imprint (Ce OS), signature (Ae OS), and inscription (Ee OS) erased. Plate number *38* added (Ea OS).

English topography . . .
London, Baldwin, Cradock and Joy. 1816.   LEEDS PL.BRL

English topography: or, geographical, historical, and statistical description of the several counties of England and Wales . . . By the Rev. J. Nightingale . . .
London, James Goodwin and Thomas MᶜLean, [1827].   BL.RGS

(iii) *Polling Places*, marked by Maltese crosses, and *Places of Election, Chichester and Lewis*, added to *EXPLANATION* (Ea). Nine Maltese crosses added on map. One asterisk erased at *HORSHAM, MIDHURST, ARUNDEL* and at *RYE;* two added at *BRIGHTHELMSTONE.* Hampshire/Surrey boundary erased. At *BRIGHTHELM-*

STONE, by Steyning 60¾M. erased and replaced by 52. *Great Bognor* erased and replaced by *GR^T. BOGNOR*. Tree symbols in forests and parks erased. *CHICHESTER* to *GR^T. BOGNOR* main road added; *Itchingfield* to *Rudgwick* road upgraded.

> *Curiosities in Great Britain. England & Wales delineated historical, entertaining & commercial . . by Thomas Dugdale, antiquarian; assisted by William Burnett, civil engineer.* [vol. 3].
> London, Tallis and Co., 1835.
>
> P

> *Curiosities of Great Britain. England and Wales delineated historical, entertaining & commercial . . . by Thomas Dugdale, antiquarian. Assisted by William Burnett.* [Vol 2].
> [London, Tallis and Co., 1838].
>
> CUL.BRL
> The publisher's name is taken from the title-page of volume 1, which is dated 1835.

(iv) *BRIGHTHELMSTONE* altered to *BRIGHTON*. St Leonards and *Kemp Town* added. Two asterisks erased at *STEYNING, WINCHELSEA, SEAFORD* and at *HASLEMERE*. Road running north from St Leonards re-routed and upgraded; new roads added, eg *HASTINGS* to *Guestling, CUCKFIELD* to north border. *to Westerham 12M^s.* added west of *Cowden. Arun Portsmouth Can.* marked and named. Railways 1, 2 and 5 (as far as *LEWES*) and *London & Brighton Railway* added.

> *Curiosities of Great Britain . .*
> London, John Tallis, [1843].
>
> BL.BOD.CUL
> Editions of this work were issued in weekly parts, and are found bound in a variety of ways. The Sussex map usually appears in volumes 3 or 4, but in one set (BOD) it is in volume I and in another set from which the Sussex map is missing (BOD) it would have been in volume 6. In some editions the publisher's name is taken from the title-page of volume 1, and in one edition (BOD) the name is *L. Tallis*. It is probable that at least some of the volumes in which Sussex appears were issued later than 1843; the Brighton to Lewes railway was authorised in 1844. Other editions of this work contain no. 114.

66 A. FIRST LITHOGRAPHIC TRANSFER

Size: 220 mm × 162 mm (7 mm)   1:572,000

SUSSEX (Ca) re-engraved in solid black capitals in place of outline lettering; hatched backround erased; four asterisks added in border to right of title panel. *London. Pub. by Henry Collins, Paternoster Row.* added (Ce OS). Plate number (Ae OS) erased. In *EXPLANATION* (Ae), references to *Polling Places* and *Places of Election* erased; reference to *Railways* added. 5¾M erased after *to Tunbridge*. Railways 1 to 14 are now shown, and directions have been added, eg *to Ashford*.

> Issued about 1854 in a county atlas, probably by H.G. Collins. The only copy found lacks a title page.
>
> CUL

State of the plate: Later than no. 66(iv). Title re-engraved. Plate number and 5¾M

erased. *EXPLANATION* amended. Railways and directions added.
Alterations on the transfer: Imprint added.

66 B. SECOND LITHOGRAPHIC TRANSFER

Size: 220 mm × 165 mm (7 mm)   1:572,000

Imprint (Ce OS) omitted. Plate number *37* added (Ea OS). Railway 16 added.

Collins' railway & pedestrian atlas of England containing forty-three maps . . .
London, Darton and Co., [1858].   BL.CUL

State of the plate: Later than no. 66A. Railway probably added.
Alterations on the transfer: Plate number probably added.

67 H. COOPER   1808

Size: 176 mm × 103 mm (1 mm)   1:728,000

Probably based on Jones and Smith no. 60, with some reference to Coltman no. 59.

The signature of H. Cooper, of Chancery Lane, appears as the engraver of a number of maps at about this period. It seems, however, that this map was both drawn and engraved by him.

Sir Richard Phillips (1767–1840), the publisher, was born in London of a Leicestershire family. His original name was Philip Richards.[1] He worked first as a school-master and subsequently as a hosier. In 1790 he set up as a book-seller in Leicester and founded the *Leicester Herald* in 1792. Three years later he was gaoled for selling Paine's *Rights of man*. He then moved to London, and started the *Monthly magazine* in 1796, with encouragement from Dr. Priestley. The editor was Dr. John Aikin (see no. 53), with whom Phillips quarrelled in 1808. He continued as a publisher in Bridge Street. He was a sheriff of the City of London in 1807 and was knighted in 1808. In 1823 he retired to Brighton where he died. *DNB* does not mention *A topographical dictionary* among his publications, and it gives his address as Little Bridge Street.[2]

George Byrom Whittaker (1793–1847), see (iii) below, was born in Southampton and worked as a schoolmaster before moving to London and setting up as a book-seller and publisher. He was a sheriff of the City of London in 1824.

1. *The gentleman's magazine* vol. 14 new series (July–Dec 1840), p. 212; Nichols, J. and J.B. 1817 to 1858 vol. 8 p. 512. Tooley, 1979 p. 503, states that he used the pseudonym *Rev. J. Goldsmith*.
2. Timperley, 1842 p. 831 gives his address in 1807 as *New Bridge Street*.

EDITIONS

(i)   *SUSSEX* (Db, in plain double line frame). *Published January 1, 1808, by R. Phillips Bridge Street Blackfriars London.* (Ce OS). *Cooper del^t. et sculp^t.* (Ee OS). *British Miles 10* = 23 mm (Ab). Compass (Aa). *Plate XXXV.* (Ea OS). *Rapes* (Ca). Statistical notes (Ba).

> *An atlas of the British islands . . .*
> London, Richard Phillips, 1808.   CUL

> *A topographical dictionary of the United Kingdom . . . Accompanied by forty-six maps, drawn purposely for this work, on an original plan. By Benjamin Pitts Capper, Esq.*
> London, Richard Phillips, 1808.   BL.CUL.BOD
> A note on the title-page of this work refers to the publication of 'the Maps coloured and done up separately, price 12s. half bound'.

> *A topographical dictionary of the United Kingdom . . . Accompanied by forty-seven maps, drawn purposely for this work, on an original plan, with additions and corrections, and the population tables published in 1812. By Benjamin Pitts Capper Esq.*
> London, Longman, Hurst, Rees, Orme and Brown, 1813.   BL.CUL.SAS

(ii)   Cooper signature (Ee OS) erased. Hill hachures retouched and extended.

> *A topographical dictionary of the United Kingdom . . . Accompanied by forty-seven maps, drawn purposely for this work, on an original plan. By Benjamin Pitts Capper, Esq.*
> London, Richard Phillips, 1808.   W
> A note on the title-page of this work refers to the publication of 'the Maps done up separately, price 9s. half-bound, or the maps neatly coloured, 3s. extra.'

> *A topographical dictionary of the United Kingdom . . . Accompanied by forty-seven maps, drawn purposely for this work, on an original plan, with additions and corrections, and the population tables published in 1812. By Benjamin Pitts Capper, Esq.*
> London, Longman, Hurst, Rees, Orme, and Brown, 1813.   BOD.W

(iii)   Imprint (Ce OS) erased and replaced by *Published by G. & W.B. Whittaker. 13 Ave Maria Lane. 1824.* Statistical notes (Ba) revised; *Houses 36,283* (formerly *25,272*), *Inhabitants 233,019* (formerly *159,311*); *Acres of Land 936,320* (formerly *935,000*). Twenty-one place-names added, eg *Lynchmere, Stopham, Lamberhurst.*

> *A topographical dictionary of the United Kingdom . . . With forty-seven maps. By Benjamin Pitts Capper, Esq. . .*
> London, George B. Whittaker, 1825 and 1826.   BL.CUL;BL

A topographical dictionary of the United Kingdom. . .
London, Sir Richard Phillips and Co., 1829 (reissued 1834).   CUL;BL

68   JOHN CARY   1809

Size: 250 mm × 199 mm (6 mm)   1:510,000

A re-engraved version of Cary no. 49, most readily identified by the scale-bar, which is now numbered consecutively from 1 to 10.

EDITIONS

(i)*SUSSEX* (Cd, in hatched frame). *By JOHN CARY, Engraver* (Cd, below title and compass). *London; Published July 1. 1809 by J. Cary, Engraver & Map-seller Strand.* (Ce OS). *Statute Miles 69½ to a Degree 10 = 33 mm* (Ce). Compass (Cd, behind title). Longitude 10' (2'); latitude 10' (2').

> *Cary's new and correct English atlas; being a new set of county maps from actual surveys . . .*
> London, John Cary, 1809.   CUL.RGS.W
> Earlier versions of this work contain no. 49.

(ii)   Date in imprint (Ce OS) altered to . . . *July 1. 1812* . . .

> *Cary's new and correct English atlas; . . .*
> London, John Cary, 1812.   CUL.W

(iii)   Imprint (Ce OS) now *London; Published by J. Cary, Engraver & Map-seller Strand. New Brighton Road* added and named.

> *Cary's new and correct English atlas; . . .*
> London, John Cary, 1818, 1821, 1823, 1825, 1826, 1827, and 1829.
>   BOD.CUL;CARDIFF PL.BRIGHTON PL;CUL;W;LEEDS PL;CHUBB[1];W

(iv)   *St Leonards* and a road from there to *Crowhurst* added. Portsmouth/Arun canal marked. Asterisks added at *BRIGHTHELMSTON* (2); erased at *EAST GRINSTEAD* (2), *WINCHELSEA* (2), *RYE* (1), *Bramber* (2); at *STEYNING* the asterisks are still visible although an attempt to erase them seems to have been made.

> *Cary's new and correct English atlas . . .*
> London, John Cary, 1831.   CUL.RGS

1.   Chubb, 1927 no. CCLXIX.

139

(v)   Borough boundaries marked by pecked lines, eg *HORSHAM*. The boundary of the parliamentary division between west and east Sussex marked by a pecked line, which runs through the *B* of *Bolney*. Railways 1 and 2 added, and a line from *BRIGHTHELMSTON* towards *LEWES* and swinging southwards to *Newhaven*. *London & Brighton Railway* named.

> *Cary's new and correct English atlas . . .*
> London, John Cary, 1840 and 1843.   BOURNEMOUTH PL;COLCHESTER PL

68 A.   FIRST LITHOGRAPHIC TRANSFER

Size: 252 mm × 200 mm (6 mm)   1:510,000

EDITIONS

(i)   Title, compass and signature (Cd) erased. New title *RAILWAY & STATION MAP OF SUSSEX WITH THE NAMES OF THE STATIONS* added (Ba). Scale moved (from Ce to De). Imprint (Ce OS) erased and replaced by *LONDON. PUBLISHED BY G.F. CRUCHLEY, MAP-SELLER & GLOBE MAKER 81, FLEET STREET. New Brighton Road* erased. Plate number *35* added (Ea OS). A number of place-names underlined to indicate stations, eg *NEW SHOREHAM. BRIGHTHELMSTON* re-engraved *BRIGHTON: G^t.Bognor or Hothampton* re-engraved *Bognor. St Leonards Jun., Wood Ga., Drayton, Paxridge Gr., Fox Ga., 3 Bridges, Rowfant* and *Pole Ga.* added. *45* and *46* erased at *Paxridge Ga.*. *53* and *55* erased north of *BRIGHTON. a Emsworth* erased. *to Croydon the London R^d* erased north of *CRAWLEY*. Railways 1 to 14 and 16 to 20 marked by solid black lines; 21, 22, 24, 27, 28 and 30 by diced[2] lines; 26 by plain double lines. *London & Brighton Railway* erased and renamed *BRIGHTON & SOUTH COAST RAILWAY. STHWESTERN R^Y., BRIGHTON & STH. COAST R^Y.* (on left border) and STH EASTERN R^Y. (in two places) also named.

> *Cruchley's county atlas of England & Wales shewing all the railways & stations with their names, also the turnpike roads and principal cross roads . . . delineated on a series of 46 county maps.*
> London, G.F. Cruchley, 1863.   BL

(ii)   Railways 21 and 22 now shown by solid black (heavy continuous) lines.

> *Cruchley's county atlas of England and Wales . . .*
> London, G.D. Cruchley. [1864].   BOD

---

2.   A double line with alternate black and white squares between the lines (see *MDTT.* 421.3).

State of the plate: Later than no.68(v). Title, compass and signature (Cd) and imprint (Ce OS) erased. Plate number added. Place-names added and amended. Railways added and named.
Alterations on the transfer: New title added. Scale moved. Railways 21 and 22 converted to solid lines on edition (ii).

68 B. SECOND LITHOGRAPHIC TRANSFER

Size: 252 mm × 200 mm (6 mm)   1:510,000

EXPLANATION added (Ea), with three items. Railway from *Eastbourne* to *Pevensey* added in solid black line; railway 25 marked by plain double lines.

> *Cruchley's county atlas of England and Wales . . .*
> London, G.F. Cruchley, 1864.   P

State of the plate: Later than no. 68A. Railway 25 added.
Alterations on the transfer: As no. 68A. Also *EXPLANATION* and *Eastbourne* to *Pevensey* line added.

68 C. THIRD LITHOGRAPHIC TRANSFER

Size: 253 mm × 197 mm (6 mm)   1:510,000

EDITIONS

(i)   Title *SUSSEX* (moved to Cd) and the remainder of the wording omitted. Scale as originally engraved (Ce). Imprint (Ce OS) and *EXPLANATION* omitted. Railways 23 to 28 and 30 added in solid black lines; 34,35 and lines from *MIDHURST* to *HASLEMERE, Pulborough* to *STEYNING,* and from W^st Grinsted to S^t. Leonards (by *CUCKFIELD, UCKFIELD* and *Hellingly*) marked by diced lines.

> *Cruchley's county atlas of England and Wales . . .*
> London G.F. Cruchley, [1868].   BL.CUL.RGS

(ii)   Railway 31 added in solid black line.

> *Cruchley's new pocket companion, or, handmaid to Bradshaw and all other railway time-tables for England & Wales, in four divisions . . . twelve county maps each . . . South-east division . . .*
> London, Cruchley, [1872].   BL.CUL.BOD

State of the plate: Later than no. 68B. All alterations listed up to no. 68C (i) above, except the addition of the railways shown by diced lines, were probably made on the plate.

Alterations on the transfer: Railway 31 and those marked by diced lines added.

68 D. FOURTH LITHOGRAPHIC TRANSFER

Size: 253 mm × 198 mm (6 mm)   1:510,000

Two lines added under title (Cd). *LONDON, PUBLISHED BY G.F. CRUCHLEY. MAP-SELLER & GLOBE MAKER. 81. FLEET STREET.* added (Ce OS). *Kemp Town* and *Lewes R^d.,* with station symbols added. Railways 29 and 32 added, 23 re-routed to the west of *Bognor* (1 to 32, excluding 15, are now marked by solid black lines). Railways 34, 35, *Pulborough* to *STEYNING* line and 42 are marked by plain double lines; other lines (formerly marked by diced lines) omitted.

Cruchley's county atlas of England & Wales . . .
London, G.F. Cruchley, 1875 (reissued 1876).   BL.CUL.BOD;BL

State of the plate: Later than no. 68C. All changes listed above except the imprint were probably made on the plate.
Alterations on the transfer: Imprint (Ce OS) probably added on the stone.

69 CHARLES COOKE   circa **1810**

Size: 100 mm × 114 mm (5 mm)   1:1,160,000

Based on Cary no. 51.

Charles Cooke (1750–1816) was a book-seller and publisher in Paternoster Row. He inherited the thriving business from his father, John Cooke (1731–1810).[1]

EDITIONS

(i) *SUSSEX* (Ca, in border which has been expanded to 6.5 mm to accommodate title). *Scale of Miles 10* = 14 mm (Be). Compass (Aa), with north to the left. *RAPES* (Ea). Longitude 10'; latitude 5'. Reference to the colours used on the *Superior Edition* (Ce OS).

Topographical and statistical description of the county of Sussex . . . by George

---

1. Nichols, J. and J.B. 1817 to 1858, vol. 8 p. 488.

Alexander Cooke . . . Illustrated with a map of the county . . .
London, C. Cooke, [1810].   SAS

This work, with title-page and pagination unaltered also formed part of:
(a)   *The modern British traveller: or, tourist's pocket directory . . . By G.A. Cooke
. . . Illustrated with maps of the counties, forming a complete British atlas.*
London, C. Cooke, [1810].   BL
(b)   *Topography of Great Britain: or, British traveller's directory . . . Illustrated
with maps of the counties, forming a complete British atlas. By George Alexander
Cooke . . .*
London, C. Cooke, [1810].   BOD
(c)   *Topography of Great Britain, or, British traveller's pocket directory . . . Illu-
strated with maps of the counties which form a complete British atlas. By G.A.
Cooke, Esq. . . vol. 5.*
London, Sherwood, Neely, and Jones, "printed by assignment from the executors
of the late C. Cooke", [1822].   W

*Topographical and statistical description of the county of Sussex . . . by G.A. Cooke
esq . . . Illustrated with a map of the county . . .*
London, Sherwood, Neely and Jones [1822].   SAS

(ii)   Plate number *39* added (Ea OS). On map, *nearest road from London to Brighton*
erased, but traces of the original engraving are still visible.

*Gray's new book of roads. The tourist and traveller's guide to the roads of England
and Wales . . . By George Carrington Gray.*
London, Sherwood, Jones & Co., 1824.   BL.CUL.RGS

*A topographical and statistical description of the county of Sussex . . . Illustrated
with engravings and a map of the county . . . by G.A. Cooke esq.*
London, Sherwood, Neely and Jones [1826].   SAS

A topographical and statistical description . . .
London, Sherwood and Co., [1831].   WORTHING PL

In the last two works the text has been reset and there is an additional title-page *Cooke's Topographical
Library* . . . The map of Hertfordshire in this series is also known in an edition published by Sherwood,
Gilbert and Piper.[2]

----

2.   Hodson, 1974, No. 67 (ii).

70 JAMES WALLIS

Size: 250 mm × 162 mm (7 mm)   1:586,000

Based on Cole no. 66.

The hill hachures, which appear on the maps of other counties in this series, are absent from the Sussex map in all editions.

EDITIONS

(i) *SUSSEX* (Ca, in hatched frame). *Engrav'd by J. Wallis.* (Cb, under title and compass). *London Published by S.A. Oddy 1812* (Ce OS). *Scale of Miles. 12 = 35* mm (Ee). Compass (Ca, behind title). *RAPES.* (Aa). *EXPLANATION* (Ea). Longitude 5'; latitude 5'.

> *Wallis's new British atlas containing a complete set of county maps . . .*
> London, S.A. Oddy, 1812 (actually issued 1813).   RGS.CUL

(ii) *Meridian of London.* added (Ce) and marked by single line. Also added:- *Longitude* (Ce), *West* and *East* (Ce, in border), shading along coastline, *Loxwood, G$^{r^t}$. Bognor or Hothamton, Ashdown Forest, Tilaute Forest* and *St Leonards Forest. Merid^n. of Greenw^h.* (Ce, in border) erased.

> *A new and improved county atlas, Wallis's new British atlas containing a complete set of county maps . . . The whole engraved in the most accurate manner from the latest actual surveys.*
> London, J. Wallis, 1812 (actually issued 1813).   CUL

> *Wallis's new British atlas containing a complete set of county maps . . .*
> London, S.A. Oddy, 1812 (actually issued 1813).   CUL

> *Wallis's second & superior British atlas, containing a complete set of county maps . . .*
> London James Wallis [1816].   P

(iii) Imprint (Ce OS) erased and replaced by *London Published by J. Wallis 1814. Second Edition with Considerable Improvements and Additions By L. Herbert, Geographer.* added (Ca OS). Nearly thirty place etc. names added, eg *Ladyholt Park, Handcross, R. Adur, Lamberhurst, Hiegate, Battle Abbey.* Several distances from London amended, eg *36¾* at *Horsham* (formerly *36*), *39½* at *Cuckfield* (formerly *59*).

> *Wallis's second & superior British atlas . . .*
> London, James Wallis, [1814 and 1816].   A;W

(iv) Wallis signature (Cb) and imprints (Ce OS and Ca OS) erased.

Ellis's new and correct atlas of England and Wales, being an entire new set of county maps . . .
London, G. Ellis [1819].   BL.CUL.W
There is no connection between this work and *Ellis's English atlas* 1766 to 1796, no. 44.

70 A. LITHOGRAPHIC TRANSFER

Size: 250 mm × 167 mm (7 mm)   1:586,000

*London. Published by Ja*ˢ. *Wyld, Charing Cross East* (Ce OS) added. Scale altered to *BRITISH MILES 12* = 35 mm (Ee). *EXPLANATION.* (Ea) re-engraved in outline capitals the last four lines replaced by six new lines commencing *Canals . . .*, and including *Population 272,328. RAPES* re-engraved in outline capitals and the note commencing *Divided into 64 . . .* omitted. The thin outside line of the border replaced by a thick line. *Brighthelmstone 60, to Godalmin* (in two places), and *to Maidstone* erased. *Pevensey Bay* and *Tunbridge Wells* re-engraved. Many additions, eg *Brighton 51, Chain Pier, Kemp Town, Martello Towers* (in two places), *Birling Gap, Tenterden,* Portsmouth and Arun canal, military canal at *Rye* and Wye canal are marked, and *Wye canal* named. The roads along the north boundary have been extended and new roads added, eg from *S*ᵗ. *Leonards* to the north. Asterisks amended, eg two added at *Brighton*, one erased at *Rye.*

Probably issued as loose maps, sold separately, [1840].   BL
This map may have been published in *Wyld's atlas of English counties*, London, 1842.[1]

State of the plate: Later than no. 70 (iv). The alterations listed above were probably made on the plate.
Alterations on the transfer: It is probable that only the outside line of the border was added on the stone.

71 JAMES WALLIS   circa **1812**

Size: 85 mm × 111 mm (4 mm)   1:1,150,000

Based on Cary no. 51.

The map of another county in the same series is known in a state later than the editions listed below. It bears the imprint *J. and F. Harwood, 26 Fenchurch St.* and was probably issued about 1840;[1] the map of Sussex may have been issued in a corresponding state.

1. Whitaker, 1948, no. 487; Chubb, 1927, no. DV.
1. Hodson, D. 1974, no. 72.

EDITIONS

(i)   *SUSSEX* (Ca, in border which has been expanded to 8 mm to accommodate title). *London. Publish'd by J. Wallis. Engraver. 77, Berwick Str. Soho.* (Ce OS). *Scale of Miles 12* = 16 mm (Ae). Compass (Ea), with north to the left. *Explanation* (Ce, in bottom border which has been expanded to 12 mm). Longitude 5'; latitude 5'.

Wallis's new pocket edition of the English counties or travellers companion . . .
London, J. Wallis [1812].   BOD.CUL.RGS

(ii)   Plate number *34* added (Ea OS).

Wallis's new pocket edition . . .
London, J. Wallis, [1814].   BL.CUL.W

(iii)   Imprint (Ce OS) replaced by *London. Publish'd by P. Martin Nº. 198. Oxford Street.* Hill hachures and shading along coastline erased. Additional shading under each letter of title. House symbols retouched and some added, eg at *Cuckfield* and *Battel.* In nearly all parks the shading has been erased and a house symbol added, eg at *Stanstead Park.*

Martin's sportsman's almanack, kalender, and travellers' guide, for 1818 [and 1819]; *containing . . .*
London, Simpkin and Marshall, 1818 and 1819.   P;WN

Lewis's, new traveller's guide, or a pocket edition of the English counties . . .
London, W. Lewis, [1819].   W

(iv)   Imprint (Ce OS) erased and replaced by *London. Publish'd by W. Lewis Finch Lane.*

Lewis's new traveller's guide . . .
London, W. Lewis, [1819].   BL.CUL.BOD

Lewis's new traveller's guide, and panorama of England and Wales . . .
London, William Lewis, 1835 and 1836.   BL.A;BL.GL.W

72 ROBERT ROWE

1814

Size: 394 mm × 321 mm (9 mm)

1:321,000

Based on Jones and Smith no. 60.

Robert Rowe (c. 1775–1843) is known as an engraver, and he may well have been the draughtsman as well as the engraver and publisher of this series of maps. The plates were used subsequently by a number of publishers: Henry Teesdale from about 1829, Henry George Collins from about 1848, William S. Orr from about 1852, W.H. Collingridge in 1858 and George Philip and Son about 1860. Another work, *The Travelling atlas* (no. 95) followed a similar succession: Teesdale in 1830, Collins about 1848, Orr about 1852 and subsequently John Heywood of Manchester. There is no evidence, however, of any direct link between these publishing houses. Teesdale started in 1828 and was taken over by Thomas Deacon in 1857. Collins must have bought the plates from Teesdale, or have come to some arrangement regarding the use of the maps. Collins' stock was sold off in 1858 (see no. 66), and it seems probable, from the fact that Orr made use both of these maps and of no. 95, that Collins was then the owner of both sets of plates and that Orr acquired them at auction. The plates ultimately passed into the hands of Philip and Heywood respectively.

George Philip (1800–82), the founder of the famous map publishers, was born in Aberdeenshire, the son of a farmer. One brother, Robert, was a writer and biographer (Whitfield, Bunyan); the other, John, became a congregational minister in Liverpool. In 1819, George followed his brother to Liverpool, and worked for William Grapel, a book-seller. In 1834 he opened his own shop, and prospered. He began by publishing educational books and maps, printed from copper plates on hand presses. In 1848 he was joined by his son, George (1823–1902), and about 1856 they opened a London office. At one time the firm employed no less than eighty girls on the hand-tinting of maps. In 1859 they moved to new premises, the Caxton Building in Liverpool, where they installed Senefelder[1] machines. These power driven lithogaphic machines revolutionised the map production process. About the same time the firm of Philip, Son and Nephew was formed to take over the retail side of the trade. In 1870 George Philip took advantage of the establishment of Board Schools to increase the output of educational aids and text-books. In 1902 the printing works was moved from Liverpool to Willesden, near London. Several descendants of George and of his brother, John, worked in the firm at one time or another.[2]

1. I. Mumford, 'Lithography, photography and photozincography in English map production before 1870'. *CJ* June 1972, p. 30.
2. Philip, 1934.

EDITIONS

(i) *A NEW MAP of the COUNTY of SUSSEX Divided into Rapes & Hundreds. By R. Rowe.* (Aa, in oval frame). *London: Printed for R. Rowe, Nº. 19, Bedford Street, Bedford Row, Janʸ. 1. 1814.* (Aa, in border of title frame). *Scale.* 1 + 12 *Miles* = 61 mm (Ce). Compass (Ca). *EXPLANATION.* (Ea), includes *CUCKFIELD 40. REFERENCE to the RAPES and HUNDREDS* (Ce). Longitude 5' (1'); latitude 5' (1').

Sold about 1814 as a folding map in slip-case.   (BRIGHTON PL)

The English atlas; being a new and complete set of county maps, divided into hundreds . . . By Robert Rowe, geographer.
London, R. Rowe, 1816.
                                                                  A

(ii) Date in imprint (Aa) altered from *1814* to *1821. by Steyning 59¼ – Findon 55⅞* added at *Worthing.*

The English atlas; . . .
London, R. Rowe, 1816.
                                                                  P

(iii) Title, signature and imprint (Aa) erased and replaced by new title *SUSSEX.* in ornamental letters without frame. Imprint added *London, Published by Henry Teesdale & Cº. 302 Holborn.* (Ce OS). County boundary re-engraved to exclude *Flimwell* area. *Great Bognor* altered to *BOGNOR, Worthing* to *WORTHING, Poleing* to *Poling. Arundel & Portsmouth Cˡ.* added and named. Park symbols added, eg at *Bayham Abbey* and east of *EAST GRINSTEAD.* Place-names added, eg *Tillington, Little Green, Turwick, Trotton.* Roads added, eg through *Rudgwick* to *Kingsfold.* Dots added along some roads raising them to status of *Mail Coach Roads,* eg *Lamberhurst* to *HASTINGS.* A number of place-names re-engraved, eg *Yapton, Barnham. Shernfold Place* and park symbol, near *Frant,* erased.

New British atlas, containing a complete set of county maps . . . The whole carefully revised & corrected to the year, 1829.
London, Henry Teesdale and Co.
                                                                  BL.W

New British atlas . . . corrected to the year, 1830.
London, Henry Teesdale and Co.
                                                                  CUL

(iv) Two asterisks added at *ARUNDEL, Bramber, CHICHESTER, EAST GRINSTEAD, HASTINGS, HORSHAM, LEWES, MIDHURST, NEW SHOREHAM, RYE, STEYNING* and at *WINCHELSEA.*

New British atlas . . . corrected to the year, 1830.
London, Henry Teesdale and Co.
                                                                  RGS

(v) *New H., Kemp Town, St Leonards* and *Lovers Seat* added, with lettering in the sea. Many other place-names added inland, eg *Maudlin, Runcton, Cokeham.* Dotted line added marking course of *Arundel & Portsmouth C^l.* from *Birdham* to left border. Minor roads added, eg at *Flansham* (north of *BOGNOR*), and two at *Selsea Bill.* Dots added to road from *CHICHESTER* to the west. Road with dots added from *Copthorn* to *Staplefield Com^n.*

> *New British atlas . . . corrected to the year, 1831.*
> London, Henry Teesdale and Co.   BL.CUL

(vi) *WESTERN DIVISION, EASTERN DIVISION,* two circles in squares, ten Maltese crosses, three double circles, four triangles half blacked, five triangles fully blacked, dotted lines to mark borough boundaries, and note starting *NEW SHOREHAM and Cowfold . . .* (Bd) added on map. The key to the symbols is on the title-page of the atlas. Notes on *Population* and *Assess^d. Taxes* added to *EXPLANATION.* (Ea). As a result of the addition of the symbols, the asterisks at *STEYNING* (2) and at *NEW SHOREHAM* (1) are not visible and may have been erased.

> *Improved edition of the new British atlas . . . corrected to the year, 1832.*
> London, Henry Teesdale and Co.   BL.CUL

(vii) Four line note on parliamentary representation added (Ab, under title). Road distances 6 and 7, Maltese cross and asterisks erased at *NEW SHOREHAM.*

> *Improved edition of the new British atlas . . . corrected to the year, 1832.*
> London, Henry Teesdale and Co.   A.W

(viii) Plate number *40* added (Ea OS).

> *Improved edition of the new British atlas . . . corrected to the year, 1835.*
> London, Henry Teesdale and Co.   CUL.W.A

> *Improved edition of the new British atlas . . . corrected to the year, 1842.*
> London, Henry Teesdale and Co.   CUL

72 A. FIRST LITHOGRAPHIC TRANSFER

Size: 400 mm × 324 mm (9 mm, excluding foliate decoration)   1:321,000

Frame line drawn round title. Imprint (Ce OS) altered to *London. Published for the Proprietors by H.G. Collins. 22 Paternoster Row. EXPLANATION* (Ea) wholly erased and replaced by new *EXPLANATION,* which includes *UXBRIDGE 14¾* in place of *CUCKFIELD 40* and nine items of electoral information. Foliate decoration added to corners of border and at centre of top and bottom borders. On the map, road directions along county boundary erased, eg *from Chichester to Havant 9¾ Miles,* except *to Westerham* and *to New Romney. To Portsmouth* added. Maltese crosses, borough boundaries and other symbols for electoral information added. *BRIGHTHELMSTONE* erased and replaced by *BRIGHTON*. Road distances under *WORTHING* and *BRIGHTON* erased. Note (Bd) relating to *NEW SHOREHAM* omitted. Alternate divisions in the border have been blacked in. Plate number omitted. Railways 1 to 9, 22 and 25 added; *London, Brighton & South Coast R*ʸ. named.

> *New British atlas, containing a complete set of county maps . . . The whole carefully revised & corrected.*
> London, Henry George Collins, [1848]. W

State of the plate: Later than no. 72 (viii). Imprint erased and new imprint added. Alterations made on the map itself as listed above, except road directions and road distances.
Alterations on the transfer: Frame line round title, foliate decoration to border and imprint (Ce OS) added. *EXPLANATION* erased and new *EXPLANATION* added from a separate engraved plate. Note re *NEW SHOREHAM* erased. Road directions and road distances erased.

72 B.   SECOND LITHOGRAPHIC TRANSFER

Size: 402 mm × 324 mm (9 mm excluding foliate decoration).   1:321,000

EDITIONS

(i)   *EXPLANATION* (Ea) is as on no. 72 (viii), including *CUCKFIELD 40,* but the last two lines, *Population* and *Assessᵈ Taxes* erased and replaced by *Railways . . .* The foliate decoration to border has been entirely revised and now appears at the four corners and at the centres of each side. Road directions along the county boundary are partially erased, *to* followed by the destination remaining, eg *from Petworth to Godalming 15½ Miles* reduced to *to Godalming; from Rye to Cranbrook 19½ Miles* wholly erased but the arrow remains. Road distances under *WORTHING* not erased.

> Issued about 1852 as a folding map. (P)
> It is probable that the map in this state was issued by Collins as a folding map with printed cover: *England depicted in a series of splendidly full-coloured maps.* Whitaker records four such maps,[3] and the map of Derbyshire (no. 8 in the series) is known. The Sussex map, with this title, is listed in the catalogue at EASTBOURNE PL.

---

3.   Whitaker, 1948, no. 516; also Cheshire no. 513, Yorkshire no. 487 and Northumberland no. 527 (see cartobibliographies in appendix XII).

(ii)   *THE BRITISH GAZETTEER* and foliate decoration above title added.

> *The British gazetteer . . . illustrated by a full set of county maps, with all the rail-*
> *ways accurately laid down; forming at once an iron road-book and county atlas. By*
> *B. Clarke, Esq . . .*
> London, H.G. Collins, 1852.   BOD
>
> There is a set of these maps at the British Library without title-page.

> Issued about 1852 as a folding map with printed title on cover: *Collins' [Sussex]*
> *with its railways. Sixpence.*
> London, H.G. Collins.   (SAS)
>
> This map (and other loose impressions found) has a triangular label with *SUSSEX* and foliate
> decoration stuck over *THE BRITISH GAZETTEER*. Sussex on the cover is also on an adhesive label.

State of the plate: Later than no. 72A. *EXPLANATION* amended. Road directions
partially erased. Road distances under *BRIGHTON* erased.
Alterations on the transfer: Foliate decoration added. Note re *NEW SHOREHAM*
erased. *THE BRITISH GAZETTEER* added in edition (ii). This transfer may be
identified by a 1 mm break in the inner line of the top longitude graduations between
22'W and 23'W.

The reversion to the earlier form of *EXPLANATION* and the partial reappearance of road directions suggest
that transfer no. 72B should preceede no. 72A. However, in placing the transfers in the above order and in
dating the two atlases, the sequence adopted by both Harvey[4] and Hodson[5] has been followed.

72 C.   THIRD LITHOGRAPHIC TRANSFER

Size: 398 mm × 320 mm (9 mm, excluding foliate decoration).   1:321,000

Title (Aa) with frame line as no. 72A; *THE BRITISH GAZETTEER* and foliate
decoration omitted; new foliate decoration added above title. Road directions along
county boundary erased, eg *to Guildford;* but *to New Romney* not erased. Roads,
place-names and road directions added outside the county boundary, eg *Seven Oaks,*
Farnham and road to the west marked *from Alton. EXPLANATION* (Ea) as no. 72A
with *Lines for which Acts have been obtained* added vertically along the left side.
Havant and *Emsworth* added. Note re *NEW SHOREHAM* not erased. Railways 10, 11
and 13 marked by continuous black lines; 14, 16, 19.20 (to *STEYNING*) and line from
Whatlington to *Icklesham* by plain double lines. *Direct Portsmouth Raily.* and *To*
Ashford added; *London, Brighton & South Coast Ry.* erased.

> Issued about 1852 as loose maps sold separately.   (BL).(BOD)
>
> The date is from the British Museum acceptance stamp.

4. Harvey, 1959, nos. 62A and C.
5. Hodson, 1975, nos. 70A and C.

State of the plate: Later than no. 72B., including the revisions to detail listed above. Railways added.

Alterations on the transfer: Foliate decoration to border and above title added. *EXPLANATION* erased and new *EXPLANATION* added from separate engraved plate.

72 D.   FOURTH LITHOGRAPHIC TRANSFER

Size: 400 mm × 325 mm (9 mm, excluding foliate decoration)   1:321,000

Imprint (Ce OS) erased. Foliate decoration above title omitted. In the *EXPLANATION* (Ea) the sample town is *LEWES 48¾*, in place of *UXBRIDGE 14¾*.

> Issued about 1852 as a folding map with printed title on cover: *[Sussex] with its railways.*
> London, William S. Orr & Co.   (P)
> Sussex is on an adhesive label.

State of the plate: Later than no. 72C. Imprint erased.
Alterations on the transfer: Foliate decoration added to border. *EXPLANATION* added from separate, but amended, plate.

72 E.   FIFTH LITHOGRAPHIC TRANSFER

Size: 400 mm × 325 mm (9 mm)   1:321,000

EDITIONS

(i)   Title *SUSSEX* (Aa) re-engraved, now 51 mm in length (formerly 74 mm) and frame line omitted. Foliate decoration to border omitted. Road distances under *WORTHING* not erased. *EXPLANATION* (Ea) as no. 72B, including *CUCKFIELD 40* and *Railways*. Railways 12 and 14 marked by continuous black lines; 23 by plain double lines.

> *Melville and Co's directory and gazetteer of Sussex* . . .
> London, W.H. Collingridge, 1858.   GL.ESCL.EASTBOURNE PL

(ii)   *GEORGE PHILIP & SON, LONDON & LIVERPOOL* added (Ce OS). Plate number *35* added (Ea OS).

> *Philips' county atlas* . . .
> London and Liverpool, George Philip and Son, [1860].   P

State of the plate: Later than no. 72D. Title erased and new title added. Railways added.
Alterations on the transfer: Imprint and plate number added in edition (ii).

72 F. SIXTH LITHOGRAPHIC TRANSFER

Size: 403 mm × 324 mm (9 mm)   1:321,000

Title as 72A (74 mm in length with plain single line frame). Imprint (Ce OS) and plate number omitted. Railways 1 to 14, 16 to 25, 27 and 28 now shown by continuous black lines; *Whatlington* to *Brede* line by plain double lines.

Issued about 1866 as a folding map with printed title on cover:
Philips popular series of county maps. Sussex.   (WORTHING PL)

State of the plate: Later than no. 72E. Railways added.
Alterations on the transfer: None.

73 EDWARD LANGLEY   **1817**

Size: 246 mm × 162 mm (6 mm)   1:582,000

Based on Cole no. 66.

Langley and Belch traded under that name from 1807 to 1820. William Belch then set up on his own, but Langley continued at 173 High Street, Borough, London, until 1835. Neither of them seems to have been interested in the reissue of this atlas, which was printed and published by Joseph Phelps from 1820. Phelps had started as a bookseller in 1809.

EDITIONS

(i) *LANGLEY'S new MAP of SUSSEX.* (Ca OS). *Printed and Publish'd by Langley & Belch, Nº. 173, High Street, Borough, London. April 1ˢᵗ. 1817.* (Ce OS). *Scale of Miles. 10* = 28 mm (Ce). *Compass* (Ca). *RAPES.* (Ae). *EXPLANATION.* (Ee). Longitude 5'; latitude 5'. *View of the Steyne at Brighton,* and vignette (Aa). *Scene on the Beach, Brighton, taken near the Steyne,* and vignette. (Ea).

Langley's new county atlas of England and Wales, embellished with a beautiful vignette to each map . . .
London, Langley and Belch, [1818].   BL
A set of these maps in the Whitaker Collection (Whitaker, 1947 no. 122) lacks the title page. The title in that catalogue is taken for the label, which is also on the cover of the atlas at the British Library,

and has the words 'alphabetically arranged' added after '. . . & Wales'.

Langley's new county atlas . . .
London, Joseph Phelps, [1820].   A

Issued as loose sheets, sold separately in slip-case with Langley and Belch imprint.

(HASTINGS PL)

(ii)   Imprint (Ce OS) erased and replaced by *Printed & Published by J. Phelps, No. 27, Paternoster Row, London, 1820. View of the Steyne at Brighton* (Aa) erased and replaced by *Pavilion at Brighton* and new vignette.

Langley's new county atlas . . .
London, Joseph Phelps, [1820].   CUL

(iii)   Title (Ca OS) and imprint (Ce OS) erased. To the left of the map a panel has been added from a separate plate measuring 112 mm × 204 mm. The panel has its top to the left and measures 96 mm × 172 mm. It contains drawings of a sailor and of a farm-worker with a blank space between them. Pasted on to this space is a new title *SUSSEX* and a new imprint *Published by J. Phelps No. 44 Paternoster Row*. This plate was presumably intended for use with a set of county maps in a new publication.

Found only as a loose sheet.   (HOVE PL)

Probably issued between 1834 and 1839 when Phelps occupied premises at 44 Paternoster Row.[1] An atlas in a private collection has a similar panel added to the map of *NORTHAMPTONSHIRE*. The address, however, is *27* (not *44*) *Paternoster Row*.

74   SAMUEL JOHN NEELE   1818

Size: 236 mm × 185 mm (5 mm)   1:549,000

Based on Cary no. 49 (iv) or (v).

James Robins (d. 1836), the publisher, also wrote under the name Robert Scott. His works include *The history of England during the reign of George III.*

Frederic Shoberl (1775–1853), the author of the third work noticed below, was also a magazine editor, and co-founder of *New monthly magazine* in 1814. With Joseph Nightingale and others he continued Brayley and Britton's *Beauties of England and Wales* (see no. 66), himself compiling vol. 14, Suffolk, Surrey, Sussex. He published *A history of university of Oxford* in 1814.

1.   Chubb, 1927, p. 446.

There is considerable variation in the dimensions of the Sussex map. Impressions have been found measuring between 232 mm and 240 mm horizontally.

Other maps in the series are known with the imprint of James Cundee dated 1812–14, or of J. & J. Cundee dated 1814–15.[1] Sussex may, therefore, have been issued in a state earlier than (i) below; alternatively the Cundee imprints may have been changed by the time vol. 4 came to be printed. The imprint (Ce OS) lies 9 mm below the border and is not visible in the first work listed below. It is possible that the map was printed in an earlier state – without the imprint. *Topographia Sussexiana*[2] lists *A topographical, antiquarian and historical description of Sussex with nine engravings and map, 1818.* This has not been found, but probably refers to the last work listed below, which contains nine engravings.

EDITIONS

SUSSEX. (Ea, in rectangular frame). *Neele Sc. Strand.* (Ee OS). *Published by J. Robins & C⁰. Albion Press London January 1. 1818.* (Ce OS). *British Miles 10 = 30 mm* (Ce). Compass (Ce, above scale). Longitude 10' (2'); latitude 10' (2').

The new British traveller; or, modern panorama of England and Wales . . . By James Dugdale, LL.D. vol. 4.
London, J. Robins & Co., 1819 (probably issued in 1820).   BL.RGS.W

Robins' atlas of England and Wales, accurately engraved by Neele, from the latest surveys.
London, J. Robins & Co., 1819.   BL.CUL

A topographical and historical description of the county of Sussex . . . by Mr Shoberl . . .
London, Sherwood, Neely and Jones; and George Cowie and Co., [1820]. SAS
The advertisement at the beginnng of this work reads 'THIS volume forms part of that elegant and interesting Work lately COMPLETED in Twenty-Five Volumes, entitled THE BEAUTIES OF ENGLAND AND WALES; . . .' (See Cole no. 66 for a note on this work). At the end of Shoberl's book is *A LIST OF THE PRINCIPAL BOOKS, MAPS, AND VIEWS* . . . which contains the entry 'The most modern as well as the most correct (map) is Laurie and Whittle's . . . It was published in 1807.' This refers to no. 59 (ii), which had in fact been re-issued in 1815.

---

1. Whitaker, 1947, no. 126.
2. Butler, 1866, p. 223.

75 THOMAS DIX   1818

Size: 425 mm × 336 mm (9 mm)   1:332,000

Based on Rowe no. 72

Thomas Dix (1769/70–1813) practised as a surveyor in Northamptonshire and Norfolk.[1] He wrote a number of books, mainly for schools. *A treatise on the construction and copying of all kinds of maps* was published in 1805.

William Darton, the publisher, was the son of the Darton of Darton and Harvey (see no. 56). The name of the firm varied from time to time; they were also publishers of nos. 66B and 81.

Maps of some other counties in the same series are known in two further states:[2] (a) an edition intermediate between the two listed below with the date in the imprint altered to 1830, and (b) a state later than (ii) below printed about 1848. The map of Sussex may have issued in corresponding states.

EDITIONS

(i) *A NEW MAP of the County of SUSSEX, Divided into Rapes, and Hundreds. by M^r. THO^s. DIX.* (Ca, in circular frame). *London, Published Jany. 8th. 1818, by W. Darton Junr. 58 Holborn Hill.* (Ce OS). *SCALE of MILES* ½ + 12 = 58 mm (Be). Compass (Bd, above scale). *REFERENCE to the RAPES and HUNDREDS.* (Aa). *EXPLANATION.* (Ae). *MARKET TOWNS AND MARKET DAYS.* (Ea). *NOTE,* comprising eleven lines of historical and parliamentary information (Ce). *Arundel Castle; the Seat of the Duke of Norfolk* and vignette (Ee). Longitude 5' (1'); latitude 5' (1').

> *A complete atlas of the English counties, divided into their respective hundreds, &c. . . to which is added, various explanatory notes . . . Commenced by the late Thomas Dix, of North Walsham; carried on and completed by William Darton, London.*
> London, William Darton, 1822.   BL.CUL.W
> Maps in this atlas bear dates from July 1816 to February 1821, and it is probable that they were first issued as loose sheets, sold separately. Some impressions (CUL and BRIGHTON PL) have traces of an erased signature (Ee OS), which appears to have ended with the word *Strand*. The Brighton impression is a folding map in slip-case with William Darton's imprint.

(ii) Title, signature and circular frame (Ca) erased and replaced by *SUSSEX, Divided into Rapes & Hundreds AND THE Parliamentary Divisions* without frame. Imprint (Ce OS) erased and replaced by *LONDON, WILLIAM DARTON & SON, 58 Holborn Hill. SCALE OF MILES* moved (from Be to Ae), and now engraved in outline capitals. Compass (Bd) erased. *EXPLANATION* (Ae) erased; new *EXPLANATION,*

---

1. P. Eden, 'Land surveyors in Norfolk 1550–1850' in *Norfolk archaeology* vol. 36 pt 2 (1975); Hannas, 1972, p. 145.
2. Hodson, 1974, no. 76.

in outline capitals, added (Be, in place of compass and scale), including a number of additional items with particular reference to electoral information. *Arundel Castle, the Seat of the Duke of Norfolk* (Ee) re-engraved in capital letters. *REFERENCE to the RAPES and HUNDREDS* (Aa) re-engraved in outline capitals, and sub-headings also re-engraved in outline capitals, eg *A Arundel Rape* now *A ARUNDEL RAPE*. In the note (Ce), the heading *NOTE* re-engraved in outline capitals and lines 6, 7 and 8 re-engraved, eg *Sends to Parliament 28 Members; . . .* altered to *Sends to Parliament 18 Members, . . .* A number of additions on the map:- *EAST DIVISION* and *WEST DIVISION;* concentric circles denoting *Principal Places of County Elections* at *CHICHESTER* and *LEWES;* crosses denoting *Polling Places,* eg at *EAST GRINSTEAD;* diamonds (two members), eg at *NEW SHOREHAM;* triangles (one member), eg at *RYE; Arun & Portsmouth Can.* with branch to *CHICHESTER; BOGNOR* in place of *Great Bognor or Hothampton; WORTHING* in place of *Worthing; BRIGHTON* in place of *BRIGHTHELMSTONE; Chain Pier* and *Kemp Town; Martello Towers; S*^t*Leonards; to Westerham;* and a number of roads, eg *Beeding* to *NEW SHOREHAM.* Some roads downgraded, eg *Beeding* to *Southwick,* and some erased, eg the branch from this road to *NEW SHOREHAM.*

The counties of England; with general maps of north and south Wales.
London, William Darton and Son, [1835].   A
Also issued by Darton and Son in about 1835 as a folding map (BRIGHTON PL).

76   W. SAUNDERS AND SON   circa **1818**

Size: 244 mm × 158 mm (5 mm)   1:591,000

Copied from Langley no. 73.

EDITIONS

(i)   *SUSSEX.* (Ca). *Scale of Miles 10* = 27 mm (Da). Compass (Ba). *Rapes* (Ea). *EXPLANATION.* (Aa), with eight items. Longitude 10' (5'); latitude 10' (5').

Rambles in the vicinity of Brighton . . . with a map of the county. By C. Wright . . .
3rd edition.
Brighton, W. Saunders, [1818].   SAS.ESCL
The date is taken from the preface to the work.

Rambles in the vicinity of Brighton . . . with a map of Sussex.
Brighton, W., Saunders and Son, [1841].   BL
The British Library copy of this work is bound with *The Stranger's guide in Brighton,* and there is a printed cover for the two works together, which is dated 1841. Earlier issues of *The Stranger's guide . . .* do not have *Rambles . . .* bound with it.

(ii)   *Kemp Town* and *S*^t*. Leonards* added. Road from *Cuckfield* to county boundary

157

upgraded and marked *to Croydon. From Guildford* added. The road from *Brighthelmstone* to *Cuckfield* and *Crawley* is marked by black dots at intervals on either side. Railway 2 and *Railroad* added.

Rambles in the vicinity of Brighton . . . with a map of Sussex.
Brighton, W. Saunders, [1843].   BRIGHTON PL.SAS
Bound with *Stranger's guide in Brighton* with a printed cover for the two works dated 1843.

77 SIDNEY HALL   1820

Size: 66 mm × 116 mm (1 mm)   1:1,080,000

Based on Gardner, Yeakell and Gream no. 57.

This is the first map of Sussex to adopt the modern spelling – *Brighton*.

EDITIONS

(i) *SUSSEX.* (Ca, in border which has been expanded to 4 mm to accommodate the title). *Sid^y. Hall sculp^t.* (Ee OS). *Pub. By S. Leigh, 18. Strand* (Ae OS). *English Miles 20* = 29 mm (Ed). Compass (Aa), with north to the left, the map being designed to be viewed from the 'south'. Plate number *36* (Ea OS).

Leigh's new pocket atlas, of England and Wales, consisting of fifty-five maps of the counties . . .
London, Samuel Leigh, 1820.   W

Leigh's new picture of England and Wales . . .
London, Samuel Leigh, 1820.   WN

Leigh's new atlas of England & Wales.
London, Samuel Leigh.
Issued bound in with *Leigh's new pocket road-book of England, Wales, and part of Scotland . . .* [1st] and 2nd edns.
London, Samuel Leigh, 1825 and 1826.   BL.RGS;CHUBB[1]

Leigh's new atlas of England & Wales
London, Samuel Leigh.
Issued bound with *Leigh's new pocket road-book of England & Wales . . . 3rd edn.*
London, Samuel Leigh, 1831.   RGS.W

1. Chubb, 1927, no. CCCLXXV.

158

(ii)   Imprint (Ae OS) erased and replaced by *Pub. by M.A. Leigh 421 Strand.* Asterisks erased at *Midhurst* (1), *Bramber* (2), *Steyning* (2), *Seaford* (2), *Winchelsea* (2), *Rye* (1), *Horsham* (1), *E. Grinstead* (2), *Arundel* (1); and added at *Brighton* (2).

> *Leigh's new atlas of England and Wales.*
> London, M.A. Leigh.
> Issued bound in with *Leigh's new pocket road-book* . . . 3rd edn.
> London, Samuel Leigh, 1831.   GL

(iii)   Division between east and west Sussex marked by pecked line.

> *Leigh's new atlas of England & Wales.*
> London, M.A. Leigh.
> Issued bound in with *Leigh's new pocket road-book* . . . 4th edn.
> London, M.A. Leigh, 1833; and 5th edn, London, Leigh and Son, 1835.
>   BL.GL.RGS;ST. ALBANS CITY MUSEUM

> *Leigh's new pocket atlas of England and Wales . . . Corrected since the passing of the Reform Bill.*
> London, M.A. Leigh, 1834.   A

(iv)   Signature (Ee OS) erased.

> *Leigh's new atlas of England & Wales.*
> London, M.A. Leigh.
> Issued bound in with *Leigh's new pocket road-book* . . . 6th and 7th edns.
> London, Leigh and Son, 1837 and 1839.   BL.CUL.W;CUL.W

(v)   Railways 1 and 2 and line from *Brighton* to *Lewes* with branch to *Newhaven* added.

> *Leigh's new atlas of England & Wales.*
> London, Leigh and Son.
> Issued bound in with *Leigh's new pocket road-book* . . . 8th edn.
> London Leigh and Co., 1840; 9th edn. London, G. Biggs, 1842; and 10th edn.
> London, G. Biggs and Orlando Hodgson, 1842 and 1843.   BOD.RGS;WN;GL;W

78 W.H. REID

circa **1820**

Size: 96 mm × 61 mm (4 mm)

1:1,340,000

Possibly based on Cary no. 49.

EDITIONS

(i) *SUSSEX* (Ca, in double line frame with hatched background). *Scale of Miles 10 =*
11 mm (Ba). Compass (Da). *Mail Coach R^{ds}. thus* . . . (Ce). Longitude 5'; latitude 10'.
Errors on the map include *Salsea Bill, Pugham Har.*.

> *The panorama: or, traveller's instructive guide; through England and Wales* . . .
> *accompanied by a description of each county.*
> London, W.H. Reid, [1820].
> BL.A.W
> There appear to have been two issues of this work in 1820. Lee[1] states "Another change in business
> affiliations accounts for the misleading imprints in the first issue of *The Panorama; or, Traveller's
> instructive guide,* published undated in 1820. Although the title page says 'Printed by J. Wallis . . .
> published by W.H. Reid', many of the maps in this issue bear the imprint: 'Published by C. Hinton . . .
> and J. Wallis'. In a reissue in the same year the imrpints were not very skillfully corrected."

(ii) Imprint *Published by Hodgson & Co. 10, Newgate Street.* added (Ce OS).

> *The panorama of England and Wales.*
> London, Hodgson and Co., [1825].
> A

79 SAMUEL JOHN NEELE AND SON

1820

Size: 156 mm × 126 mm (2 mm)

1:856,000

Probably based on Cary no. 65.

William Pinnock (1782–1843), the publisher, was born at Alton in Hampshire. He
started life as a school-master and was later a book-seller in Alton. He moved to
Newbury in 1811, and to London in 1817. In partnership with Samuel Maunder he
published a number of educational works, including a series of eighty-three
'Catechisms' covering various subjects including geography. Pinnock did well, making,
it was said, £4/5000 a year; but as a result of an unwise speculation he was forced to sell
his copyrights to Whittaker (see no. 67) and others. He married Maunder's sister and
their son, William (1813–85) went into the Church, and wrote books on ecclesiastical
subjects.

1. Lee, 1955, p. 11.

Samuel Maunder (1785–1849) came from Devon. He worked on the 'Catechisms', but was mainly a compiler of dictionaries and the like; his *Little gazetteer, or geographical dictionary in miniature* was published in 1845, and the *Treasury of geography* in 1856, having been completed by William Hughes (see no. 128).

EDITIONS

(i)   *SUSSEX* (Ca, in double line frame with hatched background). *Neele & Son sc. 352 Strand.* (Ee OS). *Scale of Statute Miles !0 = 18 mm* (Aa). Compass (Cd). *EXPLANATION.* (Ed).

The travellers pocket atlas consisting of a complete set of county maps, for England & Wales, on an original & improved plan . . .
London, Pinnock and Maunder [1820].   CUL

Pinnock's county histories. The history and topography of Sussex, with . . . and, a neat map of the county.
London, Pinnock and Maunder [1820].   HASTINGS PL

(ii)   Imprint *Published by G. & W.B. Whittaker, Ave-Maria Lane, 1821.* added (Ce OS).

The travellers pocket atlas . . .
London, G. and W.B. Whittaker, 1821 and 1823.   WN;BL.CUL

Pinnock's county histories, historical and topographical; with . . . a map of each county. vol. 5.
London, G. Whittaker and Co., [1823].   P

Pinnock's history and topography of England and Wales. vol. 5.
London, George B. Whittaker, 1825.   BL
This contains *Pinnock's county histories. The history and topography of Sussex, with . . . a neat map of the county.* London, Pinnock and Maunder [1820]. The text and pagination is unaltered. Warwickshire[1] and Hertfordshire[2] in this work have the Whittaker imprint (Ce OS) removed. The Sussex map has been cropped, but the imprint is just visible.

1. Harvey, 1959, no. 72.
2. Hodson, 1974, no. 79.

80   T. STARLING

1820

Size: 205 mm × 141 mm (6 mm)

1:601,000

Based on Gardner, Yeakell and Gream no. 57.

EDITION

SUSSEX (Ca, in frame with hatched background). *T. Starling Sc. 87 Old St. London.* (Ae OS). *Published Oct. 1. 1820, by Longman & C°. Paternoster Row.* (Ce OS). *Statute Miles 16* = 43 mm (Cb). Longitude 10' (2'); latitude 10' (2').

> *Excursions in the county of Sussex . . . including a map of the county.*
> London, Longman, Hurst, Rees, Orme, and Brown; and two others, 1822 and 1822.
> BL.SAS.ESCL;ESCL
> In one of these works (ESCL) the text has been rearranged and extended from 176 pages to 201 pages.

> *History of Sussex; or, excursions in the county; . . . including a map of the county.*
> Witham and Maldon, P. Youngman, 1822.
> SAS.WSCL
> The text, which is the same as in one of the former works, extends to 201 pages.

> The titles of the above works are taken from the second of two title-pages. The first title-page reads *Excursions through Sussex . . . Pub[l]. Jan. 1. 1822 by Longman & C°. Paternoster Row.*

81   ROBERT MILLER

circa **1821**

Size: 97 mm × 62 mm (4 mm)

1:1,300,000

Copied from Reid no. 78.

EDITIONS

(i)   *SUSSEX* (Ca, in frame with hatched background). *London Published by Robert Miller, 24 Old Fish Street.* (Ce OS). *Scale of Miles 10* = 12 mm (Aa). Compass (Da). Plate number *35* (Ee OS, sideways). Longitude 5'; latitude 10'.

> *Miller's new miniature atlas containing a complete set of county maps . . .*
> London, R. Miller, [1821].
> BL.CUL

(ii)   Imprint (Ce OS) erased and replaced by *London: William Darton; 58 Holborn Hill.*

Darton's new miniature atlas containing a complete set of county maps . . .
London, William Darton, [1822] and [1825].   BL.CUL;CHUBB[1]

81 A. LITHOGRAPHIC TRANSFER

Size: 99 mm × 62 mm (4 mm)   1:1,300,000

SUSSEX (Ca, re-engraved in smaller letters and without frame). No imprint (Ce OS).
Railways . . . added (Ca, below title) and railway 2 added on map. Views added
outside border: Brighton chain pier across top, Royal Pavillion across bottom, ruins on
left of map, sheep grazing on right. The printed area now measures 190 mm × 145 mm.

> *Reuben Ramble's travels through the counties of England. With maps and historical*
> *vignettes.*
> London, Darton and Clark, [1845].   BL

> *Reuben Ramble's travels in the southern counties of England.*
> London, Darton and Clark, [1845].   BL.RGS

> *Reuben Ramble's travels through the counties of England . . .*
> London, Darton and Co., [1850].   CUL

State of the plate: Later than no. 81 (ii). Imprint erased. Alteration to title and railway
addition probably made on the plate.
Alterations on the transfer: Views added.

82 GEORGE AND JOHN CARY   1822

Size: 90 mm × 122 mm (1 mm)   1:1,140,000

Based on Cary no. 65.

Earlier editions of *Cary's travellers companion* contain no. 51 or no. 65, of which
this is a re-engraved version. *Arun River* has been added and changes made in the table
of distances, eg *Chichester 62* (formerly *63*). The layout of the page is the same, with
title at top and north to the left. In this version, however, the scale-bar and lettering on
the map are designed to be read from the right of the page. *By J. Cary . . . Engraver* is
omitted.

---

1. Chubb, 1927, no. CCCXCV.

EDITIONS

(i) *SUSSEX* (Ca, in border which has been expanded to 9 mm to accommodate title). *London. Published by G. & J. Cary, Nᵒ. 86 Sᵗ. James's Str.* (Ce OS). *Scale of Miles 10* = 14 mm (Ed, sideways). Compass (Ca OS), north to the left. Page number *18* (Ce OS, 20 mm below bottom border). Below map, and inside bottom border, is a list of towns with distances from London.

> *Cary's traveller's companion, or, a delineation of the turnpike roads of England and Wales . . . laid down from the best authorities, on a new set of county maps.*
> London, G. and J. Cary, 1822, 1824, 1826 and 1828
>
> BL.CUL;BL.CUL.W;GL;BL.RGS.BOD
>
> In one copy of the 1828 issue (BOD) the date is obscured by a label, which reads *Sold by James Wyld (Successor to Mʳ Faden) . . . 6, Charing Cross, London.*

(ii) Roads have been added from *Hastings* to *Rye*, *Midhurst* to west boundary, *Horsham* to *Crawley*, *Lewes* to *Newhaven*, and *Battel* to *Cross in Hands*.

> *Cary's traveller's companion . . .*
> London, G. and J. Cary, 1828 (actually a reissue of 1835).   CUL

82 A. LITHOGRAPHIC TRANSFER

Size: 92 mm × 116 mm (1 mm)   1:1,140,000

Title and compass erased. Top border reduced in width. *SUSSEX* added (Ca OS). Imprint (Ce OS) erased and replaced by *London. Published by G.F. Cruchley, Map Seller & Globe Maker 81, Fleet Street.* Page number *35* added (Ae OS). Page number *18* (Ce OS) either erased or cut off in binding. *Fishbourn* and *Hampnet* erased. Place names re-engraved:- *Angmering, Brighton* in place of *Brighthelmstone, Eastbourne* in place of *E.Bourne. Bognor* added. Stations underlined, eg *Hastings;* and a number of new station names added and underlined, eg *Bosham, Pole Ga., Sᵗ Leonards.* Railways 1 to 14 and 16 to 20 added as in use; 24 and 27 as projected. *BRIGHTON & Sᵀᴴ. COAST* and *Sᵀᴴ. Eᴺ. Rᵞ.* named, the latter in two places.

> *Cruchley's railroad companion to England & Wales shewing all the railways & stations with their names, also the turnpike roads . . . delineated on a series of 42, county maps.*
> London, G.F. Cruchley, [1862].   BL.W
> The map of *SURRY* is printed on the back.

State of the plate: Later than no. 82 (ii). Probably including all the changes listed above; although some may have been made on the transfer.
Alterations on the transfer: Probably none.

83 PICKETT[1]   1822

Size: 215 mm × 168 mm (9 mm)   1:563,000

Based on Jones and Smith no. 60.

Although clearly a map of Sussex, the area covered extends as far north as London.

EDITIONS

(i) *SUSSEX* (Ca, in hatched frame, partly inside and partly outside border). *Pickett Sc.* (Ee OS). *Printed for C. SMITH, No. 172 Strand, 1822.* (Ce OS). *Scale of Miles 15* = 44 mm (Ce, along bottom edge of border). Compass (Ca OS, above title). Longitude 5' (1'); latitude 5' (1').

> *Smith's new English atlas, being a reduction of his large folio atlas containing a complete set of county maps . . . The whole carefully arranged according to the stations & intersections of the trigonometrical survey of England.*
> London, C. Smith, 1822 and 1825.   CUL.W;CUL

(ii) *Portsmouth Can.* added and named.

> *Smith's new England atlas . . .*
> London, C. Smith, 1825.   BL

(iii) Date *1822* erased in imprint (Ce OS). Roads added from *Angmering* to *ARUNDEL* via *Yapton*, *CUCKFIELD* to *St Johns* direct, *W. Grinstead* to *Billingshurst*, *Eridge* to *Pound Green* with a branch to *Wadhurst*.

> *Smith's new English atlas . . .*
> London, C. Smith, 1828 (actually issued 1829 and 1830).   A;CUL

(iv) *St Leonards* added.

> *Smith's new English atlas . . .*
> London, C. Smith, 1833 (not issued before 1834).   P
> According to Whitaker[2] there was probably an 1832 edition: 'I have seen the map of Yorkshire . . .

1. A.J. or J. Pickett, see Tooley, 1979, p. 505.
2. Whitaker, 1948, no. 416.

bearing the date 1832 in the imprint'. He is probably correct, since the map of Yorkshire in the 1833 atlas is dated 1834.

(v)   Boundary between parliamentary divisions added. Railway(s) added.

Smith's new English atlas . . .
London, C. Smith, 1844.   P
This atlas from the Gardner collection has not been examined. The additions are deduced from those made on the maps of Warwickshire[3] and Hertfordshire.[4]

84   GIDEON ALGERNON MANTELL   1822

Size: 236 mm × 295 mm (2 mm)   1:754,000

There is not sufficient detail to enable the derivation of this map to be determined. Although primarily a map of Sussex, it covers parts of Surrey and the Weald of Kent.

Dr. Gideon Algernon Mantell (1790–1852)[1] is too well-known to require more than the briefest biographical note; there has even been a television play about him. He practised as a 'surgeon' in his native town of Lewes, and later at Brighton and in London, at Clapham and at Chester Square. He contributed essays to the *Lancet* and other medical journals, and also earned an international reputation as a geologist and palaeontologist. His *Journal,*[2] covering the years 1818 to 1852, throws a fascinating light on this extraordinary man, who was born the son of a provincial shoemaker. In December 1820 he writes 'Recovered my geological maps from the lithographer; the expense was equal to copper-plate engraving, 500 cost me £13.0.0 – including paper and colouring.' The entry for June 24, 1844 reads 'Mr. Knipe called and shewed me his new Geological Map of Great Britain, a very good work – the best at present published.' This is a reference to J.A. Knipe's *Geological map of the British Isles and part of France* . . ., published that year.

The following extracts refer to *The Geology of the south-east of England* (see below). In January 1833; 'Received a note from Mr. Murray declining the publication of my book after keeping it three weeks! this is really too bad. Wrote to Mr. Relfe [Lupton Relfe was married to Mantell's sister-in-law, and had been declared bankrupt in 1828] to come down and arrange respecting its publication.' And two days later, 'Mr Relfe arrived, but I could do nothing satisfactory with him, have therefore through my kind friend Mr Bakewell [Robert Bakewell, the geologist] sent it to Longman – perhaps with a similar result. So much for the delights of Authorship!' He seems to have been

3.   Harvey, 1959, no. 76 (iii).
4.   Hodson, 1974, no. 84 (iii).

1.   Lower, 1865; Spokes, 1927; A.D. Morris in *Proceedings of the Royal Society of Medicine*, February, 1971; W.E. Swinton, in *British Medical Journal*, March 1975.
2.   E.C. Curwen, (ed) *The Journal of Gideon Mantell*, OUP, 1940.

luckier. Only seventeen days later we read, '. . . first proof sheet of my work received . . .', and a month later, 'At twelve went to Messrs Longman and arranged respecting the plates etc. of my forthcoming volume.' In November 1836: 'Received from Messrs Longman 60 copies of the Geol. S.E. of England – and thus closing the acc^t. of the first Edition – when these 60 are sold at 20/- each – I shall clear about £100 by the work – the only money I ever obtained from any literary production.' Later entries, however show a rather better return for his literary efforts.

Mantell sold his collection of fossils to the British Museum for £5,000.

The first work noticed in (ii) below forms part of *History of the western division of the county of Sussex,* by James Dallaway (1763–1834)[3], a man of many parts – antiquarian, poet and author of a number of books on the visual arts. He obtained a medical qualification and was for a time chaplain and physician to the British 'factory' in Constantinople. His book on heraldry was praised by Thomas Moule (see no. 110). Born at Bristol, he was thirty-four before establishing a connection with Sussex, when he became secretary to the Earl-Marshall. His *History of the western division* was based on the manuscript collection of Sir William Burrell at the British Museum. The work was completed by Rev. Edmund Cartwright. Unfortunately it is notorious for its inaccuracies.

Edmund Cartwright (c. 1777–1834) was a man of considerable intellectual ability. He followed a military career before going into the Church. But archaeology was his favourite pursuit, and his special interest in Sussex developed while his regiment was stationed at Chichester. He died at Littlehampton.

'Longmans' was founded in 1724 by Thomas Longman (1699–1755)[4] of Bristol, who took over the business of William Taylor in Paternoster Row, and was the first publisher of *Robinson Crusoe*. The firm published Cobbett's parliamentary debates from 1803, but handed over to Hansards in 1808. The composition of the firm kept changing; twenty-three different forms of imprint are recorded between 1724 and 1924.

EDITIONS

(i) *MAP AND SECTIONS ILLUSTRATIVE OF THE GEOLOGY OF THE S.E. PART OF ENGLAND* (Ce). *Gideon Mantell F.R.S. del^t. (Ae). Neeles' sc. 352 Strand.* (Ed). Compass (Ec). Limits of geological strata marked by pecked lines. Above and below the map, but inside the border, are nine geological sections.

The fossils of the South Downs . . . By Gideon Mantell, F.R.S.
London, Lupton Relfe, 1822.   BL.SAS.ESCL

Illustrations of the geology of Sussex: . . . By Gideon Mantell, F.R.S.
London, Lupton Relfe, 1827.   BL

---

3. Lower, 1865; F.W. Steer, 'Memoir and letters of James Dallaway', *SAC* vol. 103 (1965) pp. 1–45, and *SAC* vol. 105 (1967) pp. 62–9.
4. Cox and Chandler, 1924.

(ii) Four geological descriptions, eg *HASTINGS SAND and CLAY FORMATION* added on map. *Beds of Sussex Marble* with three groups of three commas added. Small circles added at eight places, eg at *Hastings* and at *Fairlight*.

The parochial topography of the rape of Bramber . . . by Edmund Cartwright . . .
vol. 2, part 2.
London, J.B. Nichols and Son, 1830.   BL.SAS.WORTHING PL
For other maps in this work see appendix no. VII.4.

The geology of the south-east of England . . . by Gideon Mantell, F.R.S.
London, Longman, Rees, Orme, Brown, Green and Longman, 1833.   BL.SAS

85   J. WALKER[1]   1822

Size: 118 mm × 77 mm (1 mm)   1:1,180,000

The source from which this map was derived has not been established. **See plate 26.**

Benjamin Crosby (1768–1815), the compiler of the gazetteer in which this map appears, was born near Leeds, the youngest son of a large family. On coming to London, he worked for some well-established book-sellers, before setting up on his own. He was one of the first to travel the country selling books. He suffered a severe paralysis in 1814, and his business was taken over, in part by Baldwin, Cradock and Joy, and in part by Crosby's own assistants, William Simpkin and Richard Marshall. He died at Louth, leaving a widow and two children.[2]

The well-known firm of book-sellers, J. and E. Bumpus, was founded by Thomas Bumpus in 1816.[3] The younger son, Edward (1832–96), took over from his father in 1859, and he amalgamated the firm in 1889 with that of his late brother, John (1818–80), who had earlier set up on his own. John Bumpus, publisher of this map, was probably the brother of Thomas Bumpus, and was perhaps the John Bumpus, book-seller of Skinner Street, who drowned himself in the Surrey Canal in 1832 leaving a wife and six children.[4] See no. 97 for notes on the Walker 'family'.

EDITIONS

SUSSEX. (Ca). *J. Walker del* (Ae OS). *J. Cox sculp.* (Ee OS). *London, Publish'd May 1st. 1822. by I. Bumpus, Nº. 6 Holborn Bars.* (Ce OS). *Scale of Miles 10 = 24 mm*

---

1. I am indebted to John Huddy for bringing this series of maps to my attention.
2. Timperley, 1842 addenda p. 11.
3. Boase, 1965.
4. Timperley, 1842, p. 927. Darlington and Howgego, 1964 records (no. 306) an 1827 map published by John Bumpus of 23 Skinner Street.

(Ee). Compass (Aa). *This County contains 1461 square Miles; 190,083 Inhabitants, & sends 28 Members to Parl*. (in panel 118 mm × 4 mm, immediately above bottom border). **See plate 26.**

Crosby's complete pocket gazetteer of England and Wales or traveller's companion. New edition, illustrated by two maps.
London, Baldwin, Cradock and Joy; Simpkin and Marshall; and J. Bumpus, 1818 (actually issued in 1822).   P
The 1807 edition of this work contains two general maps only. The 1815 edition and the first issue of the 1818 edition are without maps.

86   A.M. PERROT   1823

Size: 53 mm × 46 mm (single line border)   1:2,760,000

There is insufficient detail to enable the derivation of this map to be determined. Errors on the map include *Arundol* and *Haslemerce*. Although described as a map of Sussex and Surrey, much of Kent, Middlesex and other south-eastern counties is covered by it. **See plate 28 (ii).**

Aristide Michel Perrot (1793–1879) was a French geographer.
The engraver may have been Adrien Migneret (1786–1840) of Paris mentioned in *Bryan's dictionary of painters and engravers* (1904).
George Bernard Depping, the writer, was born at Munster in 1784. He moved to Paris, and became a naturalised French citizen in 1827.[1]

EDITION

SUSSEX SURREY (Ca OS, surmounted by a telescope). *McMigneret Sc* (Ee OS). *A.M. Perrot 1823* (Ae OS). The map is surrounded by decorative engravings of oak-leaves and barley, a ram, a cockerel, a cannon and a stocking. **See plate 28 (ii).**

L'Angleterre, ou description historique et topographique de Royaume Uni de la Grand-Bretagne, par G.B. Depping . . . Tome V.
Paris, Etienne Ledoux, 1823 and 1824.   WN;BL

L'Angleterre, ou description historique . . . par G.B. Depping . . . seconde edition. Tome V . . .
Paris, Etienne Ledoux, 1828.   W.WN

L'Angleterre, ou description historique . . . par G.B. Depping . . . 3me. edition . . .
Brussels, L.J. Brohez, 1828.   CUL

1. Querand, 1827.

L'Angleterre, ou description historique . . . par G.B. Depping . . . seconde edition . . .
Paris, Etienne Ledoux, 1835.

WN

Whitaker[2] has remarked on the anomalous description of this work as *seconde edition*.

87   J. THOMSON   1823

Size: 52 mm × 78 mm (3 mm)   1:1,650,000

Based on Cary no. 65.

EDITION

SUSSEX (Ca, in decorated border). *Scale of Miles 10* = 10 mm (Ae). Compass (Aa), with north to the left. Note commencing *This County contains* . . . (Ce, in border).

The new English atlas, being a complete set of county maps, neatly coloured . . .
London, J. Thompson, 1823.

BOD

The pocket tourist & English atlas, being a new and complete set of county maps . . . . Including a copious topographical account of each county.
London, O. Hodgson, [1827].

BL

88   WILLIAM EBDEN   1825

Size: 423 mm × 328 mm (9 mm)   1:306,000

Based on Gardner, Yeakell and Gream no. 57.

Little is known about William Ebden, although his name appears on maps as early as 1811 and as late as 1856.[1] In compiling the atlas described below he used the latest available large-scale surveys, but not the Ordnance Survey maps, which were available for some counties.

The publishing history of this series of maps is confusing. The Hertfordshire map[2] bears the imprint *Published Feb*y. *22 1825, by WILLIAM COLE, late HODGSON & C*o. *10, Newgate Street.* It will be seen that (i) and (ii) below were published by Cole and S. Maunder in 1825 and 1828, both from 10, Newgate Street. Orlando Hodgson,

2. Whitaker, 1948, no. 441.

1. Laurie & Whittle's map of Norfolk and Suffolk, 1811; Tooley, 1979, p. 185.
2. Hodson, 1974, no. 86.

however, originally of 10 Newgate Street, see no. 78 (ii), continued in business elsewhere.[3] No. 77 (v), for example, was published by him in 1842 and 1843. A bound collection of the maps in this series,[4] without title-page, contains maps sold by Hodgson (1824), by Cole (1825) and by Maunder (1828). It is unlikely that these maps were ever issued in atlas form, although Tooley[5] refers to an *Atlas of English counties* by S. Maunder (1828). Cowling[6] says that Cole and Maunder, with others, were partners in the firm of Hodgson and Co. The imprints suggest that Hodgson left Cole and Maunder with the rights in the original plates, and himself set up in business elsewhere.

It is probably that this is the Maunder who was associated with Pinnock (see nos. 79 and 106).

Ebden's name and that of the engravers were omitted when the maps were published in atlas form in 1833 by Duncan. Duncan is not known to have published other maps or atlases.

Hoare and Reeves also engraved no. 94.

Maps of other counties[7] in this series were issued about 1858 with the title *Collins' Railway & Telegraphic Map of* [name of county]. A map of Sussex was probably included in the series.

EDITIONS

(i)   *EBDEN'S New Map of the County of SUSSEX; Divided into Hundreds laid down from Trigonometrical Observations by W. EBDEN. Hoare & Reeves Sc. 90 Hatton Garden* (Ee). *Published Sept[r]. 21. 1825, by WILLIAM COLE, 10 Newgate Street. London.* (Ce OS). *SCALE 20 Miles* = 107 mm (Ee, under title). Compass (Aa). *EXPLANATION.* (Ea). *REFERENCE to the RAPES, HUNDREDS &c.* (Ce). Longitude 10' (2'); latitude 10' (2').

> Published as loose sheets, sold separately. The maps in this series were issued by a succession of publishers between 1825 and 1828   (CUL).(W)

(ii)   Imprint (Ce OS) erased and replaced by *Published Sept[r]. 20 1828, by S. MAUNDER, N[o]. 10, Newgate Street, London.*

> Published as loose sheets, sold separately.   (SAS)

(iii)   Title (Ee) altered to *New Map of the County of SUSSEX; Divided into Hundreds Containing the District Divisions and other LOCAL ARRANGEMENTS effected by the REFORM BILL.* Imprint (Ce OS) erased and replaced by *Published by J. Duncan. Paternoster Row. County Members 4. Elections at,* followed by square symbol, added

3.   Darlington and Howgego, 1964, no. 310 (4).
4.   Whitaker, 1947, no. 139.
5.   Tooley, 1979, p. 426.
6.   Cowling, 1959, p. 115.
7.   Whitaker, 1947, no. 319; Whitaker, 1948, no. 554.

(Ae); squares added on the map at *CHICHESTER* and *LEWES*. Five new symbols, indicating changes in parliamentary representation and polling places, added to *EXPLANATION*. (Ea), and marked on map, eg a cross at *PETWORTH*, two asterisks at *HASTINGS*.

A new atlas of England and Wales; consisting of a set of large county travelling maps . . . containing also the new district divisions . . . &c. agreeably to the provisions of the Reform Bill; thereby exhibiting on the map of each county both its present and former state of parliamentary representation.
London, James Duncan, 1833.   BRL

A complete county atlas of England & Wales, containing forty-four superior maps. With all the improvements – projected or completed. Divided into hundreds, with the district divisions, and other local arrangements effected by the Reform Bill.
London, James Duncan, 1827 (a misprint, perhaps for 1837), [1835]. 1837 and 1838.   P;BL;W.GLASGOW PL;P

(iv) *BRIGHTON AND LONDON RAILWAY* added and named.

A complete county atlas of England & Wales, containing . . .
London, James Duncan, [1840] and [1845].   BL;CUL

A complete county atlas of England & Wales, containing forty-four superior maps. With all the railroads and improvements . . .
London, James Duncan, [1845].   RGS

88 A.   FIRST LITHOGRAPHIC TRANSFER

Size: 425 mm × 330 mm (9 mm)   1:306,000

effected by the REFORM BILL erased from title (Ee). Imprint (Ce OS) erased and replaced by *London: Edward Stanford 6 Charing Cross. St Leonards, Sevenoaks, Tunbr. Wells* and much detail including roads, outside the county boundary have been added. Some roads added in the county, eg *Felpham* to *Patching* via *Ham, Billinghurst* to *Bolney*. Railways 1 to 14, 16 to 20 marked. Stations marked by black dots. Railway 2 extended to top border and *to London* added. *fr: Southampton & Gosport* added.

Issued as a folding map with printed title on cover: *Collins railway map of Sussex.*
London, Edward Stanford, [1865].   (WSRO)
The map of another county in this series is known.[8]

8.   Whitaker, 1948, no. 577.

State of the plate: Later than no. 88 (iv), including changes listed above, except the imprint (Ce OS).
Alterations on the transfer: Imprint (Ce OS) probably added.

88 B.   SECOND LITHOGRAPHIC TRANSFER

Size: 430 mm × 330 mm (9 mm)   1:306,000

Railways and Stations added at end of title (Ee). Imprint (Ce OS) erased. A four line note headed *PARLIAMENTARY REPRESENTATION* added (Ae). *County Members 4. Elections at . . .* (Ae) erased. Crosses to indicate places *for Polling* added at *BRIGHTON, Ripe* and many other towns. Railways 21 to 32 added; dots added along new lines, and some added along existing lines, eg at *Keymer Junction*, which is now named. An additional border, 38 mm at top and bottom and 57 mm at sides, containing information relating to *Railways, Antiquities,* etc. added.

> *Ready guide and tourists' handbook for Sussex. With . . . map of the County.*
> London, Ward, Lock and Co., [1878].   BL

State of the plate: Later than no. 88A. including changes above, except the additional border.
Alterations on the transfer,: Additional border added.

88 C.   THIRD LITHOGRAPHIC TRANSFER

Size: 426 mm × 176 mm (4 mm)   1:306,000

Title (Ee) erased except for *SUSSEX*, which has been raised 49 mm. *W. & A.K. Johnston, Edinburgh & London* added (Ee OS). Compass, *EXPLANATION* and *REFERENCE to the RAPES, HUNDREDS &c.* erased. Scale moved upwards by 82 mm. Border erased and replaced new border without longitude or latitude. The new border cuts out nearly all detail outside the county boundary, eg *BRIGHTON AND LONDON RAILWAY* and *ENGLISH CHANNEL*. The right border moved inwards so that *to Ramsgate* and *to Dover* now overlap the inner border. Additional station names added, eg *Hastings, St Leonards, Worthing Sta.* and *Lavant Sta.* Railways 33 to 38 and 40 to 42 added. The sea overprinted in blue.

> *A pictorial and descriptive guide to Hastings, St Leonards, Bexhill . . .*
> London, New York and Melbourne, Ward, Lock and Co., [1896]. BRIGHTON PL

State of the plate: Later than no. 88B. Railways and station names added.
Alterations on the transfer: Alterations to title, imprint (Ce OS), compass, scale and *REFERENCE to the RAPES, HUNDREDS &c.* probably made on the stone. New border added.

173

88 D.   FOURTH LITHOGRAPHIC TRANSFER

Size: 425 mm × 176 mm (4 mm)   1:306,000

Heene erased and re-engraved in the sea. *West Worthing* and *W. Brighton* added. Railway from *CHICHESTER* to *Selsey* added. Sea overprinted in blue.

> *A pictorial and descriptive guide to Hastings, St Leonards, Bexhill . . . second edition . . . map of Sussex . . .*
> London, New York and Melbourne, Ward, Lock and Co., [1898].   BL
> A later edition, issued about 1900, contains a map of the Sussex coast with George Philip imprint.

State of the plate: Later than no. 88C. including all alterations listed above.
Alterations on the transfer: As no. 88C.

89   CHRISTOPHER AND JOHN GREENWOOD   1825

Size: 1990 mm × 1214 mm (17 mm)   1:64,400

Based on the Ordnance Survey One Inch Old Series appendix VI.1(a), with a considerable amount of additional information. **See plate 29.**

Christopher Greenwood (1786–1855) was born in Yorkshire and started working as a surveyor in or before 1815. In 1818 he opened an office in London and in 1821 he was joined by his brother, John. George Pringle was associated with him for about ten years, from 1820. Pringle was a solicitor and may have put up money to get the business started. His son, also George, looked after the commercial side of the enterprise.

Between 1817 and 1831 Greenwood published maps on the scale of one inch to one mile for all but six of the English counties, starting with Yorkshire. All were based in whole or in part on original surveys, and represent, with the work of Andrew Bryant, the last attempt by private surveyors to compete with the Ordnance Survey at the national level. The maps were sold at three guineas each, and subscribers were offered the whole set (never completed) at 125 guineas. The map of Yorkshire was surveyed by Greenwood under the supervision of Netlam and Francis Giles of New Inn, London.[1] Netlam and Francis Giles surveyed the *Intended Arun and Portsmouth Canal . . .* in 1815,[2] and had been paid £148.8.0 in 1813 for planning a canal from Dell Quay to Chichester.[3] Greenwood published a map of London in 1827, of which the accuracy has been criticised.[4] By contrast, he produced in 1834 an attractive series of maps of the English counties (see no. 93), which, in Fordham's view, "constitute by far

1. Harley, 1962, p. 3.
2. Steer, 1968, p. 84.
3. SRS vol. 62, pp. xxx and 115.
4. Hyde, 1975, p. 1.

the most artistic, complete and interesting set of county maps ever issued."[5] Thereafter the business declined. The 1834 atlas was published from Burleigh Street, Strand, which was the address of Josiah Neele and of J. and C. Walker, who engraved most of the maps. It appears that Greenwood had been forced to give up his own premises. The British atlas (no. 108) published by the Walkers in 1837 was similar in style to Greenwood's atlas.

William Edwin Baxter, under whose auspices the Greenwood map was reissued in 1861, was a member of a well-known Lewes family,[6] a road in the town is named after them. William Edwin's father, John Baxter (1781–1858) was born in Surrey and lived with his grandfather at Tismans, Rudgwick until he was fourteen. He first worked for a Mr Matthew, printer, in the Strand, and then in Brighton, before moving to Lewes in 1803, where he set up as a book-seller, printer and publisher. He is credited with the invention, with Robert Harrild,[7] of the composition inking roller. His publications included a Bible, *Baxter's library of agriculture*, and several topographical works, of which Horsfield's histories of Lewes and of Sussex are of special interest. He also published *Lambert's cricketers guide*, much of which he wrote himself. He is mentioned several times in the *Journal of Gideon Mantell* (see no. 84) whose brother he employed. He achieved civic distinction, being appointed High Constable, then equivalent to Mayor, of Lewes in 1828. With his son, William Edwin, he founded the *Sussex Agricultural Express* in 1837, and retired in 1849, leaving his son to carry on the business.

William Edwin Baxter (1808–73) was educated at Lewes Grammar School. He was a staunch Conservative and took a keen interest in civic affairs, serving as High Constable in 1858, 1860 and 1863. He made a great success of the newspaper, and was active in other local enterprises; promoting, for example, the Brighton, Lewes and Hastings railway and subsequent railway developments. In 1856 he purchased the Walland estate, negotiated with Lord Abergavenny the extinction of existing 'sheep leases', and made the land available for building. According to his obituary,[8] these activities were prompted by a desire to benefit his native town. Reading between the lines, one forms a picture of a middle class Victorian businessman, with high moral standards, and motivated by enlightened self-interest.

Under William Edwin's direction the *Sussex Agricultural Express* became the recognised voice of the Conservative party. Its influence spread far beyond the boundaries of east Sussex. It circulated in both Surrey and Kent, and competed successfully with the established *Sussex Advertiser*, published in Brighton. By 1858, it had reached a circulation of over 160,000. Its expansion was attributed to Baxter's introduction of the correspondence system, whereby he established correspondents,

5. Fordham, 1914, p. 104.
6. *DNB*; G. Christian 'A Lewes Publisher'. in *SCM* vol. 26 (1952); Holman, 1927; parish records and wills. Notes on the back of a Baxter portrait at Barbican House, Lewes, suggest that John Baxter of Chichester (1755–1827) was the father of John Baxter of Lewes (1781–1858), but this is not confirmed from any other source.
7. The two families became closely connected. John Baxter's son, George, married Harrild's daughter, Mary; his daughter Mary married Harrild's son Robert. Later Edith, daughter of William Edwin Baxter, married a Frederick Harrild.
8. *Sussex Agricultural Express* for 11 January 1873.

some paid, in all the towns in his area, who sent him regular weekly newsletters. Hitherto most editors had relied on virtually fortuitous reports of local happenings. *The Times* reported in October, 1870, 'The list of English Provincial Papers still has to place first the "SUSSEX AGRICULTURAL EXPRESS", which, heading the list, took 365.000 stamps.' William Edwin was active in 1853 on behalf of the Provincial News-papers Society, of which he became President in 1854–5, in a campaign to prevent the repeal of the stamp duties. They feared that removal of the duty would cheapen the character of the Press[9] and perhaps that unscrupulous publishers would attract adver-tising on the basis of exaggerated circulation figures, which could not then be verified. Letters written by him to W.E. Gladstone, then Chancellor, on the subject, have survived.[10]

About 1865 he retired to Wynnestay Lodge, Bedford Park, Croydon, where he died in 1873,[11] after a long illness. His reasons for leaving Lewes have not been estab-lished, but he was buried in the family vault at All Saints, Lewes. He had married Anne Minshall in 1843, and he left three sons and two daughters – Wynne Edwin (see below), Minshall (died in New Zealand in 1876), Harrild (b. 1851), Mary Anne Simpson (b. 1848) and Edith Warner Harrild (b. circa 1859). Anne Minshall was the daughter of Edward Minshall and Margaret Wynne.

The identical initials of William Edwin and his eldest son, Wynne Edwin, have caused some confusion. One authority[12] refers to W.E. Baxter, author of *Feathered vocalist; a history of British singing birds* published in 1830, as being the grandson of John Baxter. In view of the fact that John was only married in 1801, it is more likely that this work was by his son, William Edwin. The same writer maintains that the firm was run for thirty years after the death of John by his grandson; but William Edwin was certainly in charge of the firm in 1861, when the map described below (no. 89A) was published. Wynne probably assumed responsibility for the paper shortly before 1865, when his father moved to Croydon. William Edwin's will (dated 15.1.1868) refers to 'The County Chronicle now being managed by my son, Wynne Edwin', and bequeathes to him half the value thereof, including goodwill. The reference to the newspaper by this name is curious.

Wynne Edwin Baxter (1844–1920), grandson of John Baxter, founded the firm of Lewes solicitors which still bears his name. He took an interest in local politics, serving as High Constable in 1879 and 1880, and as the first Mayor of Lewes in 1881. He was a founder member of the Sussex Archaeological Society. He wrote the introduction to the *Sussex domesday book,* published in 1876, and had a paper on Milton published by the Bibliographical Society in 1901. He was the owner of the Palmer and Covert map, now in the British Library (see appendix II.2). His hobby was the study of diatomaceae.

In 1906 he moved to Stoke Newington, and as coroner for the East London district conducted inquests on the victims of Jack the Ripper and on those killed at the siege of

9. Whorlow, 1886, pp. 54–5; Andrews, 1859, p. 321 et seq.
10. BL Add MS. 44374 (folio 210) and 44375 (folio 135).
11. *Who was who 1916–1928* gives the date as 1871, but this is probably a confusion with William Baxter, the botanist, who died in that year.
12. Christian, 1952 (see note 6 above).

Sydney Street. He was buried at Lewes, leaving an estate of £29,309.[13] His elder son, Reginald Truscott Baxter (1871–1939) carried on the solicitors business in Lewes, where he was Town Clerk from 1915 to 1925.

In addition to his other activities, Wynne Baxter maintained an interest in the printing and publishing business, and was made chairman when it was formed into a limited company in 1888. The manager at that time was George Holman, author of *Some Lewes men of note*. The *Sussex Express* was sold to F.J. Parsons in 1914, but the printing firm of W.E. Baxter still exists, although no member of the family is now associated with it.

The best known member of the family was George Baxter (1804–67),[14] son of John Baxter and brother of William Edwin. He was an artist and engraver, and assisted with the production of illustrations for Horsfield's *History of Lewes,* which was published by his father in 1824–7. About 1827 he moved to London and in the same year he married the daughter of his father's associate, Robert Harrild. His international reputation rests on the quality of his colour prints. The process, for which he obtained a patent in 1836, combined metal engraving with the application of colour from wood blocks. He was a cantankerous character and quarrelled with his family to such an extent that he did not even attend his father's funeral. He was also a poor businessman. In 1860 his stock of plates was sold to Vincent Brooks, Day and Son, by whom his son, George, was employed. A collection of Baxter prints was given to the British Museum in 1901 by Francis William (Frank) Baxter, the younger son of Wynne Baxter.

William Figg's name appears on the first lithographic transfer. Eden[15] lists William Figg, surveyor, as active between 1799 and 1866, and Steer[16] catalogues maps and estate plans by William Figg between 1799 and 1861. These maps and plans were the work of two William ,Figgs, father and son. There were, in fact, four generations of William Figgs of the parishes of St. Johns and St. Michaels in Lewes. The first was probably the William Figg who married Charity Verral in 1738. The Verrals were a long established Lewes family[17] with book trade connections. Edward Verral (1707–67) was a Lewes book-seller, and founder of the *Lewes Journal.* In 1759 he published, in conjunction with John Rivington, *A complete system of cookery . . .* by his brother, William, who was proprietor of the White Hart Inn. Two sisters, Elizabeth Ruth and Rebecca, married two brothers named Palmer in 1849; both were book-sellers, Samuel in Brighton and Joseph in Paternoster Row.

The second William Figg (d. 1799) served as Constable of Lewes in 1785, and was probably a baker by trade. On 25 February 1770 he married Lucy Ridgeway, and his son William was christened on 7th September in the same year.

This third William Figg (1770–1833) was the first of the two surveyors. In 1820 he read an address to the Queen in his capacity as High Constable. By his wife, Susanna (d. 1847) he had four sons and a daughter. The daughter, also Susanna, died aged

13. *The Times*, Obituary (2 Oct. 1920); Will (4 Dec. 1920).
14. Courtney-Lewis, 1908; Gohm, 1969.
15. Eden, 1975.
16. Steer, 1962 and 1968.
17. *SAC* vol. 58, pp. 99–131.

thirty in 1831. Mantell (see no. 84) wrote in his Journal 'Attended the funeral of my friend Miss Figg at St. John's, with that pompous priest the Rev. P. Crofts. The poor girl was an early and much valued friend of mine. – Am quite out of sorts . . .'[18]

Figg's eldest son, the fourth William Figg (1799–1866) took over his father's surveying practice. He was Constable in 1852, and is mentioned a number of times in the *Lewes Town Book*.[19] He was a founder member of the Sussex Archaeological Society, and in its early years formed, with Lower and Blaauw, an unofficial executive committee. He was a regular contributor to *SAC*, and also wrote booklets on religious subjects. His wife's name was Elizabeth, and it is probable that she predeceased him and that he died without issue; his will leaves his estate to his brother, John Figg. It is this fourth William Figg, whose name appears on the 1861 reissue of the Greenwood map.

Over 150 plans were executed by the two Figgs between 1799 and 1858. We know from Holman that the father was active until at least 1816,[20] and that the son was working on his own by 1825.[21] No attempt has yet been made to differentiate in more detail between the work of the two men.

Besides their own work, the Figgs assembled an outstanding collection of estate plans of the county,[22] of which most have now been deposited with the Sussex Archaeological Society.

The 1861 map was not printed at Baxter's own works at Lewes, but by Maclure, Macdonald and Macgregor, a firm of specialist lithographers, which used steam operated machines. They also printed the Palmer and Covert map reproduced by Baxter's son in 1870 (see appendix II.2). They operated from Walbrook, in London, but were probably of Scottish origin.

The map was printed from six plates, fitting together in two rows of three. It is usually found with sheets I and IV, II and V, and III and VI joined together; some-times with all six joined together. It is the first map of the county to mark the boundaries of the parishes.

The lithographic transfers are first referred to in an advertisement in the *Sussex Express* for 26 December 1857, which reads: 'We intend next year, at Midsummer, to present to each of our subscribers, at a mere nominal cost, the first part of the SPLENDID REVISED MAP OF THE COUNTY OF SUSSEX, which was originally published at four guineas. It will be completed in six parts, and in each succeeding half-year we intend to issue a part until the work is finished.' The project was again advertised in the issue of 27 February 1858: 'Proposals for republishing the Great Map of Sussex. With the new railways and other important alterations and works in the

18. Curwen, 1940, p. 95.
19. SRS vols. 69 and 70.
20. Holman, 1927. His name appears on later plans. One carries a note . . . *the boundaries between the manors of Ditchling and Lindfield as agreed in July 1830 by David Rowland Esq. & William Thorpe Esq.*, and is signed *Willm Figg & Willm Figg Jnr.*.
21. He was working, probably in his father's office and not necessarily as a surveyor, by 1817. Dickins (Lewes, 1981, p. 23) refers to a map 'copied . . . by William Figg junior 1817'.
22. *Catalogue of the maps and plans accumulated by the late William Figg of Lewes, Land Surveyor. Published by George Fuller, successor to the late Mr Figg. Lewes, 1870.*

county . . . An opportunity occurred some time ago to the proprietor of the Journal to become the purchaser of the copyright and all the plates. . . . The ordinary plan would be to publish the Map by Subscription, and thereby secure a high remuneration to the publisher; but this would not ensure a sale sufficiently extensive to effect any real amount of public good. . . . The highest remuneration we seek is the confidence and encouragement of those who for very many years have accorded us their support as journalists.' It announced the intention to print five thousand copies to be sold to subscribers at sixpence per sheet, a return of £750. An advertisement in the issue for 6 September 1859 reads: 'THE GREAT MAP OF SUSSEX. IN THE COURSE OF PUBLICATION, exclusively for the subscribers of this newspaper. Part 1 (Published) . . . Part 2 (Published) . . . Part 3 (In the hands of the engraver) . . . Part 4 (Preparing) . . . Part 5 (Preparing) . . . Part 6 (Preparing) . . . The corrections and new surveys are made under the direction of Mr Figg, FAS, Surveyor, Lewes, The object of this publication is to ensure to upwards of 5,000 influential inhabitants of Sussex and adjacent counties a first class map of the county, with the addition of the new railways, mansions, turnpike roads, and other changes made in Sussex during the last quarter of a century. It would have been impossible to bring this publication out under a cost of FOUR GUINEAS each copy, had it not been produced in conjunction with the subscribers of this newspaper, to whom it is presented at a mere nominal charge. It is not intended to publish any more copies than those required by the subscribers. The publisher will feel particularly obliged to the owners of property and mansions built within the last 25 years to furnish him with particulars of the name, the situation, and also with notice of additions made to boundaries or alterations to roads, &c. TO THE SUBSCRIBER – Those who have not received copies of Parts 1 and 2 will oblige the publishers by applying for orders to the office at Lewes . . . Parties desirous of obtaining copies of this splendid map can do so by becoming Subscribers to the Sussex Express . . .' The *Part* numbers do not correspond with sheet numbers of the original publication, but work out as follows:

Sheet I Part 6	Sheet II Part 4	Sheet III Part 2
Sheet IV Part 5	Sheet V Part 3	Sheet VI Part 1

If the period of 25 years is to be taken literally, the last intaglio issue, no. 89 (vii), must have been about 1833. The last advertisement continued to appear until the middle of 1861, the words in brackets after each *Part* being amended to mark the progress of the work. As far as can be ascertained from advertisements, the six *Parts* were actually published as follows: *Part* 1 in June, 1858, *Part* 2 in September 1859, *Part* 3 in January 1860, *Part* 4 in March 1860, *Part* 5 in May 1861 and *Part* 6 in June 1861. After June 1861 the advertisement reads: 'Just Published, THE GREAT MAP OF SUSSEX, From Original Surveys, corrected to the present time, with all the Roads and

179

Railways accurately laid down, from authentic resources, under the direction of MR. FIGG, F.A.S. SURVEYOR, LEWES . . . (the six Parts are then listed without the words in brackets) . . . As this Map is now completed, and is published for the exclusive advantage of the subscribers to this newspaper . . . The Publisher having received many orders for the Map, begs to say that it is not offered for public sale, and the only means for obtaining a copy is to become a subscriber to this journal for two years, the cost of which is only about half the price at which it would have been otherwise published.' Thomas Jull of Horsham and W. Townshend of Uckfield advertised that they would mount the parts in various ways for subscribers, in particular on rollers, in which form it is often found. One impression (GLC) has a buff label (146 mm × 109 mm) stuck on sheet III, which reads *GREAT MAP OF SUSSEX PART 2. THE NORTH-EASTERN DISTRICT. SUBSCRIBERS COPY. This Map is published exclusively to the Subscribers of the SUSSEX EXPRESS, SURREY STANDARD, KENT MAIL, HANTS AND COUNTY ADVERTISER, and one part will be issued every Half-year until completed. Originally published at Six Guineas; is now presented at the mere nominal charge of 6d. each part to the Subscribers of the above Journal.* Sheet V has a similar lable in green and designated *PART* 3.

Sheets V and VI have been found in three states (nos 89A, 89B and 89C), sheets II and III in two states (nos. 89A and 89B) and sheets IV and I in only one state (no. 89A). The eastern areas were probably published first because the paper circulated primarily in the Lewes area of Sussex, and it seems that the earlier sheets were amended before the publication of the last two parts, no doubt as a result of information sent in by subscribers. Complete copies of the map have been found in a variety of combinations of the six sheets, thus:

Location of map	State of sheet					
	I	II	III	IV	V	VI
GLC	A	A	A	A	A	A
SAS (1)	A	A	A	A	A	A
Brighton PL	A	A	A	A	A	B
WSRO PM 64	A	A	A	A	B	A
PM 248	A	A	A	A	A	C
PM 203	A	B	A	A	A	*
PM 14	A	B	B	A	A	A
PHA 3528	A	B	A	A	C	A
Hove PL	A	B	B	A	C	C
BL maps 6.e.7	A	B	B	A	C	C
SAS (2)	A	B	A	A	C	C

* Sheet missing

No 89A below, represents a map put together by a subscriber who collected the six sheets as they were first published, ie GLC and SAS(1). No 89C describes a map made up from sheets in the final state of publication, ie BL maps 6.e.7 and HOVE PL. No. 89B represents an intermediate state and shows the changes to sheets V and VI between no 89A, as originally published, and no. 89C, the final state. No set in this specific intermediate state (ie A B B A B B) has been found.

EDITIONS

(i) *MAP OF THE COUNTY OF SUSSEX. from an Actual Survey in the Years 1823 & 1824, by C. & I GREENWOOD. Most Respectfully DEDICATED TO THE Nobility, Clergy & Gentry. OF THE COUNTY. by the Proprietors GREENWOOD, PRINGLE & Cº. Nº. 13 Regent Street Pall Mall. London. March 24th. 1825* (Aa). *London. Published March 24th. 1824 by Greenwood Pringle & Cº.* (top centre outside border, on sheet IV). *London. Published March 24th. 1825 by Greenwood Pringle & Cº.* (bottom centre outside border, on sheets II and III; top centre outside border, on sheets V and VI); these imprints being cut off or pasted over when the sheets are joined. *SCALE OF STATUTE MILES* 1 + 6 = 150 mm (Be). Compass (Ea). Plate numbers in Roman numerals, top left outside borders on sheets II, III, V and VI; top right outside border on sheet IV; sheet one not numbered. *Explanation* (Be, above scale). *REFERENCE TO THE HUNDREDS* (Ce). *CHICHESTER CATHEDRAL.* and engraving (Ee). Longitude 5' (1'); latitude 5' (1'). **See plate 29 (i).**

Issued as loose sheets, sold separately from 1825. (WSRO).(RGS)

(ii) *Kemp Town* added, and windmill altered to house symbol. Windmill east of *BRIGHTHELMSTONE* moved 2 mm to north, and square-shaped symbol added at *Gas Works.*

Issued as loose sheets, sold separately. (WSRO)

(iii) *Imberhorn* erased and *Imberhorn Farm* added to the south. *TB* added at *EAST GRINSTEAD. Chantlers Farm* and *Newlands* added north-west of *EAST GRINSTEAD.*

Issued as loose sheets, sold separately. (CUL)

(iv) *Godstone* added and marked by Maltese cross.

Issued as loose sheets, sold separately. (W).(WSRO)

(v) Church symbol added at *Little Hampton.* New road from *Little Hampton* to *Bilsom,* the branch to *Yapton* raised to turnpike status, mileages 6 to 9 added, *Ferry* added where it crosses the *River Arun, Hospital* added.

Issued as loose sheets, sold separately. (BL).(BOD).(HASTINGS PL)

(vi) *PETERSFIELD, HASLEMERE, Sandhurst* and *Hawkhurst* added outside county boundary.

Issued as loose sheets, sold separately.   (SAS)

(vii)   The county boundary from the road direction *To Cranbrook* to a point north of *Ticehurst* has been extended, the addition measuring 75 mm × 40 mm. *Flimwell, Quedley, Brookgate Farm, Mumpumps, Dane Hill, Burners Hill, Little Bearsell, Ho.* (after *Pickford*), *T.B.*, and many roads and woodlands have been added. Road directions *From Tonbridge, To Hawkhurst* erased; *From Cranbrook* (at *New Bridge*), *To Maistone through Goudhurst* added. The road from *HORSHAM* to *Crawley* has been upgraded and a new section added from *Roughey Street* to *Crawley*; mileages, *1, 3, 4, 5, 6* and *7* added. *Fay Gate* erased. *North Hayling* added outside county boundary. The cloud engraving behind the spire of *CHICHESTER CATHEDRAL* (Ee) has been modified, eg the engraving does not now extend above the top of the spire. Two loops, 6 mm long, on either side of the top of the spire are now clearly visible. *Neele's Sc, 13 Newcastle S^t. Strand.* has been added near the border to the left of the engraving.

Issued as loose sheets, sold separately.   (BL)

(viii)   In the title (Aa), address altered to *N°. 3 Burleigh Street Strand; 1824* altered to *1834; CORRECTED TO APRIL 1839* added at end. *BRIGHTHELMSTONE* re-engraved *BRIGHTON*. Railways 1 and 2 shown by plain double lines, *London and Brighton Railway* added. Extra borders added at top of sheets IV and V with the words *ENVIR* (sheet IV, top right), *ONS OF WORTHING* (sheet V, top left) and *ENVIRONS OF BRIGHTON* (sheet V, top and left of centre). On each sheet *Scale of Miles 5 = 127* mm added (Da OS). (These additions, presumably designed to enable these sheets to be sold separately, are not visible when sheets IV and V are joined to sheets I and II respectively, and may have been added in an earlier state).

No impression from the plate in this state has been found, and it is probable that none was issued. There is, however, a lithographic impression from the plate in this state, but with *CHICHESTER CATHEDRAL* and the engraving (Ee) omitted and with the election information and note (Da), see no. 89A below, added (SAS, Figg 680). This impression is in sepia, sheet IV is missing, and there are numerous amendments in ink. It seems probable that the plate was prepared by Greenwood for a c.1839 edition, which was abandoned; and that the transfer (with engraving of cathedral omitted, but with information and note (Da) added) was taken from the plates by Figg some time before 1861 in order to help him up-date the plates for the 1861 publication. The ink amendments are probably in Figg's own hand.

89 A.   FIRST LITHOGRAPHIC TRANSFER[23]

Size: 2008 mm × 1232 mm (17 mm)   1:64,400

In the title (Aa) all words after . . . *In the Years 1823 and 1824* erased and replaced by *Corrected to the present time by WILLIAM FIGG, F.S.A. Surveyor PRESENTED TO*

---

23.   Not the first transfer, see 89 (viii) above, but the first published transfer.

THE SUBSCRIBERS TO THE SUSSEX EXPRESS, SURREY STANDARD & KENT MAIL. By the Proprietor, WILLIAM EDWIN BAXTER. LEWES 1861. Printed by Maclure MacDonald & Macgregor, London added (Ee OS). Neele signature to left of engraving (Ee) erased. *WESTERN DIVISION/EASTERN DIVISION* followed in each case by *PLACE OF ELECTION* and lists of *POLLING PLACES*, then *Shews the Division of the County. Boundary of Boroughs*, and a note relating to *Borough of New Shoreham* added (Da). A note relating to *Additional Poling Places since 1832 . . . from the introduction of Lord John Russell's bill in 1860* added (Ae). There are numerous changes on the map, eg additions at *WORTHING* include *Gas Works, Water Works. Ruins* altered to *Brambletye Ruins. The Vicarage* erased and *U. House* added at *East Bourne. Grand Parade* and other names added along coastline. *Church Farm* added and *Lime Farm* altered to *Parsonage F.* at *Herstmonceux. Hilders Farm* added at *Chiddingly. Cricket Ground* added at *Tunbridge Wells.* To the north and east of *Ticehurst* additions include *Seacocks Heath House, Stone Crouch, Union Ho., New Church* and a road to *Beals Bridge.* Road added from *Hawkhurst* to *Sedlescome. Sᵗ. Mary Magdalen* altered to *Sᵗ. Leonards* and two roads running north added. *PEVENSEY HARBOUR* altered to *PEVENSEY BAY.* Railways 1 to 14, 16 to 20 and 27 added as in use; 21 to 24 as projected; the lines named; *Station* added in many places. **See plate 29 (ii).**

Issued as loose sheets, sold separately, 1858 to 1861. (GLC).(SAS)

State of the plate: Later than no. 89 (viii). All the alterations listed above except the imprint (Ee OS) and the note (Da) commencing *Shews the . . .* were probably made on the plate. The note (Da) seems to be an afterthought and may well have been added on the stone, although the style resembles the note relating to . . . *New Shoreham. Alterations on the transfer:* Maclure imprint and note (Da) added.

89 B. SECOND LITHOGRAPHIC TRANSFER

Size: 2008 mm × 1232 mm (17 mm)   1:64,400

Sheets I and IV as no. 89A.

Sheet II: *Inholm Farm, Courtingham* and *South Park* added. Note (Da) commencing *Shews the . . .* omitted.

Sheet III: *Brenchley* erased. Over twenty additions, eg *Hargate Lodge, Little Rosehill Farm, Willards Hill. Beals* altered to *Bewls; Latingham* to *Gottenham. Farm* erased at *Haremare Farm.* Railway 15 added.

Sheet V: To the east of *BRIGHTON*, roads, house symbols and a park have been erased leaving only one road to *Kemp Town.*

Sheet VI: *Cornfield Ter.* and *Reddyke* added. *Bexhill* added to *Station. Hill Farm* erased and replaced by *Upper Barn Horn; Duffs Farm* replaced by *Dulvies Farm.*

Issued as loose sheets, sold separately.

State of the plate: Later than no. 89A. Altered to include all the changes listed above, except omission of the note (Da).
Alterations on the transfer: None.

89 C. THIRD LITHOGRAPHIC TRANSFER

Size: 2008 mm × 1232 mm (17 mm)   1:64,400

Sheets I, II, III and IV as no. 89B.
Sheet V: *Sta^n*. at *Bramber, Race Course* (now marked twice) and *Houndean Bottom* to the west of *LEWES* have been added. *Malt Kiln* near *Old Shoreham* erased and replaced by *Swiss Gardens.*
Sheet VI: Maclure imprint (Ee OS) omitted. Considerable alteration to the engraving of the clouds behind the spire of *CHICHESTER CATHEDRAL*, eg there is now a white patch, 20 mm × 15 mm, 50 mm to the left of the spire at 50°44'N, and the engraving on the right border now extends 8 mm above 50°43'N. The shading along the coastline has been increased; it now extends over 100 mm below the main coastline at *HASTINGS*, whereas on no. 89B it extends to less than 90 mm. About thirty place-names added, eg *Tokes F., Vale of Ecclesbourn, Oaks F., Court Lodge, The Gore, Braggs F.*. Four place-names altered, eg *Beams Farm* to *Coghurst Farm, Dulvies Farm* to *Dunks Farm* (called *Duffs Farm* on no. 89A; *Dulveys* on first edition of the One Inch Ordnance Survey Old Series).

Issued as loose sheets, sold separately.   (BL).(HOVE PL)

State of the plate: Later than no. 89B. Altered to include all changes listed above, except omission of imprint (Ee OS)
Alterations on the transfer: None.

90 JAMES PIGOT AND SON   circa **1826**

Size: 341 mm × 213 mm (7 mm)   1:396,000

Based on Cary no. 61 (vi).

James Pigot[1] is first heard of in 1794 as an engraver and printer in Manchester. In 1804 he engraved the map for Dean's Manchester directory. In 1811 he set up on his own in competition with Dean, though from 1813 to 1824 they cooperated in the issue of a Manchester directory every two years. By 1823 Pigot had agents in various parts of the country. He opened an office in London and issued his first directory covering

---

1. Norton, 1950 pp. 43–5.

London and the southern counties. His son was in business with him from about 1839, when he took Isaac Slater into partnership. He died in 1843, but Slater continued the directories, which were published, even after the latter's death, until taken over by Kelly & Co. in 1892.

EDITIONS

(i) *SUSSEX.* (Ca in border). *Engraved on Steel by Pigot & Son Manchester* (Ee OS). *Published by Pigot & C⁰. 24 Basing Lane, London & Fountain St. Manchester.* (Ce OS). *SCALE 10 Miles* = 41 mm (Ce, in border). Compass (Ba). *REFERENCE to the HUNDREDS.* (Ee). *Explanation.* (Aa). Longitude 5' (1'); latitude 5' (1'). *Longitude East from Greenwich* (De, in border). *CHICHESTER CATHEDRAL.* with engraving (Ea).

Issued about 1826 as a set of maps without title-page by J. Pigot and Co.   P

Pigot and Co's London & provincial new commercial directory, for 1826–7 . . . [of London and six counties] *. . . The volume is embellished with a new series of elegant maps of the above-named counties, engraved expressly for the work . . .* 3rd edn.
London and Manchester, J. Pigot and Co.   GL
The same firm's directory for 1823–4 of London, Sussex and seventeen other counties does not contain county maps.

Pigot and Co's London & provincial new commercial directory, for 1827–8 . . . [of London and six counties] *. . .* 3rd edn.
London and Manchester, J. Pigot and Co.
The only copy found (GL) lacks the maps.

Pigot and Co's London & provincial new commercial directory, for 1828–9 . . . [of London and six counties] *. . .* 3rd edn.
London and Manchester, J. Pigot and Co.   GL

With leather-bound copies of each of the above directories the maps were issued bound separately, without title-page.

Issued in a set of maps without title-page by J. Pigot and Co. about 1830.   W

Piggot & Cⁿˢ. British atlas. of the counties of England . . . the whole engraved on steel plates, and embellished with a correct graphic series of vignettes of the cathedrals and some of the handsomest churches in England . . .
London and Manchester, J. Pigot and Co., 1830.   BOD.GL

(ii) Canals marked from *Birdham* to *Riv. Arun* and from *Egdean* to two miles south of *GUILDFORD.* Many roads added, eg *Field Place* (near *HORSHAM*) to *Cranley* and beyond, *Burwash* to *Ashburnham.* A number of roads upgraded, eg *PETWORTH* to *Wisborough Green*. The road from *CHICHESTER* to *Lit. Hampton* via *Middleton* is partly new and partly upgraded.

Pigot & Co[s]*. British atlas . . .*
London and Manchester, J. Pigot and Co. 1831.   W

(iii)   Imprint (Ce OS) erased and replaced by *Published by Pigot & C*[o]*. 1 Basing Lane London & Fountain S*[t]*. Manchester.*

Pigot and Co[s]*. British atlas . . .*
London and Manchester, J. Pigot and Co., 1831 (actually a reissue of 1832), and 1832   CUL.P²

Pigot and Co's national London, & provincial commercial directory, for 1832–3–4.
. . [of London and six counties] . . . 5th edn.
London and Manchester, J. Pigot and Co., [July 1832 and October 1832].
GL.BRIGHTON PL; GENEALOGICAL SOC

Pigot and Co's national London, & provincial commercial directory, for 1833–4 . .
. [of London and six counties] . . . 5th edn.
London and Manchester, J. Pigot and Co.
The only copy found (GL) lacks the maps.

Pigot and Co's national London, & provincial commercial directory, for 1833–4 . . .
[of London and six counties] . . . 5th edn. 'improved'.
London and Manchester, J. Pigot and Co., 1834.   BL

With leather bound copies of each of the above directories the maps were issued bound separately, without title-page.

(iv)   Imprint (Ce OS) erased and replaced by *Published by Pigot and C*[o]*. 59 Fleet Street, London, & Fountain St. Manchester.* In the *Explanation* (Aa), after *Division of the Counties, according to the Reform Bill* has been added and the pecked line replaced by alternate short vertical lines and longer horizontal lines; in the last line, *RYE* is now followed by a town symbol with one asterisk in place of two. On the map, one asterisk has been omitted at *RYE*, both omitted at *EAST GRINSTEAD* and *WINCHELSEA*, and one added at *BRIGHTHELMSTONE or BRIGHTON*. *Polling Places* with triangle symbol and *Rail Roads* added at end of *Explanation;* nine triangles added on map. *W.D.* added 20 mm north-east of *PETWORTH: E.D.* added 8 mm south-west of *Mayfield. S*[t] *Leonards* added. Railways 1, 2 and a line from *BRIGHTON* to *LEWES* with a branch to *Newhaven* marked and *Brighton R*[y]. named. Outside the county boundary a branch line to *REIGATE* is shown, and a line running south of *TUNBRIDGE* is marked and named *South Eastern R*[y].

2.   Deighton Bell catalogue 221, item 1126.

186

Pigot & Co^s. British atlas, comprising the counties of England, (upon which are laid down all railways completed and in progress) . . .
London and Manchester, J. Pigot and Co., [1839].   BL

Pigot & Co's royal national and commercial directory and topography of . . .
[eleven counties] . . . To which is added, a directory of London and its suburbs . . .
The work is embellished with beautiful county maps; upon which is conspicuously
laid down every line of railway, for which an Act of Parliament has been obtained to
the present time.
London and Manchester, J. Pigot and Co., 1839.   GL.HASTINGS PL

(v)   Signature (Ee OS) erased and replaced by *Engraved on Steel by Pigot & Co.*
Manchester.

Pigot and Co's royal national and commercial directory and topography of . . .
[eleven counties] . . . To which is added, a classified directory of London . . .
London and Manchester, J. Pigot and Co. [1839].   BL

Pigot and Co's royal national, commercial, and street directory of London, for 1840
. . . To which are added, directories of [eleven counties] . . . The work is embel-
lished with beautiful county maps; with all railways conspicuously and faithfully laid
down. . .
London and Manchester, J. Pigot and Co.   BL.BOD

Pigot & Co^s. British atlas . . .
London and Manchester, J. Pigot and Co., [1840], [1841] and [1842].
                                                          W.A;CUL;BRL.W

Pigot & Co^s. British atlas . . .
London and Manchester, Pigot and Slater, [1843].   CUL

(vi)   Imprint (Ce OS) erased and replaced by *Published by I. Salter, Fleet Street,*
London, & Fountain St. Manchester. Signature (Ee OS) erased and replaced by
Engraved on Steel by I. Slater, Manchester. Railways 3, 4, 5, 7, 8 and 13 added.

I. Salter's new British atlas, comprising the counties of England (upon which are
laid down all railways completed and in progress) . . .
London and Manchester, Isaac Slater, [1846] and [1847].   BL;CUL.BOD

(vii)   Railways 9, 10, 11, 12, 14 (routed from *Whatlington* to *WINCHELSEA*), 16, 19
and 20 (*NEW SHOREHAM* to *STEYNING* only) added. Outside the county parts of
railways A, C, E and F added.

I. Slater's new British atlas . . .
London and Manchester, Isaac Slater, [1857].   BL

187

91 J. PASS   1827

Size: 236 mm × 173 mm (5 mm)   1:554,000

A re-engraved version of Neele no. 74.

Nothing has been discovered regarding J. Pass.

John Wilkes[1] (1750–1810), the compiler of the encyclopaedia noted below, was not connected with the John Wilkes of *North Briton* fame. He started as a printer in Winchester and was proprietor of the *Hampshire Chronicle*. He sold his Winchester business in 1784, and, in conjunction with Peter Barfoot, published *The universal British directory* . . . in 1790. Barfoot was a cantankerous gentleman from Droxford, near Southampton, and Wilkes something of a shady character. He was fined for piracy in connection with the *Encyclopaedia Londinensis;* but he managed to protect the copyrights in his own works by securing royal patents. He died at Milland House, Trotton in Sussex, but is buried in Winchester.

EDITION

SUSSEX. (Ce OS). *J. Pass sc.* (Ee, OS). *Engraved for the Encyclopaedia Londinensis, 1827* (Ce OS, below title). *British Miles 10* = 29 mm (Ce). Compass (Ce, above scale). Longitude 10' (2'); latitude 10' (2').

> *Encyclopaedia Londinensis; or, universal directory of arts, sciences, and literature . . . by John Wilkes* . . . vol. 23.
> London, G. Jones, 1828.   BL

92 SIDNEY HALL   1828

Size: 241 mm × 101 mm (1 mm)   1:793,000

The sources from which this map was derived have not been identified.

Peter John Martin (1786–1860), author of the work noted below, was the son of a Scottish doctor. He was born in Pulborough, studied medicine and took over his father's practice in that town. He was a keen gardener, but devoted most of his spare time to the study of geology and archaeology. He contributed a number of papers to *Sussex archaeological collections.*

The map covers an area to the east as far as Dover, but the information on the map relates primarily to Sussex.

---

1. Norton, 1950, pp. 32–35; Nichols, J. and J.B. 1817 to 1858 vol. 8, p. 475.

Weald Denudation (Ca OS). *Engraved by Sid*ᵞ. *Hall* (Ee OS). *London. Published by J. Booth, Duke Str*ᵗ. *Portland Place, Feb*ᵞ. *1828* (Ce OS). *Plate II* (Ea OS). *Fig. I.* (Ea). Figures 2 and 3 appear below the map on the same page and together measure 241 mm × 85 mm. The imprint and signature are at the foot of the page, below Figures 2 and 3. Geological formations are delineated on the map by pecked lines, and a colour key appears at the foot of the page above the Booth imprint.

> *A geological memoir on a part of western Sussex . . . by P.I. Martin.*
> London, John Booth, 1828.   BL.SAS.ESCL
> This work sometimes has *GEOLOGICAL MAP of the SOUTH-EASTERN part of SUSSEX. by Gideon Mantell. F.L.S. &c.* which was engraved by *J. Wyld*, and printed by *The Lithographic Press, 6 Dartmouth S*ᵗ. *West*ᵗ., bound with it.

93   CHRISTOPHER AND JOHN GREENWOOD   1829

Size: 658 mm × 548 mm (15 mm)   1:196,000

Based on Greenwood no. 89.

EDITIONS

(i) *MAP of THE COUNTY OF SUSSEX from an actual Survey MADE IN THE YEARS 1823 AND 1824 By C. & J. GREENWOOD. Published by the Proprietors, GREENWOOD & C*ᵒ. *13, Regent Street Pall Mall. London CORRECTED TO THE PRESENT PERIOD July 4*ᵗʰ. *1829. Engraved by H. FROST Goswell R*ᵈ. (Aa). *Scale of Miles* 1 + 10 = 80 mm (Ce). Compass (Ca). *Explanation* (Ea). *REFERENCE TO THE HUNDREDS.* (Ae). *CHICHESTER CATHEDRAL* and engraving (Ee). *Sussex Contains 1423 Square Statute Miles* (Ce, under scale). Longitude 5' (1'); latitude 5' (1').

> *Atlas of the counties of England, from actual surveys made from the years, 1817 to 1833, by C. & J. Greenwood.*
> London, Greenwood & Co., 1834.   BL.BOD

(ii) Roads and road directions added at *TUNBRIDGE, Tunbridge Wells, Ockley, Horley* and near *EAST GRINSTEAD*, eg *To Cranbrook. To Maidstone* moved 10 mm to north. House symbols added at *TUNBRIDGE* and *Tunbridge Wells*. Six place-names added outside the county, eg *SEVEN OAKS*. Asterisks added, eg two at *HASLEMERE*.

> *Atlas of the counties of England . . .*
> London, Greenwood and Co., 1834.   W.GL.BRIGHTON PL

(iii)   *Mary's Fm*. added north of *Falmer,* and *Wick* added at *Hove.* Cloud engraving behind top half of the spire of *CHICHESTER CATHEDRAL* erased.

Atlas of the counties of England . . .
London, Greenwood and Co., 1834.   BL.BOD.(WSRO)

(iv)   Road from *Flimwell* to *Beal's Br.* added.

Atlas of the counties of England . . .
London, Greenwood and Co., 1834.   RGS.WSRO

(v)   S*ͭ*. *Mary Magdalen* erased and replaced by S*ͭ*. *Leonards,* and house symbols added.

Atlas of the counties of England . . .
London, Greenwood and Co., 1834.   CUL.WSRO

(vi)   *EASTERN DIVISION* and *WESTERN DIVISION* added on map. *PRINCIPAL PLACES OR COUNTY ELECTION* followed by fourteen lines of text including *Division of the County* and *Boundary of the Boroughs,* which are now marked on the map, added (Da). The cloud engraving behind *CHICHESTER CATHEDRAL* has again been modified, in particular, ten birds have been added to the right of the spire.

Atlas of the Counties of England . . .
London, Greenwood and Co., 1834.   W.(WSRO)

94   T.L. MURRAY   1830

Size: 435 mm × 337 mm (10 mm)   1:317,000

Copied from Ebden no. 88, and engraved by the same firm. A number of errors have been made in copying, eg *Dallington* appears as *Ballignton, Eridge Park* as *Bridge Park, Penhurst* as *Benhurst.*

William Robson,[1] see (iv) below, published directories, mostly of the London area, between 1819 and 1842. The business was taken over by Botwell and Co., but they were forced to give up publication almost immediately because of competition from Kelly and Co.

1.   Norton, 1950, pp. 58–9.

EDITIONS

(i)   *SUSSEX.* (Ea). *Drawn under the Superintendence of T.L. Murray* (Ae OS). *Hoare and Reeves Sc.* (Ee OS). *London. Published May, 1st. 1830, by T.L. Murray, 19, Adam Street, Adelphi.* (Ce OS). *SCALE – 10 Miles* =51 mm (Ae). Compass (Aa). *EXPLANATION* (De). *REFERENCE to the RAPES, HUNDREDS, &c.* (Be). Longitude 10' (1'); latitude 10' (1').

> *An atlas of the English counties divided into hundreds &c. . . projected on the basis of the trigonometrical survey by order of the Honble., the Board of Ordnance. Under the superintendence of T.L. Murray.*
> [London, T.L. Murray, 1830].   BL.CUL

(ii)   Date in imprint (Ce OS) altered to . . . *May, 1st. 1831.* . .

> *An atlas of the English counties . . .*
> London, T.L. Murray, 1831.   BL.CUL

(iii)   Date in imprint (Ce OS) altered to . . . *May, 1st. 1832* . . . Key to parliamentary information added (Ea, under title). This includes reference to colours yellow and red, but the map is hand-coloured. On the map, boroughs returning one or two members are marked by a black dot and by a black dot with a circle round it respectively; places of election by a rectangle; *Polling Places* by a Maltese cross. The boundary between west and east Sussex is now marked by a chain dot line (formerly marked by a dotted line).

> *An atlas of the English counties . . .*
> [London, T.L. Murray].   CUL

(iv)   New imprint *William Robson & Co. Directory Office. London.* added (Ce OS). Signature (Ae OS) and inscription (Ee OS) erased. Symbols for parliamentary representation revised both on map and in key (Ea) by the addition of a circle to each of the black dots and the omission of the rectangle for places of election. *Index of Reference to the Parochial Unions* added (De), with key letters *A to T* and *U*, and followed by a note. Some spelling errors corrected, eg *Penhurst, Dallington;* but *Bridge Park* remains. Railway 2 added and named *LONDON & BRIGHTON RAILWAY.*

> *Robson's . . . commercial directory of London and the six home counties . . . with a beautifully engraved map of each of the six counties, on which is delineated the new divisions or parochial unions . . . For 1838.* 19th edn.
> London, William Robson and Co., 1838.   GENEALOGICAL SOC.SAS
> 'Nineteenth edition' refers to the whole of Robson's series of directories, and not to this particular publication which is the first of the series to cover Sussex.

> *Robson's commercial directory of* [seven counties] *with a beautifully engraved map of each of the seven counties . . . For 1839.* 20th edn.
> London, William Robson and Co., 1839.   GL

191

Size: 181 mm × 141 mm (5 mm)   1:842,000

Based on Cary no. 49 or a derivative (Neele no. 74 or Pass no. 91).

See Rowe no. 72 for discussion on the history of the plates.

John Heywood (1804–64), see nos. 95C – I below, started life as a weaver, but set up as a stationer in Manchester in 1846. He prospered, and is said to have become the most important maker of copy-books in the world.[1] He was a city councillor in 1860–61. John Heywood (1832–88) took over on his father's death. The firm continued to prosper and in 1870 he opened the Excelsior printing and binding works, which employed no less than 750 people.

The dates assigned to the atlases containing lithographic transfers must be accepted with caution. A particular problem arises in the case of the atlas in BIRMINGHAM RL (see no. 95F); c. 1862 or even later would be consistent with the information on the Sussex map, but a study of the Hertfordshire map would indicate an earlier date, possibly c. 1858.[2]

EDITIONS

(i)   *SUSSEX* (Ca. in panel with hatched rectangular background). *London, Published Sept*^r. *1830, by Henry Teesdale, & C*^o. *302, Holborn.* (Ce OS). *Scale of Miles. 10 =* 18 mm (Ce). Compass (Aa).

> *A new travelling atlas, containing a complete set of county maps . . . The whole carefully revised and corrected to the year 1830.*
> London, Henry Teesdale and Co.   CUL

(ii)   Imprint (Ce OS) erased. *London & Brighton Railway* added and named. Plate number *38* added (Ee OS, sideways).

> *A new travelling atlas, containing a complete set of county maps . . . The whole carefully revised and corrected to the year 1843.*
> London, Henry Teesdale and Co.   P

1. Boase, 1965.
2. Hodson, 1974, no. 91c.

95 A. FIRST LITHOGRAPHIC TRANSFER

Size: 182 mm × 143 mm (2 mm)   1:842,000

EDITIONS

(i) *London. Published for the Proprietors by H.G. Collins. 22, Paternoster Row.*
added (Ce OS). Hatched background to title panel omitted. Plain three line border in
place of the Ordnance Survey type border. Plate number omitted. Railways 1 to 9 and
25 marked by black lines; but 6 and 25 are mis-routed to by-pass *Newhaven* and to end
touching the coastline at *Seaford.*

> *The travelling atlas, of England & Wales . . . the whole carefully revised and
> corrected to the present time.*
> London, Henry George Collins, [1848].   BL

(ii) Railways 10 to 14, 16, 22 and 23 marked by black lines; also direct line east from
Battle, and line 20 as far as *Steyning.* No plate number.

> *The travelling atlas of England and Wales . . .*
> London, Henry George Collins, [1850].   W

State of the plate: As no. 95 (ii).
Alterations on the transfer: Hatched background to title and border erased, and new
border added. Imprint (Ce OS) added. Plate number erased. Railways added.

95 B. SECOND LITHOGRAPHIC TRANSFER

Size: 182 mm × 143 mm (2 mm)   1:842,000

Imprint (Ce OS) altered to *London: (Published for the Proprietors) by W.S. Orr & Co,
2 Amen Corner, Paternoster Row. S^t. Leonard's* added. The railways now marked by a
single cross-hatched line; railways 1 to 9, 12, 13, 14 and 25 are marked; 16, 20, 22 and
23 omitted; 6 and 25 remain mis-routed; *Fr. Portsmth.* and *to Ashford* added, and in
each case part of the border has been erased.

> *The travelling atlas of England & Wales . . .*
> London, W.S. Orr and Co., [1852].   BL

> *The travelling atlas of England & Wales . . . Revised & corrected to the present
> time.*
> London, W.S. Orr and Co., [1852].   BL.W

State of the plate: Later than no. 95A. *S^t. Leonard's* and railways added.
Alterations on the transfer: Hatched background to title and border erased. New border

and imprint (Ce OS) added. Plate number erased.

95 C.   THIRD LITHOGRAPHIC TRANSFER

Size: 189 mm × 141 mm (5 mm)   1:842,000

Hatched frame to title panel (Ca) not erased. Imprint (Ce OS) altered to *Printed and Published by John Heywood 170 Deansgate Manchester.* Form lines added to coast. Railways 10, 11 and 16 added; 1 to 14, 16 and 25 now marked by single cross-hatched lines. No plate number. Ordnance Survey type border in original style; expanded to left and right; not partially erased (see no. 95B).

> *The travelling atlas of England & Wales . . . the whole carefully revised to the present time.*
> London, W.S. Orr and Co. (actually published by John Heywood in about 1856).
> GLOUCESTER PL

State of the plate: Later than 95B. Border partly re-engraved. Railways and form lines along coast added.
Alterations on the transfer: Imprint (Ce OS) added. Plate number erased. (Title panel as originally engraved).

95 D.   FOURTH LITHOGRAPHIC TRANSFER

Size: 189 mm × 141 mm (5 mm)   1:842,00

Imprint (Ce OS) *PRINTED & PUBLISHED BY JOHN HEYWOOD. 143. DEANSGATE. & 3. BRAZENOSE S^T MANCHESTER.* Portsmouth/Arun canal added but marked *Canal. Royal Military Canal* re-engraved *Roy. Mil^y. Canal.* on one line. *to Westerham* and road erased and *to Westerham* engraved further west. *Rype, Tillington, Felpham, Heathfield* and many other place-names added. Several place-names re-engraved, eg *Northyham* altered to *Northiam, Awfold* to *Aldfold, Gardners St.* to *Gardners Str* and road re-routed. Many place-names erased, eg *Eaton Bri, Pound-Gate. Uppark.* Railways 17 and 19 added; 25 omitted; 2, 10, 11 and 16 re-routed, eg 2 now runs west of *Povey Cross; London & Brighton Railway* re-engraved.

> *The travelling atlas of England & Wales . . . Revised and corrected to the present time.*
> Manchester, John Heywood, [1860].   P

State of the plate: Later than no. 95C. Place-names &c. and railways amended.
Alterations on the transfer: Imprint (Ce OS) added. Plate number erased.

95 E. FIFTH LITHOGRAPHIC TRANSFER

Size: 189 mm × 141 mm (5 mm)   1:842,000

Railways 18, 22 and 23 added. Plate number *38* (Ee OS, sideways).

The tourist's atlas of England and Wales, with railways and coach roads, cities, towns, parks, and gentlemen's seats.
Manchester, John Heywood; London, Simpkin, Marshal and Co., [1865].   P

State of the plate: Later than no. 95D. Railways added.
Alterations on the transfer: Imprint added.

95 F. SIXTH LITHOGRAPHIC TRANSFER

Size: 189 mm × 141 mm (5 mm)   1:842,000

Imprint (Ce OS) omitted. Railways 20, 21, 24, 25, 26, 27 and 28 added.

The travelling atlas of England and Wales . . . Revised and corrected to the present time.
Manchester, John Heywood, [1862] and [1868].   BRL;BL.RGS.W

State of the plate: Later than no. 95E. Railways added.
Alterations on the transfer: None.

95 G. SEVENTH LITHOGRAPHIC TRANSFER

Size: 189 mm × 141 mm (5 mm)   1:842,000

Imprint (Ce OS) *PRINTED & PUBLISHED BY JOHN HEYWOOD, 141 & 143, DEANSGATE, & EXCELSIOR WORKS MANCHESTER.* added. Railways 29 and 30 added.

The travelling atlas, of England & Wales . . .
Manchester, John Heywood, [1875].   P

State of the plate: Later than no. 95F. Railways added.
Alterations on the transfer: Imprint (Ce OS) added.

195

95 H.   EIGHTH LITHOGRAPHIC TRANSFER

Size: 189 mm × 141 mm (5 mm)   1:842,000

EDITIONS

(i) Imprint (Ce OS) replaced by *JOHN HEYWOOD PUBLISHING & EDUCATIONAL BOOKSELLER, EXCELSIOR BUILDINGS, RIDGEFIELD, MANCHESTER, AND 18, PATERNOSTER SQUARE, LONDON, E.C.* Place-names added, eg *Groombridge, E.Guildford, Loxwood. Lon O°0'13"E* added in two places with a section of the meridian; *50°52½'N* added with a section of the parallel. A note *Contains nearly . . . Population (1871) 417.407* added (Ca, under title). Railway 31 added.

> *The travelling atlas, of England and Wales . . .*
> Manchester, John Heywood, [1876].   CUL

(ii)   Imprint (Ce OS) replaced by *PUBLISHED BY JOHN HEYWOOD, 141 & 143, DEANSGATE MANCHESTER.*

> *The travelling atlas of England & Wales . . .*
> Manchester, John Heywood, [1876].   P

State of the plate: Later than no. 95G. The alterations listed above, except the imprint and perhaps the note (Ca) were made on the plate.
Alterations on the transfer: Imprints and perhaps note (Ca) added. Edition (ii) may precede (i); they may even be separate transfers.

95 I.   NINTH LITHOGRAPHIC TRANSFER

Size: 189 mm × 142 mm (5 mm)   1:842,000

Note (Ca) altered to . . . *Population (1881) 490.316.* Imprint (Ce OS) replaced by *John Heywood. Publisher. Deansgate & Ridgefield, Manchester.* Place-name changes include *Est. Bourne* and *Sth. Bourne* erased; *Gt. Bognor or Hothampton* altered to *Bognor,* and *Lit. Hampton* to *Littlehampton; Eastbourne, Langley P^t., Ashdown Forest, Rotherfield* added. Railways 34, 35 and 36 added.

> *The travelling atlas of England & Wales . . .*
> Manchester and London, John Heywood, [1882].   MANCHESTER PL

State of the plate: Later than no. 95H., including all the alterations listed above, except imprint and perhaps the note (Ca).
Alterations on the transfer: Imprint (Ce OS) and perhaps the note added.

Size: 237 mm × 177 mm (7 mm)   1:543,000

Based on Greenwood no. 93, with certain errors, eg *Chicham* for *Chidham*, *Sted Cr* for *Steel Cross*, *Pell* for *Pett*.

John Gorton, who died 1835, was also the compiler of *A general biographical dictionary,* published in 1828. His *Topographical dictionary* (see below) was originally published in parts.

EDITIONS

(i) *SUSSEX.* (Aa, in rectangular frame). *ENGRAVED BY S. HALL* (Aa, under title). *London, Published by Chapman, and Hall Nº. 186 Strand Octʳ. 1. 1831.* (Ce OS). *English Miles. 16 = 47 mm* (Be). Compass (Ba). *REFERENCE TO THE HUNDREDS* (Ea). *The Figures prefixed to the Towns denote the distance from London* (Ee). Longitude 10' (2'); latitude 10' (2').

A topographical dictionary of Great Britain and Ireland, compiled from local information, and the most recent and official authorities. By John Gorton . . . With fifty-two quarto maps, drawn and engraved by Sidney Hall. vol. 2.
London, Chapman and Hall, 1831.   P

A topographical dictionary of Great Britain and Ireland . . . with fifty-four maps . . . vol. 2.
London, Chapman and Hall, 1833.   BL.GL

Issued about 1833 as a folding map with a printed list of maps headed *Pocket county maps . . .*
London, Chapman and Hall.   (SAS).(CUL)
In the impression at (CUL), the date in the imprint (Ce OS) has been erased by hand.

(ii) In the imprint (Ce OS) *Octʳ. 1. 1831* erased and replaced by *1833. WEST DIVISION* and *EAST DIVISION* added.

A new British atlas; comprising a series of 54 maps, constructed from the most recent surveys and engraved by Sidney Hall.
London, Chapman and Hall, 1833 and 1834.   GL.RGS.W;BL.CUL.W

(iii) Date *1833* erased from imprint (Ce OS).

Sidney Hall's British atlas.
[London, Chapman and Hall, 1835].   W.P
This atlas was published without a title-page; the title quoted is taken from the binding.

A new British atlas . . .
London, Chapman and Hall, 1836.   BL.A.W

(iv) Borough boundaries at *HASTINGS, HORSHAM, BRIGHTON* and *CHICHESTER* marked by a line of circles and dashes. *Light Ho.* added at *Beachy Head*. Railway 2 marked by single pecked line; *Brighton Rail R^d.* added.

A topographical dictionary of Great Britain and Ireland . . . With fifty-four quarto maps . . . vol. 3.
London, Chapman and Hall, 1833 (actually issued about 1836).   W

(v) Railways 1 and 2 marked by double cross-hatched lines.

A travelling county atlas: with all the coach and rail roads accurately laid down and coloured, and carefully corrected to the present time. Engraved by Sidney Hall.
London, Chapman and Hall, 1842.   BL.A.W

Issued about 1842 as a folding map.
London, Chapman and Hall.   (CUL)

(vi) *Railway Stations marked thus* . . . added (Eb, below *REFERENCE TO THE HUNDREDS*), and stations marked on map *Stat^n.* or *Station*.

A travelling county atlas . . .
London, Chapman and Hall, 1842, 1843 and 1845.   BL.RGS;CUL;BL.A.W

(vii) Railways 3, 4, 5, 7, 8, 9 and 13 added. *Hastings Rye & Ashford Extension Railway* named.

A travelling county atlas . . .
London, Chapman and Hall, 1845.   CUL.BRL

A new county atlas: with all the coach and rail roads accurately laid down and coloured. Carefully corrected to the end of the session of M.DCCC.XLVI. Engraved by Sidney Hall.
London, Chapman and Hall, 1847.   BOD.CUL.W

(viii) Railways 6, 12, 14, 15, 16 and 22 added. Also part of 20 from *SHOREHAM* to *STEYNING*.

A travelling county atlas: with all the coach and rail roads accurately laid down and coloured, and carefully corrected to the end of the last session. Engraved by Sidney Hall.
London, Chapman and Hall, 1846.   CUL

A travelling county atlas: with all the railroads accurately laid down and coloured,

and carefully corrected to the end of the last session. Engraved by Sidney Hall.
London, Chapman and Hall, 1847.   CUL.W

A travelling county atlas: with all the railroads accurately laid down and coloured.
Engraved by Sidney Hall.
London, Chapman and Hall, 1848 and [1850].   CUL;BOD.W

(ix)   In the imprint (Ce OS) *Nᵒ. 186 Strand* erased and replaced by *193 Piccadilly*.
Plate number *37* added (Ea, in border). *Sea Houses* added. Railways 10 and 11 added.
Railways are now shown by continuous black lines and the key (Eb) altered accord-
ingly; but railways 12, 14, 15, 16, part of 20 and 22 remain as originaly engraved, ie
cross-hatched double lines.

A travelling county atlas: with all the railroads accurately laid down, and the
boundaries coloured. Engraved by Sidney Hall.
London, Chapman and Hall, [1852].   CUL

(x)   Railways 12, 14 and 16 (ie all except 15, part of 20 and 22) now shown by
continuous black lines.

A travelling county atlas with all the railroads accurately laid down . . .
London, Chapman and Hall, [1853].   W

(xi)   Many more stations are now marked by stub lines at right angles to the railway
lines, and *Sta.* added, eg at *Frant*, at *Rye*.

A travelling county atlas . . .
London, Chapman and Hall, [1854].   W

Sidney Hall's travelling atlas of the English counties with all the railroads accurately
laid down, and the boundaries coloured.
London, Chapman and Hall, [1855] and [1847].   A;BOD

96 A.   FIRST LITHOGRAPHIC TRANSFER

Size: 236 mm × 176 mm (7 mm)   1:543,000

EDITIONS

(i)   Railway 17 added as black line. Railways 1 to 14, 16 and 17 are now marked by
black lines; 15, part of 20 and 22 by cross-hatched double lines.

A travelling atlas of the English counties. by Sidney Hall. With all the railroads
accurately laid down, and the boundaries coloured.
London, Chapman and Hall, [1859].   W

199

(ii)   Railway 18 added as black line.

A travelling atlas . . .
London, Chapman and Hall, [1859].   P

State of the plate: Later than no. 96 (xi). Railway 17 added.
Alterations on the transfer: Railway 18 added on edition (ii).

96 B.   SECOND LITHOGRAPHIC TRANSFER

Size: 395 mm × 290 mm (13 mm)   1:326,000

As a consequence of the enlargement, the scale is now *English Miles 16 = 79* mm (Be).

The English counties. By Sidney Hall. With all the railroads accurately laid down,
and the boundaries coloured . . .
London, Chapman and Hall, [1860].   BL.CUL.BOD

The English counties by Sidney Hall with all the railroads accurately laid down, and
the boundaries coloured . . .
London, Chapman and Hall, [1862].   CUL.RGS

State of the plate: As no. 96A.
Alterations on the transfer: Railway 18 added.

96 C.   THIRD LITHOGRAPHIC TRANSFER

Size: 236 mm × 176 mm (7 mm)   1:543,000

EDITIONS

(i)   Scale reverts to *English Miles 16 = 47* mm (Be). Railway 20 shown by black line.
Railway 18 re-routed to the south. *50' east* (Ee, in border) omitted.

A travelling atlas of the English counties . . .
London, Chapman and Hall, [1860] and [1862].   BL;CUL.W

(ii)   Railway 21 added, and 22 now shown by black line.

A travelling atlas of the English counties . . .
London, Chapman and Hall, [1864].   CUL.W

(iii)   Railways 23, 24, 25 and 27 added. Railways 1 to 18, 20 to 25 and 27 now appear
as black lines, except 15 which is still marked by a cross-hatched double line.

200

A travelling atlas of the English counties . . .
London, Chapman and Hall, [1866].   W

(iv)   Plate number *37* (Ea, in border) omitted; *N°. 40* added (Ea OS). Railway 26 added; loop line at *Ford* added.

A travelling atlas of the English counties . . .
London, Chapman and Hall, [1868] and [1869].   P;P

State of the plate: Later than no. 96C. Railways added.
Alterations on the transfer: 50' east (Ee, in border) omitted. Plate number 37 erased and *N°. 40* added on edition (iv).

96 D. FOURTH LITHOGRAPHIC TRANSFER

Size: 236 mm × 177 mm (7 mm)   1:543,000

EDITIONS

(i)   *N° 40* (Ea OS) as on·no. 96C (iv). *50'* (Ee, in border) not erased. Railways 28, 29, 30 and 31 added.

A travelling atlas of the English counties . . .
London, Chapman and Hall, [1871].   BOD

(ii)   Railway added in a smooth curve passing through the last R and E of *HASLEMERE.*

A travelling atlas of the English counties . . .
London, Chapman and Hall, [1873], [1874] and [1875].   BL.CUL;P;LEEDS PL

State of the plate: Later than no. 96C. Railways added. *N°.40* added.
Alterations on the transfer: Plate number *37* erased.

96 E. FIFTH LITHOGRAPHIC TRANSFER

Size: 236 mm × 177 mm (7 mm)   1:543,000

Plate number *37* (Ea, in border) appears, in addtion to *N°. 40* (Ea OS). Railway 19 re-engraved; it is not now a smooth curve, it turns downwards at its western end and passes through the last *E* of *HASLEMERE.*

A travelling atlas of the English counties . . .

State of the plate: Later than no. 96D. Railway 19 re-engraved.
Alterations on the transfer: None.

97   R. CREIGHTON   **1831**

Size: 223 mm × 164 mm (6 mm)   1:569,000

Based on Ebden no. 88 and Greenwood no. 93.

R. Creighton was active as a cartographer between 1818 (Greenwood's map of Lancashire) and 1855.

The map was engraved by J. & C. Walker. There were a number of Walkers, and some of the published material about them is misleading. We are mainly concerned with the sons of John Walker,[1] who worked for Alexander Dalrymple as an engraver and cartographer in 1774–5, and continued to work under him when Dalrymple was appointed Hydrographer to the East India Company in 1779 and to the Admiralty in 1795. Dalrymple died in 1808, and John Walker took over as Admiralty Hydrographer, a post which he held until his death in 1831. Walker had four sons: John (1787–1873), Michael (d. 1868). Thomas (d. 1881) and Charles (d. circa 1872). Michael[2] and Thomas worked as Admiralty draughtsmen, and Michael succeeded his father as Hydrographer in 1831. John (the eldest son) was an engraver of charts for the East India Company under James Horsburgh from 1825. He became Hydrographer and Geographer to the company following Horsburgh's death in 1836, and held these appointments, with variations in style, until about 1870. John Walker (the son) may have worked as a map engraver before joining the East India Company; a map of Jersey by M. White in 1821 was engraved by a J. Walker. A John Walker of *1 Spur S*[t]. *Leic*[tr]. *Sq.* also engraved William Watson's Fen maps published in 1827.[3]

In addition to his work with the East India Company, John Walker (the son) founded the very active firm of J. and C. Walker, in partnership with his brother Charles. Although best known as engravers, they were also successful as cartographers and as map publishers. The firm's name first appeared as engravers of the *India atlas* published by James Horsburgh in 1827, and continued to appear until about 1895 (see no. 108H). Someone else must have taken over the day to day running of the business in the late 1860s; John's heatlh deteriorated about that time and Charles is known to have retired some years before his death (c. 1872).

Further research will undoubtedly reveal more about the family and about the firm of J. and C. Walker. The above outline leaves a number of questions unanswered. For

---

1. Dawson, 1885, pp. 103 and 104; Day, 1967 passim; and information provided by Andrew Cook, India Office Library and Records. Robinson, 1962, refers to a James Walker as engraver to Dalrymple, c. 1800.
2. A Michael Walker surveyed a canal from the Itchen to Winchester, c. 1807. (see Hadfield, 1969).
3. Fordham, 1969, p. 79.

example, the firm of John and Alexander Walker was active as engravers and publishers of maps from 1823[4] to as late as 1875[5]. They started at Pool Lane, Liverpool, and were agents for the sale of Admiralty charts. No connection with the firm of J. and C. Walker has been established,[6] but it is possible that both were successors to I. Walker, for whom Cary engraved a map of Europe in 1783.[7]

A John Walker and Co. published *Bartholomew's Pocket atlas of Ireland* (1887) and *Pocket atlas and guide to London* (1889).[8] This was, perhaps, the form adopted by J. and C. Walker for some of its output after the retirement of Charles in the 1860s, and may have continued as such after the death of John in 1873.

A John Walker engraved and published *The Itinerant* in 1799. The names of other Walkers will be found on maps and estate plans during the period, in particular that of James Walker, who engraved the illustration of Arundel Castle for Dallaway's *The parochial topography of the rape of Arundel* (1832). J. Walker, who made a manuscript plan of Littlehampton (1822)[9] and who surveyed Gravesend Reach (1838),[10] is probably the cartographer of no. 85 (1822). Finally there is a possible connection with General James Thomas Walker (1826–1896) of the Indian Survey.

Little is known of Samuel Lewis, the publisher. He died in 1865. He had a son, also Samuel, who was a writer and topographer, and who died, before his father, in 1862.

The map described below is from various sources. The hills and rivers resemble Ebden no. 88; but much of the detail, eg *Todhurst* on the road from *Pulborough* to *Billingshurst*, is from Greenwood, no. 93. The map marks N^{th}. & S^{th}. *Keymer*, N^{th}. & S^{th}. *Hartfield* and E^t. & W^t. *Billinghurst*, which are not differentiated in this manner on other maps.

In addition to this topographical map, the third edition of *A topographical dictionary* contains a parliamentary map of the county, see no. 107.

EDITIONS

(i) *SUSSEX* (Ea). *Drawn by R. Creighton (Ae OS). Engraved by J. & C. Walker (Ee*

---

4. *A Plan of LIVERPOOL . . . By J. & A. Walker, AGENTS FOR THE SALE OF THE ADMIRALTY CHARTS, 33, POOL LANE . . .* 1823 (BL) and *MAP OF THE UNITED STATES; . . . by JOHN & ALEX^R. WALKER. Published by J. & A. WALKER, 47 Bernard Street Russell Square LONDON, and 33 Pool Lane LIVERPOOL, June 1st. 1827* (RGS).
5. *Map of South Wales drawn from trigonometrical survey by J. & A. Walker 1875,* and *Map of North Wales by J. & A. Walker, 1976,* both published by E. Stanford (RGS).
6. The British Library map catalogue is probably incorrect in referring to Alexander Walker as being 'in commercial association with his brother John, Geographer to the East India Company'.
7. Jervis 1936, p. 92.
8. Hyde, 1975, p. 44.
9. Steer, 1968, p. 170. John Farrant suggests that this Walker is the engineer, James Walker, who worked on the Penshurst canal in 1830, and on the Kennet and Avon canal in 1845 (see Hadfield, 1969). Steer also catalogues a plan of Littlehampton, engraved by J. and C. Walker, published by the Hydrographical Office in 1831.
10. Robinson, 1962, p. 203.

OS). *DRAWN AND ENGRAVED FOR LEWIS' TOPOGRAPHICAL DICTIONARY* (Ce OS). *Scale of Miles 15* = 41 mm (Be). Compass (Aa). Longitude 10' (5'); latitude 10' (5').

> *A topographical dictionary of England . . . with historical and statistical descriptions; illustrated by maps of the different counties and islands . . . By Samuel Lewis . . .*[1st] and 3rd ends. vol. 4.
> London, S. Lewis and Co., 1831 and 1835.   BL.BOD.BRL;WN
> Each of these editions of the work was also issued with the maps bound in a separate volume, usually without title-page; but occasionally in the first edition with title and imprint: *A topographical dictionary of England . . . By Samuel Lewis. The atlas.* London, S. Lewis and Co., 1831 (A)

(ii)   Notes relating to places of polling and election added (outside top border). *WESTERN DIVISION* and *EASTERN DIVISION* added on map and boundary marked by pecked line.

> *A topographical dictionary of England . . .* 2nd and 3rd edns. vol. 4.
> London, S. Lewis and Co., 1833 and 1835.   BL;BL.W
> Each of these editions was also issued with the maps bound in a separate volume without title-page.

(iii)   Notes relating to places of polling and election (outside top border) erased.

> Issued about 1837 in a set of maps without title-page to accompany late impressions of the third edition of *A topogaphical dictionary.*   W

(iv)   *Reference to the Unions* added (Aa); numbers *1* to *22* and boundaries marked on map. Compass (Aa) erased and re-engraved (Ca). *S^t. Leonards on Sea* added in small italics. Railway 2 marked and named *Brighton Railway.*

> Issued in a set of maps without title-page to accompany *A topographical dictionary of England . . .* 4th edn.
> London, S. Lewis and Co., 1840.   BL.W

(v)   *S^t. Leonards on Sea* erased; *S^T LEONARD'S, Bulvuhy (the Church in ruins), Sea Houses, Meads, Aldwicke, Handcross* and other place-names added. Branch of *Arun & Ports Can.* to *CHICHESTER* marked. Roads added, eg main road from *HORSHAM* to *Crawley,* minor road *HORSHAM* to *Rusper* with branches to east and west. Railway 1 added and named *Shoreham Railway.*

> *An atlas, comprising maps of the several counties, divided into unions . . .*
> London, S. Lewis and Co., 1842.   BL.CUL.W

> *Atlas to the topographical dictionaries of England and Wales . . .*
> London, S. Lewis and Co., 1844 and 1845.   CUL.W;A.W

> *Atlas to the topographical dictionary of England . . .*
> London, S. Lewis and Co., 1845.   CUL

(vi) *East Bourne* re-engraved *EASTBOURNE*. *Part of Hampshire* and boundary line erased. Railways 3 to 11, 13 and 25 added.

Atlas to the topographical dictionary of England . . .
London, S. Lewis and Co., 1848.   W

Atlas to the topographical dictionaries of England and Wales . . .
London, S. Lewis and Co., 1848 and 1849.   BL.CUL;P

98 MARK ANTONY LOWER   1831

Size: 309 mm × 164 mm (2 mm)   1:439,000

Probably based on Wallis no. 70, with some details from other sources.

Mark Antony Lower[1] (1813–76) was the son of Richard Lower of Chiddingly in Sussex. Richard Lower (1827–1865), a schoolmaster, is described by his son as the village factotum, and as a land surveyor of considerable note. Steer[2] lists eight surveys carried out by Richard Lower in east Sussex between 1823 and 1853, including the tithe award map for Southover. Mark Antony was also a schoolmaster, first in 1830 at East Hoathly where he helped his sister, then at Heathfield, at Alfriston, and from 1835–67 at Lewes. In 1867 he moved to Seaford, but on the death of his second wife in 1871 removed to London, where he died. He was a founder of the Sussex Archaeological Society, and a prolific contributor to the *Collections*. It will be observed that the work below was published when he was eighteen years old! Other works by Lower include *Patronymica Britannica* (1860), *The worthies of Sussex* (1865) and *A compendious history of Sussex* (1870), see no. 125.

The relationship of R.W. Lower, the publisher, to Mark Antony has not been established.

The map was printed from a lithographic stone on which the design had been laid down. The first lithographic map of Sussex,[3] unless no. 99 preceded it.

1. *SAC* vol. 27, pp. 132–4; *SAC* vol. 22 p. 228.
2. Steer, 1962. See also Dickins, 1981 pp. 49, 61.
3. An interesting example of the early use of lithography for a Sussex map is *PLAN of the RIVER ARUN NAVIGATION . . . Surveyed by J. Hollinsworth 1820. Scale of Miles 3* [= 160 mm]. *Lithographic Press 6 Dartmouth Str. West*. *Ja*. *Wyld del*. (SAS). The first lithographic map printed in England was in 1808 (see Twyman, 1970).

(i) *SUSSEX* (Aa, underlined). *Drawn on Stone by M.A. Lower* (Ae OS). *Published by Lower, Bookseller, Lewes.* (Ce OS). *Scale of Miles 10 = 37* mm (Be). Compass (Ea).

Sussex; being an historical, topographical and general description . . . with a correct map of the county. By Mark Antony Lower.
Lewes, R.W. Lower, 1831.   SAS

(ii) *Drawn on Stone by M.A. Lower* (Ae OS) altered to *Drawn by M.A. Lower.* Asterisks, presumably indicating parliamentary representation, remain as in state (i), in spite of the revised title to the work.

Sussex; being an historical, topographical and general description . . . and a correct map of the county. To which is added . . . alterations affected by the Reform and Boundary Act of 1832 . . . by Mark Antony Lower.
Brighton, E. Taylor,[4] 1834.   BRIGHTON PL

99 ROBERT KEARSLEY DAWSON   circa **1831**

Size (of stone): 275 mm × 223 mm (no border)   1:517,000

Based on Cary no. 68.

R.K. Dawson was the son of Robert Dawson (1776–1860), artist and surveyor. Commissioned into the Royal Engineers in 1818, he worked under Colby in Scotland and Ireland. In 1836 he was seconded to the Tithe Commission with responsibility for the approval of tithe maps. He advanced a scheme whereby the tithe maps would form the basis of a cadastral survey of the whole country on the scale of three chains to the inch (26.7 inches to the mile), but his proposals were not accepted.[1] Dawson was also charged with the vetting of maps on behalf of the Poor Law Commissioners.[2] These maps were prepared under the 'Act to regulate Parochial assessments' in 1836. Until approved by Dawson's department they could not be used for rating purposes, nor could payment to the surveyors be sanctioned.

Luke Hansard (1752–1828) the printer, see (ii) below, was born in Norwich. From 1774 he printed the *Journals of the House of Commons*, and was highly thought of by

4. Perhaps Elias Taylor, bookseller, of 95 (later 63) Western Road, Brighton. His work *An essay and familiar treatise on the art of drawing in perspective printed and published by the author* appeared in 1835.

1. Kain, 1975, p. 86.
2. Hyde, *Guildhall studies in London history* vol. 2 no. 2, 1976.

parliamentary officials and by Dr. Johnson. His eldest son, Thomas Curson Hansard (1776–1833), set up in business on his own, and his grandson, of the same name, became a barrister and wrote extensively on the history of printing. The two younger sons, James and Luke, carried on printing parliamentary reports, and were in turn succeeded by their sons.

The map described below was printed from a lithographic stone on which the design had been laid down from the original drawing; it is without a border and apart from parliamentary information shows only the rapes, main roads and some towns.

EDITIONS

(i) *SUSSEX.* (Ca). *Robt.K.Dawson. Lieut. R.E.* (Ea, a facsimile signature). *R.Martin, 124 High Holborn & 50, Carey St.* (Be). *Scale of Miles 10 = 32* mm (Be, above imprint). Compass (Ba). *Explanations.* (Ee, above signature), consisting of five items. *Polling Places . . .* with Maltese cross as symbol (De, to left of signature).

> *Parliamentary representation. Further return to an Address to His Majesty, dated 12 December 1831:- for, copies of instructions given by the Secretary of State for the Home Department with reference to parliamentary representation; likewise, copies of letters or reports received by the Secretary of State for the Home Department in answer to such instructions. Reports from Commissioners on Proposed Division of Counties and Boundaries of Boroughs. Part V.*
> 'Ordered, by The House of Commons, to be Printed, 20 January 1832.'   P
> This forms part of volume XIII of parliamentary *Accounts and papers* for the session of 6 December 1831–16 August 1832. No complete copy of this work has been found.[3] The Genealogical Society has part II (Dorset to Huntingdonshire) only. However, a loose map accompanied by the text and town plans referring to Sussex has been found, and it seems probable that part V with the maps in this state was published.

(ii) *Polling Places . . .* (De) erased and replaced by *Polling Places for the County,* and on the next line *Dᵒ. for the Borough of New Shoreham* followed by a triangle symbol. On the map a triangle has been added at *NEW SHOREHAM,* in addition to the existing triangle under *Cowfold;* the Maltese crosses have been re-engraved and are less open. *Mayfield* added.

> *Parliamentary representation. Further return to an Address to His Majesty, dated 12 December 1831 . . . Part V.*
> 'Ordered, by The House of Commons, to be Printed, 20 January 1832.' BL.CUL.W
> This forms part of volume XIII of parliamentary *Accounts and papers* for the session of 6 December 1831–16 August 1832.

3. Frank Hammond catalogue no. 208, item 643, may have contained this work.

Plans of the cities and boroughs of England and Wales: shewing their boundaries as established by the Boundaries' Act, passed 11th July 1832: together with outline maps, shewing the divisions of the counties, the principal places of election, and the polling places, as established by the same Act. Vol. II.
London, James and Luke G. Hansard and Sons, 1832.[4]   BL.CUL.BOD

100   JOHN BOWYER NICHOLS AND SON   1831

Size: 121 mm × 78 mm (1 mm)   1:1,150,000

Based on Jones and Smith no. 60, or a derivative, probably Pickett no. 83.

John Bowyer Nichols (1779–1863) was the son of John Nichols (see no. 55), and was named after the famous printer William Bowyer, to whom his father had been apprenticed. He took charge of his father's printing and publishing business from about 1803, and maintained his father's reputation as a publisher and author. From 1833 to 1856 he was mainly responsible for *The Gentleman's magazine,* and was Master of the Stationers Company in 1850. He was succeeded by his eldest son, John Gough Nichols. A large collection of letters relating to the affairs of the Nichols family was sold at Sotheby's (lot 147) on 29 Oct. 1975; a study of these papers might identify the cartographer and engraver of this series of maps. For another publication by this firm see no. 104.

Samuel Tymms (1808–71) worked on *The Gentleman's magazine.* Later he moved to Suffolk and set up as a book-seller. *The family topographer* published between 1832 and 1843 was his main work.

The scale-bar in state (ii) is grossly inaccurate.

EDITIONS

(i) *SUSSEX.* (Ca). *London, Published Novr. 1st. 1831, by Nichols & Son, 25 Parliament Street.* (Ce OS). Compass (Aa). *The figures to the Towns show the distances from London and Chichester.* (Ce OS).

A compendium of the history of the home circuit, consisting of the counties of Essex, Hertfordshire, Kent, Surrey, and Sussex . . . By Samuel Tymms, F.S.A.
London, J.B. Nichols and Sons, [1831].   GL

The family topographer: being a compendious account of the antient and present state of the counties of England. By Samuel Tymms. vol. 1.
London, J.B. Nichols and Son 1832.   BL

---

4. The report was first published on 20 January 1832, and was republished on 27 March 1832. See R. Hyde, 'Reform Bill Plans' in *Bulletin of the Society of University Cartographers'* vol. 9(2), 1975.

Camden's Britannia epitomised and continued; being a compendious account of the antient and present state of the counties of England. By Samuel Tymms. vol. 1.
London, Henry G. Bohn [1842].   BOD.W

(ii)   *Scale of Miles 10* = 25 mm added (Ed). (The length of the county on the map is 109 mm and is given in the text as 76 miles; 10 miles should, therefore, be equivalent to 14 mm. not 25 mm).

The family topographer; . . . By Samuel Tymms. vol. 1.
London, J.B. Nichols and Son, 1832.   BL

101   WILLIAM COBBETT   1832

Size: 172 mm × 99 mm   1:754,000

A very simple map, showing only the county boundary and eighteen towns. Hailsham is spelt *Harlsham*. The sources used in the compilation of this map have not been determined.

William Cobbett (1762–1835) was born in Surrey. Grandson of a farm worker, he was completely self-taught. After a spell in the army, he obtained his discharge in 1791, and devoted himself to political pamphleteering and to writing. In 1792 he settled in Philadelphia and later in New York, where he showed his strong loyalist sympathies. He returned to London, and in 1803 opened a bookshop, in Pall Mall. In the same year he commenced publication of parliamentary debates, which were taken over by Hansard in 1808. He suffered imprisonment for a libel on the government, and was a member of parliament for a short time before his death. *Rural Rides,* in which he refers to 'Mr. Baxter, stationer of Lewes' (see no. 89) is perhaps his best-known work. He had visited Lewes in 1822. He is reputed to have disinterred and brought to England the remains of Tom Paine, who had resided in Lewes from 1768 to 1774.

EDITION

SUSSEX (Ce, in double line frame). *Drawn & Engraved for Cobbett's Geographical Dictionary of England & Wales* (Ce OS). Compass (Ea).

A geographical dictionary of England and Wales . . . each county is also preceded by a map, showing . . . the local situations of the cities, boroughs and market towns . . . By William Cobbett.
London, William Cobbett, 1832.   BL.RGS.W

A geographical dictionary of England and Wales . . . 2nd edn.
London, 1854.   FORDHAM[1]

---

1. Fordham, 1914, p. 101.

Size: 228 mm × 176 mm (7 mm)   1:560,000

Copied from Hall no. 96, although a few road distances have been amended, eg *29* in place of *28* at *EAST GRINSTEAD.*

Robert Scott (1771–1841) was born in Lanarkshire and set up in business in Edinburgh. He was the best Scottish engraver of his day. His large output included many maps and plans. His sons, David and William Bell Scott, were both successful painters.

The *New and comprehensive gazetteer* included a number of articles which had been pirated by James Bell, the writer, from Lewis's *A topographical dictionary . . .* (no. 97), first published in 1831. In July 1839, Lewis obtained an injunction preventing further sale of Bell's work, which was, therefore, withdrawn. In its place, Fullarton and Co. brought out *The parliamentary gazetteer,* using the same county maps as had been used for Bell's gazetteer. *The parliamentary gazetteer* comprised four volumes, but was first published in thirty-one parts at 2s. each, or in twelve parts at 6s. each. It was superseded in 1866–9 by *The Imperial gazetteer,* in which the county maps were replaced by Bartholomew's 'THE IMPERIAL MAP of ENGLAND & WALES . . .' (see no. 129). Fullartons argued that this was preferable to the inclusion of individual county maps, which gave equal importance to each county irrespective of size, and in which the scales varied from county to county. *The Imperial gazetteer* was reissued in 1874.

EDITIONS

(i)   *SUSSEX* (Be). *Eng^d. by R. Scott.* (Ab, under the engraving). *Published by Arch^d. Fullarton & Co. Glasgow.* (Ce OS). *English Miles. 16 = 47 mm* (Ee). Compass (Ca). *REFERENCE TO THE HUNDREDS* (Ea). Longitude 10' (2'); latitude 10' (2'). *HASTINGS, FROM THE WHITE ROCKS.*, with engraving (Aa).

> *A new and comprehensive gazetteer of England and Wales . . . by James Bell . . . Illustrated by a series of maps, forming a complete county atlas of England.* vol. 4, part 1.
> Glasgow, A. Fullarton and Co., 1833, 1834 and 1836.   FORDHAM[1];P;BL

> *A new and comprehensive . . .* vol. 4.
> Glasgow, A. Fullarton and Co., 1837.   RGS

(ii)   Scott signature (Ab) erased, but traces remain. Railway 2 and *To London* added.

1.   Fordham, 1914, p. 102.

The parliamentary gazetteer of England and Wales . . . vol. 4.
London, Edinburgh and Glasgow, A. Fullarton and Co., 1840, 1842, 1843 and
1844.   CARDIFF PL;GL;BL.RGS.PRO;P

The parliamentary gazetteer of England and Wales . . . vol. 4.
London, Edinburgh and Dublin. A Fullarton and Co., 1845.   W
The 1846 issue of this work, recorded by Fordham,[2] would probably have contained the Sussex map in
this state.

(iii)   Imprint (Ce OS) erased and replaced by *Arch^d. Fullarton & Co.* Railways 1, 3, 4,
5, 7, 8, 9 and 13 added.

The parliamentary gazetteer of England and Wales . . . vol. 4.
London, Edinburgh and Dublin, A. Fullarton and Co., 1848.   BOD;WN

103   R. MARTIN   1833

Size: 338 mm × 187 mm (7 mm)   1:401,000

Copied from Pigot no. 90.

The signature of *R. Martin* also appears on no. 99, presumably as engraver,
although Tooley[1] describes him as 'publisher'.
John Docwra Parry, the writer, came from Bedford and took holy orders in 1818.
He died at Brighton in 1833. The work in which this map appears has little merit. It
was reprinted in 1970.
Wright and Son, the publishers, were perhaps connected with Charles Wright, the
Brighton book-seller, who wrote and published several topographical works, including
Brighton ambulator and *Excursions from London to Brighton.*
The map covers the whole of Sussex. The ten mile coastal strip is shown in detail,
but only roads and main towns are marked inland.

EDITION

COAST OF SUSSEX. For the History & Description of the Coast of Sussex. 1833 (Ca).
Engraved by R. Martin. 124 High Holborn. London. (Ee OS). *Scale of Miles. 20 = 82*
mm (Aa). Compass (Ea). *ARUNDEL CASTLE, FROM THE RIVER.*, and engraving
(Ae). *BATTLE ABBEY, GATE-HOUSE.*, and engraving (Ee).

An historical and descriptive account of the coast of Sussex . . . by J.D. Parry,
M.A.
Brighton, Wright and Son; London, Longman & Co., 1833.   BL.BRIGHTON PL

2. Fordham, 1914, supplement p. 29. See also Hodson, 1974, no. 99 (iv).
1. Tooley, 1979, p. 422.

211

Size: (a) East section 412 mm × 417 mm (single line border)
       (b) West section 402 mm × 415 mm (single line border)   1:195,000

Based on Greenwood no. 89 and information from other sources. It includes place-names, eg *Heathdown F. (Piddinghoe)*, which appear on Greenwood no. 89, but not on Gardner, Yeakell and Gream no. 57 or on the One Inch Ordnance Survey. It also includes some place-names, eg *Barden Farm* and *Boarders F.* (near Etchingham) which do not appear on any earlier map.

Benjamin Rees Davies was an engraver and publisher in London from about 1811;[1] but he must also have been something of a cartographer as many of his maps are signed *Drawn & Engraved by B.R. Davies.* From about 1850 he worked almost wholly through Stanfords.

Thomas Walker Horsfield (1792–1837), the writer, was born in Sheffield. He came to Lewes in 1817 as Unitarian minister at Westgate Chapel. In 1824 his history of Lewes was published by John Baxter. In 1827 he moved to Taunton, where he wrote his history of Sussex.[2] In about 1834 he again moved, to Chowbent in Lancashire, where he died.

EDITIONS

(i)   (a) *MAP OF SUSSEX, PART I. EAST.* (Ea). *Drawn & Engraved by B.R. Davies, 16 George Str. Euston Squ London.* (Eb). *Published by J. Baxter Lewes. Dec*[r]*. 1. 1834* (Eb, below signature). *Scale of Miles 10 = 82* mm (Ea, between title and signature). Compass (Da). Profiles of 12 sections of the coast are drawn vertically in the sea.

(b) *MAP OF SUSSEX, PART II. WEST* (Aa). *Drawn & Engraved by B.R. Davies, 16 George Str. Euston Squ London.* (Ab). *Published by J. Baxter Lewes. Dec*[r]*. 1. 1834* (Ab, below signature). *Scale of Miles 10 = 82* mm (Aa, between title and signature). Compass (Ca). Profiles of 9 sections of the coast are drawn vertically in the sea.

Found only as loose sheets.   (SAS)

(ii) (a) PART I. *Gad & C*[o]*. Printers, London* added (Ee OS).

The history, antiquities and topography of the county of Sussex. By Thomas Walker Horsfield F.S.A.
Lewes, Baxter; London, Nichols and Son, 1835.   SAS

1. Tooley, 1979, p. 150.
2. *The history, antiquities and topography of the county of Sussex* was reprinted in 1974 with an introduction by F.W. Steer, from which these biographical notes are taken.

212

(iii) (b) PART II. *Gad & Cº. Printers, London* added (Ee OS). The dots and dashes indicating the county boundary have been extended to show 10 mm of the Hampshire/ Surrey boundary, and also to run across the top of the Hampshire enclave from *Sussex Bell* to just north of *Baldwins*.

> *The history, antiquities and . . . by Thomas Walker Horsfield F.S.A.*
> Lewes, Baxter; London, Nichols and Son, 1835.   BRIGHTON PL

(iv) (a) PART I. *The Views drawn by T. Henwood & Engraved by B.R. Davies* added (Bd, sideways).
      (b) PART II. *The views from Drawings by T. Henwood* added (Bd, sideways).

> *The history, antiquities and . . . By Thomas Walker Horsfield F.S.A.*
> Lewes, Baxter; London, Nichols and Son, 1835.   BL

105 LONGMAN, REES, ORME, BROWN, GREEN AND LONGMAN   1834

Size: 88 mm × 76 mm (1 mm)   1:1,780,000

The detail is insufficient to enable the derivation of this map to be determined.

The Sussex map occupies the upper part of the plate; below is the map of Hampshire, within a separate border. The map is designed to test topographical knowledge.

EDITION

SUSSEX. (Ca). The map shows the county boundary, coastline and rivers. Capes and bays are lettered *A, B & C; Thorney Island* is *D; Ashdown Forest* is *E;* rivers are lettered *a* to *c;* the towns are numbered *1* to *16*.

> *The geography of the British Isles . . . illustrated with separate blank maps and explanatory keys; showing the relative situations, boundaries, principal towns, rivers &c. of each county. For the use of young persons and schools. By Mary Martha Rodwell.* vol. I.
> London, Longman, Rees, Orme, Brown, Green and Longman, 1834.   BL

Size: 215 mm × 153 mm (6 mm)   1:566,000

Based on Cole no. 66.

The map was engraved on a wood-block.

As well as appearing in the publications listed below, the maps in this series were used to illustrate a *Descriptive county atlas of England and Wales,* published in parts commencing in 1844, by R. Groombridge and by Shepherd and Sutton. Known copies (BOD) are incomplete and lack the Sussex section, which would have been no. 39 in Part IV, but which may never have been issued. The maps in known copies are in a state corresponding to that described under no. 106A below, but were printed directly from the wood-blocks by a relief process using black or pale-brown ink.

EDITIONS

SUSSEX (Aa, in plain frame). *J. Archer sc.* (Ae). *Pub^d. for the Propr^s. by Edwards Ave Maria Lane* (Aa, under title). *English Miles 20* = 57 mm (Be). Arms of the Duke of Newcastle (Ee). *No. CIX* (Ea OS, sideways). *GUIDE TO KNOWLEDGE* (Ec OS, sideways). *PRICE ONE PENNY* (Ee OS, sideways). Longitude 5'; latitude 5'.

The guide to knowledge. Edited by W. Pinnock. . . vol. 2.
London, W. Edwards, 1834.   BL.CUL
The map appeared on the front page of the issue for 19 April 1834 (WORTHING PL, Sussex pamphlets), and was printed by a relief process so that the design appeared in white on a black background. Later series of *The guide to knowledge,* published in parts commencing in 1837 and 1844, do not contain county maps. The three items printed sideways are 7 mm outside the right border.

106 A.   LITHOGRAPHIC TRANSFER

Size: 215 mm × 153 mm (6 mm)   1:566,000

Signature (Ae) and imprint (Aa) erased. Arms (Ee) erased and replaced by arms of Chichester. Three items printed sideways outside right border erased. pattern of black and white bands added to border between values of longitude and latitude. Seven road directions added, eg *Fr. Alton, To Ashford. Railway Stations marked thus* . . . added (Be, under scale). Railways 1 and 2 added and stations marked.

Johnson's atlas of England; with all the railways containing forty two separate maps of the counties and islands.
Manchester, Thomas Johnson, 1847.   BL.CUL

State of the plate: Later than no. 106. All alterations listed above having been made on the block.
Alterations on the transfer: None.

107   R. CREIGHTON

1835

Based on Dawson no. 99.

The plate from which the following lithographic transfer was taken was apparently never used for direct intaglio printing.

The purpose of the map is to give parliamentary information; apart from this it shows only the hundreds, principal towns and main roads.

107 A.   LITHOGRAPHIC TRANSFER

Size: 242 mm × 171 mm (5 mm)   1:519,000

SUSSEX (Ba). *Drawn by R. Creighton* (Ae OS). *Engraved by J. & C. Walker* (Ee OS). *Scale of Miles. 20 = 60* mm (De). Compass (Ea). *Explanation* (Be). Plate number *XC.* (Ee OS, sideways).

> *A topographical dictionary of England . . . with historical and statistical descriptions; illustrated by maps of the different counties and islands . . . With a supplementary volume, comprising a representative history of England with plans describing the electoral divisions of the several counties. . . By Samuel Lewis.* vol. 5. 3rd edn.
> London, S. Lewis and Co., 1835 and 1837.   BL.W:P
> Other editions of this work contain no. 97.

> *View of the representative history of England, with engraved plans, shewing the electoral divisions of the several counties . . . by Samuel Lewis.*
> London, S. Lewis and Co., 1835 and 1840.   RGS;P

108   JOHN AND CHARLES WALKER

1835

Size: 374 mm × 302 mm (9 mm)   1:330,000

Based on Greenwood no. 93. **See plates 30 to 33.**

William Colling Hobson, see nos. 108A to D below, also published maps of Durham (1839) and of Yorkshire (1843). Editions of the fox-hunting atlas bearing his name were published from about 1849 to about 1878. Later editions were known as *Walker's foxhunting atlas;* Hobson must have died or retired about 1878.

An interesting foxhunting map (WORTHING RL), of central Sussex only, was published in 1859–60 by C. Booty of 16, Kings Road, Brighton. It is on a scale of about half inch to one mile, and is *Engraved by G. Philip & Son, Liverpool.*

John Murray, see 108F (ii) below, was born in London of Scots descent. His father (d. 1793) retired from the marines and acquired the bookselling business of William

Sandby in Fleet Street. When John Murray (1778–1843) took over, he parted from his father's partner, who took with him the medical publications, and continued on his own. His son, also John, (1808–92) travelled extensively abroad before joining his father in 1830. He was the author of a book entitled *Scepticism in geology*. Murray's *Handbook* was well thought of, and is often quoted in *Sussex archaeological collections;* the only critical reference (and this is controversial) occurs in vol. 30 p. 104, which reads 'I am sorry to observe that the author of Murray's valuable handbook for Sussex tells us that Worth Church *was subjected to a destructive restoration in 1870.* A remark of this kind, mere echo of a charge which has been thoroughly refuted, occurring in a popular book of considerable circulation and real utility, is enough to arouse a keen sense of injustice'.

The publishing house of Letts[1] (see transfers I and J below), famous for its diaries, had been in existence since 1809. In 1884 it went into liquidation and the map plates owned by it were bought by Mason and Payne, who were the City agents for Stanfords. The diary side of the business was acquired by Cassells.

As well as appearing in the atlases listed below, the various editions were probably issued continuously from 1835 to about 1890 as folding maps sold separately. Many editions of the map have been found in this form. Impressions of the map were usually issued with all railways actually built marked by hand in red ink; these did not necessarily correspond with the railways printed on the map, which are the only ones taken into account in the descriptions below. It was by this means that old stocks of maps, printed many years before, could be used to make up new atlases without appearing out of date. This may well account for the apparent anomaly in the dating of the first editions of *Hobson's foxhunting atlas* (no. 108A below). The dates [1849] to [1851] are from Harvey[2] and Hodson[3]. The first lithographic transfer was taken from the plate in state (xv). Impressions of the map in the previous state (xiv) were included in an atlas dated 1851, whereas, if the date assigned to the first fox-hunting atlas is correct, the plate must have been altered to state (xv) by about 1849. Even more surprising, atlases dated 1861 and 1862 contain Sussex maps in states (xii) and (xiii).

EDITIONS

(i) *SUSSEX* (Aa, in double line frame). *BY J. & C. WALKER* (Aa, under title). *Published by Longman, Hurst, Rees, Orme & C⁰. Paternoster Row July 1ˢᵗ. 1835* (Ce OS). *English Miles* 1 + 14 = 70 mm (Aa, below signature). Compass (Ea). *Sussex contains 1463 Square Miles . . . 272.328 Inhabitants,* followed by note on parliamentary representation and road distances (Aa, under scale). *REFERENCE TO THE RAPES* (Ce). Electoral information (Be and De). Longitude 10' (1'); latitude 10' (1'). **See plate 30**.

1. *The romance of the business of a diary publisher: Charles Letts & Co. Ltd.*, London, 1949.
2. Harvey, 1959, no. 96A.
3. Hodson, 1974, no. 103A.

Issued from 1835 as a folding map with printed title on cover: *Walker's Sussex*. From about 1837 boxed sets of this series of folding county maps were issued, each box bearing a title-label 'Walker's county atlas'.   CUL

To their Royal Highnesses the Duchess of Kent & the Princess Victoria, this British atlas, comprising separate maps of every county in England . . . compiled from the maps of the Board of Ordnance and other trigonometrical surveys, is . . . dedicated by . . . J. and C. Walker.
London, Longman, Rees and Co. and J. and C. Walker, 1837.   BOD.CUL.W

(ii)   *Light Ho.* added at *Beachy Head.* A road added five miles south of *REIGATE* and running north-east to join the main *CROYDON* to *BRIGHTON* road.

To Her most excellent Majesty Queen Victoria, and to Her Royal Highness the Duchess of Kent, this British atlas . . .
London, Longman, Rees and Co. and J. and C. Walker, 1837.   BL

(iii)   Railways 1 and 2 marked by pecked lines; 2 named *Railroad from London to Brighton.*

. . . British atlas . . .
London, Longman, Rees and Co. and J. and C. Walker, 1837.   LEEDS PL

(iv)   Date in imprint (Ce OS) altered to *July 1st. 1837. Northbrook* (near *Angmering*) and park symbol added.

. . . British atlas . . .
London, Longman, Rees and Co. and J. and C. Walker, 1837.   CUL

(v)   *Staplehurst* (in Kent) added. Pecked lines marking boundaries of adjacent counties extended by 30 mm (Hants/Surrey) and 40 mm (Surrey/Kent). Railways 5 (as far as *LEWES*) and A added; A named *Railroad from London to Dover;* railways now marked by plain double lines.

. . . British atlas . . .
London, Longman, Rees and Co. and J. and C. Walker, 1841.   RGS

(vi)   Railways 1, 2 and A now marked by cross-hatched double lines; railway 5 by plain double lines.

Issued about 1841 as a folding map in printed cover with the title: *Walker's Sussex.*
(P)

(vii)   Date in imprint (Ce OS) altered from *July 1st. 1837* to *1841. Brighton, Hastings, Rye, Cuckfield, Worthing* and *Midhurst* added to list of polling places (Be). Outside the county boundary a number of roads and about fifty place-names, eg *Lyss Turney,*

Ewhurst, Lingfield and *Goudhurst* added. Fifteen place-names added in Sussex, eg *Ely, Stone Ho., Woodgate, Hall* (at *Worth*), *Ashfold, Loxwood Ho., Lakers, Albourne Place, Pakyns* and *House* (at *Summers Fm, Billinghurst*). About fourteen park symbols added, eg at *Dane Hill* (2), at *Stone Ho.* (3). About six new roads added in Sussex, eg *Hollington* to *HASTINGS. Arun & Wye Canal* extended 13 mm to north-east. Stations marked by black dots (eg at *Hove*); *Sta* (eg at *Keymer*) and *Station* (eg at *Stoats Nest*) added. *Horsham St* (near *Worth*), *Tunnel* (near *Merstham*) and *Croydon Ry. Terminus* added.

Issued about 1841 as a folding map in printed cover with the title: *Walker's Sussex.*
(BOD).(WSRO)

. . . *British atlas* . . .
London, Longman, Rees and Co. and J. and C. Walker, 1841.   CUL

(viii) Date in imprint (Ce OS) altered to *1842.*

Issued in 1842 as a folding map with printed title on cover: *Walker's county maps,*
London, Longman, Orme & Co., and J. & C. Walker.   (BRIGHTON PL)

Issued in 1842 as a folding map with printed title on cover: *New map of Sussex.*
London, G.F. Cruchley.   (HASTINGS PL)

. . . *British atlas* . . .
London, Longman, Rees & Co. and J. & C. Walker, 1842.   (P)
This loose map is probably from an 1842 edition of the atlas of which only the title-page is known (CUL).

(ix) Date in imprint (Ce OS) altered to *1843. Inhabitants* (Ae, under title) now *299.770* (formerly *272.328*). *Marden Sta.* and *Maidstone Road Sta* added.

. . . *British atlas* . . .
London, Longman, Rees & Co. and J. & C. Walker, 1845 and 1865.   BOD;BL

Issued as a folding map with printed title on cover: *Sussex;* and inside the cover: *Betts series of pocket maps* . . .
(CUL)

(x) Date in imprint (Ce OS) altered to *1844.*

Issued as a folding map with printed title on cover: *Walker's Sussex.*
London, Longman and Co. and J. & C. Walker.   (BL)

(xi) Date in imprint (Ce OS) altered to *1845. EPSOM* added. Railway 5, which formerly stopped at *LEWES,* now extends to *HASTINGS; Epsom & Croydon Atmospheric Railway* marked by cross-hatched double lines and named.

Found only as a loose map.   (WORTHING PL)

(xii)   Date in imprint (Ce OS) erased. Railways 1 to 5, A and B now marked by cross-hatched double lines; 6 to 16, 19, 22, 23, 25, C and E by plain double lines; lines from *Whatlington* to *Brede, SHOREHAM to STEYNING* and from *DORKING* to *EPSOM* added. *From Southampton* erased and replaced by *Rail^d. from Portsmouth to Southampt^n. &c.. Croydon R^y. Terminus* erased. Several of the new lines named, eg *Hastings & Ashford Railway.*

> . . . *British atlas* . . .
> London, Longman, Rees & Co. and J. & C. Walker, 1861.   BL

(xiii)   *Kingsfold* and *Holford* added on the north boundary.

> . . . *British atlas* . . .
> London, Longman, Rees and Co. and J. and C. Walker, 1862.   BL

(xiv)   *Swines Gate* altered to *Pole Gate, Crexley* to *Cranley. Newlands* (near *EAST GRINSTEAD*) and *State Ho.* (at *Slaugham*) added.

> Issued about 1851 as a folding map with printed title on cover: *Walker's Sussex.*
> London, Longman, Rees and Co. and J. and C. Walker.   (BL)

> . . . *British atlas* . . .
> London, Longman, Rees and Co. and J. and C. Walker, 1851.   BL

(xv)   Many place-names connected with hunting added, eg *Woolmer Pond* (in Hampshire), *Pipers, Lakers, Fitzballs, Valdoe Kennels, Balls Cross, Gravetye;* and many altered, eg *Common* (formerly *Pinkhurst Common*), *Ashington Gate* (formerly *Ashington*); and some erased, eg *Lowfield.* Nearly all these changes are in west Sussex. **See plate 31.**

> . . . *British atlas* . . .
> London, Longman, Rees and Co. and J. and C. Walker, 1852.   CUL

(xvi)   Imprint (Ce OS) altered from *Published by Longman, Hurst, Rees, Orme & Co., Paternoster Row* to *London Published by J. & C. Walker 9 Castle Street Holborn.*

> . . . *British atlas* . . .
> London, Longman, Rees and Co. and J. and C. Walker, 1854 and 1856. BL;PRO

(xvii)   *Inhabitants* (Aa, under title) altered from *299.770* to *336.844.*

> . . . *British atlas* . . .
> London, Longman, Rees and Co. and J. and C. Walker, 1860. SALT LIBRARY

(xviii)   First stage:
Railways 17, 18 and 20 marked by double lines, not cross-hatched.

No map has been found in this state, but the plate in this state was used for transfer no. 107C.

Second stage:
Sta. and black dot added at several places, eg at *Bramber* and *Cowfold*.

Issued about 1860 as a folding map with printed cover: *Walker's Sussex.*
London, Longman and Co. and J. and C. Walker.   (BL).(CUL).(WSRO)

(xix)   Railway 21 marked by plain double lines.

   . . . British atlas . . .
London, Longman, Rees and Co. and J. and C. Walker, 1864.   P

(xx)   Railways 26, 28, 29 and 34 from *HAILSHAM* to *Heathfield* only marked by plain double lines.

   . . . British atlas . . .
London, Longman, Rees and Co. and J. and C. Walker, 1869.   A

(xxi)   Railway 30 marked by plain double lines. 1 to 5 now marked by cross-hatched double lines; 6 to 30 (omitting 24 and 27) and part of 34 by plain double lines.

   . . . British atlas . . .
London, Longman, Rees and Co. and J. and C. Walker, 1870.   BL

   . . . British atlas . . .
London, Longman and Co. and J. and C. Walker, 1872, 1873, 1877, and 1879.
P;W;P;BRL.BRIGHTON PL

108 A.   FIRST LITHOGRAPHIC TRANSFER

Size: 379 mm × 300 mm (9 mm)   1:330,000

EDITIONS

(i)   Imprint *Published by Longman, Hurst, Rees, Orme & Cº. Paternoster Row* (Ce OS) and *299.770 Inhabitants* (Aa, under title) as engraved. Plate number *Nº. 35* added (Ea OS and Ee OS, sideways). Boundaries of hunts marked by pecked lines; *PLACES OF THE MEETING OF FOXHODNDS* (sic) with black dot symbol added (Aa, below scale; the dot is immediately above the *u* in *Sussex contains . . .*). On the map a number of dots have been added and place-names underlined, eg *Woolmer Pond, Ashington Gate;* these additions are mostly in west Sussex, the most easterly being *Plaw Hatch* near *EAST GRINSTEAD.* Names of hunts, *COL WYNDHAM, MᴿNAPPER,*

CRAWLEY & HORSHAM, added in outline lettering. *See Map 34*, referring to adjacent hunts, added in two places. The names of hunts and references to adjacent hunts coloured by hand in blue on all impressions examined. Railways and stations as on no. 108(xv). **See plate 32.**

> *Hobson's fox-hunting atlas; containing separate maps of every county in England . . . comprising forty-two maps . . . Compiled from the maps of the Board of Ordnance, and other surveys. By J. and C. Walker.*
> London, J. and C. Walker, [1849].   CUL.W

(ii)   The outline hunt names and the two references to adjacent hunts erased. The map overprinted in blue with the names of hunts: *COL. WYNDHAM, MR NAPPER, CRAWLEY & HORSHAM.*

> *Hobson's fox-hunting atlas . . .*
> London, J. and C. Walker, [1850] and [1851].   CUL.W;BL

State of the plate: As no. 108(xv).
Alterations on the transfer: Plate number and all hunting information added. Transfer identified by two dots on outer line of top border, 17 mm from the left.

108 B.   SECOND LITHOGRAPHIC TRANSFER

Size: 375 mm × 300 mm (9 mm)   1:330,000

Stop added after plate number, now *N°. 35.* (Ea OS and Ee OS,). Imprint (Ce OS) now *London Published by J. and C. Walker 9 ·Castle Street Holborn. Inhabitants* now *336.844. PLACES OF THE MEETING OF FOXHOUNDS* (Aa) amended and moved to the left, the symbol is now 5 mm left of *u* in *Sussex contains* . . . The black dots on the map considerably revised; they are now of more even size; dots added, eg at *CUCKFIELD* and *Hand Cross;* dot omitted at *Shillingly Park;* dots re-sited, eg that over the *va* of *E^st Lavant* is now over the *nt.* Overprinted in blue lettering 3 mm in height (formerly 4 mm) with names of hunts: *COL. WYNDHAM, M^R. NAPPER, CRAWLEY & HORSHAM.* Railways as on no. 108(xv).

> *Hobson's fox-hunting atlas . . .*
> London, J. and C. Walker, [1855].   CUL

State of the plate: As no. 108(xvii).
Alterations on the transfer: Plate number and hunting information added.

108 C.   THIRD LITHOGRAPHIC TRANSFER

Size: 375 mm × 300 mm (9 mm)   1:330,000

EDITIONS

(i)   *Langley Gate* and *Ram Inn* (at *Firle*) added and underlined; dots added. Additional dots added and place-names underlined. Hachures along coastline erased. Overprinted in blue with names of hunts: *LORD LECONFIELD, CRAWLEY & HORSHAM, SOUTHDOWN.* Railways as no. 108(xvii), first stage.

> *Hobson's fox-hunting atlas . . .*
> London, J. and C. Walker, [1860].   BL

(ii)   Railways 21, 24, 26, 27, 28 and 29 added; 24 and 27 appear as partially erased on some impressions.

> *Hobson's fox-hunting atlas . . .*
> London, J. and C. Walker, [1866] and [1868].   W;BOD

State of the plate: As no. 108(xviii), first stage.
Alterations on the transfer: Plate number, hunting information, *Langley Gate* and *Ram Inn* added. Hachures along coastline erased. Railways added in edition (ii). Transfer identified by gap in outer border, at Ee.

108 D.   FOURTH LITHOGRAPHIC TRANSFER

Size: 375 mm × 300 mm (9 mm)   1:330,000

REFERENCE TO THE RAPES (Ce) and notes giving parliamentary information (Be and De) omitted. Additional place-names underlined, eg *Dallington.* Overprinted in blue with names of hunts: *LORD LECONFIELD, CRAWLEY & HORSHAM, SOUTHDOWN, E^T. SUSSEX.* Railway 30 added.

> *Hobson's fox-hunting atlas . . .*
> London, J. and C. Walker, [1869].   W

State of the plate: Probably as no. 108(xviii), first stage. (*Sta.* not added at *Bramber* and *Cowfold*).
Alterations on the transfer: Plate number, hunting information, *Langley Gate* and *Ram Inn* added. Hachures along coastline and inscriptions (Be, Ce and De) erased. Railways added as on no. 108C(ii), and also railway 30.

108 E. FIFTH LITHOGRAPHIC TRANSFER

Size: 375 mm × 300 mm (9 mm)   1:330,000

The imprint (Ce OS) now *London Published by J. and C. Walker; 37 Castle Street Holborn.* Inscriptions (Be, Ce and De) as originally engraved. *Gospel G^n* (near *HASLEMERE*), *Rushlake* and *Magham* added; *Rushlake* is curved. Hachures along coastline not erased. Hunting information as no. 108D, except that *Mead Street* is not underlined. Railways as no. 108D. but *Sta* and black dots added at several places, eg at *Bramber* and *Cowfold*.

> *Hobson's fox-hunting atlas . . .*
> London, J. and C. Walker, [1875] and [1878].   W;BL.W

> *Walker's fox-hunting atlas; containing separate maps of every county in England . . . comprising forty-two maps . . . compiled from the maps of the Board of Ordnance, and other surveys. By J. and C. Walker.*
> London, J. and C. Walker, [1880].   W

State of the plate: As no. 108(xxi), with imprint (Ce OS) amended, *Gospel G^n* added and railways 24 and 27 added.
Alterations on the transfer: Langley Gate, Ram Inn, Rushlake and *Magham* added. Hunting information added.

108 F. SIXTH LITHOGRAPHIC TRANSFER

Size: 375 mm × 300 mm (9 mm)   1:330,000

EDITIONS

(i) *Inhabitants* (Aa) altered to *417.456.* Note (De) now reads *BOROUGHS returning 2 Members each Brighton Hastings Shoreham* (formerly *Lewes Hastings Chichester Shoreham Brighton*) and . . . *returning 1 Member each Rye Lewes Horsham Midhurst Chichester* (formerly *Rye Arundel Horsham Midhurst*). Plate number omitted. *Langley Gate* and *Ram Inn* omitted. *Rushlake* is now in a straight horizontal line. All hunting information, including symbol and note (Aa, under scale), black dots, underlinings and hunt names, omitted.

> Issued about 1879 as a folding map with printed title on cover: *Walker's Sussex.*
> London, J. and C. Walker.   (P)

(ii) Imprint (Ce OS) altered to *Published by John Murray Albemarle Street London 1879.*

> *Handbook for travellers in Sussex. Fourth edition. With map and plan.*
> London, John Murray, 1877.   SAS.HASTINGS PL

The map is loose, inserted in a pocket at the back of the work. The table of contents refers to a map of Kent and Sussex, but most copies examined contain this map, which probably became available in 1879. The British Library copy of the handbook contains a map of south-east England from the same plates as no. 147. Earlier editions entitled *Handbook for travellers in Kent and Sussex* and published on 1858, 1863 and 1868, also contain the map of south-east England. Later editions, published in 1893 and 1899, contain sectional maps.

State of the plate: Later than no. 108E. Inhabitants added. *Rushlake* and *Magham* added.
Alterations on the transfer: Imprint (Ce OS) amended in (ii).

108 G.   SEVENTH LITHOGRAPHIC TRANSFER

Size: 375 mm × 300 mm (9 mm)   1:330,000

EDITIONS

(i)   Imprint (Ce OS) *London Published by J. and C. Walker; 37 Castle Street Holborn* and plate number *N⁰. 35.* (Ea OS) as no. 108E. Hunting information as nos. 108D and E; but *Mead Street* is underlined and extra dots have been added, eg at *Brede. Langley Gate* and *Ram Inn* added. Railway 34 added; 28 re-routed.

> *Walker's fox-hunting atlas . . .*
> London, J. and C. Walker, [1882].   P

(ii)   Hunt names overprinted in blue are now *GOODWOOD, L^D. LECONFIELD, CRAWLEY & HORSHAM, BURSTOW, SOUTHDOWN* and *EAST SUSSEX.*

> *Walker's fox-hunting atlas . . .*
> London, J. and C. Walker, [1886] and 189[2].   P;P
> The last figure in the date of the later atlas has been inserted by hand in a space left blank for that purpose.

State of the plate: Later than no. 108F. Railways have been added and amended.
Alterations on the transfer: Hunting information added. *Langley Gate* and *Ram Inn* added. (The boundaries of the hunts, which are defined by hand colouring, vary from one impression to another.)

108 H.   EIGHTH LITHOGRAPHIC TRANSFER

Size: 375 mm × 300 mm (9 mm)   1:330,000

No imprint (Ce OS). Notes (Be, Ce and De) omitted. *550.442 Inhabitants* (Aa). Note (Aa) now reads . . . *returns 6 Members to Parliament for the county and 3 for 2 Boroughs.* Hunting information as no. 108G(ii), but additional underlining, eg at

Birling Gap, and eight hunt names now overprinted in blue: *GOODWOOD, LECONFIELD, CRAWLEY AND HORSHAM, BURSTOW, SOUTHDOWN, ERIDGE, EASTBOURN* and *EAST SUSSEX*. Railways 34, 35, 36, 38 and 42 added.

Walker's fox-hunting atlas; containing separate maps of every county in England . . . comprising forty-two maps . . . compiled from the maps of the Board of Ordnance. By J. and C. Walker.
London, J. and C. Walker, 189[4] and 189]5].   P;CUL
The last figure in the dates of both of these atlases has been inserted by hand in a space left blank for that purpose.

State of the plate: Later than no. 108G. Imprint (Ce OS) and notes (Be, Ce and De) erased. *Inhabitants* and note (Aa) amended. Railways added.
Alterations on the transfer: Hunting information added. *Langley Gate* and *Ram Gate* added.

108 I. NINTH LITHOGRAPHIC TRANSFER

Size: 376 mm × 302 mm (9 mm)   1:330,000

Title *Sussex* (Aa) now in plain black capitals, but the frame is unchanged. Walker signature (Aa, under title) erased and replaced by *LETTS, SON & Cᵒ. LIMITED.* Imprint *LETTS, SON & Co. LIMITED, LONDON BRIDGE, E.C.* added (Ce OS). *PLACES OF THE MEETING OF FOXHOUNDS*, underlinings, black dots and names of hunts omitted. Area, population and parliamentary information (Aa, under scale) erased; replaced by *STATISTICS,* including six items of which one is *Population 490,316. S* of *SURREY* erased. Two adjoining panels (47 mm × 57 mm and 106 mm × 57 mm) containing new key added (Ce). A number of features listed on the key are now marked on the map by overprinting in red and blue, eg red square under *CHICHESTER,* indicating *Towns where Quarter Sessions are held;* other features are marked in black, eg *L.B.S.* at *WORTHING,* meaning *Life Boat Station.* Grid (75 mm × 150 mm) with reference letters *A* to *E* and *a* to *d* added. *Cooksbridge Sta.* added. *LITTLEHAMPTON, HOVE, KEMP TOWN, NEWHAVEN, SEAFORD* and *Sᵀ LEONARDS* re-engraved in the sea in capitals. *EASTBOURNE (Old Town)* added in place of *East Bourn,* and *EASTBOURNE* in place of *Sea Houses. Rye Harbour* and *Rye Bay* added in place of *Rye Old Harbour* and *Rye New Harbour. Bopeep, Camber Cas.,* and *Winchelsea Cas.* erased. *Langley Gate* and *Ram Inn* omitted. Railways 31 and 37 added. *Whatlington* to *Brede* line erased. Overprinted to produce colours green, yellow, pink, blue and red. **See plate 33.**

Lett's popular county atlas. Being a complete series of maps delineating the whole surface of England and Wales, with special and original features . . .
London, Letts, Son and Co. Ltd., 1884.   BL.BOD.BRIGHTON PL

State of the plate: Later than no. 108H. Place-names amended. Railways added.
Alterations on the transfer: All other alterations listed above, including the grid were

probably made on the stone. In most impressions *NONE* (in black) overprinted *BRIGHTON* (in red) appears opposite *Towns with Population over 100.000* in the key (Ce). In one impression (SAS) *BRIGHTON* is in blue; in another (BL) *NONE* and *BRIGHTON* have been replaced by a red line. These variations would have been effected on the stone.

Loose impressions (WSRO. and BRIGHTON PL) have also been found with printed labels reading *JAMES WYLD. Geographer to the Queen. 11 & 12 CHARING CROSS. S.W. & 2 ROYAL EXCHANGE. E.C. LONDON*, pasted over the signature (Aa, under title) and the imprint (Ce OS).

108 J.   TENTH LITHOGRAPHIC TRANSFER

Size: 376 mm × 302 mm (9 mm)   1:330,000

WESTERN DIVISION and *EASTERN DIVISION* erased. The six parliamentary divisons are marked and named in red, eg *HORSHAM (NORTH WESTERN). Post Towns* are marked by blue triangles in place of blue dots and the key (Ce) amended. The red dots (indicating the number of members returnable by Parliamentary Boroughs) increased from 2 mm diameter to 3 mm diameter. The red circle (indicating the number of members returnable by County Parliamentary Divisons) removed in the key, and four omitted on the map. The position of symbols on the map has been changed, eg the red cross indicating County Court at *EASTBOURNE* has been moved from the right to the left of the town name. Printer's reference *ix.85* added (Ee OS). Overprinted to produce colours green, yellow, pink, purple, blue and red.

> *Lett's popular county atlas* . . .
> London, Mason and Payne, 1887.   BOD

State of the plate: Probably as no. 108I.
Alterations on the transfer: Similar to no. 108I, but modified in accordance with the changes listed above. *WESTERN DIVISION* and *EASTERN DIVISION* may have been erased on the plate.

Size: 305 mm × 303 mm (5 mm)   1:823,000

There is insufficient detail to enable the sources used in the compilation of this map to be determined.

Aaron Arrowsmith[1] (1750–1823), of Durham, came to London in 1770, and is believed to have worked under Faden or Cary. He published his first map in 1790, and his subsequent output included some excellent large maps of various parts of the world. After his death, the firm was carried on by his sons, Aaron and Samuel, until the death of Samuel in 1839. John Arrowsmith (1790–1873) was the nephew of the first Aaron. He came to London in 1810 and worked for his uncle, before setting up on his own in 1823. He took over the family business on the death of Samuel in 1839. He assisted in the founding of the Royal Geographical Society. The assets of the Arrowsmith business were sold by auction in 1874.

Another map of the diocese of Chichester by *Stanford's Geogl. Estabt.* illustrates a paper by Rev. William Hudson on *The ancient deaneries of the diocese of Chichester, and their relation to the rapes of the county of Sussex* in *SAC* 55 (1912). See also no. 137.

The design was probably laid down on the lithographic stone from an original drawing. It is an outline map measuring about 160 mm × 100 mm and occupying a position to the left of centre within the border. Only Chichester is named. Other maps in this series are listed by McGechaen and Verner.[2]

EDITION

CHICHESTER. (unaltered). (Da). *S. Arrowsmith Lithog.* (Ee OS). Plate number *5* (Ea OS). *Reference* (Be) to ecclesiastical boundaries. Key (Ed) to the deaneries in east Sussex headed *A* and numbered *1* to *5*; to those in west Sussex headed *B* and numbered *1* to *6*. *A,B* and the numbers are marked on the map.

> *Third report from His Majesty's commissioners . . . the state of the Established Church. 20 May 1836. Appendix to the third report of the church commission. . . . Maps of the several Dioceses . . . These maps are divided according to counties; and also according to Archdeaconries and Deanries; the boundaries of the latter being regulated by the maps published in the Valor Ecclesiasticus, and their names taken from Bacon's Liber Regis . . .*
> Reports from Commissioners, Session 4 Feb – 20 Aug 1836. vol. 36, 1836.
>
> BL.(BRIGHTON PL)

The signature (Ee OS) has been cut off in the British Library copy. *Valor Ecclesiasticus* was compiled c. 1536. John Ecton made a similar valuation in

1. R.V. Tooley, 'Aaron Arrowsmith' in *Map Collector* no. 9 (Dec. 1979).
2. McGechaen and Verner, 1973.

1711, when it was printed with the title *Liber Valorum et Decimarum* by I. Harrison. It was reissued in 1723, 1728, 1742, 1754 and 1763. In 1786 it was republished with the title *Liber Regis* . . . by John Bacon (without acknowledgement to Ecton) and sold by J.F. and C. Rivington, J. Robson and T. Cadell. None of these issues contained maps. In 1810 to 1834 the *Valor* was updated and reprinted in six volumes under the title *Valor Ecclesiaticus Temp. Henr. VIII* . . . *Printed by Commons of His Majesty King George III. In pursuance of an address of The House of Commons of Great Britain.* The earlier volumes contained maps showing the diocesan boundaries, but in most cases several dioceses were grouped on one map; the first volume, for example, had a map covering Chichester, Canterbury, Rochester and London and dated 1810. The last volume had a *Tabula Generalis* . . . dated 1834. All maps were signed *S. Arrowsmith delin^t*. These, presumably were the maps referred to by the Commissioners in 1836. There is a set at SAS.

110   W. SCHMOLLINGER   1837

Size: 242 mm × 168 mm (see below)   1:554,000

Based on Hall no. 96.

Nothing has been discovered about W. Schmollinger.

George Virtue (c. 1793–1868) was the founder of the publishing firm and was himself an artist. His son, James Sprent Virtue (1829–92), opened up the United States branch and eventually took over the running of the whole business.

Thomas Moule, the author of the work referred to below, was a book-seller; but for most of his life held official appointments which enabled him to pursue his writing activities. He published a number of important works on heraldry and antiquities, including *Bibliotecha heraldica Magnae Britanniae* in 1822.

The English counties delineated . . . was first published in parts commencing in May 1830.[1] The Hertfordshire section (*Moule's English counties* . . . *Hertfordshire* . . . *The English counties delineated;* . . . *a series of forty county maps* . . . *By Thomas Moule* . . . *Part XIX*) has been found[2] and was published in 1830. It is possible that a Sussex section, with map, was published about the same time.

More than one copy of *The history of England by Hume and Smollet* . . . has been found containing this series of maps, but none of the many editions in the British Library contains them. It is possible that the maps were issued separately and bound in by some subscribers to an edition originally published in parts, – possibly the 1876–7 edition published by Virtue & Co.

The map is surrounded by a decorative floral border; the dimensions given above

1. Whitaker, 1948, no. 449.
2. Hodson, 1974, no. 94(i).

are taken from the inside of the framework which supports the decorations. The maximum engraved area measures 260 mm × 206 mm.

EDITIONS

(i)   *SUSSEX* (Ce, in border). *Engraved for MOULES ENGLISH COUNTIES by W. Schmollinger* (Ce OS). *Scale of Miles 10* = 35 mm (Bd). Compass (Db). *REFERENCE to the RAPES* (Ab). *CHAIN PIER, BRIGHTON* and engraving (Ca). *CHICHESTER CATHEDRAL* and engraving (Ae). *ARUNDEL CASTLE* and engraving (Ee). *CHICHESTER* and arms (Eb), arms of the See of Chichester (Aa), arms of the Duke of Norfolk (Ea), arms of the Earl of Egremont (Ca).

> *The English counties delineated; or, a topographical description of England. Illustrated by . . . a complete series of county maps. By Thomas Moule . . .* vol. 1.
> London, George Virtue, 1837 and 1839.   BL.W.CUL;CARDIFF PL.BRL

(ii)   Form lines along coast extended to right border (formerly stopped 4 mm from border).

> *The English counties delineated . . .* vol. 1.
> London, George Virtue, 1837 and 1838.   BL.LEEDS PL;CUL

(iii)   *The County returns 4 members* added (Bd, under scale). Asterisks added, eg one at *RYE*, two at *HORSHAM*. Boundaries added to parliamentary boroughs of Horsham, Chichester, Hastings and Brighton.

> *The English counties delineated . . .* vol. 1.
> London, George Virtue, 1838 and 1839.   P;W

(iv)   Signature (Ce OS) erased and replaced by plate number *14*.

> *A complete and universal English dictionary, by the Rev. James Barclay, illustrated by numerous engravings & maps. Revised by Henry W. Dewhurst, Esq., F.E.S.L. . . .*
> London, George Virtue, [1842].   P

(v)   Railway 2 marked by double cross-hatched lines.

> *Barclay's universal English dictionary, newly revised by Henry W. Dewhurst Esq: F.E.S.L.*
> London, George Virtue, [1842].   W.CARDIFF PL

(vi)   A number of place-names added, eg *Hove, Bulverhythe, Polegate. Railway Stations thus* added (Bd, above scale), and stations marked by black dots on map. Railways 1, 3, 4 and 5 added; all railways now marked by treble cross-hatched lines.

229

A complete and universal English dictionary . . . [1844] and [1845].   W;P

The *unversal English dictionary . . . by the Rev. James Barclay* published about 1846 contains no. 114(ii).

(vii)   Railways 6 to 10 added; railway 8 misrouted to *Cuckfield* in place of *Wivelsfield.* Plate number *14* (Ce OS) erased.

A complete and universal dictionary of the English language . . . By the Rev. James Barclay. A new edition . . . by B.B. Woodward, B.A. London.
London, George Virtue, [1848] and [1850].   BL;WN

(viii)   Railways 11 and 13 added. *To Ashford* added.

A complete and universal dictionary of the English language . . .
London, James S. Virtue, [1852].   W

111   JOSHUA ARCHER   1841

Size: 215 mm × 164 mm (6 mm)   1:622,000

Based on Walker no. 108.

EDITION

CHICHESTER. (Ea). *Drawn and Engraved by J. Archer, Pentonville, London.* (Ee OS). *London, Engraved for the BRITISH MAGAZINE for Dec. 1841 & Published by T. CLERC SMITH, 13 Henrietta Street, Covent Garden.* (Ce OS). *Scale of English Miles. 20* = 51 mm (Ea, under title). *REFERENCE* (Aa) including deaneries numbered *1* to *12* on the map, boundaries of ecclesiastical divisions, and symbols for *Bishops Residence, Vicarages, &c. Arms of the Bishop* (Ca). Longitude 10' (5'); latitude 10' (5'). No roads or railways are shown on the map.

The British Magazine, and monthly register of religious and ecclesiastical information . . . vol. 20.
London, T. Clerc Smith, 1841.   BL

112   DARTON AND CLARK

circa **1841**

Size: 90 mm × 55 mm (1 mm)

1:1,410,000

The map is sufficiently detailed to enable the sources used in its compilation to be determined.

This is a miniature road-book in 32°. The text states '. . . with a map. A population table comprising the census of 1841.' The table, however, gives the figures for 1831, together with a blank column for 1841; presumably because the figures had not become available by the date of publication. Hampshire, Isle of Wight, Kent and Surrey in the same series are known.[1]

EDITION

SUSSEX (Ea). Twenty towns are named on the map and roads are shown in two categories.

The miniature road-book of Sussex.
London, Darton and Clark, [1841].

BL.BOD

113   JAMES PIGOT AND ISAAC SLATER

circa **1841**

Based on Pigot no. 90.

The plate does not appear to have been used for direct intaglio printing.
County maps in this series were published fortnightly, in about 1839, in *Pigot and Co's pocket atlas, topography, and gazetteer of England*[1] . . . The parts were issued in rough alphabetical order, but appear to have ceased after *no. 25 NOTTINGHAMSHIRE.*

113 A.   LITHOGRAPHIC TRANSFER

Size: 156 mm × 95 mm (5 mm)

1:870,000

SUSSEX (Ca, in border). *Pigot & Slater Engravers Manch*[r]. (Ee OS). *PUBLISHED BY PIGOT & Co. LONDON AND MANCHESTER.* (Ce OS). *Scale of Miles 10* = 18 mm (Ce, in border). Compass (Aa). *Explanation.* (Eb). Longitude 5' (1'); latitude 5' (1').

1. Chubb, 1927, no. DV1.
1. Hodson, 1974, no. 104A.

A pocket topography and gazetteer of England . . . Illustrated by maps of the English counties . . . By Pigot & Co. . . vol. 2.
London, Pigot and Co., Longman and Co., Sherwood and Co., and Simpkin and Marshall; Manchester, Pigot and Slater, [1841] and [1850].   BL.CUL.W;BL
It is probable that individual sections of this work, with the county map but without title-page, were offered for sale separately.

State of the plate: As originally engraved.
Alterations on the transfer: None.

114   JOSHUA ARCHER   circa **1842**

Size: 223 mm × 167 mm (7 mm)   1:575,000

Based on Walker no. 108.

Edward L. Blanchard (1820–89), the editor of some of the works listed below, was the son of William Blanchard (1769–1835), the actor-manager. He edited a number of magazines, including the *New London magazine,* and for thirty-seven years he produced the annual pantomime at Drury Lane.

EDITIONS

(i)   *SUSSEX* (Aa). *Drawn & Engraved by J. Archer, Pentonville, London.* (Ee OS). *Engraved for Dugdales England and Wales Delineated.* (Ce OS). *SCALE-16 Miles* = 47 mm (Aa, under title). Plate number *38* (Ea OS). *RAPES* (Ca). *EXPLANATION* (Ea). Longitude 10'; latitude 10'. Railways 1 and 2 marked and *London & Brighton Railway* named.

Curiosities of Great Britain. England and Wales delineated . . . by Thomas Dugdale, antiquarian. Assisted by William Burnett. vol. 4.
[London, L. Tallis, 1842].   CUL.BRL
Earlier editions of this work contain no. 66 (iii) and (iv).

Curiosities of Great Britain . . . vol. 4.
London, L. Tallis, [1846].   BL

(ii)   Inscription (Ce OS) erased.

The universal English dictionary . . . By the Rev. James Barclay.
London and Glasgow, J. and F. Tallis, [1846].   P
Other editions of Barclay's dictionary contain no. 110.

(iii)   Railways 3, 4, 5, 7, 9, 12, 13, 14 and 16, and a line from *Sedlescombe* to *Winchelsea* added and many named; *London & Brighton Railway* erased and replaced by *London Brighton & South Coast Raily.*

232

Curiosities of Great Britain . . . vol. 6.
London, J. and F. Tallis [1846] and [1847].   W.BRL;W

(iv)   Railways 6, 8, 10, 11, 15 and 25 added, and a line from *New Shoreham* to *Steyning* (part of 20).

Curiosities of Great Britain . . . vol. 6.
[London, L. Tallis, 1848].   W.BRIGHTON PL

The universal English dictionary . . .
London and New York, John Tallis and Co., [1848].   P

(v)   *New Shoreham* to *Steyning* line and railway 15 (Rye harbour extension) erased. Town symbol for *Coombs* erased. Railways 12 and 14 re-routed; 14 so as to pass through the *l* of *Salehurst,* and in the railway name *Hastings* re-engraved *Hasting. STA* added at numerous places, eg at *Frant.*

Dugdale's England and Wales delineated. Edited by E.L. Blanchard. vol. 2. part 45.
London, L. Tallis [1858].   BL

(vi)   Railways 17 and 18 added.

The topographical dictionary of England and Wales.
London, L. Tallis, [1860].   P

The topographical dictionary of England and Wales. Edited by E.L. Blanchard. vol. 2.
London, L. Tallis, [1860].   RICS LIB.SAS

Tallis's topographical dictionary of England and Wales. With a road & railway county atlas.
London, L. Tallis, [1860].   P
The imprint is taken from the spine.

115   BENJAMIN REES DAVIES   1845

Based closely on Walker no. 108.

The plate from which the following lithographic transfers were taken was apparently never used for direct intaglio printing,

The map of Hertfordshire[1] is known in a state between no. 115A and no. 115B, and it is possible that a revised map of Sussex was included in a re-issue of one of the directories listed under no. 115A. According to advertisements in the directories, the maps were also available loose, *SHEET, ON ROLLER*, or *IN CASE*.

114 A.   FIRST LITHOGRAPHIC TRANSFER

Size: 282 mm × 216 mm (2 mm)   1:461,000

POST OFFICE MAP OF SUSSEX. 1845. (Ea). *Drawn & Engraved by B.R. Davies.* (Ee OS). *Kelly & Cº. Post Office Directory Offices 19 & 20 Old Boswell Court, Temple Bar* (Ce OS). *Scale of . . . Miles 10* = 37 mm (Ea, under title). Compass (Eb). *Reference* to rapes (Ce). Parliamentary information and key (Ee). Longitude 10'; latitude 10'. Railways 1 to 5, A, D and *EPSOM RAILWAY* marked; *SOUTH EASTERN RAILWAY, SOUTH WESTERN RAILWAY, GUILDFORD RAILWAY, CROYDON RAILʸ., BRIGHTON RAILʸ.. HASTINGS RAILʸ.* and *CHICHᴿ. RAILʸ.* are also named.

> *Post Office directory of the six home counties, viz., Essex, Herts, Kent, Middlesex, Surrey and Sussex. With maps engraved expressly for the work.*
> London, W. Kelly and Co., [1845].   BL.GL.BOD

> *Post Office directory of London and nine counties; viz. . . . The maps engraved expressly for the work.*
> London, W. Kelly and Co., [1846].   BL

State of the plate: As originally engraved.
Alterations on the transfer: None.

115 B.   SECOND LITHOGRAPHIC TRANSFER

Size: 282 mm × 218 mm (2 mm)   1:461,000

The date in title (Ea) altered from *1845.* to *1852. Pl* added at *Fairlight. Courtledge* erased below *TUNBRIDGE WELLS. EPSOM* erased. Key added (De) with two items:

---

1.   Hodson, 1974, no. 107B.

Railways finished and in use to be shown by a continuous line, and . . . *D⁰ . . . in Progress or for which Acts Have been obtained* to be shown by a pecked line. Railways added as in use, 6 to 11, 13, 22, B, C, E and F; as in progress, 12, 14, 15, 16 and a line from *Whatlington* to *Brede*. Other lines added outside the county boundary, eg *S^TH. WEST^N. RAILY LONDON TO SOUTHAMPTON, MAIDSTONE RAILWAY.*

> *Post Office directory of the six home counties . . .*
> London, W. Kelly and Co., [1851]. BL

State of the plate: Later than no. 115 A., including all the changes listed above, although the date may not have been erased on the plate.
Alterations on the transfer: Date (Ea) added.

115 C.   THIRD LITHOGRAPHIC TRANSFER

Size: 282 mm × 220 mm (2 mm) 1:461,000

Signature (Ee OS) erased. Hachures in the sea strengthened along shoreline.

> *Post Office directory of the six home counties . . .*
> London, W. Kelly and Co., [1851]. BOD.GL

> *Post Office directory of Hampshire, with Essex, Herts, Kent, Middlesex, Surrey, and Sussex. The maps engraved expressly for the work.*
> London, W. Kelly and Co., [1852]. WSCL.PORTSMOUTH PL

State of the plate: Later than no. 115B. Signature (Ee OS) erased and railways added.
Alterations on the transfer: Date added.

115 D.   FOURTH LITHOGRAPHIC TRANSFER

Size: 282 mm × 221 mm (2 mm) 1:461,000

Date in title (Ea), altered from *1852.* to *1855.* Inhabitants (Ee) altered from *299.753* to *366,844.* Railways 12 and 14 now shown as in use; 19 erased.

> *Post Office directory of Essex, Herts, Kent, Middlesex, Surrey and Sussex; with maps engraved expressly for the work and corrected to the time of publication.*
> London, Kelly and Co., 1855. BL.GL.BOD

State of the plate: Later than no. 115C. Inhabitants and railways amended.
Alterations on the transfer: Date added.

115 E.   FIFTH LITHOGRAPHIC TRANSFER

Size: 280 mm × 218 mm (2 mm)   1:461,000

Date on title (Ea) altered from *1855.* to *1859.*. Railways 16, 18 and 19 shown as in use; *Whatlington* to *Brede* line erased.

> *Post Office directory of Essex, Herts, Kent, Middlesex, Surrey and Sussex* . . .
> London, Kelly and Co., 1859.   BL

State of the plate: Later than no. 115D. Railways amended.
Alterations on the transfer: Date added.

115 F.   SIXTH LITHOGRAPHIC TRANSFER

Size: 278 mm × 218 mm (2 mm)   1:461,000

No date under title (Ea). *Drawn & Engraved by B.R. Davies* added (Ee OS), now 32 mm long compared with 30 mm on no. 115A to E. In imprint (Ce OS) . . . *19 & 20* . . . altered to . . . *19, 20 & 21* . . . *Printed from Stone by C.F. Cheffins & Son. London* added (Ae OS). Railway 17 added as in use.

> *The Post Office directory atlas of England and Wales.*
> London, Kelly and Co., [1861].   BL.CUL.BOD

State of the plate: Later than no. 115E. Signature added (Ee OS). Imprint (Ce OS) amended. Railway added.
Alterations on the transfer: Cheffins imprint (Ae OS) added. Date erased.

115 G.   SEVENTH LITHOGRAPHIC TRANSFER

Size: 280 mm × 218 mm (2 mm)   1:461,000

Date *1862.* added (Ea). Inhabitants (Ee) altered from *336,844* to *363,648*. Imprint (Ae OS) omitted. Railway 20 added as in use; 21, 24, 26, 27, 29 and 30 as in progress; 22 now in progress (formerly shown as in use).

> *Post Office directory of Essex, Herts, Middlesex, Kent, Surrey & Sussex* . . .
> London, Kelly and Co., 1862.   BL.BOD

> *Post Office directory of Sussex* . . .
> London, Kelly and Co., 1862.   SAS
> This is the Sussex section of the preceding work, with special title-page but unaltered pagination.

State of the plate: Later than no. 115F. Inhabitants and railways amended.
Alterations on the transfer: Date added.

115 H.   EIGHTH LITHOGRAPHIC TRANSFER

Size: 280 mm × 218mm (2 mm)   1:461,000

Date (Ea) altered from *1862.* to *1867..* Inhabitants (Ee) altered from *363,648* to *363,735. Post Office Money Order Towns* (Ee) erased. *Littlehampton* and *Eastbourn* re-engraved as one word and on one line. Railways 21 to 28 and 30 shown as in use; line from south of *Balcombe* to *Uckfield* and on to *HAILSHAM* shown as in use; 34, 35, 42 (to *Boldbrook*) and line from *Horeham* to S^t. *Leonards* shown as in progress.

> *The Post Office directory of Essex, Herts, Middlesex, Kent, Surrey & Sussex. With maps engraved expressly for the work. Edited by E.R. Kelley, M.A.*
> London, Kelly and Co., 1866.   BL.BOD
> The Sussex section of this work was issued separately, but in the copy examined (Brighton PL) the title-page is missing.

State of the plate: Later than no. 115G. Inhabitants, place-names and railways amended. *Post Office Money Order Towns* erased.
Alterations on the transfer: Date added.

115 I.   NINTH LITHOGRAPHIC TRANSFER

Size: 280 mm × 218 mm (2 mm)   1:461,000

EDITIONS

(i)   Date (Ea) altered from *1867.* to *1871.* In the imprint (Ce OS) . . . *19, 20 & 21 Old Boswell Court, Temple Bar* replaced by . . . *51, Great Queen Street, London. J.M. JOHNSON & SONS, PRINTERS 3 CASTLE STREET. HOLBORN & 56, HATTON GARDEN. LONDON.* added (Ae OS). *Denote Polling Places* and symbol (Ee) erased, but the symbols on the map have not been erased. *EPSOM* added; it is now placed below *EPSOM RAILWAY. e* added to *Eastbourne.* Railways 34, 35 and lines from *Balcombe* to *UCKFIELD* to *HAILSHAM*, and from *Horeham* to S^t. *Leonards* erased, but traces of the original engraving remain, eg at *Whitesmith;* 29 shown as in use; M added.

> *The Post Office directory of the six home counties . . . With maps engraved expressly for the work. Edited by E.R. Kelly, M.A., F.S.S.*
> London, Kelly and Co., 1870.   BL.BOD

(ii)   Imprint (Ae OS) altered to *J.M. JOHNSON & SONS, PRINTERS 56 HATTON GARDEN, LONDON.*

The Post Office directory of Sussex. With map engraved expressly for the work. Edited by E.R. Kelly, M.A., F.S.S.
London, Kelly and Co., 1870.   BRIGHTON PL
This is the Sussex section from the preceding work, with unaltered pagination.

State of the plate: Later than no. 115H., including all alterations listed above, except date and imprints (Ae OS).
Alterations on the transfer: Date (Ea) and imprints (Ae OS) added.

115 J.   TENTH LITHOGRAPHIC TRANSFER

Size: 280 mm × 218 mm (2 mm)   1:461,000

Date (Ea) altered from *1871.* to *1874.* Signature (Ee OS) erased. Imprint (Ae OS) altered to *J.M. JOHNSON & SONS, LITHO. 56, HATTON GARDEN, LONDON.* Inhabitants (Ee) altered from *363,735* to *417,456. Pier* and symbol added at *WORTHING; on sea* added to S*t*. *Leonards. Blatchington* re-engraved, road added and railway 25 re-routed along the coast. In the key (De) reference to (railways) *in Progress* . . . erased. Railway 31 added as in use; 42 erased; 29 re-routed.

The Post Office directory of the six home counties . . .
London, Kelly and Co., 1874.   BL.BOD

The Post Office directory of Sussex. With map engraved expressly for the work. Edited by E.R. Kelly, M.A., F.S.S.
London, Kelly and Co., 1874.   BRIGHTON PL
This is the Sussex section from the preceding work, with unaltered pagination.

State of the plate: Later than no. 115I. Signature erased. Inhabitants, place-names and railways amended.
Alterations on the transfer: Date added. Imprint (Ae OS) added.

115 K.   ELEVENTH LITHOGRAPHIC TRANSFER

Size: 390 mm × 290 mm (2 mm)   1:332,000

In the title (Ea) *POST OFFICE MAP OF* erased. Date (Ea) altered from *1874.* to *1878. Scale of . . . Miles 10* = 52 mm (Ea, under title). No imprint (Ae OS). Railways 32 and 34 to 37 added as in use. (Railways in Sussex are now 1 to 32, 34 to 37, and are all shown as in use except 15).

The Post Office directory of the six home counties . . .
London, Kelly and Co., 1878.   BL.BOD

The Post Office directory of Sussex . . .
London, Kelly and Co., 1878.   BRIGHTON PL
This is the Sussex section from the preceding work, with unaltered pagination.

State of the plate: Later than no. 115J. Imprint (Ae OS) erased. Railways added.
Alterations on the transfer: Title and date amended.

116   F.P. BECKER AND CO.   circa **1845**

Size: 335 mm × 264 mm (7 mm)   1:361,000

Based on Walker no. 108.

Henry Fisher,[1] see below, published his first map in Liverpool in 1816; the firm was then known as Nuttall, Fisher and Co. Fisher moved to London in 1821, following a fire at his 'Caxton Press' in Liverpool. In 1825 he took his son, Robert, into partnership. The firm then became Fisher, Son and Co. In 1833 they were joined by Peter Jackson. Henry Fisher died in 1837. An 1843 map bears the imprint *Peter Jackson, late Fisher, Son and Co.,* which may mean that Robert Fisher had died or retired, or perhaps merely that Jackson had set up on his own, which would account for the Fisher imprint on the map below and on other post-1843 maps in the same series.

The atlas in which these maps appeared was started by James Gilbert in 1842 with maps engraved by Archer, but after seven maps had been issued, it was taken over by Fisher and subsequent maps were engraved by F.P. Becker and Co. Francis Paul Becker also engraved maps, but not Sussex, for Kelly's Post Office Directories (see no. 115). In about 1850 he introduced *Becker's Patent Process.*[2]

EDITION

SUSSEX (Aa). *Drawn by F.P. Becker & C⁰. Albion Road Holloway.* (Ae OS). *Engraved on Steel by the Omnigraph, F.P. Becker & C⁰. Patentees.* (Ee OS). *FISHER, SON, & C⁰. LONDON & PARIS.* (Ce OS). *SCALE OF MILES* 1 + 14 = 65 mm (Ae); zero is not marked on the scale-bar, which makes it confusing to read. Electoral information (Ab, under title). Key to four ecclesiastical symbols (Ae, under scale). Longitude 10' (2'); latitude 10' (2').

Fisher's county atlas of England and Wales. Compiled from authentic surveys, and corrected to the present time. . .
London, Liverpool and Manchester, Fisher, Son and Co., [1845]. BL.CUL.WSRO

1. Gardiner, 1973, pp. 59–60.
2. Hyde, 1975, nos. 10 and 32.

117 JOHN EMSLIE   1848

Size: 226 mm × 165 mm (4 mm)   1:560,000

Based on Hall no. 96; Pett appears as *Pell*.

John Emslie[1] (1813–75) was born at Newington in Surrey. He was apprenticed to Thomas Harwood, the engraver, in Gray's Inn Road. He set up on his own in 1843, and co-operated with Reynolds in the production of maps and diagrams. He was the father of John Philip Emslie (1839–1913), the topographical artist.

The plate, from which this map was printed, continued in service until at least 1927. Maps derived from it appeared until that year in successive editions of H.B. Woodward, *Stanford's geological atlas of Great Britain.*

Hertfordshire in this series is grouped with three other counties, and is, therefore, omitted by Hodson.[2]

EDITIONS

(i) *SURREY AND SUSSEX.* (Ea). *Drawn and Engraved by John Emslie* (Ae OS). *Published by J. Reynolds 174 Strand.* (Ce OS). *ENGLISH MILES 12* = 36 mm (Eb). Compass (Ec). Plate number *28* (Ee OS). *RAILWAYS Open* . . . continuous line, *Constructing* . . . fine double lines (Eb, between title and scale). Railways shown as *Open*, 1 to 5, 7 and 8, A, C, D and K; as *Constructing*, 6, 9, 12, 14, 15, 16, 19, 20 (part) and 22 to 25, E, F and line from *Whatlington* to *WINCHELSEA*. A single cross-hatched line marked *Railway* runs from *REIGATE* to *Putney* via *Croydon*.

> *Reynolds's travelling atlas of England: with all the railways and stations accurately laid down. Constructed from the surveys of the Board of Ordnance, railway companies and other authorities.*
> London, Simpkin, Marshal and Co. and James Reynolds, 1848.   BL.CUL

(ii) Railways 6, 9 to 14, E and F now shown as *Open*.

> *Reynolds's travelling atlas . . .*
> London, Simpkin, Marshal and Co. and James Reynolds, [1854] and [1856]. W;WN

(iii) Geological formations marked by thin lines and numbered in accordance with a key in the front of the atlas. *67 Bognor* erased. *Bognor* added to the east of *S*th. *Bersted*. House symbols added on the west side of *BRIGHTON*. Railways 1 to 19 now shown as *Open*; 22, 23, 24 and line from *Whatlington* to *Winchelsea* shown as

---

1. J.C. Phillips, 'John Philip Emslie and his topographical drawings of the London area'. *Guidhall studies in London history* vol. 2 no. 2, 1976.
2. Hodson, 1974.

Constructing. Outside Sussex, the cross-hatched line from *REIGATE* and *Railway* erased; another line from *Epsom* and some further lines in north Surrey added.

Reynolds's geological atlas of Great Britain, comprising a series of maps in which the roads, railways and geological features are accurately laid down . . . The whole complied from the most authentic sources.
London, James Reynolds, 1860.   BL.W

Reynolds's geological atlas of Great Britain, comprising a series of maps in which the roads, railways, and geological features of England and Wales are clearly shown; with a geological map of Scotland. Preceeded by . . .
London, James Reynolds, [1860].   P

117 A.   FIRST LITHOGRAPHIC TRANSFER

Size: 230 mm × 170 mm (single line border)   1:560,000

Hill hachures added and some hills named, eg *Box Hill, Leith Hill.* Signature (Ae OS) and imprint (Ce OS) erased. Outer border erased, single line border remains. Plate number (Ee OS) erased; *28* added (Ee). Railway 20 now shown as *Open;* 21, 26, 27, 28, 29, 30 and M as *Constructing.*

Portable atlas of England and Wales; with tourist's guide . . . Thirty-two maps.
London, James Reynolds, [1864].   BL

Reynolds's geological atlas of Great Britain, comprising a series of maps geologically coloured, from the best authorities; preceded by a description of the geological structure of Great Britain . . .
London, James Reynolds [1864].   BL.BOD.W

State of the plate: Later than no. 117 (iii). Hills and railways added.
Alterations on the transfer: Signature, imprint, outer border and plate number (Ee OS) erased. New plate number (Ee) added.

117 B.   SECOND LITHOGRAPHIC TRANSFER

Size: 230 mm × 170 mm (single line border)   1:560,000

Railways 26 and 29 now shown as *open.*

Reynolds's geological atlas of Great Britain . . .
London, James Reynolds [1867].   P

State of the plate: Later than no. 117A. Railways added.

Alterations on the transfer: As no. 117A.

117 C.   THIRD LITHOGRAPHIC TRANSFER

Size: 230 mm × 170 mm (single line border)   1:560,000

Railways 21, 22, 23, 24, 25, 27, 28, 30, 31 and M now shown as *Open*. Many station symbols added, eg between *Southwick* and *Hove*, and between *Hove* and *BRIGHTON*.

> *Reynolds's geological atlas of Great Britain . . .*
> London, James Reynolds, [1869].   P

State of the plate: Later than no. 117B. Railways added.
Alterations on the transfer: As no. 117A.

117 D.   FOURTH LITHOGRAPHIC TRANSFER

Size: 230 mm × 170 mm (single line border)   1:560,000

Imprint *London: Published by James Reynolds & Sons, 174, Strand.* added (Ce OS). *Index to Sheets of Geological Ord^{ce}. Map* below the appropriate numbered squares added (Eb). *East Bourne* replaced by *EASTBOURNE*. Numerous geological notes added, eg *MIDDLE BAGSHOT FOSSILS* (to the west of *Selsey Bill*). Grid (102 mm × 66 mm) added. Railways 32, 34, 35, 36, 37, 38 and 39 added as *Open*; 40 as *Constructing*. Railways 1 to 32, 34 to 39 and 42 now shown as *Open*; 40 as *Constructing*.

> *Reynolds's geological atlas of Great Britain . . .* 2nd edn.
> London, James Reynolds and Sons, 1889.   BL

State of the plate: Later than no. 117C. *EASTBOURNE* re-engraved, geological notes and railways added.
Alterations on the transfer: As no. 117A, together with new imprint (Ce OS), *Index . . .* (Eb) and grid.

242

118 DAY AND SON   1852

Size: 539 mm × 270 mm (1 mm)   1:234,000

Possibly based on Cary no. 50 or no. 61.

William Day, a printer, and Louis Haghe, a Belgium painter who had settled in England as a young man, went into partnership in the 1830s, and specialised in lithography.[1] The imprints *William Day, W. Day* or *W.D.* appeared from about 1830. An unusual item on which the imprint appeared was Pocock's inflatable globe (c. 1835).[2] From 1837 the imprint *Day & Haghe, Lithographers to the Queen* came into use. A map of east Sussex was engraved by them for the poll book published by Baxter in 1837 (see appendix VII.1). Haghe retired in 1852 in order to concentrate on painting. Fom then to about 1868 the form *William Day & Son* or *Day and Son* was used. The firm later amalgamated with Vincent Brooks, and as Vincent Brooks Day and Son continued in business until a few years ago. Railway plans by *Vincent Brooks,* by *Day & Son* and by *Vincent Brooks, Day & Son* are catalogued by Steer.[3] The royal appointment was not exclusive; Maclure, Macdonald and Macgregor (see no. 89) also held the appointment from at least 1853.[4]

The imprint *Corrected and brought up to the present time by J. Day and Son* appeared on *King's school atlas* (c. 1869). No connection between the two firms has been established.

The design for this map was probably laid down on the lithographic stone from an original drawing. It is the first Sussex map to have been printed in colour.

EDITION

Map of THE COUNTY OF SUSSEX, SHEWING THE TURNPIKE ROADS. 1852. (Ea). *Day & Son Lith^rs. to The Queen* (Ee). Compass (Ee). Railways 1 to 9, 12, 13 and 14 are marked. Map overprinted to produce colours yellow, green and brown. The roads are numbered 1 to 51 to correspond with the numbering of the Trusts in the text and tables.

Turnpike trusts. County reports of the Secretary of State, . . . N°.3 Sussex.
London, HMSO, 1852.   BL.GL
In *Accounts and Papers,* Session 3 Feb to 1 July 1852. Vol. XLIV.

1. Twyman, 1970.
2. Woodward, 1975, p. 101.
3. Steer, 1968, see index.
4. Steer, 1968, p. 104.

119 JOSHUA ARCHER   circa **1852**

Probably based on Old Series One Inch Ordnance Survey, appendix VI. 1(a).

This is one of a series of maps made by taking a separate transfer for each county (or group of counties) from plates engraved with a map of the whole of England and Wales. It was the first map of Sussex to be produced by this method. Lithographic transfers of the entire map are to be found in *Collins' indestructible atlas of the earth* and in *Collins' one shilling atlas of the world*, both published by Henry George Collins, probably in 1858. The map was almost certainly issued in other books as well. The signature *Drawn & Engraved by J. Archer, Pentonville, London.* is on the general map.

119 A. LITHOGRAPHIC TRANSFER

Size: 52 mm × 74 mm (2 mm)   1:2,380,000

Sussex.25. (Ca OS). North is to the left and the lettering on the map is designed to be read from the 'south'. The map extends north as far as London. Grid 29 mm × [45 mm]. Railways in Sussex, 1 to 8 and 10 to 14.

> *Collins' pocket ordnance railway atlas of Great Britain.*
> London, H.G. Collins, [1852].   BL

State of the plate: Earlier than the state when transfers were taken for the two atlases mentioned above. The railway from *Farnham* to *Alton* not yet added.
Alterations on the transfer: Border drawn round map and some place-names partially erased, eg *Folk*(stone). Title and plate number added (Ca OS).

120 STANFORDS GEOGRAPHICAL ESTABLISHMENT
1859

The lithographic transfer below was taken from Stanford's *Railway and Road map of England and Wales*, 1856. On that map the inscriptions *Vincent Brooks Imp.* and *Engraved by J. & C. Walker* appear outside the bottom border. It was probably based on Old Series One Inch Ordnance Survey, appendix VI.1(a).

Edward Standford[1] (1827–1904) was born in London. He was apprenticed to a printer in Malmsbury; but on the death of his master he returned to London. In 1848 he went to work for Trelawny William Saunders, whose map business he took over in 1853. In 1854 he became a fellow of the Royal Geographical Society, and started to

---

1. Hyde, 1975, pp. 11–13. The note on p. 11 gives valuable bibliographical references.

produce and publish his own maps. B.R. Davies (see no. 104) published through him. In 1858 he acquired the map plates of H.G. Collins (see no. 72). His series of large-scale library maps, constructed and engraved by Alexander Keith Johnston (see no. 147), were particularly well received.

His son, Edward Stanford (1856–1917), took over the firm on his father's retirement in 1882. In 1885 he was awarded a ten year contract for the distribution of Ordnance Survey maps in England and Wales. As a result Standford's own share of the business rose from about 33% to over 95%.[2] Stanfords were acquired by George Philip and Son in 1946.

Mackenzie Edward Charles Walcott (1821–80), the writer, was born at Walcot, near Bath, the son of a member of parliament. He went to Winchester College and then into the Church. From 1863 until his death he was Precenter of Chichester Cathedral and Prebendary of Oving. He contributed to the *Sussex archaeological collections* and wrote widely on antiquarian and topographical subjects. His works include *A guide to the cathedrals of England and Wales* (1858), *Battle abbey* (1867), *An introduction to the sources of Salopian topography* and several volumes concerning Chichester.[3]

120 A. LITHOGRAPHIC TRANSFER

Size: 208 mm × 120 mm (2 mm)   1:700,00

COUNTY OF SUSSEX. (Ca OS). *Stanfords Geographical Establishment, 6 Charing Cross, London.* (Ee OS). *English Statute Miles* 10 + 50 = 112 mm (Ce). Compass (Ee).

A guide to the coast of Sussex . . . by Mackenzie Walcott M.A. . . .
London, Edward Stanford, 1859.   SAS.EASTBOURNE PL

State of the plate: Almost certainly as originally engraved.
Alterations on the transfer: Border drawn round map and overlapping place-names erased, eg *Warnford;* but some remain, eg *Military C* (anal). Title, scale, imprint and compass added. A number of place-names added or re-engraved, eg *Gosport, ISLE OF WIGHT.* Some place-names outside Sussex erased, eg *Bishop Sutton.*

2. J. Aylward, 'The retail distribution of Ordnance Survey maps . . .' *CJ.* June 1971.
3. Anderson, 1881, p. 282.

Based on Old Series One Inch Ordnance Survey, appendix VI.1(a).

John Cassell[1] (1817–65), the founder of the publishing house (see transfers B to D below), was born in Manchester, although the family had been settled in Kent for three generations. He started life as a carpenter and soon became deeply involved with the teetotal movement. This led to the formation of Cassell and Co., tea and coffee merchants. His reforming zeal led him into publishing, starting with *The standard of freedom* in 1848. Cassell, Petter and Galpin was formed in 1858. In 1863 they acquired the stock and plates of the series of maps previously published by the *Weekly Dispatch.* The maps were reissued in the form of supplements to the *Family Paper,* which was already published by the firm and which had secured a wide circulation.

G.W. Bacon and Co., the well-known London map-makers and publishers (see E to H and K to Q below), was founded in about 1863 by George Washington Bacon[2] (1830–1922). He started with American connections, and published American maps and biographies of United States presidents, an activity appropriate to his name. In 1866 he became a Fellow of the Royal Geographical Society, one of his proposers being Edward Standford. He went bankrupt in 1867, but was soon back in business, and he built up a thriving publishing house in competition with Stanfords and Philips. In addition, Bacon was something of a health faddist. He wrote and published a number of booklets, including *A practical guide to health and longevity,* for which he proved himself a good advertisement.

The plate from which the following lithographic transfers were taken was apparently never used for direct intaglio printing.

121 A. FIRST LITHOGRAPHIC TRANSFER

Size: 426 mm × 289 mm (7 mm)   1:288,000

THE DISPATCH ATLAS SUSSEX BY B.R. DAVIES: FROM THE ORDNANCE SURVEY. (Aa, the first three words form part of a design showing Mercury above a hemisphere). *B.R. Davies* (Aa, in very small letters below the *TCH* of *DISPATCH*). *Engraved by B.R. Davies, 16 George Str. Euston Squ.* (Ee OS). *Day & Son Lith^{rs}. to The Queen.* (Ce OS). *Weekly Dispatch Atlas: 139 Fleet Street* (Ae OS). *British Statute Miles, 69.1 = 1 Degree.* 15 = 86 mm (Ce). Compass (Ee). Seven lines of parliamentary &c. information and key commencing *The County of Sussex consists of 934.851 Acres . . .* (Ab, under title). Longitude 10' (1'); latitude 10' (1'). Railways 1 to 14, 16, A to F, H and K marked by continuous lines as in use; 19 by pecked line as in progress; railways named in capitals.

1. Nowell-Smith, 1958.
2. Hyde, 1975, pp. 14–15.

Weekly Dispatch. Issue no. 2973 of 10th October 1858.   BL
This issue also contains a description of the county.

The Dispatch atlas.
London, 'PUBLISHED AT THE "WEEKLY DISPATCH" OFFICE', 1863.
                                                    BL.CUL.W

Published as loose sheets, sold separately, between October 1858 and 1863.

Some impressions of the map have page number *40* printed from type (Ee OS, sideways). There were various editions of this transfer which may be distinguished by a reference number (Ee, in border): *7*, *10* (Brighton PL, atlas without title-page), *11* and *12* have been found.

State of the plate: As originally engraved, including all information above, except Day & Son imprint.
Alterations on the transfer: Day & Son Lith^rs. to the Queen and reference numbers added.

121 B.   SECOND LITHOGRAPHIC TRANSFER

Size: 426 mm × 289 mm (7 mm)   1:288,000

THE DISPATCH ATLAS and *B.R. Davies* under the *TCH* of *DISPATCH*, together with the hemisphere and Mercury design (Aa) have been erased. *Weekly Dispatch Atlas: 139 Fleet Street* (Ae OS) erased and replaced by *Cassell, Petter & Galpin, Belle Sauvage Yard Ludgate Hill. CASSELL'S COUNTY MAPS.* added (Ca OS). Day & Son imprint (Ce OS) replaced by *E. Weller Lithog^r. 34, Red Lion Square.* Plate number *49* added (Ee OS, sideways). Railways 17, 18, 20 and J added; 17 and 18 named; 19 now in use; line from *Epsom* to *Leatherhead* added. *Sta* added on new lines, eg at *STEYNING.*

Issued in 1863 as loose sheets sold separately, and perhaps in *Cassell's folio county atlas,* of which no copy has been found.   (P)

State of the plate: Later than no. 121A. The alterations listed above have been made, except extra title (Ca OS), Weller imprint (Ce OS) and plate number (Ee OS).
Alterations on the transfer: Extra title (Ca OS), Weller imprint (Ce OS) and plate number (Ee OS) added. There are no reference numbers (Ee, in border).

121 C.   THIRD LITHOGRAPHIC TRANSFER

Size: 429 mm × 290 mm (7 mm)   1:288,000

Weller imprint (Ce OS) omitted. Davies signature (Ee OS) replaced by *LONDON, PUBLISHED BY CASSELL, PETTER & GALPIN, LA BELLE SAUVAGE*

247

YARD, LUDGATE HILL, E.C.. Railways 21 and 22 added as in use.

Cassell's complete atlas containing two hundred and sixty folio maps . . .
London, Cassell, Petter and Galpin. [1863].

P

State of the plate: Later than no. 121B. Davies signature (Ee OS) erased; railways
added.
Alterations on the transfer: Extra title (Ca OS), plate number and imprint (Ee OS)
added.

121 D.   FOURTH LITHOGRAPHIC TRANSFER

Size: 430 mm × 289 mm (7 mm)   1:288,000

Scale moved (from Ce to Ee, below compass). Statistical &c. notes added in four
columns; *AREA* and *POPULATION* (Ae), *MARRIAGES, 1861* (Be), *PHYSICAL
GEOGRAPHY*, in two columns (Ce). Imprint (Ee OS) somewhat blurred, two full-
stops and two commas are not visible. Plate number *49* (Ee OS) omitted. Plate number
31. added (Ee OS) on most impressions.

*Cassell's British atlas: consisting of the counties of England, with large divisional
maps of Scotland, Ireland, and Wales . . .*
London, Cassell, Petter and Galpin, [1867].   BL.CUL.SAS

*Cassell's topographical guides. The county of Sussex: its history, antiquities and
topography. With an itinerary for the tourist.*
London, Cassell, Petter and Galpin. [1865].   BL.BRIGHTON PL

Issued as a loose sheet with *Cassell's illustrated family paper.* vol. 14. no. 344 'New
Series'.
London, Cassell, Petter and Galpin, Issue for 2 July 1864.   BL

State of the plate: As no. 121 C.
Alterations on the transfer: Statistical notes &c. and imprint (Ee OS) added. Scale
moved. Plate number *31* added (Ee OS) on most impressions.

121 E.   FIFTH LITHOGRAPHIC TRANSFER

Size: 587 mm × 411 mm (10 mm)   1:195,000

EDITIONS

(i)   *BACON'S MAP OF* added (Aa, above *SUSSEX*) and lower part of letters in
SUSSEX hatched. *LONDON, G.W. BACON & Cº. 337, STRAND.* added (Ce OS).

248

Statistical &c. notes (Ae, Be and Ce), extra title (Ca OS). imprints (Ae OS and Ee OS) and plate number (Ee OS) omitted. *British Statute Miles, 69.1 = 1 Degree.* 15 = 132 mm (Ce). Compass (Ee) moved to right and now 17 mm from right border (formerly 37 mm). Notes under title altered, line two now . . . *14 Members . . .* (formerly . . . *18 Members*); line four now *Brighton, Hastings and Shoreham* (*Chichester* and *Lewes* omitted); line five now *Horsham, Chichester, Midhurst and Rye.* (*Arundel* omitted, *Chichester* added). In the key, the station symbol has been blacked in. Railways 23 to 31, 39 and 40 added; 35 and line from *Pulborough* to *STEYNING* shown as in progress; 19 re-routed further south; outside the county, railway M shown as in use; N, R, T, part of P and U with extensions to *CRANBROOK* and *TENTERDEN* shown as in progress. A number of stations added, eg *Rotherfield*. The area enclosed by the border has been reduced, *Epsom* being omitted at the top, and a number of place-names, eg *Bethersden*, on the east border. *Smarden* has been re-engraved on two lines so as not to extend beyond the border. The county boundary now extends 34 mm beyond the outside of the right border.

> *Bacon's county atlas: comprising forty-two beautifully engraved and coloured maps of the counties of England and Wales . . .*
> London, G.W. Bacon and Co., 1869. CUL

(ii)   Title (Aa) now *BACON'S ILLUSTRATED MAP OF SUSSEX BY B.R. DAVIES: FROM THE ORDNANCE SURVEY.* Bacon imprint (Ce OS) replaced by *LONDON, G.W. BACON & Cº. 127, STRAND.* Scale erased; new scale *British Statute Miles 69.1 = 1 Degree.* 10 = 88 mm added (Aa, below key). Compass (Ee) erased; new compass added (Ae). *ENGLISH CHANNEL* erased. No plate number. Four illustrations added (Be to Ee); *CHICHESTER CATHEDRAL* with note referring to the steeple rebuilt in 1866, *BRIGHTON, BATTLE ABBEY* with note, and *HASTINGS.* *Pier* added at *BRIGHTON,* in addition to *Chain Pier* and *Steyne* on earlier editions. Railway 12 added.

> Probably issued about 1870 as loose sheets sold separately (CUL).(WSRO)
> Known impressions of this map are hand coloured in red and green and varnished.

(iii)   Title as no. 121E(i). *ENGLISH CHANNEL* not erased. Illustrations omitted. *Pier* omitted and *NEW PIER* added at *BRIGHTON. COMMENCEMENT OF SEWER* (at *Hove*) and *OUTFALL OF BRIGHTON SEWER* (east of *Rottingdean*) added.

> Issued about 1870 as a folding map in printed cover; *Bacon's new tourist map of Sussex from the Ordnance Survey.*
> London, G.W. Bacon and Co. (WORTHING PL)

State of the plate: Later than 121D. Railways 23 to 31 and M added. Stations added. *Alterations on the transfer:* Top and right borders moved inwards. Title, parliamentary information and key amended. Imprint (Ce OS) added. Scale and compass moved or erased, and new scale and compass added. *ENGLISH CHANNEL* erased, and illustrations added on edition (ii). *Pier* or *NEW PIER* added. References to *SEWER* added on edition (iii). Other railways added. Transfer identified by smudge on left side of centre line of outer right border at 51°11½'N.

121 F.   SIXTH LITHOGRAPHIC TRANSFER

Size: 425 mm × 288 mm (7 mm)   1:288,000

SUSSEX BY B.R. DAVIES: FROM THE ORDNANCE SURVEY (Aa, as no. 121B, C and D). Imprint (Ce OS) omitted. *G.W. Bacon & Cº. 127 Strand, London* added (Ae OS). *British Statute Miles, 69.1 = 1 Degree.* 15 = 88 mm (Ce, as originally engraved). Compass moved (to Ed, 16 mm from right border). Parliamentary information (Aa, below title) as originally engraved. In key (Aa) the station symbol replaced by black circle. No plate number. Illustrations (Be to Ee) omitted. Engraving, *BRIGHTON from the New Pier.*, and *W. Dickes Sc London* added (Ee). *NEW PIER* and references to *SEWER* (at *BRIGHTON*) omitted. *Sᵗ Leonards (W. Marina)* and *Sᵗ Leonards (Warrior Square)* added. Railway 35 omitted; L and N added as in use; R, U and part of P omitted. A number of extra station names added, eg *Southwater, Brighton* in place of *Station, Rye* in place of *Sta.* In *Kingston by Sea, by* omitted to make space for *Southwick, on* added and name now reads *Kingston on Sea.* Stations marked by circles on map. The borders revert to their original positions.

> Issued about 1874 as a folding map with printed title on cover: *Bacon's new pocket map of Sussex.*
> London, G.W. Bacon and Co.   (CUL)

State of the plate: Later than no. 121E. Additions made at *Sᵗ Leonards.* Railways and stations added.
Alterations on the transfer: Bacon imprint (Ae OS) and engraving (Ee) added. Compass moved. Key amended.

121 G.   SEVENTH LITHOGRAPHIC TRANSFER

Size: 426 mm × 289 mm (7 mm)   1:288,000

Title (Aa) now *BACON'S MAP OF SUSSEX BY B.R. DAVIES; FROM THE ORDNANCE SURVEY;* with *SUSSEX* in checked lettering. Imprint (Ae OS) altered to *Bacons Map Establishment, 127 Strand London.* Compass (Ee, 37 mm from right border as originally engraved). The parliamentary information (Aa, below title) now reads . . .*18 Members . . . 2 each for the Boroughs of Brighton, Hastings and Shoreham; and 1 each for Horsham Medhurst Chichester and Lewes.* In the key (Aa) the symbol for *(Boundary) of Boroughs* is now a pecked oval, and the station symbol is a black dot. Plate number *47* added from type (Ea OS). *East Bourne* re-engraved *EASTBOURNE. Pier* added at *WORTHING* and at *Sᵀ LEONARDS* (formerly *Sᵗ*

250

Leonards). A *Note* relating to station names beginning *The official . . .* and giving as example *Ludgate* added (Ea). Railway 15 added as in use; outside Sussex railways A to N are now shown as in use.

> *Bacon's new quarto county atlas: comprising 55 beautifully engraved and coloured maps of the counties of England and Wales.*
> London, G.W. Bacon and Co., [1876].   BL

State of the plate: Later than no. 121F. Title, parliamentary information and key amended. *Pier* added and place-names amended. Railways added.
Alterations on the transfer: Imprint (Ae OS), plate number and *Note* (Ea) added.

121 H. EIGHTH LITHOGRAPHIC TRANSFER

Size: 634 mm × 434 mm (9 mm)   1:195,000

In the title (Aa) *BY B.R. DAVIES* erased. *British Statute Miles, 69.1 = 1 Degree. 15 = 130 mm* (Ce). Compass (Ee, 55 mm from right border). A number of place-names added outside Sussex, eg *Charlwood, Horley, Box Hill*. Railways 33 to 37 added as in use; 38 as in progress; line from *Pulborough* to *STEYNING* omitted. *Note* relating to station lettering omitted.

> Issued about 1880 as a folding map with printed title on cover: *Bacon's new tourist's map of Sussex.*
> London, G.W. Bacon and Co.   (CUL).(WORTHING PL)
> Another impression (BL) has the title: *Bacon's tourist's map of Sussex.*

State of the plate: Later than no. 121G. Title amended. Place-names added. Railways added.
Alterations on the transfer: Imprint (Ae OS) added. Some railways (see no. 121I), which appear to have been erased from the plate, may have been added on the stone on this transfer.

121 I. NINTH LITHOGRAPHIC TRANSFER

Size: 538 mm × 344 mm (9 mm)   1:222,000

Title (Aa) now *MAP OF SUSSEX REDUCED FROM THE ORDNANCE SURVEY.* Bacon imprint (Ae OS) omitted. *British Statute Miles, 69.1 = 1 Degree. 20 = 111 mm* (Ce); *20* is an error for 15. Compass (Ee, 32 mm from right border). *Sheet 8* added (Ea OS). In the key, reference to railways in progress and the words *in use* erased. *Sea Houses* erased and replaced by *EASTBOURNE (New Town), (Old Town)* added to existing *EASTBOURNE, S*th. *Bourne* unchanged. Additional house symbols added on west side of *BRIGHTON. Cliftonville* erased and replaced by *West Brighton* Railways 33, 36 and 37 erased; 38 in progress erased.

251

New Ordnance atlas of Brighton.
London, National Map Company, 1882.   CUL.SAS³

State of the plate: Later than no. 121H. Title and key amended. Place-names and house symbols added. Railways erased, although these additions may originally have been made on the stone.
Alterations on the transfer: Scale amended.

121 J.   TENTH LITHOGRAPHIC TRANSFER

Size: 430 mm × 178 mm (7 mm)   1:288,000

Title (Ee) now *SUSSEX REDUCED FROM THE ORDNANCE SURVEY Divided into 5 mile squares. British Statute Miles. 69.1 = 1 Degree 15 = 88* mm (Ee, under title). Parliamentary information, key, *Note,* compass and plate number omitted. Top and bottom borders moved inwards, *ENGLISH CHANNEL* erased, most of the detail north of the county boundary omitted. Grid (29 mm × 29 mm) added, with reference letters *C* to *H* and numbers *1* to *15. THORNEY ISLAND* erased and the island joined to the mainland and road added. *(New Town)* erased at *EASTBOURNE.* At *BRIGHTON, Aquarium* and *West Pier* added. House symbols added at *CHICHESTER;* built-up areas extended at *BRIGHTON, HASTINGS, LEWES* and *EASTBOURNE* and marked by diagonal shading. *Pigeon Ho F.* (at *Rustington*), *Kingston* (near *Southwater*) and *Barracks* (at *Selsea* and at *Aldwick*) erased. *Aldwick Place* added. *Blue Ho Fm* (north of *Peasmarsh*) altered to *New Ho., Betshurst* to *Belhurst, Udymer* to *Udimore, West Bourn* to *West Bourne, Fish Houses* to *Fishop Fm. Fletching & Sheffield Park* station added. A 5 mm loop added to road south of *MIDHURST* and a new road added north/south through *CU* of *CUCKFIELD.* Railways 33, 36, 37 and 38 added.

> *Royal archaeological institute of Great Britain and Ireland . . . Annual meeting at Lewes . . . July 31st to August 6th, 1883 . . . Compiled by Frederick Ernest Sawyer F.M.S.*
> Lewes, Sussex Archaeological Society, 1883.   BRIGHTON PL

State of the plate: Later than no. 121I. Title amended. Place-names &c. changes as listed above. Railways added.
Alterations on the transfer: Top and bottom borders moved inwards, and detail north of border erased. ENGLISH CHANNEL erased. Title (Ee), scale (Ee) and grid added.

3. Complete, but disbound.

252

121 K.   ELEVENTH LITHOGRAPHIC TRANSFER

Size: 438 mm × 290 mm (7 mm)   1:288,000

EDITIONS

(i)   Title and scale, as no. 121J, moved (to Aa). Parliamentary information erased. In the key (Aa, below scale), *Station* replaced by *Bognor* and *Division of County* added. Compass (Ee, 37 mm from right border). Plate number *41* added from type (Ea OS and on back). Grid, has reference letters *A* to *I;* the line between reference numbers *3* and *4* passes through the 15 mile mark on the scale-bar. The grid is interrupted for the compass. The *Note* relating to station names (Ee) gives as example *Clayton*. A number of station names added outside Sussex, eg *Brookwood, Stoats Nest, Boxhill and Burford Bri., Penshurst*, which now appears twice. Roads added outside Sussex. The left border moved outwards 5 mm so that the county boundary does not extend into the border. *40'* appears in error in left border at latitude 50°54'. Railways A to N and P are shown as in use. *READING RY* omitted.

> *New large scale Ordnance atlas of the British Isles . . .*
> London, George W. Bacon, F.R.G.S., [1883].   BL

(ii)   In the key (Aa), *Bognor* replaced by *Station*, which is written above and left of the symbol.

> *New large scale Ordnance atlas of the British Isles . . .*
> London, George W. Baçon, F.R.G.S., 1884.   P

State of the plate: Later than no. 121J. Parliamentary information erased. Railway P and station names added.
Alterations on the transfer: Left border added. Key amended. Grid and *Note* (Ee) added. *READING RY* erased. *40'* added in left border. Plate number added from type. Transfer identified by 1 mm gap in outer line of right border, 5 mm from Ee.

121 L.   TWELFTH LITHOGRAPHIC TRANSFER

Size: 438 mm × 290 mm (7 mm)   1:288,000

EDITIONS

(i)   In the key (Aa), *Division* now starts under *w* of *Railways* (formerly under *R*). The vertical line between reference numbers 3 and 4 of the grid passes to the left of the 15 mark on the scale-bar. The grid is not interrupted for the compass. Railways 41, 42, R, S, T, U and W added as in progress. *READING RY* not omitted.

> *New large scale Ordnance atlas of the British Isles . . .*

253

London, George W. Bacon, F.R.G.S., [1883], 1884 and [1885].

BL;RGS.A;BL.BOD.W

(ii)   Plate number omitted.

Bacon's new county guide and map of Sussex from the Ordnance Survey . . .
London, G.W. Bacon, [1885].   BRIGHTON PL

State of the plate: Later than 121 K. Railways added.
Alterations on the transfer: Left border added. Key amended. Grid and *Note* (Ee)
added. *40'* added in left border. Plate number added from type on edition (i).

<h2 align="center">121 M.   THIRTEENTH LITHOGRAPHIC TRANSFER</h2>

Size: 438 mm × 290 mm (7 mm)   1:288,000

EDITIONS

(i)   Key erased. New key, having *Railways* . . . with *Station* written above and to the
right of the symbol, added (Aa, below scale). The horizontal grid line between reference letters *B* and *C* stops at *GODALMING*. In the *Note* (Ee), *Ludgate* is given as the
example in place of *Clayton*. A colour key to seven *Parliamentary Divisons* added (Ee,
between compass and *Note*); each division in the key is represented by a separate
rectangle; the boundaries are marked on the map by pecked lines. *WESTERN
DIVISION* and *EASTERN DIVISION* erased. All the railways now shown as in use.

New large-scale Ordnance atlas of London & Suburbs with supplementary maps . . .
London, George W. Bacon, F.R.G.S., [1885].   BL.CUL.BOD

New large scale Ordnance atlas of the British Isles . . .
London, George W. Bacon, F.R.G.S., [1886].   P

New large scale Ordnance map of the British Isles . . .
London, George W. Bacon, F.R.G.S., [1887].   P
In the first work listed above there is no plate number on the map, but *72* printed from type appears
on the back. In other two works *41* printed from type has been added on the map (Ea OS) and on the
back.

(ii)   In the key (Ee) the colours are now contained in a single rectangle with five
internal divisions. Railway 40 added as in use.

New large scale Ordnance atlas of the British Isles . . .
London, George W. Bacon, F.R.G.S., [1888].   W
Plate number *41* printed from type appears (Ea OS) and on back.

Issued about 1888 as a folding map with printed title on cover: *A guide to the*
254

county of Sussex.
London, G.W. Bacon. (ESCL)
There is no plate number on the map.

State of the plate: Later than no. 121L. Key (Aa), *WESTERN DIVISION* and *EASTERN DIVISION* erased. Railways S added.
Alterations on the transfer: Left border added. Keys (Aa and Ee), grid, *Note* (Ee) and railways 40 added. *40'* added in left border. Plate numbers added from type. Transfer identified by 4 mm white strip in centre line of left border at 51°03'N.

121 N.   FOURTEENTH LITHOGRAPHIC TRANSFER

Size: 728 mm × 444 mm (7 mm) 1:170,000

MAP OF added (Aa, above *SUSSEX*). Scale-bar erased, and new bar *10 = 100 mm* added. Key to *Parliamentary Divisions,* as 121M(i), moved (to Aa, below scale). Key to railways erased; new key *Railways & Stations* with *Falmer* as the example added (Aa, below key to *Parliamentary Divisons*). No plate number. *Bacon's Geog^l. Establishment, 127 Strand, London* added (Ae OS). *40'* in left border omitted. *Stoat's Nest* erased; station names added, eg *Lenham, Hollingbourne, Cobham, Marden Park, The Dyke.* Railways 41, 42 and R added as in use; T, U and W as in progress. *Pagham Harbour* and hachures erased; *leigh* in *Highleigh* erased; *Reclaimed Land* added. Bottom border now at 50°39'N.

Issued about 1889 as a folding map with printed title on cover: *Bacon's county guide and map of Sussex.* (WORTHING PL)

State of the plate: Later than no. 121M. Railways and some station names added. *Stoat's Nest* erased.
Alterations on the transfer: Scale-bar erased and new bar added. Left and bottom borders, keys (Aa), grid and imprint (Ae OS) added. Alteration made at Pagham. Station names added.

121 O.   FIFTEENTH LITHOGRAPHIC TRANSFER

Size: 438 mm × 290 mm (7 mm) 1:288,000

EDITIONS

(i)   General layout, title, scale, keys and *Note* (Ee) as on no. 121M(i). In the key (Aa), *& Stations* added to *Railways* and *Station* replaced by *Falmer*. The line between reference letters *B* and *C* extends to the left border, and the vertical lines between reference numbers *1* and *2* and between *2* and *3* extend to 2 mm above it; the vertical line between *3* and *4* passes to the right of *15* on the scale-bar; there are 7 mm and 1.5

mm smudges where *SOUTH WESTERN RAILY.* and *READING RY.* have been erased. *The Dyke* omitted. 51° is 1 mm lower than on previous editions. The *Note* (Ee) has *Clayton* as the example (as on no. 120K). Outside Sussex, *Marden Park* and *Cobham* omitted; roads added in Kent, eg running north to south through the first *O* of *CRANBROOK*. Railways 1 to 42 and A to R now appear as in use; T, U and W as in progress. Alterations in area of *Pagham Harbour* (see no. 121N) have not been made. Bottom border reverts to 50°35'N.

New large scale atlas of the British Isles from the Ordnance Survey . . .
London, George W. Bacon, F.R.G.S., [1889].   BL
SUSSEX.41. (Ea OS) and *41* on back added from type.

(ii)   The two smudges referred to above do not appear, but there are 8 mm and 5 mm gaps in the vertical grid line.

New large-scale atlas of the British Isles from the Ordnance Survey . . .
London, G.W. Bacon and Co. Ltd., 1890.   P

(iii)   *Pagham Harbour* and the hachures behind it erased, and replaced by a river running west to east. Station symbol added on railway between *Warlingham* and *Oxted*.

New large-scale atlas of the British Isles from the Ordnance Survey . . . Edited by G.W. Bacon, F.R.G.S.
London, G.W. Bacon and Co. Ltd., 1891.   P

New large-scale atlas of the British Isles from the Ordnance Survey with . . . census of 1891. Edited by G.W. Bacon, F.R.G.S.
London, G.W. Bacon and Co. Ltd., 1891 and 1893.   BL;P

Bacon's new large-scale atlas of London and suburbs reduced from the Ordnance Survey with supplementary maps . . . edited by G.W. Bacon, F.R.G.S.
London, G.W. Bacon and Co. Ltd., 1891.   GL.HOLBORN PL

In the first two works listed above *SUSSEX 41* has been added (Ea OS) and *41* on the back, in each case from type. In the third work the plate number has been changed to *72*.

State of the plate: Later than no. 121N. Some station names added, eg *Hollingbourne*. *Alterations on the transfer:* Left border and *Note* (Ed) added. Grid added; *READING RY* and *SOUTH WESTERN RAILY.* erased. Key (Aa) amended. *Pagham Harbour* erased and roads added. This transfer can be identified by scratches across outer section of top border at 09' and 24'W.

121 P.   SIXTEENTH LITHOGRAPHIC TRANSFER

Size: 438 mm × 290 mm (7 mm)   1:288,000

EDITIONS

(i)   In the title (Aa) *REDUCED FROM THE ORDNANCE SURVEY* erased and replaced by *REVISED THROUGHOUT BY THE NEW ORDNANCE SURVEY.* Compass omitted. *SUSSEX 41* added (Ea OS) and on back. Key (Aa, below scale) now has five items: *Railways thus* . . with *Tilehurst* as the example, *Roads, Boundary of County,* . . . *of Divisions,* and . . .*of Parliamentary Boroughs.* 64 mm of the horizontal line between reference letters *B* and *C* has been omitted to make space for the key; 7 mm of the vertical line between numbers *3* and *4* omitted to allow for the scale-bar. *Note* (Ee) omitted. *REFERENCE TO COLOURS* added (Ea), with population figures for 1881 and 1891; *Hollingbourne* and other detail erased to make space. *S^{th}.Bourne* erased and replaced by *Southbourne. Fishergate* added and *Low Water Mark* erased to the west of *BRIGHTON. St Leonards* added. *St Leonards (W. Marina), St Leonards, S^T LEONARDS, St Leonards (Warrior Square)* and *Pier* are now marked. *READING RY* omitted; *SOUTH WESTERN RAIL^Y.* not omitted. Much detail added outside Sussex, eg *Cobham* (to the south of *Church Cobham*), *Small Hithe* (south of *TENTERDEN*) and *High Oak* (near right border). Station names added, eg *Bookham.* Reference to maps of *ADJOINING COUNTIES* added (Ea OS), *KENT 40* and *SURREY 41* being in error. Railway T shown as in use. Map overprinted to produce colours pink, brown, yellow, purple, blue and two shades of green.

> *Commercial and library atlas of the British Isles from the Ordnance Survey* . . .
> *Edited by G.W. Bacon, F.R.G.S.*
> London, G.W. Bacon and Co. Ltd., 1895.   BL

(ii)   In *ADJOINING COUNTIES* (Ea), *KENT 40* corrected to *KENT 22,* and *SURREY 41* to *SURREY 40.* Railway U shown as in use. *West Brighton* erased.

> *Commercial and library atlas of the British Isles* . . .
> London, G.W. Bacon and Co. Ltd., 1896 and 1897.   BL.RGS.W;FORDHAM[4]

(iii)   In the key (Aa), *Tilehurst* replaced by *Hever,* and *Light Railways,* to be indicated by single cross-hatched lines, added. *Chain Pier* erased at *BRIGHTON.* Manhood light railway added. Printer's reference *28M10* added (Ee OS).

> *Commercial and library atlas of the British Isles* . . .
> London, G.W. Bacon and Co. Ltd., 1898.   W

---

4. Fordham, 1914, p. 155.

Commercial and library atlas of the British Isles from the new Ordnance Survey . . .
Edited by G.W. Bacon, F.R.G.S.
London, G.W. Bacon and Co. Ltd., 1899.   BL

(iv)   Manhood light railway extended to *Selsea* and stations added. Printer's reference
(Ee OS) altered to *118M10*.

Commercial and library atlas of the British Isles . . .
London, G.W. Bacon and Co. Ltd., 1899 and 1900.   P;LEEDS PL

State of the plate: Later than no. 121 O. *Pagham Harbour* erased and roads added.
Place-names added and amended. Railway T added.
Alterations on the transfer: Left border moved. Title amended. Grid, key (Aa).
REFERENCE TO COLOURS (Ea), *ADJOINING COUNTIES* (Ea OS), plate
number, railway U and light railway, and printer's reference added. Compass, *Chain
Pier, Hollingbourne* and detail, *READING RY* and *West Brighton* erased. The plate
number on the back of the map is added from type. Transfer identified by faintness of
inner line of bottom border 44 mm from Ae.
This transfer was also used in an edition of the atlas published in 1901.

121 Q.   SEVENTEENTH LITHOGRAPHIC TRANSFER

Size: 600 mm × 395 mm (10 mm)   1:204,000

Title (Aa) now   *BACON'S MAP OF SUSSEX REVISED THROUGHOUT BY THE
NEW ORDNANCE SURVEY DIVIDED INTO 5 MILE SQUARES. British Statute
Miles 69.1 = 1 Degree.* 15 = 119 mm (Ce). Compass (Ee, 52 mm from right border).
G.W. BACON & CO., 127 Strand, London. added (Ae OS). Key (Aa) erased. The
horizontal line between reference letters *B* and *C* does not extend to left border; the
vertical line between *3* and *4* is complete; the grid is interrupted for the scale and the
compass. *Note,* with *Ludgate* as the example, appears (Ae). New *REFERENCE,* with
nine items, added (Ae, above *Note*). *REFERENCE TO COLOURS* (Ea) and
ADJOINING COUNTIES (Ea OS) omitted. *West Brighton* not erased. The county
boundary extends into the left border, which is now in its original position. The map
extends 15 mm above the top border in the centre where *CROYDON* and considerable
detail has been added. *READING RY* not erased. Many place-names added outside
Sussex, eg *Knockholt, Cudham, Halsted.* There is no printer's reference, or plate
number.

Bacon's county map and guide Sussex.
London, G.W. Bacon and Co. Ltd., [1898].   BL

State of the plate: Later than no. 121P. Detail outside Sussex and railways added.
Alterations on the transfer: Title amended. Scale and compass moved. Imprint (Ae

OS), *Note* (Ae), grid and *REFERENCE* (Ae) added. Key erased. It is probable that *CROYDON* and detail in that area was added on the plate and the necessary part of the top border erased; but this may have been done on the stone.

122 JOHN BARTHOLOMEW   1860

Based on Old Series One Inch Ordnance Survey, appendix VI.1(a).

George Bartholomew (1784–1871) was an Edinburgh engraver. His son, John (1805–61), specialised from 1826 in map engraving, and may be regarded as the founder of the famous firm of map makers.[1] He was succeeded by his son, also John (1831–93), who added the use of lithography to engraving and introduced the technique known as contour layer colouring. He was again succeeded by his son, John George (1860–1920), who took over the management in 1888. About that time the business moved to new premises and was henceforth known as the *Edinburgh Geographical Establishment*. He did much to improve the techniques of map production and the skilled use of colour. His work has been described[2] as 'perhaps the most notable individual contribution to British map-making since John Cary'. He was a founder of the Scottish Geographical Society in 1884. He died in 1920, but the family tradition was maintained by his son, another John (1890–1962). The business became a limited company in 1919, and three sons of John Bartholomew (d. 1962) were directors of the company in 1976.

Adam Black (1784–1874), the publisher, was born in Edinburgh where he lived and worked as a book-seller and publisher, except for a short spell with Lackington, Allen and Co. in London. He took his nephew, Charles, into partnership, and in 1827 they acquired the copyright in the *Encyclopaedia Britannica*. Their business seems to have thrived for in 1851 they were able to pay £27,000 for the copyright of the works of Sir Walter Scott. Adam Black was a liberal politician, and was twice Lord Provost of Edinburgh. He declined a knighthood. The firm was carried on by his sons after his death.

The plate from which the following lithographic transfers were taken was apparently never used for direct intaglio printing. No. 122A covers a larger area than nos. 122B to E, indicating that all these transfers were taken from a general map.

Later editions of Black's guides to Sussex contain no. 129 in place of this map. The works listed below, together with later editions of Black's guides to Sussex and *Black's guide to Brighton and vicinity* (1866 and later) all contain the index or railway map no. 123.

1. Gardiner, 1976.
2. *DNB*

122 A.   FIRST LITHOGRAPHIC TRANSFER

Size: 380 mm × 213 mm (2 mm)   1:505,000

KENT & SUSSEX. (De). *Drawn and Eng^d. by J. Bartholomew Edin^r.* (Ee OS). *Printed by W H McFarlane Edin^r.* (Ae OS). *PUBLISHED BY A. & C. BLACK. EDINBURGH* (Ce OS). *English Miles 15 = 47 mm* (De, under title). Compass (Ea). Railways 1 to 14, 16, 17, 19 and A to H shown by continuous lines; 15 by pecked line. The map extends as far north as London, but outside Kent and Sussex the topographical detail is limited.

> *Black's handbook for Kent and Sussex.*
> Edinburgh, Adam and Charles Black, 1860.   BL

State of the plate: As originally engraved.
Alterations on the transfer: Border drawn round map and projecting place-names erased. Title, inscriptions, scale, *ENGLISH CHANNEL* and compass added.

122 B.   SECOND LITHOGRAPHIC TRANSFER

Size: 260 mm × 130 mm (2 mm)   1:505,000

SUSSEX. (Ed, the full-stop is 10 mm from the right border). *Drawn & Eng^d. by J. Bartholomew Edin^r.* (Ee OS). *Printed by W H McFarlane, Edin^r.* (Ae OS). *PUBLISHED BY A. & C. BLACK EDINBURGH* (Ce OS). *English Miles 10 = 31 mm* (Ee, below title). No compass. *SURREY* and *KENT* added, *HAMPSHIRE* re-engraved. Railways as no. 122A. This transfer covers Sussex and extends northwards as far as *Tunbridge.*

> *Black's handbook for Sussex with map . . .*
> Edinburgh, Adam and Charles Black, 1860.   BRIGHTON PL.
>   GENEALOGICAL SOCIETY

> *Black's guide to the south-eastern counties of England. Sussex.*
> Edinburgh, Adam and Charles Black, 1861 and 1862. BL,WSCL;SAS.BRIGHTON PL

State of the plate: As originally engraved.
Alterations on the transfer: Border drawn round map and projecting place-names erased. Title, inscriptions, scale and *ENGLISH CHANNEL* added. *Farnham* has been added in smaller lettering than on the plate and a little lower in order to enclose it within the top border. *SURREY* and *KENT* added. *HAMPSHIRE,* originally in hatched capitals, erased and added in plain black capitals to match the other adjoining counties.

122 C. THIRD LITHOGRAPHIC TRANSFER

Size: 260 mm × 132 mm (2 mm)   1:505,000

Bartholomew signature (Ee OS) and McFarlane imprint (Ae OS) omitted. *Farnham* omitted. *KENT* moved, the *K* being nearer to *Tunbridge Wells*. Many place-names and roads added in the north-west corner, eg *Selborne, Headley, Kingsley*; some added elsewhere, eg *E. Sutton, W. Leigh*. Railways 15, 18 and 20 to 27 shown by continuous lines.

> *Black's guide to the south-eastern counties . . .*
> Edinburgh, Adam and Charles Black, 1866.   HASTINGS PL

State of the plate: Later than no. 122B. Place-names &c. added, but some of the alterations near the border may have been made on the transfer. Railways added.
Alterations on the transfer: Border drawn round map and projecting place-names erased. (On the left border, *N. Hayling* and *Charlton* appear, but were erased on no. 122B. On the top border, *Farnham* has not been omitted, but *Street* and other place-names have been included.) Title, imprint (Ce OS), scale and *ENGLISH CHANNEL* added *SURREY, KENT* and *HAMPSHIRE* added.

122 D. FOURTH LITHOGRAPHIC TRANSFER

Size: 262 mm × 132 mm` (2 mm)   1:505,000

SUSSEX. (Dd, the stop is now 26 mm from the right border). *J. Bartholomew, Edin^r*. (Ee OS). Scale moved (to De, under title). *ENGLISH CHANNEL* moved upwards, now 13 mm from bottom border. Compass added (Ed). Names of adjoining counties omitted; *SUSSEX* added on map in hatched capitals. Railways 28, 29 and 30 shown by continuous lines.

> *Black's guide to Sussex and its watering places . . .*
> Edinburgh, Adam and Charles Black, new edn., 1873.   BRIGHTON PL.SAS

> *Black's picturesque guide to the county of Sussex:*
> Edinburgh, Adam and Charles Black, 3rd edn., 1875.   WSCL

State of the plate: Later than no. 122C. Railways added.
Alterations on the transfer: Border drawn round map and projecting place-names erased. (The map is larger than no. 122C, being extended on the right border and detail not erased, eg *Kenningto, Rucking*). Title, inscriptions (Ee OS and Ce OS), scale, compass, *ENGLISH CHANNEL* and *SUSSEX* added.

122 E. FIFTH LITHOGRAPHIC TRANSFER

Size: 262 mm × 132 mm (2 mm)   1:505,000

Imprint (Ce OS) replaced by *A. & C. BLACK, EDINBURGH.* Scale (De) omitted; new scale *English Miles 15* = 48 mm added (Be). There is a gap of about 1 mm between the top border and the printed detail, and certain names which appear on no. 122D. are now omitted, eg *Four Elms.*

> *Black's picturesque guide to the county of Sussex.*
> Edinburgh, Adam and Charles Black, 4th edn., 1877.   SAS
> A copy of this work has been found (WSCL) with no. 122D in place of this map.

State of the plate: As no. 122D.
Alterations on the transfer: Border drawn round map and projecting place-names erased. Title, inscriptions, scale, compass, *ENGLISH CHANNEL* and *SUSSEX* added.

123   JOHN BARTHOLOMEW   1860

Based on Old Series One Inch Ordnance Survey, appendix VI.1(a).

This map appeared on the inside front cover of Black's Sussex handbooks, except for *Handbook for Kent and Sussex,* 1860, in which it was inside the back cover. It was referred to as *INDEX MAP;* but in later editions, when the references to page numbers were dropped, it was called *SKETCH MAP* and was sometimes described as *railway map.* The earlier editions of these handbooks also contained no. 122 or no. 129. The works listed under nos. 123M and N below contained sectional maps taken from the same general map as no. 153. An 1898 guide contained no. 144D.

The first edition of *Black's guide to Brighton and vicinity* was published in 1866. The next edition so far found is described as '6th ed., 1874'. There were probably other editions with maps between these dates.

The plate from which these transfers were taken was probably never used for direct intaglio printing. The references to pages seem to have been engraved on the plate; evidenced by the fact that *530*, after *Mayfield* on nos. 123C and D, is omitted on E and F, but reappears on G.

123 A. FIRST LITHOGRAPHIC TRANSFER

Size: 169 mm × 129 mm (1 mm)   1:718,000

EDITIONS

(i) *INDEX MAP TO ACCOMPANY BLACK'S GUIDE TO SUSSEX. Note. The* *numbers after the names refer to the page in Guide Book where the description is to be found.* (Ea). *Guide to Sussex* (Ae). *J. Bartholomew, Edin*ʳ. (Ee OS). *Printed by W H Mᶜ*Farlane Edin*ʳ. (Ae OS). *Bound by H. Bowie.* (Ce OS), commencing 90 mm from left corner. Railways 1 to 14. No roads are marked.

> *Black's handbook for Sussex.*
> Edinburgh, Adam and Charles Black, 1860.   P

(ii) *Bound by H. Bowie Edin*ʳ. added (Ce OS, commencing 85 mm from Ae) in place of *Bound by H. Bowie.*

> *Black's handbook for Sussex.*
> Edinburgh, Adam and Charles Black, 1860.   BRIGHTON PL

State of the plate: As originally engraved.
Alterations on the transfer: Mᶜ Farlane imprint (Ae OS) and Bowie inscription (Ce OS) probably added. It is possible that the references to pages were added on the transfer and that spaces were left for this purpose when the place was engraved. Transfer identified by gap in inner line of right border, 6 mm from Ea.

125 B. SECOND LITHOGRAPHIC TRANSFER

Size: 167 mm × 127 mm (1 mm)   1:718,000

The reference numbers on the map altered, eg *Mayfield 233* (formerly *75*), *Midhurst 242 (84)*, *BRIGHTON 168 (10)*, *Bolney 166 (8)*. *Guide to Sussex* (Ae) altered to *Guide to Kent & Sussex.* Inscription (Ce OS) reverts to *Bound by H. Bowie* and now starts 76 mm from left corner. Railway 17 added.

> *Black's handbook for Kent and Sussex.*
> Edinburgh, Adam and Charles Black, 1860.   BL.ESCL

> *Black's handbook for Sussex.*
> Edinburgh, Adam and Charles Black, 1860.   GENEALOGICAL SOCIETY
> The latter work is the Sussex section from the former work with a new title-page, but the pagination is unaltered.

State of the plate: Later than no. 123A, probably including changes to reference numbers and addition of railway.
Alterations on the transfer: Guide to Kent & Sussex (Ae) added and *Guide to Sussex* erased. Mᶜ Farlane imprint (Ae OS) and Bowie inscription (Ce OS) added.

123 C. THIRD LITHOGRAPHIC TRANSFER

Size: 168 × 128 mm (1 mm)   1:718,000

Guide to Kent & Sussex (Ae) reverts to *Guide to Sussex. Bound by H. Bowie* (Ce OS) replaced by *Bound by J. Ramage.* Some erasures, eg *W. Hampnet 187,* and *234* under *Bayham Abbey.* Many place-names added, eg *Linchmeke 633, Salehurst 483.* Page references again altered, eg *Mayfield* now *530, Midhurst 630, BRIGHTON 54, Bolney* no number, *533* added at *Uckfield* which formerly had no reference number. Roads added, *Lewes* to *Mayfield* and on to *Rotherfield,* several radiating from *Pulborough;* but none from other important centres, eg *BRIGHTON.* Railways as no. 123B.

    Black's guide to the south-eastern counties of England — Sussex.
    Edinburgh, Adam and Charles Black, 1861.   BL

State of the plate: Later than no. 123B, including alterations above.
Alterations on the transfer: McFarlane imprint (Ae OS) and *Bound by J. Ramage* (Ce OS) added.

123 D. FOURTH LITHOGRAPHIC TRANSFER

Size: 168 mm × 128 mm (1 mm)   1:718,000

Guide to Sussex (Ae) as no. 123C. McFarlane imprint and *Bound by J. Ramage* omitted. Railways 16, 18 to 23, 25 and 27 added.

    Black's guide to the south-eastern counties . . .
    Edinburgh, Adam and Charles Black, 1862.   SAS

State of the plate: Later than no. 123 C. Railways added.
Alterations on the transfer: None.

123 E. FIFTH LITHOGRAPHIC TRANSFER

Size: 168 mm × 128 mm (1 mm)   1:718,000

Title (Ea) erased and replaced by *SKETCH MAP OF SUSSEX.* Note under title erased, and reference numbers omitted on map. *Guide to Sussex* (Ae) omitted. *Burgess Hill* added. Railway 24 added; cross-hatching on 27 erased.

    Black's guide to Brighton and vicinity.
    Edinburgh, Adam and Charles Black, 1866.   BL

Black's guide to the south-eastern counties . . .
Edinburgh, Adam and Charles Black, 1866.
The map is missing from the only copy (Hastings PL) examined.

State of the plate: Later than no. 123D. Title altered, note erased, *Burgess Hill* and railway added.
Alterations on the transfer: Guide to Sussex and reference numbers erased. Cross-hatching on railway 27 erased.

123 F.   SIXTH LITHOGRAPHIC TRANSFER

Size: 168 mm × 128 mm (1 mm)   1:718,000

EDITIONS

(i)   Railways 26, 28, 29 and 30 added; 27 again cross-hatched.

Black's guide to Sussex and its watering places . . . new edition.
Edinburgh, Adam and Charles Black, 1873.   SAS

Black's guide to the county of Sussex . . . third edition.
Edinburgh, Adam and Charles Black, 1875.   SAS

(ii)   *Guide to Sussex* added (Ae).

Black's guide to Brighton and vicinity . . . sixth edition.
Edinburgh, Adam and Charles Black, 1874.   BRIGHTON PL

State of the plate: Later than no. 123E. Railways added.
Alterations on the transfer: Guide to Sussex erased on edition (i). Reference numbers erased.

123 G.   SEVENTH LITHOGRAPHIC TRANSFER

Size: 168 mm × 128 mm (1 mm)   1:718,000

Guide to Sussex omitted. Bartholomew signature (Ee OS) omitted. Reference number *530* after *Mayfield* as on nos. 123C and D.

Black's picturesque guide . . . fourth edition.
Edinburgh, Adam and Charles Black, 1877.   SAS

State of the plate: As no. 123F.
Alterations on the transfer: Guide to Sussex erased. Reference numbers erased, except

530 after *Mayfield*. Bartholomew signature (Ee OS) erased.

123 H.   EIGHTH LITHOGRAPHIC TRANSFER

Size: 168 mm × 128 mm (1 mm)   1:718,000

J. Bartholomew Edin^r^. (Ee OS) as originally engraved. *530* after *Mayfield* omitted.

> *Black's picturesque guide . . . fifth edition.*
> Edinburgh, Adam and Charles Black, 1879.   BARBER INST. BIRMINGHAM UNIV.

> *Black's guide to Brighton and vicinity . . . eighth edition.*
> Edinburgh, Adam and Charles Black, 1881.   BL

> *Black's guide to Sussex and its watering places . . .*
> Edinburgh, Adam and Charles Black, 1882.   WSCL.BRIGHTON PL

State of the plate: As no. 123 F and G.
Alterations on the transfer: Guide to Sussex erased. Reference numbers erased.

123 I.   NINTH LITHOGRAPHIC TRANSFER

Size: 168 mm × 128 mm (1 mm)   1:718,000

Eastbourne and town symbol erased. *Southborne* erased and replaced by *Eastbourne*.

> *Black's guide to the county of Sussex . . . sixth edition.*
> Edinburgh, Adam and Charles Black, 1883.   BL.SAS

State of the plate: Later than no. 123H. *Eastbourne* and *Southborne* erased. *Eastbourne* added.
Alterations on the transfer: Guide to Sussex erased. Reference numbers erased.

123 J.   TENTH LITHOGRAPHIC TRANSFER

Size: 168 mm × 128 mm (1 mm)   1:718,000

Railways 34, 35, 36 and 37 added.

> *Black's guide to the county of Sussex and its watering places . . . seventh edition.*
> Edinburgh, Adam and Charles Black, 1885 and 1886.   BL.WSCL;P[1]

1. See A.J. Coombes *catalogue 77* (July 1981), item 46. The map has not been inspected and may be in a later state.

Black's guide to Brighton and vicinity . . . ninth edition.
Edinburgh, Adam and Charles Black, 1885.   BL

State of the plate: Later than no. 123I. Railways added.
Alterations on the transfer: Guide to Sussex and reference numbers erased.

123 K.   ELEVENTH LITHOGRAPHIC TRANSFER

Size: 168 mm × 128 mm (1 mm)   1:718,000

Guide to Sussex (Ae). *J. Bartholomew, Edin^r* altered to *John Bartholomew & Co. Edin^r.* (Ee OS). Railway 38 added.

    Black's guide to the county of Sussex . . . eighth edition.
    Edinburgh, Adam and Charles Black, 1889.   BL.SAS.WSCL

State of the plate: Later than no. 123J. Railway added.
Alterations on the transfer: Bartholomew signature altered. Reference numbers erased.

123 L.   TWELFTH LITHOGRAPHIC TRANSFER

Size: 168 mm × 128 mm (1 mm)   1:718,000

Railways 31, 33 and 41 added.

    Black's guide to Brighton including Newhaven . . . Edited by Frederick E. Sawyer, F.S.A. . . . tenth edition.
    Edinburgh, Adam and Charles Black, 1890.   BRIGHTON PL

State of the plate: Later than no. 123K. Railways added.
Alterations on the transfer: Bartholomew signature (Ee OS) altered. Reference numbers erased.

123 M.   THIRTEENTH LITHOGRAPHIC TRANSFER

Size: 168 mm × 128 mm (1 mm)   1:718,000

Signature (Ee OS) reverts to *J. Bartholomew, Edin^r. Published by A. & C. Black, London.* added (Ce OS). *Shoreham, Worthing, BRIGHTON, Battle* and other place-names re-engraved nearer to the town symbols, thus filling in the gaps left by the erasure of the reference numbers. Railways 15 and 41 added. (Railway 40, the direct Littlehampton line, was shown as a direct line from no. 123E onwards).

267

Black's guide to the county of Sussex . . .
Edinburgh, Adam and Charles Black, 9th edition 1892; 10th edition 1896. SAS;BL

State of the plate: Later than no. 123L. Place-names re-engraved. Reference numbers erased. Black imprint (Ce OS) added. Railways added.
Alterations on the transfer: None.

123 N.   FOURTEENTH LITHOGRAPHIC TRANSFER

Size: 168 mm × 128 mm (1 mm)   1:718,000

Horizontal line added under title (Ea). Railway 42 added. Railways 1 to 42 are now shown, omitting 32 (the Polegate loop) and 39 (the Newhaven harbour extension), which would be difficult to mark on such a small scale map.

> *Black's guide to Sussex and its watering places . . . Edited by A.R. Hope Moncrieff
> . . . tenth edition.*
> Edinburgh, Adam and Charles Black, 1896.   BRIGHTON PL
> This work also contains no. 129J in pocket of back cover.

State of the plate: Later than no. 123M. Railway added.
Alterations on the transfer: Line added under title.

123 O.   FIFTEENTH LITHOGRAPHIC TRANSFER

Size: 168 mm × 128 mm (1 mm)   1:718,000

Line under title and full stop after title omitted.

> *Black's guide to Sussex and its watering places . . . eleventh edition.*
> Edinburgh, Adam and Charles Black, 1898.   BL.SAS
> The 1898 edition of *Black's guide to Brighton and its environs* (BL and Brighton PL) has a map of Hampshire on the inside front cover. See also no. 144D.

State of the plate: As no. 123N.
Alterations on the transfer: Full stop erased.

124 JOHN BARTHOLOMEW   circa 1862

Based on Old Series One Inch Ordnance Survey, appendix VI.1(a).

The plate from which the following lithographic transfers were taken was apparently never used for direct intaglio printing.

124 A. FIRST LITHOGRAPHIC TRANSFER

Size: 407 mm × 323 mm (5 mm)   1:304,000

SUSSEX. (Aa). *Drawn & Engraved by J. Bartholomew & Son.* (Ee OS). *GEORGE PHILIP & SON. LONDON & LIVERPOOL* (Ce OS). *English Miles. 10* = 54 mm (Aa, under title). Key to *Railways* and *Roads* (Aa, below scale). Railways 1 to 14 and 16 to 19. Map overprinted to produce four colours, yellow – *WESTERN DIVISION*, purple – *EASTERN DIVISION*, blue – sea, and green – parks.

Issued as loose sheets or possibly in a cover bearing the title *Philips new series of county maps. From Ordnance Survey,*[1] [1862].   (BL).(BOD)

State of the plate: As originally engraved.
Alterations on the transfer: None.

124 B. SECOND LITHOGRAPHIC TRANSFER

Size: 407 mm × 325 mm (5 mm)   1:304,000

Bartholomew signature (Ee OS) erased. *BY J. BARTHOLOMEW, F.R.G.S.* added (Aa, below title above scale). Railway 20 added; 24, 27, 28, 29 and 30 shown by thin double lines. Map overprinted to produce three colours, yellow – *WESTERN DIVISION*, pink – *EASTERN DIVISION*, and blue – sea.

Philips' atlas of the counties of England, reduced from the Ordnance Survey. By Edward Weller, F.R.G.S.
London and Liverpool, George Philip and Son, 1965.   GLOUCESTER PL.
                                                            LIVERPOOL PL

State of the plate: Later than no. 124A. Signature erased (Ee OS). New signature added (Aa). Railways added.
Alterations on the transfer: None.

1. Harvey, 1959, no. 110A.

124 C.   THIRD LITHOGRAPHIC TRANSFER

Size: 407 mm × 325 mm (5 mm)   1:304,000

Railways 24, 27, 28 and 29 now shown as in use; 30 remains as on no. 121B; (21, 23 and 26 marked by pecked lines which appear to have been added by hand). Colours as no. 121B. Plate number *35* (on back).

> Probably from an edition of *Philips' atlas of the counties of England* issued in 1866 or 1867.   (WSRO)

State of the plate: Later than 124B. Railways added.
Alterations on the transfer: None.

124 D.   FOURTH LITHOGRAPHIC TRANSFER

Size: 406 mm × 326 mm (5 mm)   1:304,000

Railway 30 now shown as in use; (15, 21, 22, 23, 26 and 31 shown by pecked lines which appear to have been added by hand). Colours as no. 124B. Plate number *35* (on back) as no. 124C.

> *Philips' atlas of the counties of England* . . .
> London, George Philip and Son, 1868.   P

State of the plate: Later than no. 124C. Railway 30 added.
Alterations on the transfer: None.

124 E.   FIFTH LITHOGRAPHIC TRANSFER

Size: 406 mm × 326 mm (5 mm)   1:304,00

EDITIONS

(i)   Bartholomew signature (Aa, under title) erased. Plate number *35* added (Ea OS). Philip Imprint (Ce OS) re-engraved and full stop added; it is now 54 mm in length and starts 181 mm from bottom left corner. *E.Bourn* altered to *EASTBOURNE, Sth Bourn* to *Southbourne. Baynards Sta* added. *PT OF HAMPSHIRE* erased. *Rivals* re-engraved outside the county boundary. Longitude 10'; latitude 10' added. Graticule at 10' intervals with reference numbers *1* to *4* and letters *A* to *L* added. Boundaries of parliamentary boroughs marked by dotted lines. Railways 1 to 32 are now shown as in use. *Sta* added at several places, notably outside the county boundary. Map overprinted to produce colours red, yellow, pink, green and blue. No plate number on back.

270

Philips' atlas of the counties of England, reduced from the Ordnance Survey. By Edward Weller, F.R.G.S. New edition, with a complete consulting index, by John Bartholomew, F.R.G.S.
London and Liverpool, George Philip and Son, 1875, 1876 and 1880

BL.RGS.W;BL;W

(ii)   Plate number omitted.

Issued about 1875 as a folding map with printed title on cover: *Philips new series — Sussex — from the Ordnance Survey — of county maps.*   WORTHING PL

State of the plate: Later than no. 124D. Signature (Aa) and imprint (Ce OS) erased. Place-names and *Sta.*, graticule &c. and railways added.
Alterations on the transfer: Imprint (Ce OS) added. Plate number added in edition (i). Transfer identified by dot above inner line of outer bottom border, 10 mm from Ee.

124 F.   SIXTH LITHOGRAPHIC TRANSFER

Size: 407 mm × 328 mm (5 mm)   1:304,000

Title (Aa) erased and graticule extended to cover the space. Plate number (Ea OS) and Philip imprint (Ce OS) omitted. *THE "PICTORIAL WORLD" MAP OF SUSSEX.* added (Ca OS). *SUPPLEMENT TO THE PICTORIAL WORLD, July 29th. 1876* added (Aa OS, 32 mm above top border and starting 53 mm to the left of the left border. On most impressions this inscription is cut off in binding). Printer's mark ± or + added (Ce OS). County overprinted in yellow; the sea in blue. Topographical notes and statistics printed on back of map.

Issued as a supplement to *The Pictorial World An illustrated weekly newspaper.* vol. 5.
Issue no. 126, 29 July 1876.   BL.GL.W

State of the plate: As no. 124E.
Alterations on the transfer: Title (Aa) erased and graticule extended. Imprint (Ce OS) erased. Title (Ca OS) and inscription (Aa OS) added. Printer's mark added.

124 G.   SEVENTH LITHOGRAPHIC TRANSFER

Size: 405 mm × 328 mm (5 mm)   1:304,000

Title (Ca OS), inscription (Aa OS) and printer's mark omitted. Title *SUSSEX* (Aa) as originally engraved. *GEORGE PHILIP & SON, LONDON & LIVERPOOL.* added (Ce OS, now 64 mm long, starting 172 mm from bottom left corner, and in heavier print). Plate number *35* added (Ea OS). A note commencing *The Colouring represents*

. . . added (Aa, under key). Map overprinted to produce colours pink, red, yellow, green and blue.

> Issued about 1881 as a folding map with printed title on cover: *Philips new series — Sussex — from the Ordnance Survey — of county maps.*
> London, George Philip and Son.
>   (ESRO)

State of the plate: As no. 124F.
Alterations on the transfer: Imprint (Ce OS) and plate number added. Note re colouring (Aa) added; this addition must have been made on the stone since its position varies from one edition to another relative to that of the title, scale, key and parliamentary information (see no. 124 K), which maintain exact registration as between themselves.

124 H.   EIGHTH LITHOGRAPHIC TRANSFER

Size: 405 mm × 328 mm (5 mm)   1:304,000

The Philip imprint (Ce OS) is now 68 mm long, 174 mm from bottom left corner, and in light print. *(Old Town)* added under *EASTBOURNE, Southbourne* erased and replaced by *EASTBOURNE, Hove* re-engraved nearer to coastline, *West Brighton* added. Railways 33 to 37 and 39 added as in use; 38, 41 and 42 marked by plain double lines, the last two labelled *Constructing* and *(constructing)* respectively; T and U marked by plain double lines and extended to *CRANBROOK. Sta* added at a number of places, eg at *SEAFORD. Red Hill Junc., Ockley Sta.* and *Hayes Sta.* added. Map overprinted to produce colours pink, green, yellow and blue.

> *Philips' atlas of the counties of England . . . Reduced from the Ordnance Survey. New edition, with complete consulting index by John Bartholomew, F.R.G.S.*
> London and Liverpool, George Philip and Son, 1883.
>   COUNTY OF CLEVELAND LIB.

> Issued about 1883 as a folding map with printed title on cover: *Philips' new series of county maps. Sussex. From the Ordnance Survey.*
> London and Liverpool, George Philip and Son.
>   (P)

State of the plate: Later than no. 124G. Imprint (Ce OS) added. Place-names amended as listed above. Railways added.
State of the plate: Plate number and note about colouring added.

124 I.   NINTH LITHOGRAPHIC TRANSFER

Size: 406 mm × 326 mm (5 mm)   1:304,000

Railway 38 shown as in use. Railway R and line running north from *Milton* shown by heavy pecked lines, which may have been added by hand. Map overprinted to produce colours yellow, pink, blue and two shades of green.

Philips' atlas of the counties of England . . .
London, George Philip and Son, 1885.   A.BRIGHTON PL

State of the plate: Later than no. 124H. Railways added.
Alterations on the transfer: Plate number and note about colouring added.

124 J. TENTH LITHOGRAPHIC TRANSFER

Size: 404 mm × 325 mm (5 mm)   1:304,000

Plate number (Ea OS) and note about colouring (Aa) omitted. *(constructing)* on railway 42 erased; railway R and line running north from *Milton* are now shown by diced lines as are other railways; *Puckley Sta* added. Map overprinted in red with arrows to indicate major hills and with *H., C.* and *X.* to indicate appointed hotels, consuls of the Cyclists Touring Club and bicycle repairers. Also overprinted in blue (sea) and brown (roads).

Issued about 1885 as a folding map with printed title on cover: *Philips' cyclists' map of the county of Sussex . . .*
London and Liverpool, George Philip and Son.   (BL).(BOD).(CUL)
The impression in the British Library was received in May 1888; but it is probably that the map was published earlier. The map omits changes made on the plate for the 1885 atlas (no. 124K), and other maps in the same series were published in 1885.[2]

State of the plate: Later than no. 124I. Railways amended.
Alterations on the transfer: Plate number and note about colouring erased.

124 K. ELEVENTH LITHOGRAPHIC TRANSFER

Size: 406 mm × 326 mm (5 mm)   1:304,000

EDITIONS

(i) Plate number *35* (Ea OS) and note relating to colouring (Aa) added. Reference to parliamentary representation added (Aa, under note about colouring). *WESTERN DIVISION* and *EASTERN DIVISION* erased. The six parliamentary divisions named, eg *N.W. OR HORSHAM* and the boundaries marked by chain dots. *Sittingbourne*

---

2. Harvey, 1959, no. 110F; Hodson, 1974, no. 115H.

added. *H., C. X.* and arrows omitted. Map overprinted to produce colours blue, yellow, pink, purple, brown and two shades of green. *SUSSEX* added from type on back.

Philips' atlas of the counties of England . . . Reduced from the Ordnance Survey, and coloured to shew the new political divisions, according to the Redistribution Bill, 1885. New revised edition.
London and Liverpool, George Philip and Son, 1885.   BL.CUL.RGS

(ii)   Plate number (Ea OS) omitted.

Issued about 1888 as a folding map with printed title on cover: *Philips' new series of county maps. Sussex. From the Ordnance Survey.*
London and Liverpool, George Philip and Son.   (BL)

(iii)   Plate number *35* (Ae OS). Railway 42 shown as in use; 41 marked by heavy pecked line in addition to the plain double lines, but this must have been added by hand as the route varies from one impression to another.

Philips' atlas of the counties of England . . . coloured to shew the new parliamentary divisions . . .
London and Liverpool, George Philip and Son, [1889] and [1890].   W;P

(iv)   Railways T and U added as in use.

Philips' atlas of the counties of England . . . new and revised edition, with a complete consulting index.
London and Liverpool, George Philip and Son, [1896].   P

State of the plate: Later than no. 124J. Reference to parliamentary representation added (Aa). *WESTERN DIVISION* and *EASTERN DIVISION* erased; six parliamentary divisions marked and named. Place-names added.
Alterations on the transfer: Plate number on editions (i), (iii) and (iv), and note about colouring added. Railway 42 added on edition (iii) as in use; railways 42, T and U added on edition (iv). Transfer identified by 1 mm gap in outer line of left border, 1 mm from Ae.

124 L.   TWELFTH LITHOGRAPHIC TRANSFER

Size: 415 mm × 327 mm (5 mm)   1:304,000

Plate number, notes about colouring and parliamentary representation (Aa) and Philips' imprint (Ce OS) omitted. *ILIFFE & SON, MAP PRINTERS, COVENTRY & LONDON.* added (Ce OS). Railway 41 shown as in use and *Constructing* erased. *Sta* at *Devils Dyke* erased.

274

The way-about series, no. 6. The way about Sussex . . . by H.S. Vaughan.
London, Iliffe and Son, [1896].   BL.BRIGHTON PL
The date in the introduction is 1893; but the copy in the British Library was not received until 18 July
1896. The map is in a later state than no. 124K(iv), which Hodson[3] dates as circa 1896.

State of the plate: Later than no. 124K. Railway 41 amended and *Sta* erased.
Alterations on the transfer: Imprint (Ce OS) and reference to parliamentary representation (Aa) erased. Iliffe imprint added.

124 M.   THIRTEENTH LITHOGRAPHIC TRANSFER

Size: 415 mm × 327 mm (5 mm)   1:304,000

Railways T and U shown as in use and extending almost to *Hawkhurst.*

*The way-about series of gazetteer guides . . . no. 6. The way about Sussex . . . by
H.S. Vaughan . . . Edited by A. Baines, M.J.I.*
London, Iliffe and Son, [1896].   BL.SAS

State of the plate: Later than no. 124L. Railways added as in use.
Alterations on the transfer: As no. 124L.

124 N.   FOURTEENTH LITHOGRAPHIC TRANSFER

Size: 415 mm × 327 mm (5 mm)   1:304,000

Holmwood Sta. and two stations on the line to *ROCHESTER* added. Reference letters
and numbers in the border omitted.

The way-about series of gazetteer guides . . .
London, Iliffe and Son, [1896].   SAS.WSCL

State of the plate: Later than no. 124M. Stations added.
Alterations on the transfer: Imprint (Ce OS) and reference to parliamentary representation (Aa) erased. Iliffe imprint added. Reference letters and numbers erased.

3.   Hodson, 1974, no. 115M.

275

124 O.   FIFTEENTH LITHOGRAPHIC TRANSFER

Size: 334 mm × 253 mm (1 mm)   1:374,000

Title *SUSSEX* (Aa) is the same size as originally engraved, in spite of the reduced scale of this transfer. *PEARSON'S "ATHLETIC RECORD" COUNTY CYCLING MAPS, No. 6.* (Ca OS), *George Philip & Son, London and Liverpool* (Ee OS), *Pearson's "Athletic Record" Published from Pearson's Weekly Buildings, Henrietta Street, London, W.C., every Wednesday morning, price 1d. Full of Interest to Cyclists and all other sportsmen. One of these Maps will be given each week the next being DEVONSHIRE* (Ce OS), *SUPPLEMENT* (Aa OS) and *21st. JULY 1897* (Ea OS) have been added. *English Miles 10 = 43 mm* (Aa, under title). In the key (Aa, under scale) *Cycling Roads,* with symbol in red, added. *1°,* in red, *The line indicates the hill top, while the dot shows the direction of the dangerous descent* added (Aa, under key). Inner and outer lines of border, values for longitude and latitude, and reference letters and numbers (but not graticule) omitted. Map overprinted in red to show cycling roads and hill tops.

> *Pearson's Athletic Record.* vol. 1.
> Issued no. 16, 21 July 1897.
>   BL

State of the plate: As no. 124N.
Alterations on the transfer: All alterations and additions listed above were made on the stone. The title was erased on the stone, and subsequently the title in its original size transferred from the plate to the reduced sized stone.

124 P.   SIXTEENTH LITHOGRAPHIC TRANSFER

Size: 405 mm × 326 mm (5 mm)   1:304,000

The additions made on the previous transfer omitted. The title, scale, imprint (Ce OS) and border as as no. 124K. Key (Aa) erased and replaced by new key: *Main Roads Coloured Brown . . ., Cross Roads . . .,* and *Railways . . .,* with *Station* to the left of the symbol. Map overprinted in red with cycling symbols as on no. 124J, and in blue and brown.

> Issued about 1890 as a folding map with printed title on cover: *Philips' Cyclists' map of the county of Sussex.*
> London and Liverpool, George Philip and Son.   (GENEALOGICAL SOCIETY)

State of the plate: As no. 124N and O.
Alterations on the transfer: Key erased and new key added. Reference to parliamentary representation (Aa) erased. Cycling symbols overprinted.

124 Q. SEVENTEENTH LITHOGRAPHIC TRANSFER

Size: 405 mm × 326 mm (5 mm)   1:304,000

Chain Pier erased at *BRIGHTON.*

Issued about 1891 as a folding map with printed title on cover: *Philips' Cyclists' map of the county of Sussex.*
London and Liverpool, George Philip and Son.   (P)

State of the plate: Later than no. 124P. *Chain Pier* erased.
Alterations on the transfer: Key erased and new key added. Reference to parliamentary representation erased. Cycling symbols overprinted.

124 R. EIGHTEENTH LITHOGRAPHIC TRANSFER

Size: 404 mm × 326 mm (5 mm)   1:304,000

Key (Aa) as originally engraved. Reference to parliamentary representation (Aa) as engraved for no. 124K. Note about colouring as on no. 124K. Plate number *35* added (Ea OS, in larger size than previously). *Steyne* erased. Railway 43 added; all railways now marked by continuous black lines; the Manhood light railway added. Map overprinted to produce colours green, pink, yellow, purple, buff and blue.

Philips' atlas of the counties of England . . .
London and Liverpool, George Philip and Son, [1899] and 1900.   WN;W

State of the plate: Later than no. 124Q. *Steyne* erased. Railway added.
Alterations on the transfer: Plate number and note about colouring added.

125 MARK ANTHONY LOWER   1864

Size: 358 mm × 173 mm (6 mm)   1:336,000

Based on Walker no. 108.

George Peter Bacon,[1] the publisher, was the son of Richard MacKenzie Bacon, editor of the *Norwich Mercury*. He settled in Lewes in 1843 as proprietor and editor of the *Sussex Advertiser*. He was president of the Provincial Newspaper Society in 1848–9.[2]

---

1. *SAC* vol. 29 (1879) p. vii; Boase, 1965.
2. Whorlow, 1886, p. 89.

277

He printed the *Sussex archaeological collections* from 1861 to 1878, and took a keen interest in the work of the society. He died in 1878.

The Reverend Frederick Henry Arnold (1831–1906), see second lithographic transfer below, came from a Sussex family and lived his whole life in the county. His father was George Frederick Handel Arnold of Petworth, a man with considerable musical interests One son, Dr. G.B. Arnold, became organist at Winchester Cathedral; another, Edward, practised as a solicitor in Chichester. Frederick Henry was appointed to the living of Appledram on 21st May 1861, the day that the spire of Chichester Cathedral collapsed. In 1863 he was appointed Chaplain at Chichester workhouse, a post he held for forty-three years. As well as being a keen botanist, he wrote the *History and antiquities of Chichester* and other books, and was a regular contributor to the *Sussex archaeological collections,* including an analysis of the Sussex place-names on Andrea Bianco's portolano of 1436.[3]

The second transfer of the map described below is signed *Dawson Sc.* This statement is incorrect and it is tempting to identify the signature with the notorious Charles Dawson of Piltdown fame, who would have been twenty-three at the time. Dawson in fact produced a fictitious map of Maresfield Forge in about 1912.[4] However, Dawson's signature, which appears on the fly-leaf of the SAS copy of his book *Sussex Iron Work and Pottery,* cannot be identified with the signature on the map.

EDITION

SUSSEX REDUCED FROM THE ORDNANCE SURVEY. to accompany Papers in Vols. XV & XVI of "Sussex Archaeological Collections", By Mark Antony Lower, F.S.A. 1864. (Ea). Engraved for the Suss: Arch: Soc: by J. & C. Walker July 1864. (Ae OS). Longitude 10' (1'); latitude 10' (1'). The map shows only the boundaries of the rapes, towns and rivers, of which many are named.

> *Sussex archaeological collections* . . . vol. 16.
> Lewes, George P. Bacon, 1864.
> The map illustrates a paper by Lower on *The Rivers of Sussex.*

BL.SAS.BRIGHTON PL

125 A.   FIRST LITHOGRAPHIC TRANSFER

Size: 366 mm × 171 mm (6 mm)   1:336,000

In the title (Ea) *to accompany . . . Collections* has been erased and replaced by *with the addition of the Railways.* Signature (Ae OS) altered to *Engraved by J. & C. Walker.* Railways 1 to 5, 7 to 14, 16 to 18, 20 to 22, 24 and 26 to 30 added and named.

---

3. *SAC* vol. 20 (1868), pp. 224–5.
4. *SAC* vol. 112 (1974), p. 165; note by J.H. Combridge, *Sussex archaeological newsletter,* August 1977.

A compendious history of Sussex, . . . By Mark Antony Lower, M.A. . . . vol. 1.
Lewes, George P. Bacon, 1870.   BL.SAS.BRIGHTON PL
Some copies of this work were issued without the map.

State of the plate: Probably as no. 125; but the alterations to title (Ea) and signature
(Ae OS) may have been made on the plate.
Alterations on the transfer: Railways added, and probably the alterations made to title
and signature.

125 B.   SECOND LITHOGRAPHIC TRANSFER

Size: 195 mm × 92 mm (3 mm)   1:629,000

Title and date (Ea) erased and replaced by *SUSSEX. REDUCED FROM THE
ORDNANCE SURVEY.* (Ea, but nearer to the top border). *Dawson Sc.* added (Ea
OS). Walker signature (Ae OS) omitted. *DISTRICTS FOUNDED ON RIVER
DRAINAGE* added (Eb, under title). Seven districts are named and numbered on the
map, and the watersheds marked by heavy pecked lines. No railways are shown, the
map itself being in the same state as no. 125. It is printed on blueish paper.

Flora of Sussex . . . by the Rev. F.H. Arnold, M.A., LL.B.,
London, Hamilton Adams and Co., 1887.   BL.BRIGHTON PL.WORTHING PL
The 1907 edition of this work has the same map overprinted to produce six colours identifying the seven
drainage districts.

State of the plate: Probably as no. 125.
Alterations on the transfer: Title (Ea) and signature (Ae OS) erased. New title, signature (Ee OS) and note relating to drainage districts added. Roman numberals I to VII
and pecked lines added on map.

126   W.J. SACKETT   **1864**

Size: 410 mm × 311 mm (9 mm)   1:396,000

The sources on which this map, and no. 127, were based have not been determined. Considering the period it
is an inaccurate map; the coastal promontory at Langney Point, for example, is grossly exaggerated.

The lithographic transfer below was probably derived from a drawing, not from an
engraved plate.

EDITION

CHICHESTER (Bd, with foliar decoration). *W.J. Sackett, Printer & Lithog^r. 11, Bull
S^t. Birm^m.* (Ce OS). *REFERENCE. A Archdeaconry of CHICHESTER* with the

279

deaneries numbered *1* to *7*, *B Archdeaconry of LEWES* with the deaneries numbered *1* to *5* (Ee). *Arms of the Bishop* (Db). The map marks towns, rivers and boundaries of Deaneries only. On the back of the left half is part of map no. 127.

> *A new set of diocesan maps by James Thos. Law, Lich. Cancel. and William F. Francis. Lich(field), Theol. Schol.,* 1864.
>
> BL.W
>
> The date is taken from the preface. This work also contains no. 127.

127   W.J. SACKETT   1864

Size: 450 mm × 318 mm (2 mm)   1:581,000

The sources used in the compilation of this map have not been determined.

The map was printed from a lithographic stone on which the design had been laid down direct from the original drawing.

EDITION

CHICHESTER (Aa, with foliar decoration, but not the same as no. 126). *W.J. Sackett, Printer & Lithographer, 11 Bull S*t*. Birmingham.* (Ce OS). *Reference* to boundaries (Ab). Key to archdeaneries and deaneries with reference letters *A* and *B*, and numbers *1* to *7* and *1* to *5* as no. 126 (Eb). The map is in outline showing rivers but giving no place-names other than *Selsey Bill, Beachey Head* and *PEVENSEY BAY*. It occupies a panel 450 mm × 148 mm at the top of the page. In a separate panel below the map is a list of parishes in the diocese. On the back of the left half of the map is *Synopsis of the Diocese of Chichester* and on the back of the right half is part of map no. 126.

> *A new set of diocesan maps by James Thos. Law, Lich. Cancel. and William F. Francis. Lich(field), Theol. Schol.,* 1864.
>
> BL.W
>
> The date is taken from the preface. The work also contains no. 126.

Based on Old Series One Inch Ordnance Survey, appendix VI.1(a), but with additions, eg *Cliftonville*, perhaps from Cary no. 61C.

William Hughes, FRGS (1817–76) was employed as an assistant librarian at the British Museum from 1841 to 1843 to catalogue the geographical collection. He was Professor of Geography at King's College from 1863 to 1875.[1] Between 1840 and 1870 he published a large number of educational works,[2] including *Maunder's treasury of geography* (1843), *Treatise on the construction of maps* (1864) and *The geography of British history* (1870). Neither Boase[3] nor Cowton[4] refer to him as Professor of Geography, whereas his obituary[5] omits any reference to his work for the British Museum. Nevertheless the dates and the similarity in lists of published works makes it clear that they refer to the same person. Hughes also edited a series of school atlases published by George Philip and Son. What is not clear is whether William Hughes, the engraver, was the same man. Maps engraved by William or W. Hughes are known in 1846, 1851 and 1852.[6] Tooley[7] supposes that they were the same and describes him as 'Geographer and engraver' of Paternoster Row. The combination of skills was uncommon at such a late date, and there is another possible candidate as engraver – William Hughes, wood engraver (1803–61).[8]

The plate from which the following lithographic transfers were taken was apparently never used for direct intaglio printing.

128 A. FIRST LITHOGRAPHIC TRANSFER

Size: 300 mm × 223 mm (7 mm)   1:416,000

EDITIONS

(i) *SUSSEX* (Ea). *W. Hughes* (Ee OS). *LONDON, VIRTUE & C⁰.* (Ce OS). *English Miles 10* = 38 mm (Ea, under title). Key to *Boundary between East & West Sussex* and *Railways* (Ee). Longitude 10' (5'); latitude 10' (5'). Railways 1 to 14, 16 to 22, 24 and A to L are shown. The county is overprinted in brown and the sea in blue.

1. *Calendar of King's College*, London, 1875–6.
2. Anderson, 1881, pp. 20 and 21; Boase, 1965; Lister, 1965, p. 180; Tooley, 1979, p. 259; *Proceedings of the Royal Geographical Society* vol. 21 (1876–7), p. 429, obituary.
3. Boase, 1965.
4. Cowton, 1872, p. 221.
5. *Proceedings of RGS* vol. 21.
6. *An Historical atlas . . . new edition.* Seeley, Burnside and Seeley; Hyde, 1975, no. 15; and Chubb, 1927. no. XL (Scotland).
7. Tooley, 1979, p. 318,
8. *DNB*.

The national gazetteer: a topographical dictionary of the British Islands. Compiled from the latest and best sources, and illustrated with a complete county atlas, and numerous maps. vol. 3.
London, Virtue and Co., 1868 and [1875].   BL.CUL;W
Originally published in parts from 1863 to 1868; the section containing the map of Sussex was issued in 1868.

(ii)   *W. Hughes* (Ee OS) omitted. Overprinted to produce colours as on no. 128A (i).

The national gazetteer . . . vol. 9 (of twelve).
London, Virtue and Co., [1868].   CUL

State of the plate: As originally engraved.
Alterations on the transfer: Signature (Ee OS) erased on edition (ii).

128 B.   SECOND LITHOGRAPHIC TRANSFER

Size: 300 mm × 225 mm (7 mm)   1:416,000

W. Hughes (Ee OS) as on no. 128A(i). *Chanctonbury Ring* added. *Heights in feet.* added (Ea, under scale); spot heights added on map eg *814* at *Chanctonbury Ring, 702* at *Rooks Hill.* Railways 23, 25, 26, 27, 28 and 29 added. Colours as no. 128A(i).

The national gazetteer . . . vol. 3.
London, Virtue and Co., 1868.   HERTFORD MUSEUM

The national gazetteer . . . vol. 3.
London, Virtue and Co. Ltd., [1870].   BL

State of the plate: Later than no. 128A. *Heights in feet* and railways added.
Alterations on the transfer: None.

128 C.   THIRD LITHOGRAPHIC TRANSFER

Size: 300 mm × 225 mm (7 mm)   1:416,000

St. added to railway symbol in key (Ee). Railways 30 and M added. The county is overprinted in pink and green; the sea in blue.

A new county atlas of Great Britain and Ireland containing sixty-eight coloured maps by W. Hughes Esq., F.R.G.S.
London, Virtue and Co., [1873].   BL.BOD.CUL

282

The national gazetteer . . .
London, Virtue and Co., [1875].   W

This edition of the work is bound in twelve volumes. The map of Sussex is in vol. 9. Vol. 12 includes an appendix, which gives Poor Law returns to April 1875.

State of the plate: Later than no. 128B. *St.* and railways added.
Alterations on the transfer: None.

128 D.   FOURTH LITHOGRAPHIC TRANSFER

Size: 300 mm × 223 mm (7 mm)   1:416,000

Imprint (Ce OS) erased and replaced by *LONDON, J.S. VIRTUE & Cº LIMITED.* Six parliamentary divisions outlined and named in red, eg *HORSHAM.* Railways 34 to 38 added. Map overprinted in red, yellow and blue.

> *A new parliamentary and county atlas of Great Britain and Ireland containing seventy-two coloured maps by W. Hughes, Esq., F.R.G.S. and others edited by Professor A.H. Keene, B.A. . .*
> London, J.S. Virtue and Co., [1886].   BL

State of the plate: Later than no. 128C; railways added.
Alterations on the transfer: Names and boundaries of parliamentary divisions and new imprint (Ce OS) probably added on the stone.

129   JOHN BARTHOLOMEW   circa **1868**

Based on Old Series One Inch Ordnance Survey, appendix VI.1(a).

Thomas Houlston[1] (1804–69), the publisher, was a book-seller in the Strand from 1835 to 1844, and later at Paternoster Row, first with John Stoneman from 1844 to 1856 and then with Henry Wright from 1857 to 1869. He died on the Isle of Wight.

William Topley[2] (1841–94), who drew the geological map, was a geologist by profession. He was born at Greenwich and died at Croydon. He carried out the geological survey of the Weald between 1863 and 1873, and superintended publication of maps at the Survey Office from 1880. In 1881 he was appointed to superintend the publication of the British section of the geological map of Europe, and he helped, in 1888, with the making of the geological map of Europe, which was published in Professor Preswich's *Geology.* He took a special interest in an international scheme for

---

1. Boase, 1965.
2. Boase, 1965.

the colouring of geological maps, and was president of the Geologists Association in 1885.

Frederick Dixon, the author, was a surgeon and practised at Worthing.[3] He was a victim of the cholera epidemic of 1849.

Thomas Rupert Jones[4] (1819–1911), who revised Dixon's work, was Assistant Secretary of the Geological Society between 1851 and 1862, professor at Sandhurst in 1862, and President of the Geologists Association from 1879 to 1881.

No. 129B below and some later lithographic transfers were published by W.H. Smith and Sons. The brothers Henry Edward Smith and William Henry Smith (1792–1865) started in business as H. & W. Smith, newsagents, at Duke Street, Grosvenor Square about 1820.[5] In 1829 the indolent elder brother resigned, and the energetic W.H. Smith took over and ran the firm alone until 1846, when his son, William Henry Smith II (1825–91) became a partner; 'and Son' was added to the name. In 1848 they secured their first railway bookstall concession from the London and North Western Railway and took over the stall at Euston station. By 1862 they were established at nearly all railway stations and were the leading newspaper distributors in the country. Their activities expanded in various directions, including railway advertisement concessions and lending libraries. The elder W.H. Smith retired in 1858 and died at Bournemouth. The younger became a member of parliament in 1868 and held a number of distinguished cabinet offices, including that of First Lord of the Admiralty under Disraeli in 1877. He had wanted to go into the Church, but had been persuaded to join the family business; his reputation for honesty caused *Punch* to refer to him as 'Old Morality'. In 1891 he was appointed Lord Warden of the Cinque Ports, and he died at Walmer Castle in the same year.

The following transfers were taken from the plates of *THE IMPERIAL MAP OF ENGLAND & WALES ACCORDING TO THE ORDNANCE SURVEY . . . BY JOHN BARTHOLOMEW F.R.G.S.* The plates, much revised, were in service until at least 1938 when they were used for the map in *Methuen's Little Guides, 9th edn*. Sussex is from two plates. Most of the county, *SELSEA BILL* to Kent, is from Sheet 13; the area west of *SELSEA BILL* from Sheet 14. The join can be detected in those maps noticed below which show the whole county. Transfers from this map were also used for (i) *The royal atlas of England and Wales . . . edited by J.G. Bartholomew, F.R.G.S.* In the [1898] edition, *PLATE 47 — SECTION XXVIII*, BRIGHTON, covers most of Sussex, extending from *Havant* to *Ninfield* and northwards as far as *GUILDFORD;* (ii) *Brighton and the south coast*, 1897–98, published by Darlington & Co., Llangollen in the series *Darlington's handbooks*. This transfer covers the area from *Climping* to *W. Hythe* and inland to *HORSHAM*. It has the title *THE SOUTH COAST*, and it was taken from the plate in a state between no. 129K and no. 129L; and (iii) *MAP OF THE ENVIRONS OF BRIGHTON, HASTINGS &c.* in *Abel Heywood's tourist guide to the Kent & Sussex watering places*, published about 1873, by Abel Heywood and Son, Manchester and by Simpkin, Marshall & Co., London.

3. *SNQ* no. 7; Smail, 1949, p. 149.
4. *Proceedings of the Geological Society* vol. 67, May 1911; *The Geological Magazine*, November 1909.
5. Pocklington, 1921.

129 A. FIRST LITHOGRAPHIC TRANSFER

Size: 333 mm × 246 mm (2 mm)   1:260,000

ENVIRONS OF BRIGHTON &c. (Ce). *Drawn & Engraved by J. Bartholomew Edin*ʳ.
(Ee OS). *Scale of Miles 8* = 48 mm (Ce, under title). Grid (67 mm × 72 mm). Railways
1 to 29 shown as in use (heavy centre line and two thin lines); 30, 31, 34, 35, lines from
Naldry to *Uckfield, Uckfield* to *Hailsham, MIDHURST* to *HASLEMERE,* and from
West Grinstead to *Haywards Heath* shown as projected (three thin lines). Map over-
printed in blue.

> Issued about 1868 as a folding map with printed title: *Tourists' Handy Map from
> the Ordnance Survey, Brighton and Neighbourhood. Price Fourpence.*
> London, Houlston and Wright.   (BL)

State of the plate: Probably as originally engraved for *THE IMPERIAL MAP;* except
that the *K* of *KENT* has been erased, railway M shown as in use, and part of the *10
Fathoms Line* has been erased.
Alterations on the transfer: Title, signature and scale added. Border drawn round map
and projecting place-names wholly erased on the top and right border, eg *Catsfield.*
This transfer extends from *SELSEA BILL* to just west of *Bexhill* and north as far as
GUILDFORD.

129 B. SECOND LITHOGRAPHIC TRANSFER

Size: 437 mm × 335 mm (6 mm)   1:259,000

Title (Ce) and signature (Ee OS) omitted. New title *ENVIRONS OF BRIGHTON &
SUSSEX COAST* (Ca OS). *by J. Bartholomew, Edin*ʳ. (Ee OS). *London, W.H. Smith
& Son 186 Strand.* (Ce OS). *Engraved & Printed in colours.* (Ae OS). Scale moved
(from Ce to Be OS). *The Mizan,* under *SELSEA BILL,* erased. *W.* and *E.* (in
SUSSEX), *W.* and *M.* (in Kent), and *W.* and *M.* (in *SURREY*) added in hatched
capitals. Railway 30 now shown as in use. Overprinted to produce colours pink, green,
yellow and blue.

> Issued about 1875 as a folding map with printed title: *W.H. Smith & Son's reduced
> Ordnance map of Brighton & Sussex coast — scale 4 miles to an inch.*
> London, W.H. Smith & Son.   (P)

State of the plate: Later than no. 129A; the railways and hatched capitals added.
Alterations on the transfer: The title, signature, imprint, note (Ae OS) and scale added.
Border drawn round map. Projecting place-names and *The Mizan* erased. This transfer
extends from *Havant* to *HASTINGS* and north to *LONDON* (Ca, in border).

129 C.   THIRD LITHOGRAPHIC TRANSFER

Size: 706 mm × 251 mm (2 mm)   1:257,000

Title (Ca OS), note (Ae OS), imprint (Ce OS) and scale omitted. New title
*GEOLOGICAL MAP OF SUSSEX By W. Topley, F.G.S., Assoc. Inst. C.E.,
Geological Survey of England & Wales* (Ed). *J. Bartholomew, Edin*[r]*.* (Ee OS).
DIXON'S "GEOLOGY OF SUSSEX", 2ND. EDITION. (Ea OS). *SCALE 1:253,440
Scale of Miles (1 Inch to 4 Miles) 10 = 63 mm, Scale of Kilometres 10 = 40 mm (Ee).
(This Map, reduced from the Geological Survey, is part of that employed in a
"Geological Model of the South E. of England" by W. Topley & J.B. Jordan, 1873. The
Topography by J. Bartholomew.)* (Ed, between title and scales). *INDEX TO
COLOURS AND SIGNS.* (Eb). *SECTION FROM THE ENGLISH CHANNEL,
NEAR SEAFORD, TO THE ISLE OF SHEPPEY.* (Bd). *LINE OF SECTION* with
line drawn across map from *SEAFORD* to *Staplehurst.* The divisions of the various
geological strata outlined on the map. *RAISED BEACH* added east of *BRIGHTON.
SUB. FOREST* added in five places and *SUB. FOR.* in one place along coast. A row of
small circles (Martello towers) added at *Pevensey Bay. Light Ho.* in sea at *RYE* erased.
Ecclesbourne Glen and *Dripping Well* erased; *Lee Ness Point, Fairlight Glen* and
Ecclesbourne Glen (now written in a straight horizontal line) added east of
HASTINGS. Wittersham Level added. *Spring Tides Rise 20 Feet* added at *BEACHY
HEAD. The Mizan* not erased. Railways 31 and 32 now shown as in use. Overprinted
to produce nine colours.

> *The geology of Sussex . . . by the late Frederick Dixon esq., F.G.S. New edition
> revised . . . T. Rupert Jones F.R.S. F.G.S. etc.*
> Brighton, William J. Smith,[6] 1878.   BL.SAS
>
> The first edition of this work, 1850, did not contain a map. The map in this state was also sold loose ". .
> coloured, folded in to case, 2s 6d; 1878".[7]

State of the plate: Later than no. 129B. Outlines of geological strata, *RAISED
BEACH, Spring Tides . . ., SUB. FOREST,* and place-name changes added or made
on the plate. Railways added.
Alterations on the transfer: Title, note and scale, signature (Ee OS), imprint (Ea OS),
INDEX (Bd) and *LINE OF SECTION* added. A new border drawn round map and
projecting place-names erased. The map extends from *FAREHAM* to *W. Hythe* and
north to *Horley.*

---

6.   Melville's *Directory* for 1868 lists 'William Joshua Smith (late H.H. Cullis), 43 North Street'. The imprint
     also appears on a work published in 1912.
7.   See W.J. Smith's advertisement on last page of *Smuggling and Smugglers in Sussex.* Brighton, n.d.

129 D.   FOURTH LITHOGRAPHIC TRANSFER

Size: (a) West Sussex 266 mm × 195 mm (2 mm)
(b) East Sussex 264 mm × 195 mm (2 mm)   1:259,000

The map now appears in two sections, sometimes bound facing each other, overlapping by 2.7 mm. The title, inscriptions &c. completely revised as follows:

(a) *WEST AND MIDDLE SUSSEX* (Ee). *J. Bartholomew, Edin^r.* (Ee OS). *PUBLISHED BY A. & C. BLACK, EDINBURGH.* (Ce OS). *Scale of Miles. 8 = 49 mm* (Ee, under title).

(b) *EAST SUSSEX* (Ee) on two lines. *J. Bartholomew, Edin^r.* (Ee OS). *PUBLISHED BY A. & C. BLACK, EDINBURGH* (Ce OS). *Scale of Miles. 8 = 49 mm* (Ee, under title).

Railways as no. 129C. *SUSSEX,* which formerly appeared across the centre of the map, has been erased, but traces of the original lettering remain, eg a rectangular mark on the road 6 mm south of *Cowfold.* These maps are usually found uncoloured.

Black's picturesque guide . . . fifth edition.
Edinburgh, Adam and Charles Black, 1879.   BARBER INST BIRMINGHAM UNIV

Black's guide to the county of Sussex and its watering-places. Sixth edition with map . . .
Edinburgh, Adam and Charles Black, 1882.   WSCL.BRIGHTON PL
Earlier editions of this work contain no. 122. Map no. 123 appears on the fly-leaf.

State of the plate: As no. 129C.
Alterations on the transfer: Titles, signatures, imprints and scales added. New borders drawn round each section of the map; projecting place-names erased, some partially, eg *Shadoxh*(urst), *Horste*(d Keynes), some wholly, eg *Froxfield. SUSSEX* erased.

129 E.   FIFTH LITHOGRAPHIC TRANSFER

Size: 461 mm × 333 mm (4 mm)   1:259,000

The map is on one sheet. Title, inscriptions &c. completely revised and now read: *ENVIRONS OF BRIGHTON & SUSSEX COAST* (Ca OS). *J. Bartholomew Edin^r.* (Ee OS). *LONDON: W.H. Smith & Son, 186 Strand.* (Ce OS). *Scale of Miles 8 = 50 mm* (Ce). *SUSSEX* written across map. Railway 34 now shown as in use. Overprinted to produce colours red, pink, green, yellow, brown and blue.

Issued about 1883 as a folding map with printed title: *W.H. Smith & Son's reduced Ordnance map of Brighton & Sussex coast. Scale 4 Miles to an inch.*
London, W.H. Smith and Son.   (BRIGHTON PL)

State of the plate: Later than no. 129D. Railway 34 now 'in use'.
Alterations on the transfer: Title, signature, imprint and scale added. border drawn

round map and projecting place-names erased. This transfer covers an area from west of *HAVANT* (*Butser Hill* and *Langrish* appear in full) to *Pett*, and north to *LONDON*.

129 F.   SIXTH LITHOGRAPHIC TRANSFER

Size: (a) 260 mm × 195 mm (2 mm)
(b) 263 mm × 195 mm (2 mm)   1:259,000

The map is in two sections and compares with nos. 129D. as follows:
   (a) Title (Ee) altered to *WEST & MID. SUSSEX*. Signature (Ee OS) now reads *J. Bartholomew*. Imprint (Ce OS) omitted. Right border moved inwards 6 mm.
   (b) Imprint (Ce OS) omitted. *Grt. Cheyne* added.
   SUSSEX erased. Overprinted to produce two shades of pink marking the county boundary.

> *Black's guide to the county of Sussex and its watering-places. Sixth edition with map . . .*
> Edinburgh, Adam and Charles Black, 1883.   BL

> *Black's guide to the county of Sussex . . . seventh edition . . .*
> Edinburgh, Adam and Charles Black, 1885 and 1886.   BL.WSCL;P[8]

State of the plate: Probably later than no. 129E. *SUSSEX* erased, although this alteration may have been made on the stone.
Alterations on the transfer: Titles, signature and scales added. Borders drawn round each section of the map; most projecting place-names erased, but several remain, eg on left border of west section (Oxe)*nbourne*, (Butser) *Hill* and (Lan)*grish*; on left border of east section (Ho)*llingbury;* and on the right border *PEAT* erased. *Clanfield, Froxfield, Chiltington, Ovingdean* and *Balcombe* now overrun the border. *Grt. Cheyne* added.

129 G.   SEVENTH LITHOGRAPHIC TRANSFER

Size: (a) 260 mm × 195 mm (2 mm)
(b) 261 mm × 195 mm (2 mm)   1:259,000

House symbols added at *BRIGHTON, Eastbourne, TUNBRIDGE WELLS* and *HASTINGS*. *Barracks* added north of *BRIGHTON*. *Southbourne* re-engraved *EASTBOURNE*, and *(Old Town)* added under *Eastbourne*. *Tivoli Gardens* (north of

---

8.   See A.J. Coombes *catalogue* 77 (July 1981), item 46. The map has not been inspected and may be in a later state.

HASTINGS) re-engraved *Silver Hill*. An extra meridian added just west of *CHICHESTER*. Station symbol added at *Keymer Junction*. Railway 35 now shown as in use; 36 to 38 added; projected line from *Naldry* to *Uckfield* erased. Overprinted in pink to mark the county boundary.

> *Black's guide to the county of Sussex and its watering-places with map . . . edited by Frederick E. Sawyer, F.S.A. eighth edition.*
> Edinburgh, Adam and Charles Black, 1889.   BL.SAS.WSCL

State of the plate: Later than no. 129 F; the changes listed above were most probably made on the plate.
Alterations on the transfer: As for no. 129F, except that on the left border of the west section *Langrish* and *Oxenbourne* wholly erased, *Charlton* added. On the east section, left border *Clayton* wholly erased, *Hollingbury Cas.* appears in full; on right border *Shadoxhurst* in full overruns the border, *PEAT* erased, *Grt. Cheyne* added. On the top borders of both sections many place-names are not now erased, eg *Ockley, Puckley*.

129 H. EIGHTH LITHOGRAPHIC TRANSFER

Size: (a) 256 mm × 206 mm (1 mm)
        (b) 282 mm × 206 mm (1 mm)   1:259,000

The map is still in two sections, but the titles, inscriptions &c. are completed revised as follows:
    (a) *WEST SUSSEX* (Ee)*. John Bartholomew F.R.G.S. Edin^r.* (Ee OS). *Scale of Miles 8 = 50 mm* (Ee). *Map N°. 4* (Ea OS). *Copyright* (Ae OS). *Key to Carriage Roads . . ., Foot Routes . . .* (Ce OS).
    (b) *EAST SUSSEX* (Ee) re-engraved on one line. *John Bartholomew F.R.G.S Edin^r.* (Ee OS). *Scale of Miles 8 = 50 mm* (Ee). *MAP N°. 1* (Ea OS). *Copyright* (Ae OS). Key to *Carriage Roads . . ., Foot Routes . . .* (Ce OS).
    Fathom lines and much detail in the sea, eg *Kingmere Rocks, Royal Sovereign Shoals* omitted. Grid omitted. *Selsey* in place of *Selsea* in two places. *Puckley Sta* re-engraved and *Helgerden* erased. *Lewes Rd.* and *Marina Sta.* added. *PEAT* appears once. House symbols added at *Preston. Grt. Cheyne* omitted. Railways 39, 41 and 42 added; 1 to 39, 41 and 42 now shown as in use. Projected lines from *West Grinstead* to *Haywards Heath* and from *Uckfield* to *Hailsham* erased; projected line from *MIDHURST* to *HASLEMERE* remains. Overprinted in blue (sea) and brown (roads).

> *Thorough guide series. Surrey and Sussex (including Tunbridge Wells) by C.S. Ward, M.A. . . . sixteen maps and plans by Bartholomew.*
> London, Dulau & Co., 1890.   BL.SAS

State of the plate: Later than no. 129G. Place names and railways 39, 41 and 42 added. Grid erased. *The Mizan* erased.
Alterations on the transfer: Titles, signature, scales, map numbers, *Copyright* and keys

added. Projected railway lines from *West Grinstead* to *Haywards Heath* and from *Uckfield* to *Hailsham* erased. Border drawn round each section and projecting place-names erased. On west section left border extended by 4 mm, *Clanfield* and *Froxfield* now lie inside the border and *Oxenbourne Down* appears in full; top border extended by 7 mm and new place-names are included, eg *GODALMING;* right border reduced by 9 mm and some detail excluded, eg *Wivelsfield;* bottom border raised by 2 mm. On east section, left border extended by 18 mm and new place-names included, eg *Hurstpierpoint;* top border extended by 9 mm and new place-names included, eg *Lingfield;* right border unchanged but *Warehorne* now *Warehor, Shadoxhurst* in full overlapping border, *Gr^t. Chart* in full, *PEAT* not erased. *Grt. Cheyne* added. Detail in sea erased.

129 I. NINTH LITHOGRAPHIC TRANSFER

Size: (a) 261 mm × 195 mm (2 mm)
     (b) 264 mm × 195 mm (2 mm)   1:259,000

Titles, inscriptions &c. now as follows:
  (a) *WEST & MID SUSSEX.* (Ee). *John Bartholomew Edin^r.* (Ee OS). *Published by A. & C. Black, London* (Ce OS). *Scale of Miles 8* = 49 mm (Ee, under title).
  (b) *EAST SUSSEX.* (Ee). *John Bartholomew Edin^r.* (Ee OS). *Published by A. & C. Black, London* (Ce OS). *Scale of Miles 8* = 49 mm (Ee, under title).
  Detail in sea not erased. Railways 1 to 39, 41 and 42 shown as in use; lines from *Uckfield* to *Hailsham,* from *MIDHURST* to *HASLEMERE* and from *West Grinstead* to *Haywards Heath* shown as projected. Overprinted in pink.

> *Black's guide to the county of Sussex and its watering-places with map . . . edited by Frederick E. Sawyer, F.S.A. ninth edition.*
> London and Edinburgh, Adam and Charles Black, 1892.   WSCL.SAS

State of the plate: As no. 129H.
Alterations on the transfer: Titles, signatures, imprints and scales added. Border drawn round each section and projecting place-names erased. On west section, left border has *Idsworth Ho.* added and *Butser Hill* erased; on top border some place-names which appeared on nos. 129G and H are now omitted, eg *Ockley;* on right border *Kingscote Sta.* and other place-names have been added. On the east section, on left border (B)*alcombe* partly erased; on top border *Dormans* omitted; right border has *Shadoxhu*(rst) partly erased. *Grt. Cheyne* added.

129 J.   TENTH LITHOGRAPHIC TRANSFER

Size: (a) 265 mm × 195 mm (2 mm)
      (b) 265 mm × 195 mm (2 mm)   1:259,000

Grt. Cheyne omitted. *West Pier* and symbol added at *BRIGHTON*. Railway 40 added. Overprinted in brown.

> *Black's guide to Sussex and its watering-places . . . Edited by A.R. Hope-Moncrieff . . . tenth edition.*
> Edinburgh, Adam and Charles Black, 10th edn., 1896.   BRIGHTON PL
> The maps are loose and contained in a pocket at the back of the book. This work also contains no. 123N. Later editions contain no. 144D and sectional maps from the same plates as no. 153.

State of the plate: Later than no. 129I. *West Pier* and railway 40 added.
Alterations on the transfer: As no. 129I, except that *Butser Hill* appears in full, *Balcombe* in full overlapping the border, *Dormans* and *Shadoxhurst* erased, *Grt. Cheyne* not added.

129 K.   ELEVENTH LITHOGRAPHIC TRANSFER

Size: 464 mm × 336 mm (2 mm)   1:259,000

The map is on one sheet. Title, inscriptions &c. completely revised and now read: *SURREY & SUSSEX* (Ca OS). *John Bartholomew & Co. Edin^r* (Ee OS). *Copyright.* (Ae OS). *SCALE OF 4 MILES TO AN INCH 8* = 50 mm (Ce).

> Issued about 1896 as a folding map with printed title on cover: *W.H. Smith and Sons series of reduced Ordnance maps for tourists by J. Bartholomew F.R.G.S. . . . Surrey & Sussex. Scale 4 miles to an inch.*
> London, W.H. Smith and Sons.   (SAS)

State of the plate: As no. 129J.
Alterations on the transfer: Title, signature, *Copyright* and scale added. Border drawn round map and projecting place-names erased. On left border, *Langrish* appears in full, *Froxfield* wholly erased, *Hayling Island* overlaps border. This transfer covers Sussex as far east as *Udimore* and extends north to *London*.

129 L.   TWELFTH LITHOGRAPHIC TRANSFER

Size: 588 mm × 240 mm (2 mm)   1:257,000

Title, inscriptions &c. completely revised and now read: *COUNTY OF SUSSEX* (Ee). *John Bartholomew & Co. Edin^r.* (Ee OS). *SCALE 4 MILES TO AN INCH 8* = 50 mm (Ee, under title). *Copyright* (Ae OS). Key to *Driving & Cycling Routes, Other Roads, County Boundaries* and *Railways* (Ee, under scale). A number of changes on the map, eg in the *BRIGHTON* area, *Steyne, Light, Black Rock, RAISED BEACH* and *West Pier* omitted; *Electric Railway* added; *Pier* and *Electric Railway* are now the only lettering in the sea near *BRIGHTON*. Railway from *CHICHESTER* to *Selsey Beach Station* added; projected lines erased. *Sta.* added to *Lewes R^d*. Driving and cycling routes coloured brown.

> *Sussex by F.G. Brabant. M.A. . .*
> London, Methuen and Co., 1900.   BL
> This work also contains no. 155.

State of the plate: Later than no. 129K. *Electric Railway* added and other changes made on the map. Railways altered.
Alterations on the transfer: Title, signature, scale, *Copyright* and key added. Border drawn round map and projecting place-names erased. The left border extended to include *PORTSMOUTH: Thorpe* (9 mm north of *Froxfield*) omitted; top border extended to include *TUNBRIDGE;* right border extended to include *Dymchurch,* the county boundary extended and *Fairfield* erased and replaced by *Brookland;* bottom border extended, detail added includes *ENGLISH CHANNEL.*

130   SEELEY, JACKSON AND CO. and S.W. PARTRIDGE AND CO.   1870

Size: 50 mm × 31 mm (single line border)   1:2,550,000

The map is insufficiently detailed to determine the sources used in its compilation. It names fifteen towns and two rivers. East Grinstead is shown as *Grinstead.*

EDITION

SUSSEX (Ae, in double line frame).

> *The Children's Friend.*
> London, Seeley, Jackson and Co. and S.W. Partridge and Co. Issue for May 2, 1870.   BOD
> The map appears top right on page 68.
>   The whole page forms a hieroglyphical puzzle, which commences 'The Downs, a range of VERD[ANT] O[PEN] hills, form the most REM[ARK]ABLE [FEAT]URE in the county of [SUSSEX]. . . .' Drawings from engraved wood-blocks have been substituted for the words in brackets, and the map appears in place of [SUSSEX].

Based on the Old Series One Inch Ordnance Survey, appendix VI.1(a).

William Borrer[1] (1814–98), the author of *The birds of Sussex* (see no. 131L below) lived at Cowfold. He was the son of the distinguished botanist, William Borrer (1781–1862) of Henfield, and a member of a long established Sussex family. They were the owners of Pakyns Manor House, which had been purchased by his great-grandfather, and at which his grand-daughter, Mrs. Orlebar, lived until her death in 1953. William Borrer himself did not live at Pakyns because it had been let by his father to the latter's brother, Nathanial, for a period of forty years. Borrer was a founder member of Sussex Archaeological Society.

The plate from which the following lithographic transfers were taken was apparently never used for direct intaglio printing.

131 A. FIRST LITHOGRAPHIC TRANSFER

Size: 197 mm × 145 mm (3 mm)   1:629,000

THE COUNTY OF SUSSEX (Aa). *PHILIPS' EDUCATIONAL SERIES OF COUNTY MAPS.* (Ca OS). *GEORGE PHILIP & SON LONDON & LIVERPOOL.* (Ce OS). *English Miles 10 = 26 mm* (Aa, under title). *Parliamentary Divisions I. WEST 2. EAST* and key to *Railways, Roads* and *Canals* (Aa, under scale). Longitude 30' (10'); latitude 30' (10'). Railways 1 to 14, 16 to 31. Overprinted to produce colours yellow, pink, buff and blue.

The geography of Sussex, for use in schools, by Rev. J.P. Faunthorpe, M.A. F.R.G.S. vice-principal of S.John's College, Battersea . . .
London, George Philip and Son, 1872.   BL.CUL
The work was reissued in 1876, but the known copy (Worthing RL) lacks the map.
    The work also contained two small sketch maps of Sussex which do not justify separate entries in the catalogue: **(i) On page 6.** 77 mm × 38 mm (1 mm). One mile = 0.7 mm approximately. §2. Hills (Ca OS). The map marks the main ranges, eg *SOUTH DOWNS*, rivers, and a few towns (nine in Sussex). *NOTES.* (below the map) includes *I.* key, with numbers *1* to *12*, to the major hills in the county, and *II.* a note to the effect that figures in the sea express the average depth in feet and the rise of the tide. The text below the map starts *A. SOUTH DOWNS.* **(ii) On page 13.** 78 mm × 39 mm (1 mm). One mile = 0.7 mm approximately. The main geological formations are named; also a few towns, eg *BOGNOR.* Three fishing areas are indicated. There is text above and below the map.

State of the plate: As originally engraved.
Alterations on the transfer: Heading (Ca OS) added.

1. *SAC.* vol. 11 (1859); *SCM.* no. 9 (1935), p. 468; Lower, 1865.

131 B.   SECOND LITHOGRAPHIC TRANSFER

Size: 197 mm × 145 mm (3 mm)   1:629,000

Heading (Ca OS) and imprint (Ce OS) omitted. *BUTCHER & CO'S SERIES OF DIRECTORY MAPS.* added (Ca OS). *LONDON: ST. PAUL'S CHAMBERS, PATERNOSTER ROW, E.C.* added (Ce OS). Coloured as no. 131A.

> *Butcher & Co's borough of Portsmouth directory . . . for 1874–75.*
> London, Butcher and Co., [1874].   BL

State of the plate: As no. 131A.
Alterations on the transfer: Heading (Ca OS) added. Imprint (Ce OS) erased and new imprint added.

131 C.   THIRD LITHOGRAPHIC TRANSFER

Size: 197 mm × 145 mm (3 mm)   1:629,000

Heading (Ca OS) omitted. Imprint (Ce OS) as no. 131A. Plate number *33* added (Ee OS, sideways) and on back. Overprinted to produce colours as no. 131A.

> *Philips' handy atlas of the counties of England, by John Bartholomew, F.R.G.S.*
> London and Liverpool, George Philip and Son, 1873.   BL.CUL.W

State of the plate: As no. 131A and B.
Alterations on the transfer: Plate number (Ee OS) added.

131 D.   FOURTH LITHOGRAPHIC TRANSFER

Size: 197 mm × 145 mm (3 mm)   1:629,000

Plate number *33* (Ee OS) erased and added (Ea OS). Overprinted to produce colours as no. 131A. No plate number on back.

> *Philips' handy atlas of the counties of England . . .*
> London and Liverpool, George Philip and Son, 1874.   W

State of the plate: As no. 131A, B and C.
Alterations on the transfer: Plate number (Ea OS) added.

131 E. FIFTH LITHOGRAPHIC TRANSFER

Size: 197 mm   145 mm (3 mm)   1:629,000

Graticule added at 10' intervals with reference letters *A* to *K* horizontally and *1* to *4* vertically. *Southwater* and *Faygate* added. Railway 32 added. *Sta.* added in key (Aa, below title), but not on map. Overprinted to produce colours yellow, blue and pink; east and west Sussex outlined in red.

> *Philips handy atlas of the counties of England: new and revised edition, with a consulting index. By John Bartholomew, F.R.G.S.*
> London and Liverpool, George Philip and Son, 1876 and 1877.   BL.CUL.BOD;P

State of the plate: Later than no. 131A–D. All the above additions have been made on the plate.
Alterations on the transfer: Plate number (Ea OS) added.

131 F. SIXTH LITHOGRAPHIC TRANSFER

Size: 197 mm × 145 mm (3 mm)   1:629,000

No plate number. *10 PATERNOSTER SQUARE, LONDON* added. (Ce OS), in place of Philips imprint. Heading *EYRE BROTHERS' SERIES OF GUIDE MAPS* added (Ca OS). Overprinted to produce colours yellow, pink, orange and blue. The back carries advertisements and page numbers *29* and *32*.

> *Eyre's shilling county guide . . . of Sussex.*
> London, Eyre Brothers, 1878.   SAS.WSCL

State of the plate: As no. 131E.
Alterations on the transfer: Imprint (Ce OS) erased. Heading (Ca OS) and new imprint (Ce OS) added.

131 G. SEVENTH LITHOGRAPHIC TRANSFER

Size: 198 mm × 146 mm (3 mm)   1:629,000

Imprint (Ce OS) erased and replaced by *GEORGE PHILIP & SON LONDON & LIVERPOOL* as on no. 131E. Heading (Ca OS) omitted. Plate number *33* (Ea OS) as on no. 131E. Railway N added. Map overprinted to produce colours yellow, pink, blue and orange. Back plain.

> *Philips' hand atlas of the counties of England . . .*
> London and Liverpool, George Philip and Son, [1878] and 1879.   P;P

Philips' handy atlas of the counties of England: by John Bartholomew, F.R.G.S.
New and enlarged edition, with consulting index.
London and Liverpool, George Philip and Son, 1880. NORWICH PL

State of the plate: Later than no. 131F. Railway added.
Alterations on the transfer: Plate number added.

131 H.   EIGHTH LITHOGRAPHIC TRANSFER

Size: 197 mm × 145 mm (3 mm)   1:629,000

Plate number *33* (Ea OS) re-engraved, the centre point on each 3 now has a distinctive
downwards slope. Railways 15, 34, 35, 36, 37, 38, 39 and P added. Map overprinted to
produce colours yellow, blue and two shades of pink.

Philips' handy atlas of the counties of England. By John Bartholomew, F.R.G.S.
New and enlarged edition, with consulting index.
London and Liverpool, George Philip and Son, 1882. W

State of the plate: Later than no. 131G. Plate number and railways added.
Alterations on the transfer: None.

131 I.   NINTH LITHOGRAPHIC TRANSFER

Size: 197 mm × 145 mm (3 mm)   1:629,000

Parliamentary Divisions 1. WEST 2. EAST (Aa, under title) erased. *The Colouring*
represents the Parliamentary Divisions each returning 1 member added (Aa, under title).
Pagham Har. erased and the coastline straightened. The six parliamentary divisions are
marked and named, eg *N.W. OR HORSHAM.* Map overprinted to produce colours
green, pink, brown, yellow, purple and blue.

Philips' handy atlas of the counties of England . . . Reduced from the Ordnance
Survey, and coloured to shew the new parliamentary divisions, according to the
Redistribution Bill, 1885. New and revised edition . . .
London and Liverpool, George Philip and Son, 1885 and 1886.   BL.RGS;BL
In the 1886 edition, *SUSSEX* has been printed from type on the back of the map.

State of the plate: Later than no. 131H. Key amended. Note about colouring added
(Aa). Parliamentary divisions marked and named. *Pagham Har.* erased.
Alterations on the transfer: None.

131 J.   TENTH LITHOGRAPHIC TRANSFER

Size: 197 mm × 145 mm (3 mm)   1:629,000

As no. 131I.

> *Philips' handy atlas of the counties of England . . .*
> London and Liverpool, George Philip and Son, 1887.   BL.CUL

State of the plate: As no. 131I.
Alterations on the transfer: None. (This transfer can be identified by a scratch running 7 mm NNW from a point 13 mm from the top of the outer left border.)

131 K.   ELEVENTH LITHOGRAPHIC TRANSFER

Size: 198 mm × 146 mm (3 mm)   1:629,000

Railways 41 and 42 added. Colours as no. 131I.

> *Philips' handy atlas of the counties of England . . .*
> London and Liverpool, George Philip and Son, 1891.   P

State of the plate: Later than no. 131J. Railways added.
Alterations on the transfer: None.

131 L.   TWELFTH LITHOGRAPHIC TRANSFER

Size: 198 mm × 146 mm (3 mm)   ⚓ 1:629,000

Imprint (Ce OS) omitted. *George Philip & Son London & Liverpool* added (Ee OS).
Plate number erased.

> *The birds of Sussex. By William Borrer, M.A., F.L.S.*
> London, R.H. Porter, 1891.   BL.HASTINGS PL.EASTBOURNE PL

State of the plate: As no. 131K.
Alterations on the transfer: Imprint (Ce OS) erased and new imprint added (Ee OS).
Plate number erased.

131 M.   THIRTEENTH LITHOGRAPHIC TRANSFER

Size: 197 mm × 145 mm (3 mm)   1:629,000

Imprint (Ce OS) as no. 131K. Imprint (Ee OS) omitted. Plate number *33* (Ea OS). Railways in Sussex as no. 131K; 1 to 32, 34 to 39, 41 and 42 are now marked. Map overprinted to produce colours green, pink, two shades of yellow and two shades of blue.

> *Philips' handy atlas of the counties of England . . .*
> London and Liverpool, George Philip and Son, 1893.   W

State of the plate: As no. 131K.
Alterations on the transfer: None.

131 N.   FOURTEENTH LITHOGRAPHIC TRANSFER

Size: 197 mm × 147 mm (3 mm)   1:629,000

Note commencing *Note. Railway Stations* . . . added (Aa, above key). Key lowered to level of *GUILDFORD*. The boundaries of the parliamentary boroughs of *BRIGHTON* and *HASTINGS* now marked and coloured. Part of railway line west of *GUILDFORD* erased. A number of place-names added, eg *Ifield, Southwick Sta. West Brighton Sta; Sta* added at many places in Sussex, eg *Southwater Sta; Crawley* re-engraved. Railway 33 added. Map overprinted to produce colours green, pink, brown, blue, and two shades of yellow.

> *Philips' handy atlas of the counties of England . . . New and enlarged edition, shewing every railway station in England and Wales . . .*
> London and Liverpool, George Philip and Son, 1895 and [1896].   BL.CUL.BOD;SAS

> *Philips' handy atlas of the counties of England . . .*
> London, George Philip and Son; Liverpool, Philip, Son and Nephew, 1898.   P
> A later edition of this work (P), undated, but probably after 1900, contains the same map with railway 43 added.

State of the plate: Later than no. 131M. Probably including all the alterations noted above.
Alterations on the transfer: Probably none.

132   VINCENT BROOKS, DAY AND SON   circa **1872**

Size: 179 mm × 135 mm (3 mm)   1:682,000

Possibly based on Cary no. 61E or a derivative.

David Thomas Ansted F.R.S. (1814–81), the author, was a professional geologist.

EDITION

THE COUNTY OF SUSSEX (Ea). *Vincent Brooks Day & Son, Lith* (Ee OS). *CASSELL'S COUNTY GEOGRAPHIES.* (Ca OS). Key (Eb, under title). Railways 1 to 14 and 16 to 31 marked by continuous lines and named in capitals; 35 and a line from *Pulborough* to *Steyning* marked by pecked lines. Longitude 10'; latitude 10'.

County geographies by D.T. Ansted, M.A., F.R.S. . . Sussex.
London, Paris and New York, Cassell, Petter and Galpin, [1872].   BL.CUL
The date has been taken from the British Library copy, which was received on 9 July 1872.

133   F. BRYER   **1874**

Based on Old Series One Inch Ordnance Survey, appendix no. VI.1(a).

The maps were also issued as loose sheets, sold separately. The advertisement in the 1882 edition of *Kelly's directory* reads 'The maps are sold separately at the following prices:– Plain Sheet . . . 2 s 0d/On Roller . . . 4s 0d/In Case . . . 5s 0d'.

Earlier editions of Kelly's directories covering Sussex contain nos. 115 A to K.

The plate from which the following lithographic transfers were taken was probaby never used for direct intaglio printing.

133 A.   FIRST LITHOGRAPHIC TRANSFER

Size: 960 mm × 630 mm (3 mm)   1:130,000

POST OFFICE MAP of SUSSEX, 1874. (Ee). *Engraved by E. Bryer, 19 Craven Street, Strand, London* (Ee OS). *J.M. Johnson & Sons, Steam & Chromo Printers, 56, Hatton Garden, E.C.* (Ae OS). *Kelly & Co. Post Office Directory Office, 51 Gᵗ. Queen Street, London. W.C.* (Ce OS). *SCALE OF MILES 10* = 125 mm (Ee, under title). Compass (Cd). *EXPLANATORY NOTE.* including *934,006 acres* and *417,456 Inhabitants, Reference to the Rapes,* and to parliamentary representation (Ce, under compass). Railways 1 to 32.

Probably produced as a proof in readiness for inclusion in Kelly's directories, although the directories covering Sussex for 1874 and 1878 contain no. 115J to K.

State of the plate: As originally engraved.
Alterations on the transfer: Johnson imprint (Ae OS) added.

133 B.   SECOND LITHOGRAPHIC TRANSFER

Size: 960 mm × 630 mm (3 mm)   1:130,000

Title (Ee) erased and replaced by *SUSSEX. E. Bryer* (Ee OS) altered to *F. Bryer.*
Johnson imprint (Ae OS) omitted. In the *EXPLANATORY NOTE* (Ce), *Inhabitants*
altered to *490,316.* Railways 33 to 38 added.

> *Kelly's directory of the six home counties . . . with large maps engraved expressly*
> *for the work. Edited by E.R. Kelly, M.A., F.S.S.* vol. 2.
> London, Kelly and Co., 1882.   BL

> *Kelly's directory of Sussex, with large map engraved expressly for the work. Edited*
> *by E.R. Kelly, M.A., F.S.S.*
> London, Kelly and Co., 1882.
> This is the Sussex section from the previous work with new title-page, but unaltered pagination. In the
> only copy examined (Brighton PL) the map is missing.

State of the plate: Later than no. 133A. All alterations listed above have been made on
the plate.
Alterations on the transfer: None.

133 C.   THIRD LITHOGRAPHIC TRANSFER

Size: 960 mm × 630 mm (3 mm)   1:130,000

Bryer signature (Ee OS) erased.

> *Kelly's directory of Sussex. With large map engraved expressly for the work.*
> London, Kelly and Co., 1887.   BRIGHTON PL

> *Kelly's directory of Kent, Surrey and Sussex . . .*
> London, Kelly and Co., 2nd edn., [1887].   ESRO

State of the plate: Later than no. 133B. Signature (Ee OS) erased.
Alterations on the transfer: None.

133 D.   FOURTH LITHOGRAPHIC TRANSFER

Size: 960 mm × 630 mm (3 mm)   1:130,000

In the *EXPLANATORY NOTE* (Ce, under compass) *Inhabitants* altered to *490,505.* *Friars Bay* added near *Newhaven. Pier* at *Eastbourne* re-engraved; it now points south-east. Railways 39, 41 and 42 added.

> *Kelly's directory of Sussex. With large map engraved expressly for the work.*
> London, Kelly and Co., 1890 and 1891.   GL;GL
> Both copies in the GUILDHALL LIBRARY have the title-page missing. A copy of the 1890 edition in
> BRIGHTON PL has the title-page, but lacks the map.

State of the plate: Later than no. 133C., including all alterations noted above.
Alterations on the transfer: None.

133 E.   FIFTH LITHOGRAPHIC TRANSFER

Size: 960 mm × 633 mm (3 mm)   1:130,000

Imprint (Ce OS) now *London — Kelly & Cº. Ltd. Directory Offices, 182 to 184 High Holborn, W.C. Charles Hooper & CO., Ld., White Hart Court, and Alderman's Walk, London, E.C.* added (Ae OS). Other additions include *River Arun, West Brighton, Pier* (at *Sᵗ. Leonards on Sea*), road to *Signal Ho. (Selsey Bill). Camber Castle* in place of *Winchelsea Castle. Middleton Ledge* erased.

> *Kelly's directory of Sussex . . .*
> London, Kelly and Co., 1895.   GL

State of the plate: Later than no. 133D. Imprint (Ce OS) erased. Place-names &c. added and erased.
Alterations on the transfer: New imprint added (Ce OS). Hooper imprint added (Ae OS).

133 F.   SIXTH LITHOGRAPHIC TRANSFER

Size: 960 mm × 630 mm (3 mm)   1:130,000

Title (Ee) and imprint (Ae OS) omitted. Imprint (Ce OS) altered to *London — Kelly's Directories Limited, 182 to 184 High Holborn. W.C.* In the *EXPLANATORY NOTE* (Ce), area altered from *934,006* to *933,269* acres, reference to parliamentary representation altered to include key to *6 divisions,* which are now outlined by pecked lines on the map and marked *A* to *F.* Some alterations on the map, eg *Bolmer* (near *Stanmer*) changed to *Balmer.* Railway 40 added. *SELSEY RAILWAY* added and

301

named; there are signs of re-engraving, an earlier route seems to have passed through the *b* of *Stockbridge*.

> *Kelly's directory of Sussex. With new map.*
> London, Kelly's Directories Limited, 1899.   BRIGHTON PL

State of the plate: Later than no. 133E. Key amended. Place-names altered. Railways added. Some of these alterations may have been made on the stone.
Alterations on the transfer: Probably the title erased and imprint (Ce OS) added.

134   EDWARD WELLER   circa 1875

Probably based on Bartholomew no. 124D.

William Collins, Sons and Company,[1] the publishers, was founded by William Collins (1789–1853), of Glasgow. Sir William Collins (1817–95) succeeded his father in 1853. He was Lord Provost of Glasgow in 1877–80 and was knighted in 1881. At one time he employed nearly 2000 persons.
The plate from which the following lithographic transfers were taken was apparently never used for direct intaglio printing

134 A.   FIRST LITHOGRAPHIC TRANSFER

Size: 201 mm × 154 mm (2 mm)   1:626,000

SUSSEX (Aa). *Edwd. Weller.* (Ee OS). *William Collins Sons & Co. London & Glasgow.* (Ce OS). *English Miles 10* = 26 mm (Aa, under title). Key to *Railways, Canals* and *Roads* (Aa, under scale). *The County coloured into its Parliamentary Divisions 1 Western Division 2 Eastern Do.* (Aa, under key). Railways 1 to 28 and 30. Overprinted to produce colours red, green and blue.

> *Collins' county geographies. Edited by W. Lawson, F.R.G.S. Geography of the county of Sussex . . .*
> London, William Collins, Sons & Co., [1875].   BL.CUL

State of the plate: As originally engraved.
Alterations on the transfer: None.

---

1.   Boase, 1965.

134 B.   SECOND LITHOGRAPHIC TRANSFER

Size: 201 mm × 154 mm (2 mm)   1:626,000

Weller signature (Ee OS) erased. Plate number *29* added (Ea OS, sideways). Plate number also appears on the back.

> *Collins' series of atlases. Atlas of England and Wales . . .*
> London, William Collins, Sons and Co., 1877 and [1877].   CUL;BL.CUL

State of the plate: Later than no. 134A. Signature erased.
Alterations on the transfer: Plate numbers probably added on the stone.

135   EDWARD STANFORD   1877

Based on Old Series One Inch Ordnance Survey, appendix VI.1(a).

The following lithographic transfers were taken from *A map of England & Wales . . . projected from the triangulation for the Survey made under the direction of the Honourable Board of Ordnance on a scale of five miles to an inch . . . Drawn by R. Creighton Engraved by J. Dower. London Edward Stanford . . . Additions in 1860.* This map had first been published in 1855.

Stanford's tourist guides to some other counties[1] contain transfers from *STANFORD'S LIBRARY MAP OF ENGLAND & WALES*, which, in the case of Sussex, was used for Stanford no. 139.

Chambers handy guide to the Kent and Sussex coast, 1863 (BRIGHTON PL) contains a map of south-east England.

135 A.   FIRST LITHOGRAPHIC TRANSFER

Size: 440 × 145 mm (2 mm)   1:316,000

A MAP to accompany the GUIDE TO SUSSEX (Ee). *London; Published by Edward Stanford, 55 Charing Cross.* (Ce OS). *Scale of Statute Miles* 5 + 10 = 50 mm (Ce). Grid (one line horizontally, two lines 225 mm apart vertically). Railways 1 to 14, 16 to 31; 15 shown as projected (plain double lines). Border interrupted at *Selsey.*

> *Handbook of the county of Sussex . . . by George F. Chambers, F.R.A.S. . . . with map and plan.*
> London, Edward Stanford, 1887.   BL.SAS

---

1. Harvey, 1959, no. 122; Hodson, 1974, no. 131.

State of the plate: As amended for the 1860 edition of *A map of England & Wales.*
Alterations on the transfer: Border drawn round map and projecting place-names erased. Place-names added, eg *Droxford, Soberton, Hambledon* near the left border, but omitted on later transfers. Title, scale and imprint added. Railways 20 to 31 added.

135 B.   SECOND LITHOGRAPHIC TRANSFER

Size: 440 mm × 145 mm (2 mm)   1:316,000

TO ACCOMPANY THE (Ee) now in capital letters. Imprint (Ce OS) re-engraved now 74 mm long (formerly 109 mm). *SCALE OF STATUTE MILES* now in capital letters, and scale-bar re-engraved. *Stanford's Geog[l]. Establish[t].* added (Ee OS). Left border moved inwards by 2 mm,[2] and many place-names omitted, eg *Meon Stoke. BEACHY HEAD* re-engraved to south of headland and border interrupted. *The Park, SELSEY BILL* added.

> *Tourist's guide to the county of Sussex . . . by George F. Chambers, F.R.A.S. . . with map and plan. Second edition.*
> London, Edward Stanford, 1880.   BL

State of the plate: As 135A.
Alterations on the transfer: Border drawn round map and projecting place-names erased. Title, scale and imprints added.

135 C.   THIRD LITHOGRAPHIC TRANSFER

Size: 440 mm × 145 mm (2 mm)   1:316,000

Railways 32 to 36 and 40 added; 37 and 38 shown as projected (pecked triple lines). Stars, indicating stations, have been added where appropriate on new lines, and one on an existing line at the *F* of *Farringdon.*

> *Tourist's guide to the county of Sussex . . .. 3rd edition.*
> London, Edward Stanford, 1883.   WSCL

State of the plate: Later than no. 135B. Railways and stars added.
Alterations on the transfer: As no. 135B.

---

2.   In spite of this change the horizontal dimension of most impressions examined remains 440 mm.

135 D. FOURTH LITHOGRAPHIC TRANSFER

Size: 440 mm × 145 mm (2 mm)   1:316,000

Railways 37 and 38, formerly shown as projected, now marked by continuous cross-hatched lines. Railway 42 added.

> *Tourist's guide to the county of Sussex . . . 4th edition.*
> London, Edward Stanford, 1887.   BL.SAS

State of the plate: Later than no. 135 C. Railways added and amended.
Alterations on the transfer: As no. 135B.

135 E. FIFTH LITHOGRAPHIC TRANSFER

Size: 440 mm × 145 mm (2 mm)   1:316,000

Imprint (Ce OS) altered to *London: Edward Stanford 26 & 27 Cockspur St. Charing Cross S.W. Devil's Dyke* added. Railway 41 and branch line to *South Sea Castle* added.

> *Tourist's guide to the county of Sussex . . . 5th edition.*
> London, Edward Stanford, 1891.   BL.HASTINGS PL

State of the plate: Later than no. 135D. *Devil's Dyke* and railways added.
Alterations on the transfer: As no. 135B.

136 EDWARD STANFORD   1881

Probably based on Old Series One Inch Ordnance Survey, appendix VI.1(a).

The following lithographic transfers appear to have been taken from the plate of a map of the whole of England and Wales, which has not been identified.

136 A. FIRST LITHOGRAPHIC TRANSFER

Size: 132 mm × 75 mm (3 mm)   1:973,000

MAP OF A COUNTY (Ca OS). *Stanford's Geog^l. Estab^t. London* (Ee OS). *ENG. STAT. MILES 20* = 33 mm (Ae OS). Longitude 0° only; latitude 51° only. Graticule, one vertical and one horizontal line only. *SUSSEX* is printed across the centre of the map. Railways 1 to 14 and 16 to 32. The map extends northwards as far as *Leatherhead*.

The London geographical series. Geographical readers for elementary schools. By Charlotte M. Mason. Book I for Standard II.
London, Edward Stanford, 1881.   BL
On the back of the map is page 81 of text, headed *MAP OF A COUNTY LESSON XXXII*. The map in this volume is given as an example of a county map. The work also contains a plan of Chichester as an example of a town plan. The actual map of Sussex is 136B in *Book III*.

State of the plate: Probably as originally engraved.
Alterations on the transfer: Border drawn round map and projecting place-names erased; *Hayling* extends into the border.

136 B.   SECOND LITHOGRAPHIC TRANSFER

Size: 138 mm × 79 mm (1 mm)   1:863,000

Title (Ca OS) omitted. Scale altered to *ENGLISH MILES 20* = 38 mm (Ae OS). The border reduced to a narrow double line, *51°* and *0°* omitted, but the two graticules remain. *ENGLISH CHANNEL* re-engraved, the C is now on the 0° graticule; on no. 136A it was to the right of the line. A number of place-names added, eg *Fairlight, Castle* at *Pevensey* and at *LEWES, Pevensey, Charterhouse, Holt Forest, Forest* at *Selborne, Bosham*. Place-names erased include *Havant, Maidstone, Leeds, Charing, Staplehurst*, and towns along the top border. *Selsey Bill* re-engraved to right of the headland. Two pecked lines running south from *Beachy Head* added. Railway 34 added. The map extends northwards as far as *Guildford*.

The London Geographical series. Geographical readers for elementary schools. By Charlotte M. Mason. Book III for standard IV . . . The counties of England.
London, Edward Stanford, 1881.   BL
On the back of the map is page 294 of text headed *SUSSEX*.

State of the plate: Later than no. 136 A. Scale altered, and probably other alterations on the map itself as noted above.
Alterations on the transfer: Border drawn round map and projecting place-names erased; the county outline now extends 8 mm beyond the right border and *Tenterden, Fairlight* and *HASTINGS* extend into the border.

136 C.   THIRD LITHOGRAPHIC TRANSFER

Size: 138 mm × 79 mm (1 mm)   1:863,000

EDITIONS

(i)   *SUSSEX* added (Ec OS, sideways). *50* added (Ee OS, sideways). The county is coloured yellow; the six parliamentary divisions are outlined and named in red, eg

HORSHAM. The parliamentary boroughs of *BRIGHTON* and *HASTINGS* are also marked; the former in a darker shade of yellow, the latter in red, which appears to have been added by hand. Figures indicating parliamentary representation have been altered, *B.2.* under HASTINGS altered to *B.1.; B.1.* under Rye to *B.; C.B.1* under Chichester to *C.B.* Railways 35, 36, 37, 38 and 42 added.

> *Stanford's handy atlas and poll book of the electoral divisions of Great Britain and Ireland.*
> London, Edward Stanford, 1886 (preface dated June 1886). BL

(ii) *1886* added (Ec, sideways and to the left of title). The borough of *HASTINGS* is now coloured, as is *BRIGHTON*, in dark yellow.

> *Stanford's handy atlas and poll book . . . 2nd edn.*
> London, Edward Stanford, 1886 (preface dated October 1886). BL

State of the plate: As no. 136B.
Alterations on the transfer: All alterations listed under (i) and (ii) above. Transfer identified by gap in outer line of bottom border, above *10* of scale.

137 STANFORD'S GEOGRAPHICAL ESTABLISHMENT
1881

Size: 287 mm × 124 mm (1 mm)   1:451,000

Probably based on *STANFORD'S LIBRARY MAP . . .* (See no. 139).

William Richard Wood Stephens (1839–1902), the author, was born in Gloucestershire. As a young man he travelled abroad with A.J. Symonds. Ordained in 1864, he became vicar of Mid Lavant in 1870, prebend of Wittering in 1875, rector of Woolbeding in 1876, and finally Dean of Winchester. He was an historian and biographer, and at one time a lecturer at Chichester Theological College. He died from typhoid fever.

The map seems to have been printed from a lithographic stone on which the design had been laid down from the original drawing and from type.

EDITION

A MAP TO ILLUSTRATE THE ANNALS OF THE SOUTH SAXON DIOCESE (Ed). *Published by the Society for Promoting Christian Knowledge.* (Ce OS). *Stanford's Geog^l. Estab^t.* (Ee OS). *English Miles 10 = 36 mm* (Ee, under title). *REFERENCE* (Ee, under scale).

Diocesan histories. The South Saxon diocese, Selsey — Chichester. By W.R.W. Stephens . . . with map and plan.
London, Society for promoting christian knowledge, 1881.   BL.SAS.HASTINGS PL

138   ORDNANCE SURVEY   1885

Based on material in possession of the Ordnance Survey.

The following lithographic transfers were taken from the plates of a larger map, which probably covered the whole of England and Wales. The precise order in which the transfers were taken is uncertain.

Similar Ordnance Survey maps on a scale of four inches to one mile are catalogued, see nos. 146 and 154. *Rye Bay* on this map is 13 mm long.

138. A   FIRST LITHOGRAPHIC TRANSFER

Size: 684 mm × 262 mm (48 mm top, 4 mm other borders)   1:188,000

SUSSEX. NEW DIVISIONS OF THE COUNTY. (Ca, in border). *R. Owen Jones L*[t] *Colonel R.E.* (Ee). *Zincographed at the Ordnance Survey Office, Southampton 1885.* (Ce OS). *Scale of this Index Three Miles to One Inch* 3 + 12 Miles = 103 mm (Ca, in border below title). *REFERENCE.* (Ed, above signature). Opposite each of the three items under *REFERENCE* are rectangles indicating the colours used on the map as follows: *Boundaries of proposed Parliamentary Divisions* — red, *Boundaries of Petty Sessional Divisions* — blue, *Parliamentary Boroughs* — mauve. The six parliamentary divisions and eighteen petty sessional divisions are outlined and named in red and blue respectively; the two boroughs are coloured mauve; the boundaries are marked by pecked or dotted lines; the names of the Parliamentary Divisions and the names and boundaries of the Petty Sessional Divisions have been added by overprinting; the boundaries of the Parliamentary Divisions and the areas of the Parliamentary Boroughs appear to have been hand-coloured. The sheet lines and numbers of the six inch and twenty-five inch maps are marked, but do not extend beyond the county boundary. Adjoining counties are not named. Railways 1 to 32.

Boundary Commission (England and Wales). Report of the Boundary Commissioners for England and Wales. 1885. Part I. — Counties. Presented to both Houses of Parliament by command of Her Majesty.
London, printed by Eyre and Spottiswoode, 1885.   BL.CUL.W
This forms Volume VI of *Reports from Commissioners, Inspectors, and others* for the parliamentary session of 23 October 1884–14 August 1885. Some impressions have a printer's mark (Ae OS, 22 mm below the border): +++6 (BL), +++4 (Worthing PL).

State of the plate: Apparently unrevised since about 1871, when railway 32 was opened.
Alterations on the transfer: Projecting place-names and detail outside the county

boundary erased, except *TUNBRIDGE WELLS* and *Emsworth*. Border, title, signature, key, imprint and scale added. Divisional names and boundaries overprinted. Sheet lines and sheet numbers probably added; although unerased traces of sheet lines remain visible in place-names engraved in the sea.

138 B.   SECOND LITHOGRAPHIC TRANSFER

Size: 684 mm × 262 mm (48 mm top, 4 mm other borders)   1:188,000

Under *REFERENCE* (Ed) the rectangle coloured blue has been erased and replaced by a black line; on the map, the boundaries of the *Petty Sessional Divisions* are now outlined in black. The names of the parliamentary and petty sessional divisions are also in black, in place of red and blue. The names of the six parliamentary divisions have been expanded, eg *HORSHAM DIVISION* is now *NORTH WESTERN OR HORSHAM DIVISION.*

> *Redistribution of Seats Act, 1885 (Contents of County Divisions) . . . County of Sussex.*
> London, Henry Hansard and Son 1885.   BL.W
> This forms part of volume XIX of parliamentary *Accounts and papers* for the session of 23 October 1884–14 August 1885. In the British Library impression, a piece of paper has been pasted over the word *proposed* in the item *Boundaries of proposed Parliamentary Divisions.*

State of the plate: As no. 138A.
Alterations on the transfer: As no. 138A, except that the divisional names and boundaries (in black) were probably added on the stone, rather than by overprinting.

138 C.   THIRD LITHOGRAPHIC TRANSFER

Size: 910 mm × 635 mm (the engraved area; no border)   1:190,000

Border, title, scale, signature, imprint and *REFERENCES* omitted. New title *INDEX to the ORDNANCE SURVEY OF THE COUNTY OF SUSSEX. ON THE SCALE OF SIX INCHES TO ONE STATUTE MILE = 1/10560.* added (Ca). There are two scale-bars, *Scale of this Index Three Miles to One Inch* 3 + 12 *Miles* = 102 mm, and *Scale of Ordnance Survey Six Inches to One Statute Mile — 1/10560 10 chains + 1 Mile/80 Chains* = 152 mm (Ce). *Engraved and transferred to zinc at the Ordnance Survey Office. Southampton. 1883.* added (Ce, below scales). *AREAS OF PARISHES.* (Ad to Ed, in panel 857 mm × 184 mm between map and scales). *REFERENCE BY LETTERS TO THE CINQUE PORT . . .* (Aa, in panel 258 mm × 163 mm). *CHARACTERS USED IN THE WRITING AND . . .* (Ea, in panel 173 mm × 177 mm). *References* (Ec, in panel 114 mm × 80 mm). *LIBERTY OF THE SLUICE* (Dd) erased. The names of the six parliamentary divisions omitted. The sheet lines are now marked in full, ie where applicable they extend beyond the county boundary. There is additional engraving to the west of *Chichester Harbour*. The three adjoining counties are named. The map is uncoloured.

Issued in 1883 as loose sheets sold separately.   (BL).(CUL).(RGS)

State of the plate: Later than nos. 138A and B. *LIBERTY OF THE SLUICE* erased. *Alterations on the transfer:* Projecting place-names and detail outside the county boundary, except *TUNBRIDGE WELLS, Emsworth* and some engraving west of *Chichester Harbour,* erased. Title, scales, imprint and the four panels added. Sheet lines and numbers probably added on the stone.

138 D.   FOURTH LITHOGRAPHIC TRANSFER

Size: 910 mm × 635 mm (the engraved area; no border)   1:190,000

Imprint (Ce) altered to *Engraved and Published at the Ordnance Survey Office Southampton 1882. Price Two Shillings and Sixpence uncoloured. Parliamentary divisions coloured, Three Shillings.* In *AREAS OF PARISHES* (Ad to Ed) the summary gives the totals for the whole county, whereas in no. 138C, the totals are given for the two divisions separately. The grand total is unchanged, but some of the detail has been amended, eg *Alfriston (part of)* in *LONGBRIDGE* hundred has been decreased from *1814.309* acres to *1811.749* acres; and part of the same parish in *ALCISTON* hundred has been increased from 630.957 acres to *633.517* acres. In *REFERENCE BY LETTERS TO THE CINQUE PORT . . .* (Aa) an additional line, starting n and ending k^3, has been added in the final column. In *References* (Ec) the six lines headed *SCALE OF PRICES* have been omitted and panel reduced to 114 mm × 38 mm *Note. The names and boundaries of the Parliamentary Divisions of the County shown on this index are those of the Act of 1885* added (Ed). A note commencing *Y & Z . . .* added (Bc). The six parliamentary divisions are named, eg *NORTH WESTERN OR HORSHAM DIVISION,* in hatched capitals (formerly in black capitals). *WESTERN DIVISION* and *EASTERN DIVISION* erased. All place-names outside the county boundary, except *Emsworth,* and the engraving west of *Chichester Harbour* erased. Sheet numbers *LXXII., 1* and *5* (twenty-five inch) erased.

Issued after 1885 as loose sheets sold separately.   (CUL).(WSRO)

State of the plate: As no. 138C.
Alterations on the transfer: Projecting place-names and all detail outside the county boundary, except *Emsworth,* erased. Title, Scale, imprint, the four panels and the notes (Ed and Bc) added. *WESTERN DIVISION* and *EASTERN DIVISION* erased. names of the parliamentary divisions added. Sheet lines and numbers probably added.

138 E. FIFTH LITHOGRAPHIC TRANSFER

Size: 800 mm × 420 mm (the engraved area; no border)   1:190,000

Title and all inscriptions and notes outside the county boundary omitted. New title *ENGLAND & WALES. DIAGRAM OF THE ADMINISTRATIVE COUNTIES OF EAST SUSSEX & WEST SUSSEX, Shewing Unions, Sanitary Districts, Boroughs and Civil Parishes; AND THE SHEET LINES OF THE ORDNANCE SURVEY MAPS OF SUSSEX, ON THE SCALE 25.344 INCHES TO 1 MILE (1/2500). SURVEYED IN 1869–75.* added (Ca). Scales as no. 138C. Imprint *Engraved and Published at the Ordnance Survey Office, Southampton 1900. Price 3/-. All rights of reproduction reserved.* added (Ce, below scales). *REFERENCE BY LETTER TO THE SMALL PARISHES* . . . added (Eb, in panel 143 mm × 93 mm). *A. ENLARGED SKETCH OF THE TOWN OF LEWES.* added (Ed, in panel 75 mm × 51 mm). *B. ENLARGED SKETCH OF A PORTION OF THE TOWN OF HASTINGS.* added (Be, in panel 77 mm × 51 mm). *REFERENCE* to colours added (Cd); followed by *N.B. The Boundaries on this Diagram are revised up to date (3.1.1900).* The six parliamentary divisions are not named. The names and boundaries of the rural and urban districts, the unions, the boroughs and the county boroughs are marked in colours according to the key. The six inch and twenty-five inch sheet lines extend beyond the county boundary, which has been amended. At the eastern extremity, the boundary now extends beyond sheets *XLVI.10* and *14; TUNBRIDGE WELLS* and *LAMBERHURST* erased and the boundary reduced, sheet numbers *VIII.13* and *14* omitted; in the north-west corner, the county area has been reduced and *BRAMSHOTT* erased. Names of hundreds, eg *MANHOOD*, erased. A number of other minor erasures, eg *UPPER BEEDING (Det), SOUTH* in *SOUTH BERSTED.* The map is overprinted to produce colours blue, brown, red, green and purple.

Issued about 1900 as loose sheets sold separately.   (CUL)

State of the plate: As no. 138C.
Alterations on the transfer: Projecting place-names and detail outside the county boundary erased, except *Emsworth*. Names of hundreds and other names erased on the map; although it is possible that the hundreds were never engraved on the plate and were added on the stone on all transfers. Title, scale, imprint, four panels and *REFERENCE* added.

Based on the Ordnance Survey.

The following lithographic transfer was taken from the plates of a map of the whole country entitled *STANFORD'S LIBRARY MAP OF ENGLAND & WALES*. This was first published about 1881 and Stanford's tourist guides for Hertfordshire[1] and Warwickshire[2] contain maps which are transfers from it. Stanford's tourist's guides for Sussex, however, contain no. 135.

139 A.   LITHOGRAPHIC TRANSFER

Size: 168 mm × 218 mm (4 mm)   1:480,000

SUSSEX. (Ca OS). *Stanford's Geographical Estab^t.* (Ee OS). *London: Edward Stanford, 55 Charing Cross.* (Ce OS). *SCALE OF MILES* 54 = 175 mm (Ae, in border. The scale is marked all round the border, 54 miles top and bottom, 73 miles at the sides). Plate numbers *67* and *II.3.* (Ee OS, sideways). The map is in two parts, west Sussex above and east Sussex below, within a single border. In addition to the title, *SUSSEX* is written across the map in two halves; and also across the borders, *SUS* (Ad) and *SEX* (Eb). The names and boundaries of the parliamentary divisions, the county boundaries, and diagonal shading (defining the boroughs of *BRIGHTON* and *HASTINGS*) have been overprinted in red. Other colouring is by hand.

> *Stanford's parliamentary county atlas and handbook of England and Wales . . .*
> London, Edward Stanford, 1885.   BL.RGS

State of the plate: As originally engraved.
Alterations on the transfer: Border drawn round map and projecting place-names erased, eg *Newhaven* in the top section. Title, signature, imprint, plate numbers and *SUS SEX* added.

1.   Hodson, 1974, no. 131.
2.   Harvey, 1959, no. 122.

140   JOHN BEAL AND SON

circa **1885**

Size: 427 mm × 790 mm (2 mm)

1:147,000

Based on New Series One Inch Ordnance Survey, appendix VI.1(b).

This map was probably printed from a lithographic stone on which the original design was laid down.

EDITION

JOHN BEAL & SON'S HUNTING & TOURISTS' MAP OF SUSSEX &c. Showing the Meets of the WARNHAM STAG HOUNDS, SOUTHDOWN, CRAWLEY AND HORSHAM, EAST SUSSEX, BURSTOW AND GOODWOOD FOXHOUNDS, And the BRIGHTON, BROOKSIDE AND EASTBOURNE HARRIERS (Ee). *Published by John Beal & Son, 55 East Street, Brighton (Registered).* (Ce OS). *Scale of Miles* 1/2 + 10 = 105 mm (Ee). Key to the colours of county boundaries (Ce). The meets are shown by variously shaped, coloured and numbered symbols. Red arcs mark distances from *BRIGHTON* at four mile intervals. Overprinted to produce colours red, blue, green and yellow.

> *The Brighton and Sussex hunting map and map of the environs of Brighton showing . . .*
> Brighton, John Beal and Son, [1885].   (BL).(BOD).(SAS)
> The map was received by the British Museum in 1885. The pamphlet includes a key to the meets and other information on the map. Another hunting map by the same publisher (no. 145B) has the same title-page with only the price altered.

141   J. WEST

1885[1]

Size: 371 mm × 151 mm (2 mm)

1:338,000

Possibly based on Bartholomew no. 124K.

This map was printed from a lithographic stone on which the design was probably laid down directly from a drawing. The circumstances surrounding the publication of this map are obscure. No other map in the series has been found, and no other maps by J. West are known. A very different series of archaeological maps of several counties was published between 1889 and 1902,[2] but Sussex was not included.

---

1. Noted in *Proceedings of the Royal Geographical Society* vol. 7 (1885), p. 697, 'Price 6d.'
2. Hodson, 1974, no. 130D.

AN ARCHAEOLOGICAL MAP OF SUSSEX shewing all the Manor Houses, Priories, Churches, Ruined Abbeys, Palaces & Castles, British or Roman Remains, and other objects of interest in this county with the nearest railway station. (Ee). *Designed, drawn & published by J. West 5 Fenchurch Street, London. E.C. Copyright.* (Ee, under title). *Where unassociated with any object of interest the names of Railway Stations are omitted as also churches whose interest has not survived "restoration"* (Ce). This an outline map marking only places of interest as described in the title, and railways 1 to 38.

Issued in 1885 as loose maps, sold separately. (RGS)

142   FREDERICK ERNEST SAWYER   1886

Size: 302 mm × 207 mm (6 mm)   1:467,000

Probably based on *STANFORD'S LIBRARY MAP* . . . see no. 139.

F.E. Sawyer (1852–91), F.S.A., F.R. Met. Soc., was a Brighton man; his grandfather, G.W. Sawyer, had been an alderman. He was educated at Brighton Grammar School, qualified as a solicitor, and practised in Ship Street. He married May Weston in 1887 and left a son, George. He was a prolific contributor to *Sussex archaeological collections* (including a Sussex bibliography) and to learned journals and newspapers. His primary interest was meteorology, but he was also a knowledgeable antiquarian and edited some of Black's Sussex guides. He was instrumental in dispelling certain local myths regarding the escape of Charles II. He suffered from asthma, which accounted for his early death.

The map described below gives the impression that the northern part of the county was virtually uninhabited at that time. This was not in fact the case. There were settlements in much of the weald; but being 'dependent' on holdings in the southern part of the county, they were not recorded separately in Domesday.[1]

EDITION

DOMESDAY SUSSEX (Ee). *F.E. Sawyer, F.S.A. del^t.* (Ee, under title). *Stanford's Geog^l. Estab^t.* (Ee OS). *Scale of English Stat. Miles 20 = 65 mm* (Ee, under signature). Key, three items (Ee, under scale). Longitude 1°, latitude 1°.

Domesday book in relation to the county of Sussex . . . by W.D. Parish . . .
Lewes, H. Wolff, 1866.   BL.SAS.ESCL
The southern part of each rape has been coloured by hand, using five colours, which correspond on all copies examined. It would appear that some form of template was used to assist the colourists.

1. Brandon, 1978, p. 204.

142 A. LITHOGRAPHIC TRANSFER

Size: 165 mm × 64 mm (the engraved area; no border)   1:728,000

Title, signature, scale, key, border and most detail outside the county boundary erased, together with part of Sussex in the Rye area. New title *DOMESDAY SUSSEX (compiled from Domesday Book by the late M*ʳ*. F.E. Sawyer F.S.A. an Old Boy who has left his mark in the school Annals).* added from type (along bottom of map). Page number *6* (Ec, to right of map).

> *Past and present. The magazine of the Brighton grammar school. Edited by H.A. Payne.* vol. 30.
> Brighton, "Published at the School", 1895.   HOVE PL

State of the plate: Probably as originally engraved.
Alterations on the transfer: It is probable that all alterations noted above were made on the stone.

143 ORDNANCE SURVEY   circa **1886**

Based on New Series One Inch Ordnance Survey, appendix VI.1(b).

This map was produced by photolithography from Ordnance Survey one inch sheets measuring 12" × 18", which were joined together for the purpose. These photographic reproductions were laid down on three lithographic stones measuring about 39" × 24". The vertical and horizontal lines, along which the original Ordnance Survey sheets were joined can be detected, eg to the right of and below *Pevensey Bay*. In edition (ii) a fourth stone was used for the area of Sussex lying east of *RYE*, and additional stones were used for the town plans. The sheets did not always match up; for example, *Sᵀ. ANNE,* west of *LEWES,* appears as *Sᵀ. ANᴺᴺE.*

W.T. Pike, the publishers, specialised in the publication of directories at Brighton and Hastings from 1872 to 1889. The business then continued as Robinson, Son and Pike.

Harry and Charles Treacher, publishers of the second edition below, flourished in Brighton from the 1850s[1] to 1926, and the name continues today as Holleyman and Treacher, the distinguished antiquarian booksellers.

This map may be the 'pirated' edition of the Ordnance Survey map referred to by Stanford.[2] In 1886, he complained 'I brought a very flagrant case of piracy before the controller of H.M. Stationery Office. The new 1-inch map of Sussex had been reproduced on the same scale by photolithography, and was being sold, in Brighton and

---

1. Melville's *Directory* for 1858 gives the address as 1 North Street.
2. Stanford, 1891, p. 25.

elsewhere, at about half the price of the real Ordnance map. No steps were taken by Government, pour encourager les autres'. He clearly had desperate remedies in mind. Stanford had then been agent for the Ordnance Survey for two years.

143 A. LITHOGRAPHIC TRANSFER

Size: 1865 mm × 995 mm (27 mm)   1:64,100

EDITIONS

(i) *ORDNANCE MAP OF SUSSEX SHOWING THE NEW PARLIAMENTARY DIVISIONS, BOROUGHS, PARISHES, RAILWAYS AND STATIONS &c.* (Ce). *SCALE 4 MILES* = 100 mm (Ce, below title). *Published by W.T. PIKE,at the office of the "SUSSEX BLUE BOOK", 62 Queen's Road, HASTINGS.* (Ce, below scale). *Plan of HASTINGS. Scale of one Mile* 2000 ft = 77 mm (Ee, in panel). *Plan of BRIGHTON. Scale of one Mile* 2000 ft = 93 mm (Ae, in panel).

Issued about 1886 as a folding or wall map.
Hastings, W.T. Pike.   (WSRO)

(ii) Title, scale, imprint, town plans and border omitted. Border, 5 mm wide, added round three sides of map; along the bottom a strip of paper has been pasted on and the border completed in ink. The dimensions, excluding border, are now 1865 mm × 795 mm. Above the map are four panels: *TREACHER'S NEW MAP OF SUSSEX FROM THE NEW ORDNANCE SURVEY REVISED TO DATE SHOWING THE NEW PARLIAMENTARY DIVISIONS, BOROUGHS, PARISHES, RAILWAYS, STATIONS, &c. Scale — 1 Inch to a Mile* 1 + 4 = 101 mm. *Published by H. & C. TREACHER THE ROYAL LIBRARY, BRIGHTON* (Ea OS, in panel 254 mm × 385 mm); *PLAN OF TUNBRIDGE WELLS Scale* ¼ *of a Mile* = 56 mm (Aa OS, in panel 254 mm × 330 mm); *PLAN OF BRIGHTON & HOVE Scale of a* ¼ *Mile 2 furlongs* = 40 mm (Ba OS, in panel 254 mm × 570 mm); *PLAN OF HASTINGS & St. LEONARDS Scale of* ¼ *Mile 2 furlongs* = 52 mm (Da OS, in panel 254 mm × 535 mm). Some minor additions have been made to the map, eg *The Hall* added (under *Ovingdean*). A panel containing the area east of *RYE* added (Ee, 173 mm × 128 mm, with 4 mm border).

Issued about 1886 as a folding map with embossed title on cover: *Treacher's new map of Sussex.*
Brighton, H. and C. Treacher.   (SAS).(WORTHING PL)

State of the one inch sheets: The map, excluding the continuation east of *RYE*, is compiled from sheets 300 to 304, 316 to 320 and 331 to 334, which were first published between 1876 and 1882; and minor revisions, mainly railways, were made prior to publication of the fully revised edition in 1895–6. The *RYE* continuation is from sheet 321, published in 1880. The latest available sheet seems to have been used in each case, eg the south-west section is from an edition of sheet 331, which was from an electrotype taken in 1884. Ordnance Survey maps were also used for the town plans.

Alterations on the transfer: Ordnance Survey border, longitude and latitude and all information outside the border erased or cut off before photographing. Alternate spaces 'blacked-in' on cross hatched railway lines. Station names added in black capitals, eg *HORSTED KEYNES.* Parliamentary divisions named, eg *HORSHAM,* Minor changes on the map, eg *Coast Guard Sta.* added (somewhat smudged) east of *BRIGHTON, River Cuckmere* re-engraved (*River* is now to the south of *Exceat Br.*), *Station* erased at *Willingdon. The Hall* added on edition (ii). (It is possible that these alterations were made on a later edition of sheet 333, which the compiler has not found.)

144   JOHN BARTHOLOMEW   1887

This map appears to be based on Bartholomew no. 129.

The plate from which the following lithographic transfers were taken was apparently never used for direct intaglio printing. Besides the issues catalogued below, there were several other issues of the ninth edition of *Encyclopaedia Britannica* between 1890 and 1900 which have not been traced, but which probably contained this map.

144 A.   FIRST LITHOGRAPHIC TRANSFER

Size: 237 mm × 164 mm (4 mm)   1:543,000

SUSSEX. (Ca OS). *J. Bartholomew* (Ee OS). *ENCYCLOPAEDIA BRITANNICA, NINTH EDITION* (Ce OS). *Scale of Miles 10* = 30 mm (Ee). *PLATE XI.* (Ea OS). *VOL. XXII.* (Aa OS). *Page 723* (Ae OS). Key to *Parliamentary Divisions* (Ee, above scale). Longitude 10'; latitude 10'. Railways 1 to 32, 34 to 38, A to R. Overprinted to produce colours brown, pink and blue.

> The encyclopaedia Britannica. A dictionary of arts, sciences, and general literature.
> 9th edn. vol. 22.
> Edinburgh, Adam and Charles Black, 1887.   BL.CUL

State of the plate: As originally engraved.
Alterations on the transfer: Title and inscriptions outside the border added.

144 B.   SECOND LITHOGRAPHIC TRANSFER

Size: 237 mm × 164 mm (4 mm)   1:543,000

SUSSEX. (Ca OS) as no. 144A. Signature (Ee OS) erased and replaced by *John*

317

Bartholomew & Co.. Imprint (Ce OS), plate number (Ea OS), volume number (Aa OS) and page number (Ae OS) omitted. *Black's Handy Atlas of England & Wales* (Aa OS), *The Edinburgh Geographical Institute* (Ae OS), *Published By A. & C. Black, London* (Ce OS) and *Plate 41* (Ea OS) added. In the key (Ee), *1885* added after *Parliamentary Divisions,* and *Boroughs, 7. Brighton 8. Hastings* added to the list. *Harb Sta* and *Newhaven Harbour, L. Ho* (at *Beachey Head*) and *Devil's Dyke* added. *Seaford Bay* erased. Railways 33, 39, 41, 42 and S added; all lines except 22, to *Littlehampton,* are now marked by heavy black lines. Overprinted to produce colours green, yellow, red and two shades of blue. The six parliamentary divisions are outlined in colour. *SUSSEX* and *Plate 41* appear on the back of map.

> *Black's handy atlas of England & Wales. A series of county maps and plans with descriptive index and statistical notes edited by John Bartholomew, F.R.G.S. &c.*
> London, Adam and Charles Black, 1892.   BL.BOD.CUL

State of the plate: Later than no. 144A. Parliamentary boroughs outlined and numbered on map. Place-names added and erased as above. Railways added.
Alterations on the transfer: Title and inscriptions outside border added. Black lines drawn over railway lines.

144 C.   THIRD LITHOGRAPHIC TRANSFER

Size: 237 mm × 164 mm (4 mm)   1:543,000

Title and inscriptions outside border as no. 144A. except that the full-stop is omitted at end of title, and Bartholomew signature (Ee OS) replaced by *W. & A.K. Johnston. Page 723* (Ae OS) is in a different style. The boroughs of *Brighton* and *Hastings* are not referred to in the key or numbered on the map, but the dotted outlines of the boundaries remain. Railways 1 to 39, 41, 42 and A to S (as on no. 144B) are not overprinted in black, but are marked (as on no. 144A) by cross-hatched double lines. Overprinted to produce colours brown, pink and blue. The whole county is now coloured in brown.

> *Encyclopaedia Britannica . . .* 9th edn. vol. 11.
> Edinburgh, Adam and Charles Black, 1887 (actually a reissue made in 1899).   P

State of the plate: As no. 144B.
Alterations on the transfer: Title and inscriptions outside border added. Reference to parliamentary boroughs erased.

144 D. FOURTH LITHOGRAPHIC TRANSFER

Size: 239 mm × 164 mm (4 mm)   1:543,000

SUSSEX (Ca OS) as on no. 144C. *J. Bartholomew* (Ee OS), and scale as no. 144A. *Published by A. & C. Black, London.* (Ce OS) as no. 144B. All other inscriptions omitted. Key to *Parliamentary Divisions* (Ee) and numbers *1* to *6* on map erased. Railways as no. 144C. Overprinted in pink to mark county boundary.

> *Black's guide to Sussex and its watering-places . . . Edited by A.R. Hope Moncrieff*
> *. . . eleventh edition.*
> London, Adam and Charles Black, 1898.   BL.SAS
> The map is found loose in a pocket at the back of this work, which also contained the fifteenth lithographic transfer of no. 123, and sectional maps being transfers from the same map as no. 153. Earlier editions of the work contained no. 129D, E, F, G, I and J in place of this map.

State of the plate: Later than no. 144C. Key (Ee) and numbers *1* to *6* erased.
Alterations on the transfer: Title, signature and imprint added.

145 JOHN CARY   circa **1887**

The Sussex section appears to be based on Old Series One Inch Ordnance Survey, appendix VI.1(a).

The following transfers were taken from the plates of a complete map of England and Wales published by John Cary between 1820 and 1830. In 1832 the sixty-five sheets were reissued by G. and J. Cary in a volume entitled *Cary's improved map of England and Wales, with a considerable portion of Scotland, planned upon a scale of two statute miles to one inch, drawn from the most authentic surveys & parliamentary documents.* Like those of Cary's county maps, the plates passed first to G.F. Cruchley; by the 1880s when the first of the transfers below was taken, they were in the hands of Gall and Inglis. Sussex is covered by plate 13 and by parts of plates 12, 14, 19 and 20. Plate 13 in the 1832 edition has the imprint *PUBLISHED BY G. AND J. CARY, 86 S^T JAMES'S STREET, APRIL 2nd. 1832* (Ce OS). When reissued by Cruchley in 1856–7 this was altered to *LONDON. PUBLISHED BY G.F. CRUCHLEY MAP-SELLER & GLOBE MAKER, 81 FLEET STREET.* Amongst a number of other changes, railways and several station names were added, house symbols were added at *BRIGHTON* and other towns, the coastline re-engraved at *Langley P^t.*, and *BRIGHTON or BRIGHTHELMSTONE* erased and replaced by *BRIGHTON*, which was written in the sea.

The plates were used for a variety of maps. Sometime prior to 1840, sheets 13 and 20 were published with the printed title (stuck on, Ce) *Plan of Railway BETWEEN London & Brighton . . . Joseph Gibbs, Engineer.* The line is marked in red ink, but does not follow the route finally adopted (ESCL). A folding map was published towards the end of the century with the title *Reduced Ordnance Survey around Brighton. Scale two miles to an inch. Published by G. Richmond, Nechells Park Road, Birmingham on* the cover (SAS). It included the whole of Sussex, and covered the area from the Isle of Wight to Dymchurch and north to London. Shortly after 1900 another folding map was issued with the title *Gall & Inglis large map of Sussex*. This map is in two sections – *WEST SUSSEX* and *EAST SUSSEX* – one of which is printed on each side of a single sheet (BRIGHTON PL).

145 A.   FIRST LITHOGRAPHIC TRANSFER

Size: 616 mm × [483 mm] (12 mm)   1:125,000

Scale of English Miles. 20 Miles = 258 mm (Ca OS). Plate number *No. 13* (Ea OS). Longitude 10' (1'); latitude 10' (1'). *Continuation North – Sheet 20* (Ba and Da OS), *Continuation West – Sheet 12* (Ac OS). [This is plate 13 of the original map and covers the coast from *West Ferring* to *HASTINGS* and north to *HORSHAM* and *Balcombe*. In the only known copy, the bottom section below 50°43'N is missing. The vertical dimension has, therefore, been taken from plate 13, although it is possible that a new border was drawn on the stone in a different position. The imprint (Ce OS) and other inscriptions below the border may, or may not, have remained as on the Cruchley edition of plate 13. It is also possible that a title was added.] Railways 1 to 6, 8 to 14, 17, 18, 20, 25, 26, 30, 31, 32 and 39 are marked by double lines; 33, 37, 41, 43 and 44 are omitted; 34 seems to have been partially added or partially erased, *HOREHAM STA* is named and traces of an alternative route passing through *Park* at *Heathfield* are visible; 36 also partially added or partially erased; others fall outside the extent of this transfer. Railway 39 was opened in 1886.

> Issued as a folding map with printed title: *Bacon's new tourist map of Sussex from the Ordnance Survey with the name of every railway station.*
> London, G.W. Bacon and Co., [1887].   (BRIGHTON PL)

State of the plate: Later than the Cruchley edition of 1856–7. Additional railways and station names eg *West Worthing* added. Numerous other additions and changes, eg *Shoreham New. Br.* altered to *Suspension Br.*, *Barrow Hd* added.
Alterations on the transfer: Border, with longitude and latitude added. Projecting place-names erased. Scale and plate number added.

145 B.   SECOND LITHOGRAPHIC TRANSFER

Size: 856 mm × 448 mm (3 mm)   1:150,000

The original scale, borders, longitude and latitude, plate numbers and marginal notes omitted. Title, *JOHN BEAL & SON'S HUNTING & TOURISTS' MAP OF SUSSEX &c. Showing the Meets of the WARNHAM STAG HOUNDS, SOUTHDOWN, CRAWLEY AND HORSHAM, EAST SUSSEX, BURSTOW AND GOODWOOD FOXHOUNDS, And the BRIGHTON, BROOKSIDE AND EASTBOURNE*

320

HARRIERS. JOHN BEAL & SON, BOOKSELLERS AND PUBLISHERS, 55 EAST STREET, BRIGHTON (Ea). PUBLISHED BY JOHN BEAL & SON, 55 EAST STREET, BRIGHTON (Registered) (Ce OS). Scale of Miles. 20 Miles = 216 mm (Ee OS). Other changes include: HASTINGS re-engraved, MARINA STA. in place of LEONARDS J^N STA., HOREHAM ROAD STA. in place of HOREHAM STA., HARBOUR STA. in place of WHARF STA. at Newhaven; Convalescent Hosp. added near EASTBOURNE, and many additions, eg Sweethill, Water Hall, Round Hill, Verndean, Windmill, Milcoat Cott, New England, in the area northwest of BRIGHTON. Depths and other detail in the sea erased. Railways 1 to 39, 41 and 42 shown by continuous black lines. The meets are shown by variously shaped, coloured and numbered symbols. Black arcs mark distances from BRIGHTON at four mile intervals. Overprinted to produce colours red, blue, yellow, brown and green.

> The Brighton and Sussex hunting map and map of the environs of Brighton showing . . .
> Brighton, John Beal and Son [1889]. (BL).(BOD).(BRIGHTON PL)
> The map was received by the British Museum in 1889. The pamphlet includes a key to the meets and other information on the map. For another hunting map by the same publisher, see no. 140.

State of the plate: Plate 13 later than no. 145A. Railways and place-names changed as above. Other plates later than the Cruchley edition of the general map, eg SELSEA PENINSULAR added, Fish Houses altered to Fish Shop F.
Alterations on the transfer: Border added and projecting place-names erased. All depths and other detail in the sea erased. Title, imprint, scale and hunting information added.

145 C. THIRD LITHOGRAPHIC TRANSFER

Size: 722 mm × 343 mm (3 mm) 1:171,000

EDITIONS

(i) Title (Ee), imprint (Ce OS), scale (Ee OS) and hunting information omitted. New title, GALL & INGLIS' COUNTY MAP OF SUSSEX SHOWING THE ROADS, RAILWAYS, STATIONS &c. (Ee). Gall & Inglis. Edinburgh (Ee OS). SCALE OF MILES. 12 = 113 mm (Ee, under title). Printer's reference M2⁺ (Ae OS). Railways in Sussex, 1 to 39, 41 and 42. Overprinted to produce six colours, two shades of yellow, of green and of pink, marking boundaries of the parliamentary divisions.

> Issued about 1890 as a folding map. (HASTINGS PL)

(ii) Manhood light railway added. Printer's reference (Ae OS) altered to P4⁺. The map is hand coloured.

> Cruchley's county maps of England. Sussex for cyclists, tourists, &c.
> London and Edinburgh, Gall and Inglis [1890]. (WSRO)

State of the plate: As 145B.
Alterations on the transfer: Border added, projecting place-names erased, and detail in sea erased. Title, scale, imprint and printer's references added. Manhood railway added on edition (ii). This transfer can be identified by two dots on the inner side of the outer line of the top border at 3 mm and 17 mm from the left.

.

146   ORDNANCE SURVEY   1888

Based on material in possession of the Ordnance Survey.

The following lithographic transfers were derived from a drawing reproduced by photozincography, not from an engraved plate. *Rye Bay* on this map measures 10 mm. For a later re-engraved version of this map on the same scale, see no. 154.

146 A.   FIRST LITHOGRAPHIC TRANSFER

Size: 555 mm × 443 mm (the engraved area; no border)   1:250,000

INDEX *to the* ORDNANCE SURVEY *of the County of* SUSSEX *shewing* CIVIL PARISHES (Ca). *Scale of this Index 4 Miles to 1 Inch* (Ca, below title). *Photozincographed and Published at the Ordnance Survey Office, Southampton, 1888. Price 2d. All rights of reproduction reserved.* (Ce). REFERENCE BY LETTER TO THE SMALL PARISHES (Ee, in panel 119 mm × 33 mm). *The largest rectangles with the thickest lines & large Numbers thus . . . 319 indicate the one inch Map. The Secondary rectangles . . .* (Ed). CITY OF CHICHESTER (Be), TOWN OF LEWES (Ce, above imprint) and TOWN OF HASTINGS (Ec) with, in each case, a panel below enclosing a plan of the town and a key to the parishes; the scale is noted below each panel.

Issued about 1888 as loose sheets sold separately.   (ESRO)

State of the drawing: As originally designed.
Alterations on the transfer: Title, scale, insert plans, sheet lines and numbers, and all information outside the county boundary added.

146 B.   SECOND LITHOGRAPHIC TRANSFER

Size: 520 mm × 415 mm (the engraved area; no border).   1:250,000

In the title (Ca), INDEX *to the* erased and replaced by DIAGRAM *of the.* Scale altered to *Scale of this Diagram 4 Miles to 1 Inch.* REFERENCE BY LETTER . . . and

322

panel (Ee) and note commencing *The largest . . .* (Ed) omitted . The sheet lines and numbers of one inch and six inch maps and the sheet-lines of the twenty-five inch maps omitted. *References* listing nine items added (Ee, in panel 111 × 65 mm). Scales below town plans omitted. Three rectangles, indicating the area covered by the town plan panels, added on the map.

Issued about 1888 as loose sheets sold separately. (BL)

State of the drawing: As originally designed.
Alterations on the transfer: Title and all information outside the county boundary added. Three rectangles added on map.

146 C.   THIRD LITHOGRAPHIC TRANSFER

Size: 520 mm × 415 mm (the engraved area, no border). 1:250,000

Title (Ca) amended to read *DIAGRAM of the SANITARY DISTRICTS in the County of SUSSEX shewing also CIVIL PARISHES. Price 2d* (Ce) altered to *Price 6d. REFERENCE TO COLOURS,* with five items, added (Da). Rectangles on map omitted. *WEST WORTHING* and *BURGESS HILL* and other district names added. *WESTERN DIVISION* and *EASTERN DIVISION* added in green. Names of the unions added and boundaries overprinted in red. Map overprinted to produce colours red, brown, blue and green; the insert plans in red only.

Issued about 1888 as loose sheets sold separately.   (BL).(CUL).(WSRO)

State of the drawing: Probably later than no. 146B. District names added.
Alterations on the transfer: Title and all information outside the county boundary added. (On some impressions additional colouring has been added by hand).

146 D.   FOURTH LITHOGRAPHIC TRANSFER

Size: 540 mm × 495 mm (the engraved area; no border) 1:250,000

Title and scale (Ca) replaced by *LOCAL GOVERNMENT BOUNDARIES COMMISSION. DIAGRAM of the ALTERATIONS PROPOSED BY THE BOUNDARIES COMMISSION, In the COUNTY of SUSSEX (EAST AND WEST) Showing CIVIL PARISHES ADDED TO THE COUNTY . . . Hatched Red* – followed by a rectangle and by seven similar items. *Scale of the Diagram 4 Miles to 1 Inch.* (Cb). *R. Owen Jones,* facsimile signature added (Cb, below scale). Imprint, price and reference to reproduction rights (Ce) omitted. *REFERENCE TO COLOURS* (Da) omitted. *To face page 379* added (Ae). Map and inserts overprinted in red and green.

Local Government Boundaries Commission. Report of the Boundary Commis-

sioner of England and Wales, 1888. Vol. 1.
'Ordered to be printed 11th August 1888.'
BL
This forms volume XXVIII of *Reports from Commissioners, Inspectors, and others* for the parliamentary session of 9 February–24 December 1888.

State of the drawing: As no. 146C.

Alterations on the transfer: Title and all information outside the county boundary added.

147 WILLIAM AND ALEXANDER KEITH JOHNSTON
1889

Based on Old Series One Inch Ordnance Survey, appendix VI.1(a).

The firm of W. and A.K. Johnston was founded in Edinburgh in 1825 by Sir William Johnston (1802–88). He was Lord Provost in Edinburgh from 1844 to 1851. His younger brother, Alexander Keith (1804–71), joined him in 1826, and by 1830 the business was expanded from engraving and printing to include map publishing. Alexander Keith was a cartographer of considerable standing; in 1851 the firm was awarded a medal for exhibiting the first ever globe of physical geography; he exposed deficiencies in the work of the Ordnance Survey in Scotland which led to reforms; he undertook cartographic work for Stanfords;[1] he was a member of many learned societies; and he fathered eleven children. His son, also Keith Alexander (1844–79), was employed by Stanfords in 1866, and later studied in Germany. He ran the London end of the business, and was map draughtsman and assistant curator at the Royal Geographical Society. He was appointed geographer on a survey of Paraguay in 1876, and led an expedition to Lake Nyassa in 1878, during which he died.

The following lithographic transfers were taken from the plates of a map of the whole country entitled *Modern map of England and Wales constructed by W. & A.K. Johnston . . .*, which does not seem to have been published until 1889, although transfers from various parts of the plates had been used to prepare maps for use in guide books from as early as 1856. *Handbook for travellers in Kent and Sussex* published by John Murray in 1858, 1863 and 1868, and some copies of *Handbook for travellers in Sussex* also published by John Murray in 1877, contained transfers from the map, which covered the whole of south-east England. Most copies of the last-named work contained no. 108F. The maps in these guide books are to be found 'in a pocket at the end' and are often missing, or may in some cases have been replaced by a map from another source.

1. Hyde, 1975, p. 12.

147 A.   FIRST LITHOGRAPHIC TRANSFER

Size: 327 mm × 234 mm (4 mm)   1:439,000

SUSSEX (Ce). *W. & A.K. Johnston. Edinburgh & London* (Ee OS). *English Miles* 5 +
10 = 36 mm (Ce, under title). Grid (72 mm × 142 mm) with reference letters *a* to *c*
vertically and *A* to *D* horizontally. Railways 1 to 38 and 41. Overprinted to produce
colours green (county boundary) and blue (sea). Plate number *49* on back.

> *The modern county atlas of England & Wales comprised in fifty seven maps, all on*
> *one scale . . .*
> Edinburgh and London, W. & A.K. Johnston. 1889.   BL.RGS

State of the plate: As for the 1889 edition of the general map.
Alterations on the transfer: Border drawn round map, projecting place-names erased
and the amount of topographical detail outside the Sussex reduced. Title, signature,
scale, grid and reference letters added. *SUSSEX,* across map, erased; *HANTS*
re-engraved.

147 B.   SECOND LITHOGRAPHIC TRANSFER

Size: 304 mm × 133 mm (single line border)   1:440,000

EDITIONS

(i)   Title (Ce), scale, grid and reference letters, and plate number omitted. *SUSSEX,*
across map, not erased. New title *DEACON'S SUSSEX, POLITICAL.* added (Ca
OS). *W. & A.K. Johnston. Edinburgh & London* (Ee OS). *Charles William Deacon &
Co., London* added (Ae OS). *English Miles* 5 + 10 = 36 mm (Ce OS). Railways 1 to
38, 41, 42 and T and U. Overprinted to give colours green, blue, pink and yellow.

> *The Sussex court guide and county blue book.*
> London, Charles William Deacon, 1894.   BL.BRIGHTON PL
> An 1881 edition of this work did not contain maps.

(ii)   New title *DEACON'S SUSSEX, HYDROGRAPHICAL.* (Ca OS). *Explanation*
added (Ce) giving key to *Boundaries of River Basins* (in red) and to rainfall areas,
which are delineated by shades of blue on the map. Overprinted in red and two shades
of blue.

> *The Sussex court guide . . .*
> London, William Charles Deacon, 1894.   BL.BRIGHTON PL

(iii)   New title *DEACON'S SUSSEX, GEOLOGICAL.* (Ca OS). New *Explanation*
(Ea) giving colour scale for five strata, which are delineated by single lines on the map.
Overprinted to give two shades of brown and three of green,

325

The Sussex court guide . . .
London, Charles William Deacon, 1894.   BL.BRIGHTON PL

(iv)   New title *DEACON'S SUSSEX, CLIMATOLOGICAL.* (Ce OS). *Mean Wind* and red arrow pointing north-eastwards added (Ce). New *Explanation* (Ee), relating to temperatures and rainfall. Map overprinted in red to indicate inches of rainfall, eg *25* at *Beachy Head*. Temperatures indicated by grey numbers (July) and black numbers and lines (January), eg *62°7* (in grey) and *40°9* (in black) outside left border. Foreshore overprinted in blue.

The Sussex court guide . . .
London, Charles William Deacon, 1894.   BL.BRIGHTON PL

State of the plate: Later than no. 147A. Railways 42, T and U added.
Alterations on the transfer: Border drawn round map and projecting place-names erased. Titles, signature, imprint, scale, explanations and other special information added.

148   BURNS AND OATES   1893

Size: 178 mm × 105 mm (1 mm)   1:695,000

The map is insufficiently detailed to enable the sources used in its compilation to be determined.

EDITION

CARTE DU SUSSEX. (Ce OS). An outline map designed to show places referred to in the text, eg *DISTRICT DE PEVENSEY.*

West-Grinstead et les Caryll.[1] *Etude historique et religieuse sur le comté de Sussex . . .*
Max de Trenqualen. vol. 1.
Paris, M. Torré; Horsham, Denis; London, Burns and Oates, 1893.   BL.SAS

1. See *Sussex County Magazine* vol. 2, p. 302; vol. 12, pp. 397, 454, 544; vol. 19, p. 97.

149   FREDERICK BOOTHBY[1]   circa **1893**

Based on New Series One Inch Ordnance Survey, appendix VI.1(b).

The following lithographic transfers were probably derived from a drawing reproduced by photozincography, not from an engraved plate.

149 A.   FIRST LITHOGRAPHIC TRANSFER

Size: 800 mm × 387 mm (1 mm)   1:174,000

MAP OF SUSSEX (Ca, framed by ribbon design in red). *F. BOOTHBY, Del. et Litho.* (Ae, in border). *PUBLISHED BY THE GREAT TOWER STREET TEA COMPANY LIM^D.* (Ee, in border). *A HANDBOOK OF SUSSEX WITH REDUCED COPY OF THIS MAP AND 20 ILLUSTRATIONS Containing a vast amount of useful information CAN BE OBTAINED OF ALL AGENTS FOR TOWER TEA* (Aa, in red). *DRINK TOWER TEA.* (Ea, in red). *COPYRIGHT.* (Aa OS). *ENT.STA.HALL* (Ea OS). Key (Ee). *Scale of Miles 3/8 Inch to 1 Mile 6* = 92 mm (Ed), the scale-bar actually represents 10 miles, the 6 being a misprint. There are population figures after each town, eg *BRIGHTON 115,402.* The map is printed in red and black.

> Issued about 1893 as loose sheets.   (BL).(SAS)
> Received by the British Museum in 1893.

State of the original drawing: Apparently unaltered.
Alterations on the transfer: Probably none.

149 B.   SECOND LITHOGRAPHIC TRANSFER

Size: 490 mm × 244 mm (8 mm)   1:285,000

Title, scale and all inscriptions listed under no. 149A omitted. *MAP.OF.SUSSEX* (Ca, on black scroll design). *BOOTHBY Del.* (Ae, in border). *Scale of Miles* [10] = 56 mm (Ed). *Explanation* (Ee). Uncoloured.

> *A handbook of Sussex for the pocket, the library, or the tea table . . . by Edward F. Skinner.*
> London, John Haddon and Co., 1893.   BL.SAS

State of the drawing: Probably as no. 149A.
Alterations on the transfer: Original title, scale and inscriptions erased. New title, signature, scale and *Explanation* added.

---

1.   Hyde, 1975, no. 259 gives first name.

Size: 443 mm × 145 mm (1 mm)   1:312,000

A very close copy of Stanford no. 135. There are, however, minor differences in the engraving of many place-names, and the Addison signature is a further indication that this map is from a separate plate.

Augustus John Cuthbert Hare[1] (1834–1903), the writer (*Memorials of a quiet life, The story of my life* and a number of other books, including topographical works), was born in Rome. He was the great-great-grandson[2] of Dr. Francis Hare, Bishop of Chichester, who died in 1740. Dr. Hare's first wife was Bethaia, sister of 'Counceller' Naylor, who purchased Herstmonceux Castle in 1708 (see no. 14). The castle was sold by Augustus J.C. Hare's grandfather to Thomas Kemp, founder of Kemp Town, for £60,000 in 1807.[3] It now houses the Royal Observatory. A.J.C. Hare lived a great part of his life abroad, mainly in Italy, with his aunt, Maria Lycester, by whom he had been adopted in 1835. He lived for a time (c. 1860) at Herstmonceux, where he is buried; but he died at St. Leonards where he had passed the last years of his life. Hare has been accused of 'borrowing' rather too heavily from other writers for his topographical works.

George Allen (1832–1917), the publisher, was also an engraver and illustrator. He started life as a joiner, and became a pupil of Ruskin at the Working Men's College. He later published Ruskin's works. He was also a good amateur geologist. He lived at Orpington, Kent.

EDITION

SUSSEX (Ee). *Engraved by J. Addison Junr.* (Ee OS). *SCALE OF STATUTE MILES* 5 + 10 = 50 mm (Ee, under title).

Sussex by Augustus J.C. Hare . . .
London, George Allen, 1894.   BL.BRIGHTON PL

Sussex by Augustus J.C. Hare . . . second edition
London, George Allen, 1896.   BL.BRIGHTON PL

1. See *DNB*; Hare, 1896; *SNQ* no. 13 (1951) p. 157; *SAC* vol. 4 (1851) p. 162.
2. A.J.C. Hare, *The years with mother.* Edited by Malcolm Barnes, London, 1952, contains a family tree.
3. Lower, 1865.

151   F.S. WELLER   circa **1894**

Probably based on New Series One Inch Ordnance Survey, appendix VI.1(b)

The plate from which the following lithographic transfer was taken was apparently never used for direct intaglio printing.

151 A.   LITHOGRAPHIC TRANSFER

Size: 270 mm × 205 mm (4 mm)   1:459,000

SUSSEX (Ee). *F.S. Weller. F.R.G.S.* (Ee OS). *WILLIAM MACKENZIE. LONDON, EDINBURGH & GLASGOW.* (Ce OS). *Scale of Miles 10* = 35 mm (Ee, under title). Key to *Railways, Roads* and *Canals* (Ee, under scale). The six parliamentary divisions and two parliamentary boroughs are outlined in red and differentiated by five colours. Longitude 20' (1'); latitude 20' (1'). Graticule at 20' intervals. Railways 1 to 32, 34 to 39, 41 and 42. Overprinted to produce colours red, pink, yellow, green, buff and two shades of blue.

> *The comprehensive gazetteer of England and Wales. Edited by J.H.F. Brabner, F.R.G.S. . . .* [vol. 6].
> London, Edinburgh and Dublin, William Mackenzie, [1894][1].   BL.CUL

State of the plate: As originally engraved.
Alterations on the transfer: The imprint (Ce OS) may have been added on the stone.

152   BRIGHTON GAZETTE   **1895**

Size: 90 mm × 51 mm (single line border)   1:1,370,000

The map is insufficiently detailed to enable the sources used in its compilation to be determined.

The map was probably printed from a lithographic stone on which the design had been laid down from the original drawing.

EDITION

ROMAN SUSSEX (Ca OS). There are no place-names on the map, only letters and numbers with a reference key below the map, eg *a, a, Anderides-Wald.* Three rivers and seven towns are named.

---

1. The publication of this work in six volumes is recorded in *Geographical Journal* vols. 3 and 4. The first volume of the work was published in 1893, and the next two volumes in 1894; the publication of later volumes of the work is not recorded.

The Sussex coast defences. Report from the Brighton Gazette.
Issue for Thursday, Sept. 26. 1895.
The British Library impression is marked *HEB* in ink. An earlier article on the same subject, without map, published on 18th April 1895 is marked *RCEB*, again in ink.

153   JOHN BARTHOLOMEW   circa **1896**

Probably based on New Series Ordnance Survey, appendix VI.1(b).

This map has been included in the main catalogue because it carries the title *SUSSEX*, although it extends only from 51'W (*Earnley*) to 23'E (*Pevensey*). An earlier edition (CUL) was published c. 1890 with the title *NEW REDUCED ORDNANCE SURVEY MAP OF ENVIRONS OF BRIGHTON WITH SUSSEX COAST* (Ca OS). A later transfer from the same plate published after 1900, with the title *BACON'S NEW LIBRARY MAP OF SURREY AND SUSSEX,* covers Sussex as far east as *HASTINGS.* The reference on no. 153A to continuation sheets and the production of a combined Surrey and Sussex map from the same set of plates, makes it clear that this is a transfer from a general map, which was also used for the sectional maps in *Black's guide to Sussex,* 1898 (no. 144D), and which has not been identified.

This is not the same map as no. 129B or E. An advertisement on the cover of this map (no. 153A) lists it as *No. 8,* and also includes *No. 125 Surrey and Sussex* on a scale of 4 Miles to one inch. *No. 125* could be no. 129K or an earlier version of *BACON'S NEW LIBRARY MAP OF SURREY AND SUSSEX.*

153 A.   FIRST LITHOGRAPHIC TRANSFER

Size: 685 mm × 460 mm (11 mm)   1:126,000

SUSSEX (Ca). *NEW REDUCED ORDNANCE SURVEY OF ENGLAND AND WALES – Scale, 2 miles to an inch.* (Aa OS). *By JOHN BARTHOLOMEW, F.R.G.S.* (Ea OS). *THE EDINBURGH GEOGRAPHICAL INSTITUTE.* (Ae OS). *COPYRIGHT – JOHN BARTHOLOMEW, F.R.G.S.* (Ee OS). *Scale 2 Miles to an Inch 5 = 64 mm* (Ce OS). Key to *Railways, County Boundaries, Driving & Cycling Roads, Other Roads* (Ce OS, either side of scale). Longitude 10' (1'); latitude 10' (1'). *For continuation Eastward see KENT* (Ec, in border). *For continuation Northward see SURREY* (Ca, in border). Key to *SCALE OF COLOURS* (contours) in eight colours (Ee). Overprinted to produce blue, two shades of green and five shades of brown. The area covered by this transfer lies between 51'W and 23'E; and between 50°44'N and 51°13'N.

Issued as a folding map in printed cover with title: *The new reduced Ordnance Survey map. Brighton and Sussex coast . . .*

330

London, W.H. Smith and Son. (BL).(CUL)
British Museum impression received in 1896.

State of the plate: Probably as originally engraved.
Alterations on the transfer: Title (Ca) added. Some other information, eg the items referred to in the key, may have been added on the stone.

154 ORDNANCE SURVEY   1899

Based on materials in possession of the Ordnance Survey.

The following lithographic transfers were derived from a drawing reproduced by photozincography, not from an engraved plate. The map is a revised version of no. 146 on the same scale. In general the place-names are smaller, eg *BEACHY HEAD* is 15.5 mm compared with 21 mm on no. 146; *Rye Bay* is 7 mm compared with 10 mm.

154 A. FIRST LITHOGRAPHIC TRANSFER

Size: 692 mm × 478 mm (the engraved area; no border)   1:250,000

EDITIONS

(i) *ORDNANCE SURVEY OF ENGLAND AND WALES. COMBINED INDEX SHEWING CIVIL PARISHES AND THE ORDNANCE SURVEY MAPS OF SUSSEX ON THE 1-INCH, 6-INCH, AND 25-INCH SCALES Surveyed in 1869–75. Revised in 1895–99.* (Ca). *Scale of this Index Four Miles to One Inch.* 2 + 12 = 76 mm (Ce). *Heliozincographed and Published by the Director General at the Ordnance Survey Office, Southampton 1899. Price of this Index, 2d. All rights of reproduction reserved.* (Ce, under scale). *References* (De, in panel 97 mm × 60 mm). *TOWN OF LEWES,* with plan (Cd). *TOWN OF HASTINGS,* with plan (Ed). Note commencing *Six-inch Quarter Sheets are composed* . . . (Be). Note commencing *The Sheets along* . . . (Bd).

Issued about 1899 as loose sheets sold separately   (CUL)

(ii) Note (Bd) omitted. Note headed *DETACHED PARTS OF PARISHES IN THE COUNTY* . . . added (Ae, in panel 86 mm × 142 mm).

Issued about 1899 as loose sheets sold separately.   (CUL)

State of the drawing: As originally designed.
Alterations on the transfer: Title, scale, imprint, *References*, town plans and notes &c. added. Sheet lines of one inch, six inch and twenty-five inch maps, added.

331

Size: 950 mm × 527 mm (the engraved area; no border)   1:250,000

New title *ORDNANCE SURVEY OF ENGLAND AND WALES. DIAGRAM OF SUSSEX SHEWING CIVIL PARISHES WITH A TABLE OF THEIR AREAS AND THE NUMBERS OF THEIR 1-INCH INDEXES, Surveyed in 1869–75. Revised in 1895–98* (Ca). The imprint (Ce, under scale) revised to read *Heliozincographed and Published at the Ordnance Survey Office, Southampton, 1900. Price of the Diagram 6d. All rights of reproduction reserved.* In the scale (Ce), *Index* altered to *Diagram.* Sheet lines and numbers of six inch and twenty-five inch maps omitted. *References,* in panel 115 mm × 60 mm moved (from De to Be), and second line, which refers to the six inch sheets, omitted. The notes *Six-inch Quarter Sheets* . . . (Be) and *DETACHED PARTS* . . . (Ae) omitted. A new table, *AREAS OF PARISHES,* added to right of map (in panel 247 mm × 520 mm).

Issued about 1900 as loose sheets, sold separately.   (BL).(CUL)
The map was reissued the following year. An impression at SAS has *Note . . . Boundaries Revised to October 1901* added (Cb, under title).

State of the drawing: As originally designed.
Alterations on the transfer: Title, scale, imprint, *References,* town plans and notes &c. added. Sheet lines and numbers of one inch maps added.

155   B.C.B.   **1900**

Size: West section 81 mm × 81 mm (1 mm, top and bottom only)
          East section 81 mm × 81 mm (1 mm, top and bottom only)   1:811,000

The map is insufficiently detailed to enable the sources used in its compilation to be determined.

The map was probably printed from a lithographic stone on which the design was laid down from the original drawing.

EDITION

RAIL ROADS OF SUSSEX (in panel 6 mm deep across top of map outside border with 1 mm double line border above. The words are preceeded, separated and followed by representations of martlets). *BCB* (Ee, west section). *1900* (Ae, east section). *Scale.of.Miles: 15* = 30 mm (Ee, east section). Key:*a* to *c* indicating London termini, *1* to *24* marking places of interest (in panel below map). Only stations are named on the map. Insert of *BRIGHTON* area showing railways and stations in greater detail (Aa, west section). Drawings of two sailing ships and a steamer. Railways 1 to 39, 41, 42 and line to *Selsey Bill.*

Sussex by F.G. Brabant.M.A. . . .
Lonon, Methuen & Co., 1900.   BL
The map forms the front fly-leaf. The work also contains no. 129L.

PRINTED MAPS
OF
SUSSEX

APPENDIXES

I   MANUSCRIPT MAPS

1   LAURENCE NOWELL[1]   circa **1563**

Size: c. 280 mm × 205 mm (no border; two sheets)   [1:608,000]

Laurence Nowell (d. circa 1569) was perhaps the first to see the need for a national atlas. In 1563 he wrote to Sir William Cecil complaining of the inaccuracy of existing maps and setting forth his design for the construction of maps of all the counties. Two sets of Nowell's maps have survived in manuscript form. They would probably have been available to Saxton, since Nowell and Seckford, Saxton's patron, were friends.

Two of Nowell's sheets cover Sussex (**see plate 2**). There is a grid (16 mm × 16 mm), and the grid lines are numbered. Place-names – a subject in which Nowell was especially interested – are shown in old English characters. The names of some major landowners have been added in another hand. The map marks the county boundary and thirty-eight places, all of which can be identified except *Burn,* about five miles inland from Pevensey, and *Hide,* on the coast five miles east of Pevensey. Saxton markes *Borne* (Eastbourne); but the location of Nowell's *Burn* makes it more likely that it was intended for Boreham, which Saxton names as such. *Hide* is probably Bulverhide which Nowell marks on his c.1560 map *A general description of England and Irelande . . .* (reproduced in Crone, 1961). Two of Nowell's place-names, *Hide* and *Cudleagt* (Cudlow) are omitted by Saxton. Palmer and Covert (see appendix II, 2) mark *Cudloe,* but Saxton was probably right to omit it since by then the bulk of the parish must have been under the sea for some years.[2]   BL (MS Domit A.XVIII)

2   [JAMES COLBRAND]   circa **1599**

Size: 430 mm × 233 mm (single-line border)   [1:290,000]

Six towns, the rapes and eleven other features are named. Each rape is divided into four parts, each of which is marked with a flag. The map accompanies a document addressed by James Colbrand, deputy lieutenant of the county, to 'the Lord High Treasurer, and the Lord High Admiral of England, the Quene's most excellent Majestie's Liuetenauntes of this county of Sussex.' Colbrand makes recommendations designed to improve the efficiency and speed of the musters.[3]   BL (MS Royal 17 AL)

---

1 R.M. Warnicke 'The Laurence Nowell manuscripts in the British Library', *British Library Journal* vol. 5, no. 2 (1979), pp. 201–2, points out that there were two Laurence Nowells, cousins, and that the cartographer was not the Dean of Lichfield and Prebendary of Chichester (d. 1576). See also R. Flower, 'Laurence Nowell and the discovery of England in Tudor times', in *Proceedings of the British Academy* vol. 21 (1935). The map is reproduced in Crone, 1961, plate 18.
2 *SAC* vol. 44, p. 149.
3 *SAC* vol. 11, pp. 147–70. *SAC* vol. 40, pp. 1–37 refers to another interesting manuscript relating to musters.

3 WILLIAM ROY

1757

Size: c. 3840 mm × 740 mm (no border).

SURVEY & SKETCH OF THE COAST OF SUSSEX &c — WITH PART of the COUNTRY adjoining to the Coast. As Reconnoitred by Lieu^t. Willm. Roy. Feb^{ry}. 1st. 1757 (Ce). *Scale of 5000 yards* = 127 mm. *Scale of 2 English Miles* = 89 mm (Be and De). Compass (Be and De, to right of scales). This is a most attractive map, which extends to the north side of the Downs, and shows field boundaries along the roads, and the towns in plan. BL (King's Library 42.11. 11TAB)

4 BOARD OF ORDNANCE

circa **1736**

A PLAN of the COAST of SUSSEX from RYE to CHICHESTER. Scale of Geometrical Miles 2 + 5 = 76 mm. In panels below the map are plans of *Arundel Haven, New Haven, East Fort at Seaford, Seaford, West Fort at Hastings* and *Hastings.* The impressions of this map at Public Record Office appear to consist of an original and four copies. Two of the maps do not have the panels. One bears the imprint *Chas. Holloway June 1771,* and another *Copied by F. Gould.* PRO (MR 915)

There is another version of this map at SAS. The British Library has a manuscript map (MT 6 d 1.3), which is a continuation in the same style from Winchelsea to Ramsgate.[4]

4 J.H. Farrant 'The defences of Sussex in 1736', *SAS Newsletter* no. 12 (January 1974).

II MAPS OF THE COAST OF SUSSEX

The Sussex coast appears, as part of far larger areas, on portolan charts which were issued in manuscript from the start of the fourteenth century. From 1583, maritime atlases were printed containing more detailed charts, of which a few referred specifically to the coast of Sussex. Some of the earlier charts (prior to 1650) are listed below; reference to other charts, by Doncker, Goos, van Keulen, Seller and others, will be found in Tooley[1] and in the catalogue of the National Maritime Museum, vols. 3 and 4 pp. 803–5. Gerard van Keulen, for example, produced a chart with the title *A new gradually encreasnig* (sic) *compass-map of part of the seacoasts of England, in which is contined the coasts of Sussex, extending from eastwards of Hastings, to Arundel Haven* . . . It appeared in his *De groote niewe vermeerderde zee-atlas*, 1695, and in later collections of charts.

As well as appearing in charts of the south coast, the county is often represented in some detail in charts of the English Channel. Seller's *The English pilot*, first published in 1671, contained no. 7 below. The 1701 edition contained a very fine chart (dated 1702) by Captain Edmund Halley. Between 1804 and 1807 Lieutenant John Murray RN drew three detailed and attractive charts covering the coast from Selsey Bill to Winchelsea. Murray's charts, which measure 910 mm × 590 mm, were published by the Hydrographical Office.

The Cary and Paterson maps (nos. 9–11 below) show the coastal area of Sussex in considerable detail.

One map with the title *COAST OF SUSSEX* is included in the catalogue, see Martin no. 103 (1833).

1 LUCAS JANSZOON WAGENAER   1583

Size: 500 mm × 315 mm (4 mm)   1:404,000

EDITION

Die Canael tuffchen Engelandt en Franctryct (across centre of map). On some impressions there is a second title, *CANALIS INTER ANGLIAM ET FRANCIAM,* added below the first. *Beschrijuinghe der Zee Custen van Engelandt . . . Lucas Iansz Wagenaer* . . . (De); *Ioēs ā Doetaū* (Ae), ie engraved by Jan van Doetichum, or Deutecum, the elder. Scales of Spanish and Dutch leagues with the date *1583* (Ae). Compass (Cd). The chart extends from *Polle* (Poole) to *Doueren* (Dover). A number of towns as far inland as *Amberley, Cattestret* and *Opletre* (Appledore) are named; soundings are marked, and above the map are profiles of the coastline.

---

1 Tooley, 1949, p. 60 et seq.

Teerste deel vande spieghel der zeevaert.
Amsterdam, Christoffel Plantin, 1584.   BL.AD
This was the first printed martime atlas. It was reissued with Dutch, Latin and French texts up to 1605.[2]

2   THOMAS PALMER AND WALTER COVERT   1587

Size: First chart: 422 mm × 255 mm (4 mm)
         Others: 354 mm × 255 mm (4 mm)   [1:684,000]

There are no titles. Reynolds' signature appears on all charts (Ee) as follows: *N. Reynolds fecit* (first chart), *Nicholaus Reynolds fecit Maij 1587* (second chart), *Authore N. Reynolds Londiniensis*[3] (third chart), *Reynolds fecit* (fourth chart), *NR 1587* (fifth chart). Scale of *English Myles* (Ae on second and third charts), and *Englishe Myles* (Ae on fourth chart). Compass (Ab and Dd on first chart, De on second chart, Bc on third chart, Ee on fourth and fifth charts). In the only known copy of this manuscript (BL, Add MS 57494) the charts are on vellum.

The text which accompanies the charts commences *A Suruey made by Sʳ. Thomas Palmere knight, and Mʳ. Waltar Couerte esquire Deputie Lieuteññts of her Maᵗⁱᵉˢ. Countie of Sussex of all the places of descente alongste the sea coaste of the said Shire.* The report goes on to make detailed recommendations regarding the defence of all landing places and havens.

Palmer[4] and Covert[5] were both members of distinguished Sussex families. A report made by the Deputy Lieutenants in 1625 states, 'And for our Certificate unto yᵒᵘ. Loᵖᵖˢ. of such places along the sea coste as are leaste defensible, and likest to invite an enemy to land, we Cannot better certifye yᵒʳ. Loᵖᵖˢ. therein, than the Deputie Leueteññts did in 88, who did plott downe the sea coaste from Chichester Haven to Rye, and sent one plott thereof in cullors to the Lo: Howard then Lord Admirall, and one other to the then Lo; Buckhrust Lord Lieveteññts of this county.'[6]

It is apparent from this quotation that two original versions (or one original and a copy) of the charts were made in 1587. The manuscript now in the British Library was reproduced in 1870 with notes by M.A. Lower, published by W.E. Baxter of Lewes. According to Lower's preface 'The Document is on vellum, and this lithographic fac-simile is extremely accurate.' In fact, only the charts are on vellum; the text is on paper. Although the text was reproduced in facsimile, the charts were redrawn; the Reynolds signatures were omitted, and there were other minor errors, eg *Heind Stade*

---

2   Koeman, 1970, p. 469.
3   The word is difficult to read, and could be *Londinensis;* on Saxton's map of Hertfordshire he signs *Nicholaus Reynoldus Londinensis Sculpsit.*
4   Sir Thomas Palmer of Angmering (d. 1626). Not to be confused with Sir Thomas Palmer of Parham (d. 1605), or with Sir Thomas Palmer of Wingham, Kent, (d. 1608), who was the author of *How to make our travailes into foraine countries more profitable* (See Tooley, 1979, Palmer, 1918).
5   *SAC* vol. 47 (1904), pp. 116–50. Sir Walter (1543–1631), the co-author of these charts, is described as 'the greatest of the Coverts'.
6   *SAC* vol. 40 (1896), p. 9.

is omitted. The original at that time was in the possession of Wynne E. Baxter, and the reproduction was engraved by Maclure, Macdonald and Macgregor[7] (see no. 89). The second version of the original has not been found.

The British Library has a copy of the charts made in 1737 by William Burge and De La Tessoniere (K. Top. xlii.10.a). The Reynolds signatures are omitted, but the text and the topographical detail on the charts correspond precisely with the surviving original (Add MS 57494). If the 1737 copy was made from the surviving original, it is surprising that the manuscript turned up in private hands in 1870; if it was copied from the other original, which has since disappeared, the two originals must have agreed in every detail.

Sussex County Magazine vol. 2 (1928), p. 142 had an article about the Armada preparations, and reproduced a map then in the possession of W.W. Grantham.[8] This map included the Reynolds signature, and was probably traced, both as to text and map, from the original then in the possession of Wynne Baxter. Both text and map are very accurate copies of the original, the only difference being that *Waltar* in the title has been copied as *Walter*.

3   LUCAS JANSZOON WAGENAER   1588

Size: 500 mm × 315 mm (4 mm)   1:404,000

EDITION

THE SEA COASTES OF ENGLAND Betweene the Ile of Wight & Douer, . . . (Ee in elaborate cartouche). *THE CHANEL BETWEENE ENGLAND AND FRAVNCE* (across centre of map, as in no. 1 above, of which this is a re-engraved version). Scales of English, Spanish and Dutch leagues (Be). Compass (Cd).

> *The mariners mirrovr . . . by that famous navigator Luke Wagenar . . . for the use of Englishmen by Anthony Ashley . . .*
> [London], [1588].   BL
> This translation of *Spieghel der zeevaerdt* was arranged by Sir Christopher Hatton,[9] and the charts were engraved in London; but details of its publication are not given on the title-page. The work was republished in 1605 at Leyden with additions to the charts in Dutch by Hondius.

---

7   Advertisement in *Sussex Agricultural Express,* 3 Jan. 1871.
8   Recently donated by Mr Ivor Grantham to the Sussex Archaeological Society (Grantham MSS, accn 1384).
9. Taylor, 1956, p. 210; the title-page is reproduced. Chart no. 2 is reproduced in Tooley, 1949, p. 56. See also Koeman, 1964.

4 ROBERT ADAMS   1588

Size: 484 mm × 360 mm (7 mm)   1:452,000

One of eleven maps by Robert Adams, engraved by Augustine Ryther, to illustrate the progress of the Spanish Armada.

EDITION

Roberto Adamo authore (Be). Plate number *8* (Ee). *The Scale of English miles* 24 = 104 mm (Be).

Expeditionis Hispanorum in Angliam vera descriptio.[10]
London, A. Hadfield, 1588.   BL.RGS
Tapestries based on these charts were designed by Hendrik Cornelius Vroom and woven by Francois Spierinck of Delft. These tapestries hung in the House of Lords until destroyed by fire in 1834. Engravings, made from the tapestries by John Pine, were published in 1739. Each plate is marked *H. Gravelot delin.* and *J. Pine sculp.* Chart VIII covers the coast from Portsmouth to Sandwich. The charts were republished by T. Bowles in 1753.

5 WILLEM JANSZOON BLAEU   1608

Size: 545 mm × 245 mm (4 mm, left and right borders only)   1:615,000

EDITION

Vertooninghe hae't leven vande Zeecust van Engelant tusschen Poorlant eñ Doveren . . . Representation au vif des Costes marines D'Angleterre entre Portlande et Douvres (Da). Three scales (Ba). Both the title and the scales are in elaborate surrounds, which include engravings of seven animals. Plate number *19* (Ee). Latitude 10' (1').

Het licht der zee-vaert . . .
Amsterdam, Willem Janszoon, 1608, 1610, 1613, 1617, 1618, 1620 and 1630.
                                                                 KOEMAN[11]

The light of navigation . . .
Amsterdam, William Johnson, 1612 and 1622.   BL;BL

Le flambeav de la navigation . . .
Amsterdam, Gvillavme Jensz., 1619 and 1625.   KOEMAN;BL

10 D. Schrire, 'Adams' and Pine's maps of the Spanish Armada', *MCS* no. 4 (1963); *Lord Howard of Effingham and the Spanish Armada with exact facsimiles of the 'tables of Augustine Ryther' AD. 1590 and the engravings of the hangings of the House of Lords by John Pine AD. 1739 with introduction by Henry Yates Thompson.* Roxburghe Club, 1919.
11 Koeman, 1970, vol. 4, p. 30 et seq.

In the English and French editions, the title is usually engraved on a slip of paper, which is pasted over the original *Het licht . . .* title.

6   JAN BLAEU   1625

Size: 357 mm × 258 mm (single-line border)   [1:400,000]

EDITION

De Cust van Engelandt tusschen de Singels en de drooghten van Weembrugh (Da). Scales of Dutch, Spanish and English miles (Aa). Plate number *67* (Ee). Compass (De). Marks soundings, but only a few place-names. **See plate 36.**

> *The sea-mirrour . . . translated . . . by Richard Hynmers.*
> Amsterdam, William Johnson Blaevw, 1625 and 1635.   BL;NMM
>
> *Eerste deel der seespiegel.*
> Amsterdam, Willem Iansz Blaeuw, 1627 and 1652.   BL;BL.AD
>
> *The sea-beacon . . . translated . . . by Richard Hynmers.*
> Amsterdam, Willem Johnson Blaev. 1643.   BL

7   JAN JANSSON   1620

Size: 545 mm × 245 mm (4 mm, left and right borders only)   1:615,000

From 1620 Jansson published copies of the Blaeu marine atlas (no. 5 above). The charts were re-engraved, but differed little from the originals. In the English and French editions of the work the title is usually engraved on a slip of paper, which is pasted over the original *Het licht . . .* title.

In the English editions the imprint William Johnson refers to Blaeu, and John Johnson to Jansson.[12]

EDITION

As no. 5 above, except that the titles and scales have been transposed from (Da to Ba); the Dutch wording in the title has been altered to *Vertoninghe naar't leven vande Zeecusten van Engelant tussen Portlant ende Doeveren . . .;* the decorative surrounds contain only four animals.

---

12 Howse and Sandeson, 1973, p. 49.

Het licht der zee-vaert, 1620, 1623, 1627 and 1629; *The light of navigation*, 1620 and 1625; *Le flambeau de la navigation*, 1620 (BL.NMM) *Le nouveau phalot de mer*, 1635 and 1637; *Het nieuw vermeerde licht, 1634.* KOEMAN[13]

A heavily amended version of the chart appeared in Sellers' *The English pilot, 1671.* The title has been altered to *A Description of the Sea Coast of England*, place-names have been anglicised, and there is no plate number or right border.[14]

8 ROBERT DUDLEY   1646–7

Size: 383 mm × 490 mm (no border)   [1:660,000]

Sussex occupies only a small section of the chart described below, which has nevertheless been included in this appendix because of the many qualities of the work in which it appears. Sir Robert Dutley's *Dell'arcano del mare* was the first marine atlas to be published by an Englishman, and the first to have all the charts drawn on the Mercator projection. Beautifully engraved by Antonio Francesco Lucini, who spent eight years working on the copper-plates, it is without ornamentation, and far in advance geographically of other atlases of the period.[15]

EDITION

Carta particolare della costa d'Inghilterra è Francia che comincia con l'Isola di Garnesy e Finisce con il C. di Fecam nella costa di Normandia. La longitudine comincia da l'Isola de Picco d'Asores di Europa Carta XXVII (Dc). *A.F. Lucini Fece* (Ee). Compass (Bc).

Dell'arcano del mare di D. Rvberto Dvdleo . . .
Florence, Francesco Onofri, 1646–7.   BL.NMM
The work is in six 'books'. Books I to V were published in 1646; book VI (the atlas), in which this chart appears, in 1647. Book II contains another chart (467 mm × 365 mm) with the title *Carta quinta generale di Europa* (Ec) and *A.F. Lucini Feci* (Ee OS). This chart encompasses the English Channel, called *The Narrow Seaes,* and names fourteen places and features in Sussex. The work was reissued in 1661 (NMM).

---

13 Koeman, 1970 vol. 4, pp. 30–1.
14 Howse and Sanderson, 1973, p. 65.
15 Tooley, 1949, p. 21.

Size: 218 mm × 164 mm (1 mm) [1:135,000]

The page is divided into two parts by a 2 mm horizontal border, similar in style to the outer border. The two parts together cover the coast from *CHICHESTER* to *Rottingdean,* and extend inland as far as *Boxgrove* and *Offham.*

EDITIONS

(i) Top part 218 mm × 80 mm, with title *LITTLE HAMPTON, BOGNOR, WORTHING, ARUNDEL &c* (Ce). Bottom part 218 mm × 83 mm, with title *ENVIRONS OF BRIGHTON* (Ce), and *SCALE* 4 miles = 48 mm (Ce above title). *Published by J. Cary, Sepr. 25. 1809* (Ce OS). *For Cary's New Itinerary.* (Ea OS).

> *Cary's new itinerary . . .* 4th edition.
> London, J. Cary, 1810.
> RGS
> The 1st (1798), 2nd (1802) and 3rd (1806) editions do not contain this map. The work is often bound with Cary's *Traveller's companion.*

(ii) In the reprint of the 4th edition and in later editions of the work, the map was amended as set out below. It is possible that new plates were engraved for some of the later editions, and that the maps in the 1828 edition may be from lithographic transfers.

4th edition, 1810	Imprint (Ce OS) altered to . . . *J. Cary. Jany. 2nd. 1810.*
5th edition, 1812	Imprint (Ce OS) altered to . . . *J. Cary May 1st. 1812.* Some place-names re-engraved.
6th edition, 1815	Imprint (Ce OS) altered to . . . *J. Cary N°. 181 Strand. SIXTH EDITION* added (Aa OS). All subsequent editions have the edition number in capitals (Aa OS).
7th edition, 1817	Plate re-engraved. Dimensions reduced by 1 mm. *Combe,* near *LEWES,* omitted. *Finden* and *Hamsey* no longer overlap right border. *Lit Buckingham* appears as *Little Buckingham.*
8th edition, 1819	Horizontal dimension 214 mm.
9th edition, 1821	Imprint (Ce OS) altered to . . . *J. Cary N°. 86, S^t. James's Str.* Hill hachuring reduced, marshland pictographs erased, trees erased near *ARUNDEL PARK. Priory F.* and *Marsh F.* erased and replaced by *Priory Fm* and *Marsh Fm. Little Buckingham* erased. *STEYNING* re-engraved.
10th edition, 1826	Probably re-engraved. Now 78 mm × 210 mm and 80 mm × 210 mm. Imprint (Ce OS) altered to . . . *G. & J. Cary, N°. 86, S^t. James's Street. NEW SHOREHAM* and *Kingston by Sea* clearly re-engraved. Left border of top part moved 2 mm inwards. *Arundel & Portsmouth Canal* added, *Barn Rocks* and roads from *Beeding* to *NEW SHOREHAM* and *Kingston by Sea* omitted.
11th edition, 1828	Now 78 mm × 205 mm and 80 mm × 205 mm. No indication of re-engraving.

Size: See below

Daniel Paterson[16] (1738–1825) was commissioned in the army in 1765, and served in the Quartermaster General's department. He was Assistant Quartermaster General from 1804 until his retirement in 1812. He then received the sinecure appointment of Lieutenant-Governor of Quebec, which perhaps indicates the esteem in which he was held. The copyright in the work below was acquired by Francis Newbery in 1788; Paterson had no connection with the publication at the time of the Cary legal action (see no. 49). Three pages of maps in the work refer to Sussex. Each page is divided into two parts by a 2 mm horizontal border; each part is designated 'plate'.

EDITION

Plates 2 and 3. 212 mm × 168 mm (2 mm); upper part 212 mm × 74 mm, lower part 212 mm × 92 mm. *ROUTE FROM DEAL TO HYTHE* (Ca OS). *ROUTE FROM HYTHE TO RYE* (Ce OS). *Plate 2* (Ea OS). *Plate 3* (Ee OS). *Thomson Sculp^t.* (Ae OS). *SCALE OF STATUTE MILES* 4 = 50 mm (Cc, between parts). Compass (Ee, on each part).

Plates 4 and 5. 222 mm × 168 mm (2 mm); each part 222 mm × 83 mm. *ROUTE FROM RYE TO EAST BOURNE* (Ca OS). *ROUTE FROM EAST BOURNE TO NEW SHOREHAM* (Ce OS). *Plate 4* (Ea OS). *Plate 5* (Ee OS). *Thomson Sculp^t.* (Ae OS). *SCALE OF MILES* 5 = 49 mm (Cc, between the two parts). Compass (Be on upper part, and Ce on lower part).

Plates 6 and 7. 219 mm × 170 mm (2 mm); upper part 219 mm × 86 mm, lower part 219 mm × 82 mm. *ROUTE FROM NEW SHOREHAM TO CHICHESTER* (Ca OS). *ROUTE FROM CHICHESTER TO FAREHAM* (Ce OS). *Plate 6* (Ea OS). *Plate 7* (Ee OS). *Thomson Sculp^t.* (Ae OS). *SCALE OF MILES* 5 = 49 mm (Cc, between the parts). Compass (Ce on upper part, and Ae on lower part).

A new and accurate description of all the direct and principal cross roads in England and Wales. 15th edition.
London, Longman, Hurst, Rees, Orme and Brown, and Mr. Faden, 1811. BL.RGS
The first fourteen editions, 1771 to 1808, do not contain these maps. Later editions, with the title *Paterson's Roads*, were published by Edward Mogg. The sixteenth edition (1822) contained the maps described above. For later editions see next following.

16   H.G. Fordham, 'Paterson's roads', *The Library* 4th ser. vol. 5 (1925).

Size: See below.

EDITION

Re-engraved versions of the maps in no. 10 above. The titles and plate numbers remain the same. The Thomson signatures are omitted. The dimensions are as follows:

Plates 2 and 3. 223 mm × 176 mm (2 mm); upper part 223 mm × 72 mm, lower part 223 mm × 102 mm. *ENGLISH MILES* 3 = 37 mm (Cc, between the parts). Compass (Ee, on both parts).

Plates 4 and 5. 223 mm × 172 mm (2 mm); each part 223 mm × 85 mm. *ENGLISH MILES* 6 = 54 mm (Cc). Compass (Be, on both parts).

Plates 6 and 7. 223 mm × 172 mm (2 mm); each part 223 mm × 85 mm. *SCALE OF STATUTE MILES* 5 = 49 mm (Cc). Compass (Ee on upper part, Ae on lower part).

Paterson's roads . . . Seventeenth edition. By Edward Mogg.
London, Longman and others, 1824.   RGS
The same maps appeared in the eighteenth edition which was published in 1826, c. 1829 and c. 1832.

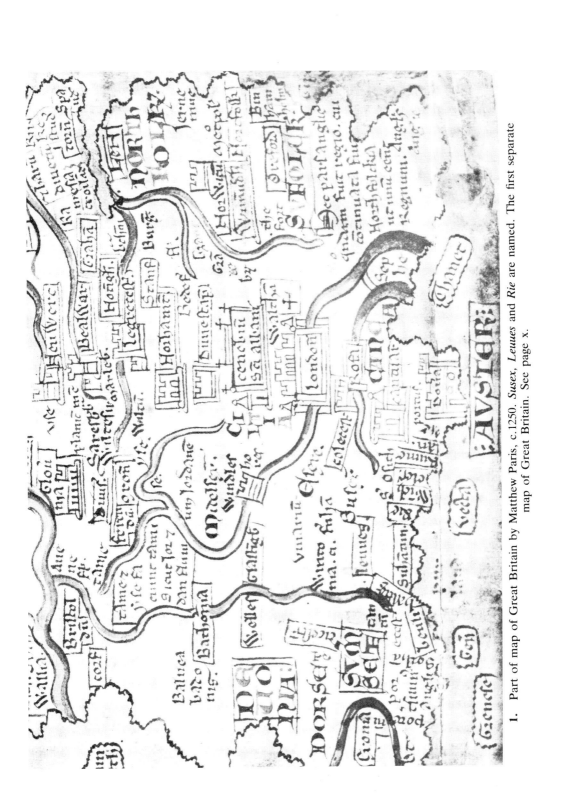

1. Part of map of Great Britain by Matthew Paris, c.1250. *Susex*, *Leuues* and *Rie* are named. The first separate map of Great Britain. See page x.

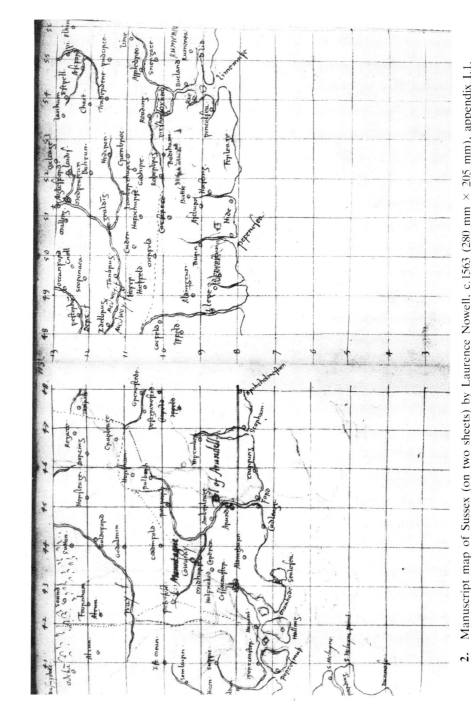

2. Manuscript map of Sussex (on two sheets) by Laurence Nowell. c.1563 (280 mm × 205 mm). appendix I.1. From the first known series of county maps.

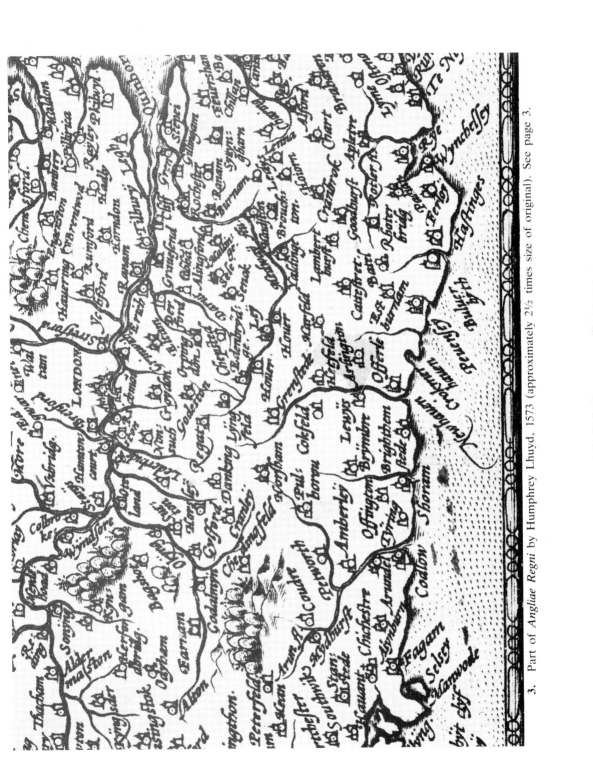

3. Part of *Angliae Regni* by Humphrey Lhuyd, 1573 (approximately 2½ times size of original). See page 3.

4. Map of Sussex by Christopher Saxton, 1575 (544 mm × 406 mm), no. 1(i). From the first printed series of county maps.

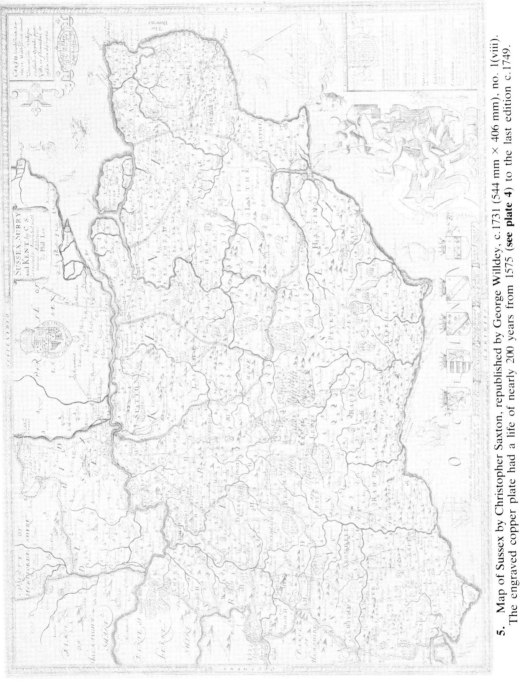

5. Map of Sussex by Christopher Saxton, republished by George Willdey, c. 1731 (544 mm × 406 mm). no. 1(viii). The engraved copper plate had a life of nearly 200 years from 1575 (**see plate 4**) to the last edition c. 1749.

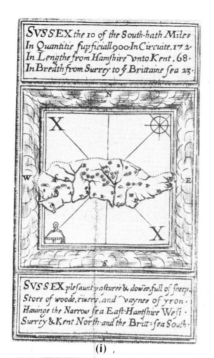

SVSSEX the 10 of the South·hath Miles
In Quantitie supficiall 900 In Circuite. 172·
In Lengthe from Hamshire vnto Kent. 68·
In Bredth from Surry to ʒ Brittaine sea 23·

X

X

SVSSEX plesaunt pastures & dower full of sheep.
Store of woode, riuers, and vaynes of yron·
Hauinge the Narrow sea East·Hantshire West·
Surry & Kent North·and the Britt sea South·

(i)

(ii)

SVSSEX

Sussex on the South Bordereth Vpon
the Brittish Ocean, toward the Sea it
is full of high white Hills, which confist

Chechester

of a fat kind of Chalk, and is very fruit·
full. In the midst are Goodly meddows,
pastures, fields, and many pleasant
groves: the Hether part hath many wood
and hath many veins of Iron.
It hath many Rivers, and hath 312
Parishes.

(iii)

4 Sussex.

Miles
5   10

Length.———————————— 53.
Bredth.———————————— 16.
Circunference.———————— 172.
Chichester { D. from Lon. 50. 57.
           { Lattitude. 50. 48.

(iv)

6. Maps of Sussex on playing-cards. **(i)** William Bowes, 1590 (56 mm × 94 mm), no. 2. **(ii)** William Bowes, c.1605 (52 mm × 89 mm), no. 4. **(iii)** William Redmayne, 1676 (51 mm × 89 mm), no. 16(ii). **(iv)** Robert Morden, 1676 (57 mm × 93 mm), no. 17(i). See also **plate 27(i).**

7. Map of Sussex by John Speed, c.1770 (510 mm × 384 mm), no. 7(ix). The last edition of a map first published in 1611. The wear on the copper plate is noticable in the battle scene (below Royal arms). The damage to the bottom left corner had occurred before 1676.

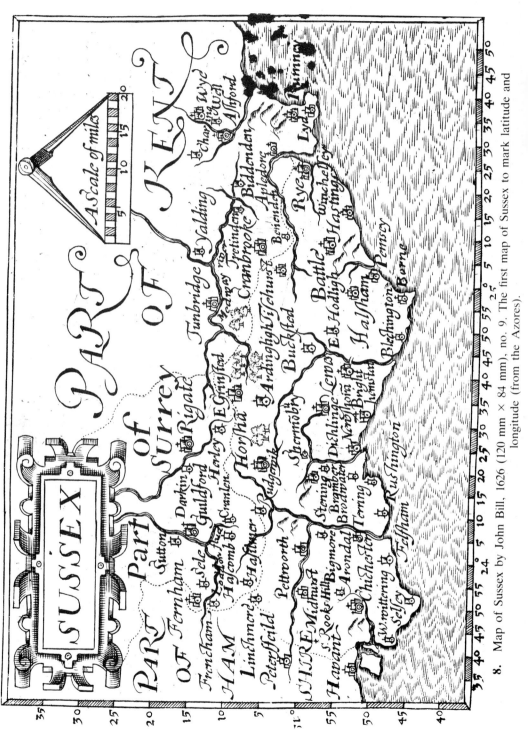

8. Map of Sussex by John Bill, 1626 (120 mm × 84 mm), no. 9. The first map of Sussex to mark latitude and longitude (from the Azores).

Suſſex	Chicheſter	Midhurſte	Petvvarth	Arondell	Terring	Stening	Horſham	Shoreham	Grinſted	Buckehurſt	Ditcheling	Brighthelmſt	Lewes	Haylſham	Battell	Eaſtbourne	Haſting	Winchelſey	Rye	Pemſey	Mayfelde	Buckeſled	Headleygh	Ardingleigh	Pulboro	Billinghurſt
Rotherfeilde N E	17	35	39	40	15	17	19	21	9	5	15	18	13	11	12	16	20	21	22	16	2	5	8	11	25	23
Billingſhur N E	15	12	7	10	21	7	6	12	16	20	23	15	18	27	38	30	19	43	43	33	12	20	22	13	4	35
Pulboro N E	11	11	5	7	7	9	11	23	23	15	18	9	36	34	44	45	32	26	22	23	15	35				
Ardingleigh N E	17	24	19	20	15	13	8	14	5	8	8	13	12	8	13	22	18	31	12	23	13	9	12	25		
Headleigh E	33	33	28	19	20	17	20	16	13	10	10	12	6	6	13	11	17	22	21	11	7	4	7			
Buckeſled E	32	32	26	25	20	7	17	16	9	6	10	13	8	9	15	14	20	23	23	15	5	74				
Mayfeilde E	38	36	30	30	25	22	20	20	10	6	14	18	12	9	12	15	18	19	20	14	77					
Pemſey E	42	43	37	35	28	16	30	14	23	20	19	10	4	6	7	4	9	11	15	47						
Rye E	54	55	49	48	40	18	19	13	30	16	31	12	27	18	10	18	8	2	47							
Winſhelſey E	54	54	48	46	40	18	39	36	30	25	30	12	26	27	8	17	6	49								
Haſting E	50	50	45	43	37	14	12	28	14	27	28	22	13	7	12	50										
Eaſtbourne E	48	48	43	41	34	18	20	22	20	18	17	12	6	10	49											
Battell E	44	45	40	37	32	29	30	28	22	18	23	14	18	9	45											
Haylſham E	38	38	32	30	24	21	25	20	18	14	15	15	10	45												
Lewes E	28	28	23	20	14	12	17	9	14	4	6	6	40													
Brighthelmſt E	23	24	19	15	9	7	15	4	18	7	5	45														
Ditcheling E	25	23	18	16	10	7	11	6	12	12	36															
Buckehurſte N E	33	41	26	27	22	18	15	19	4	28																
Grinſted N E	31	28	22	25	20	16	11	18	25																	
Shoreham E	19	20	15	10	5	5	13	43																		
Horſham N E	21	17	12	15	13	10	47																			
Stening N E	17	17	11	9	4	39																				
Terringe E	14	16	11	7	45																					
Arondell E	8	10	8	47																						
Petworth N	10	6	46																							
Midhurſte N	8	45																								

Da rum wood, haſt.
Deane eaſt, Peven.
Deane weſt, Chich.
Deane eaſt, chich.
Deane weſt, Peven.
Delſham, bram.
Deaton, Peven.
DICHELING, Le.
Didleſford, Arun.
Didling, chich.
Downe forreſt, PeCan.
Downly, chich.

Downton, Arun.
Drayton, chich.
Drungwick, Arun.
Dunhurſt, Arun.
Dunnington, chich.
Duddleſwell, Peven.
Dumpford, chich.
Durrington, bram.
Dyke, Peven.

E
Eartham, chich,
Eaſtergate, Arun.

Eaſton, chich.
Eawood, haſt.
Eborn, chich.
EBOURN, Peven.
Edburton, bram.
Ellſted, chich.
Emley, chich.
Emſworth, chich.
Euſtons, haſt.
Eridge, haſt.
Eridge, Peven.
Eringham, bram.
Erling-

X

9. Map of Sussex with triangular table of distances by Thomas Jenner, 1668 (106 mm × 165 mm), no. 11(ii).

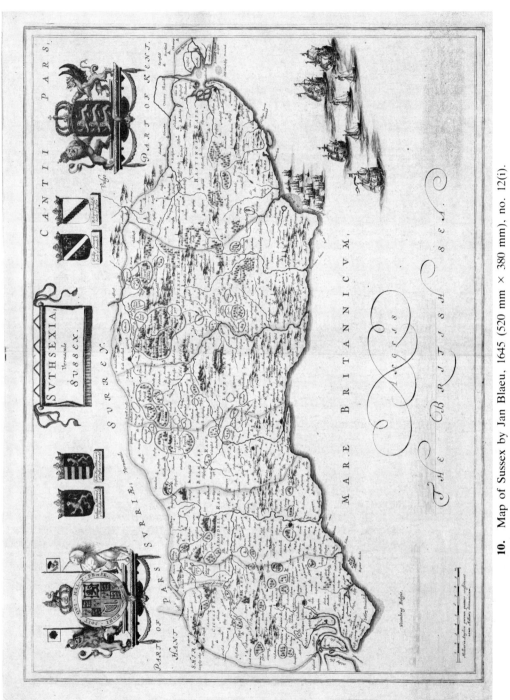

10. Map of Sussex by Jan Blaeu, 1645 (520 mm × 380 mm), no. 12(i).

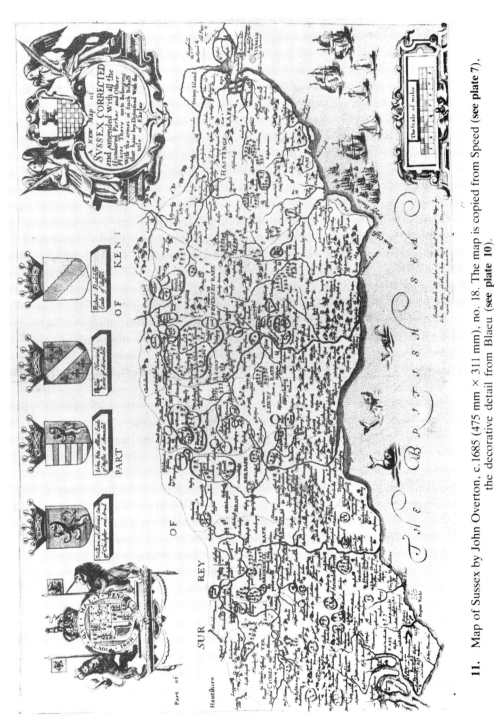

11. Map of Sussex by John Overton, c.1685 (475 mm × 311 mm), no. 18. The map is copied from Speed **(see plate 7)**, the decorative detail from Blaeu **(see plate 10)**.

12. Top half of third sheet of Richard Budgen's map of Sussex, 1723 (510 mm × 360 mm), no. 24(ii). The first large-scale map of the country.

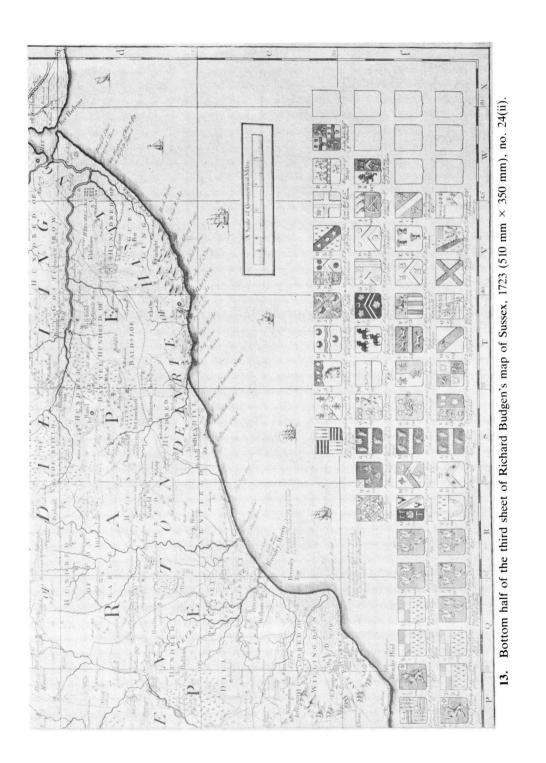

13. Bottom half of the third sheet of Richard Budgen's map of Sussex, 1723 (510 mm × 350 mm), no. 24(ii).

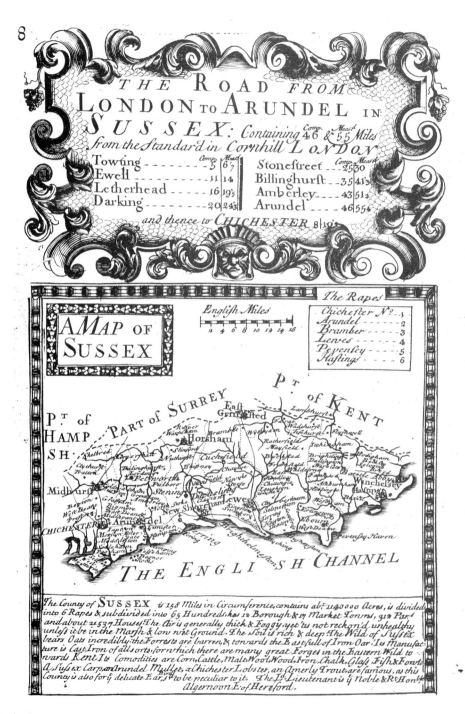

14. Map of Sussex from Emanuel Bowen's *Britannia Depicta*, 1720 (120 mm × 183 mm). no. 23(i). **Plate 38** is from the same book.

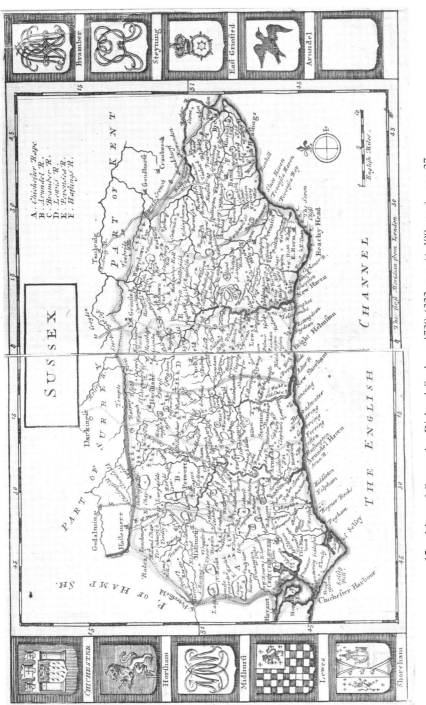

15. Map of Sussex by Richard Seale, c.1730 (322 mm × 190 mm), no. 27.

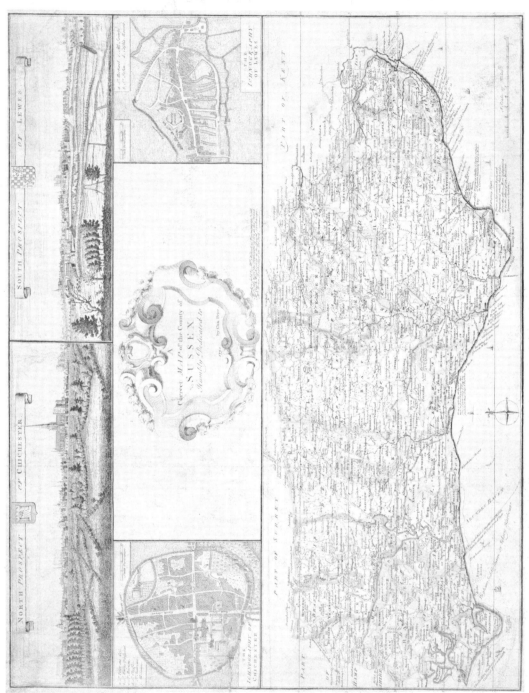

16. Map of Sussex by Charles Price, 1730 (587 mm × 463 mm), no. 28(i).

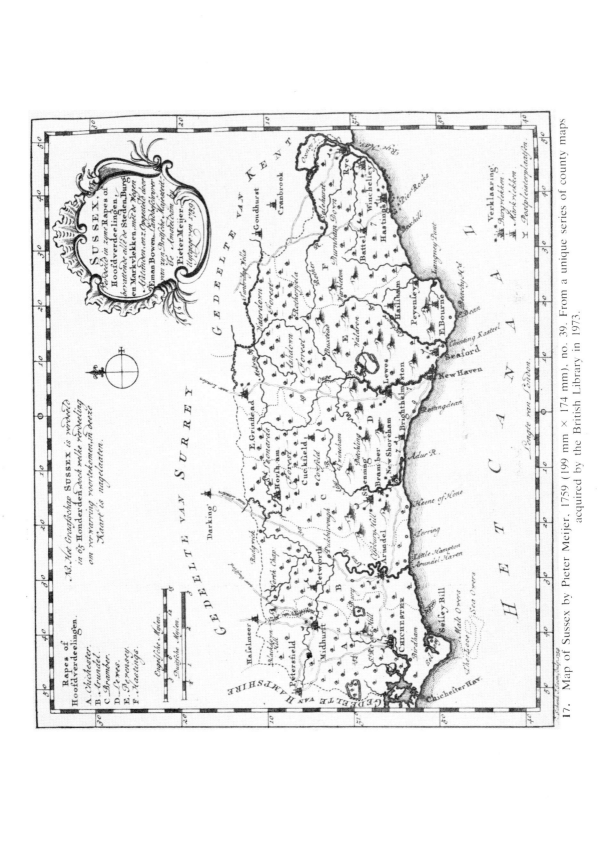

17. Map of Sussex by Pieter Meijer, 1759 (199 mm × 174 mm), no. 39. From a unique series of county maps acquired by the British Library in 1973.

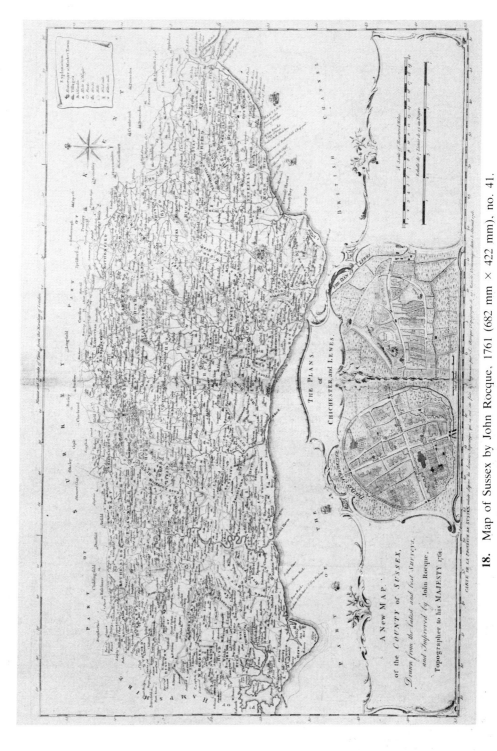

18. Map of Sussex by John Rocque. 1761 (682 mm × 422 mm), no. 41.

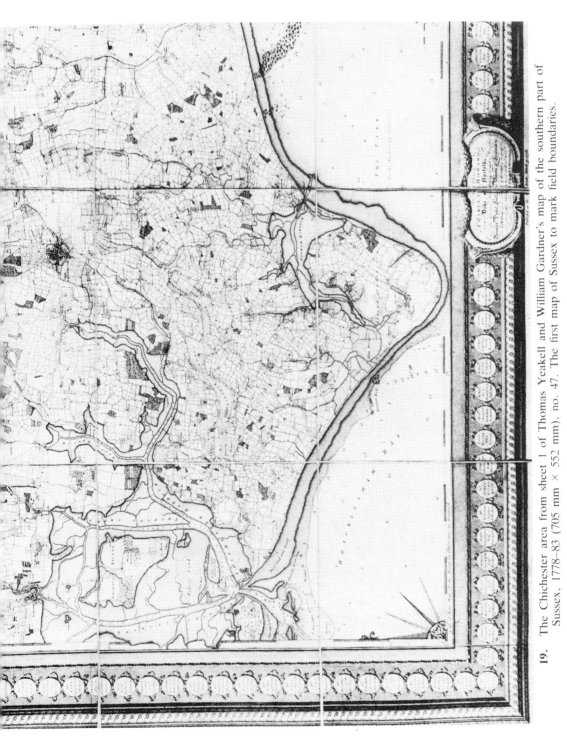

19.   The Chichester area from sheet 1 of Thomas Yeakell and William Gardner's map of the southern part of Sussex, 1778–83 (705 mm × 552 mm), no. 47. The first map of Sussex to mark field boundaries.

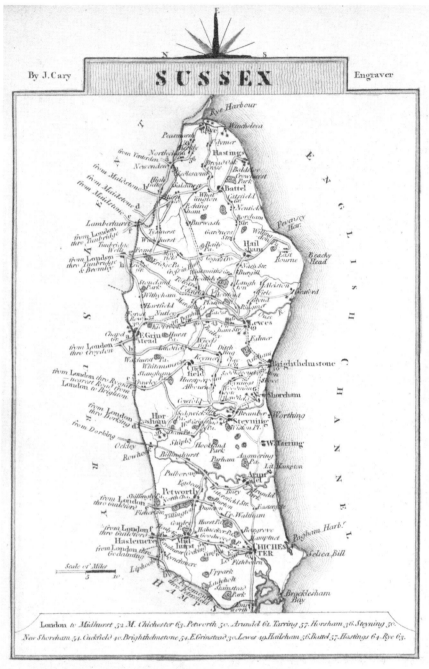

20. Map of Sussex by John Cary, 1792 (93 mm × 147 mm), no. 51(iv). Plate 21 illustrates a very similar map by Cary from a separately engraved plate.

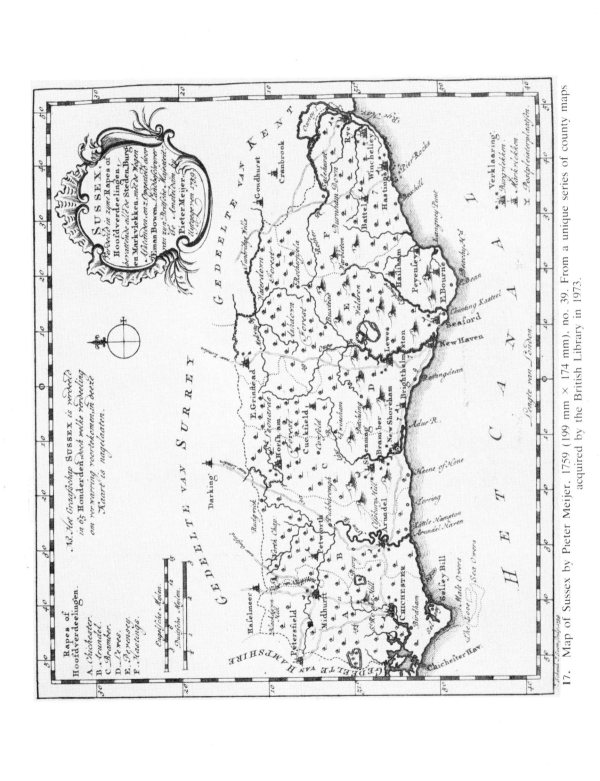

17. Map of Sussex by Pieter Meijer. 1759 (199 mm × 174 mm). no. 39. From a unique series of county maps acquired by the British Library in 1973.

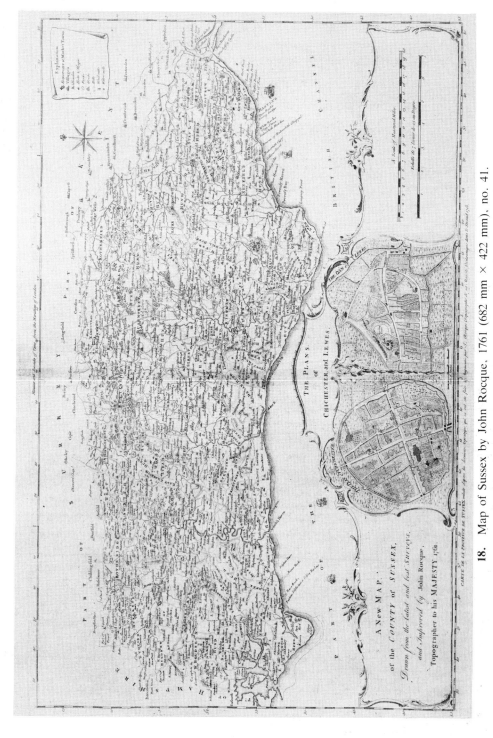

18. Map of Sussex by John Rocque, 1761 (682 mm × 422 mm). no. 41.

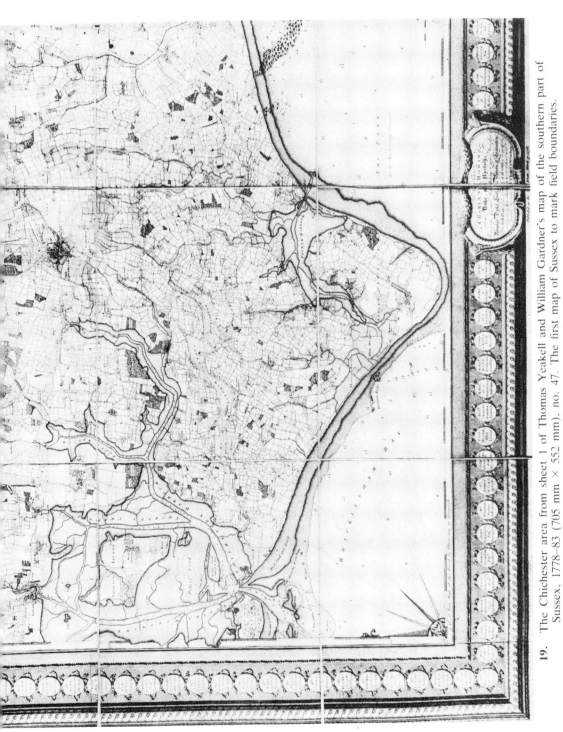

19. The Chichester area from sheet 1 of Thomas Yeakell and William Gardner's map of the southern part of Sussex, 1778–83 (705 mm × 552 mm), no. 47. The first map of Sussex to mark field boundaries.

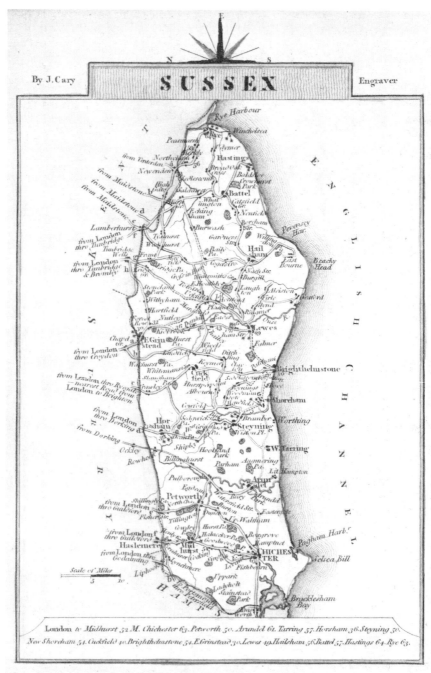

20. Map of Sussex by John Cary, 1792 (93 mm × 147 mm), no. 51(iv). Plate 21 illustrates a very similar map by Cary from a separately engraved plate.

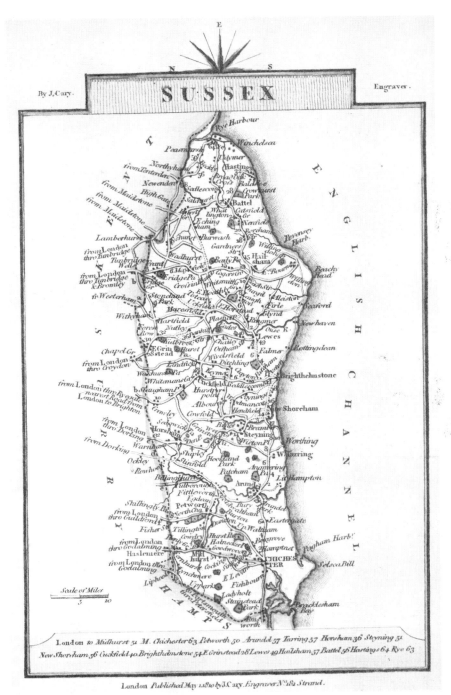

21. Map of Sussex by John Cary, 1810 (92 mm × 146 mm), no. 65(ii). **See plate 20.**

22. Part of sheet four from map of Sussex by William Gardner, Thomas Yeakell and Thomas Gream, 1795 (500 mm × 480 mm), no. 57(ii). The first map of Sussex to be based on a scientific trigonometical survey, and a forerunner of the Ordnance Survey maps.

23. Lattendens Farm, Ashburnham from: **(i)** Estate plan by W. Pearce, 1793–4; **(ii)** Yeakell and Gardner, 1778–83, no. 47; **(iii)** Gardner, Yeakell and Gream, 1795, no. 57; **(iv)** Ordnance Survey drawing on scale of 2" to one mile, surveyed c.1795. Pecked lines added by compiler to indicate the farm boundary on **(ii)** and **(iii)**. Field boundaries on the 1778–83 map **(ii)** correspond well with the estate plan **(i)**: field boundaries on **(iii)** and **(iv)** do not correspond with the estate plan or with each other. See page 92.

24. Map of Sussex by John Cary, 1856 (540 mm × 480 mm), no. 61B. **See plate 25.**

25. Map of Sussex by John Cary, 1863 (540 mm × 480 mm), no. 61D. Note (by comparison with **plate 24**) the rearrangement of features – title, scale, reference to hundreds, explanation and geological legends – made possible by the lithographic process.

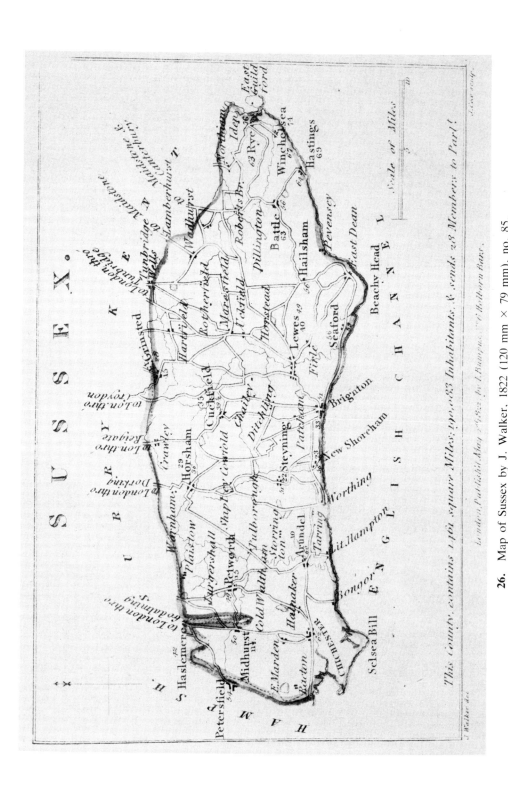

26. Map of Sussex by J. Walker, 1822 (120 mm × 79 mm), no. 85.

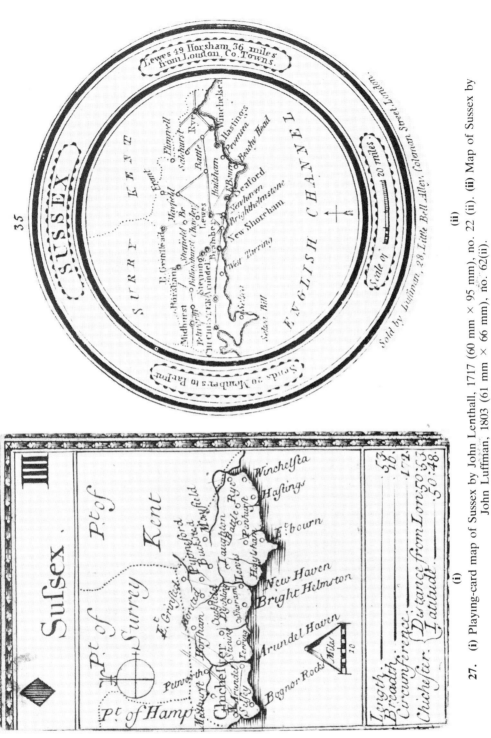

27. **(i)** Playing-card map of Sussex by John Lenthall, 1717 (60 mm × 95 mm), no. 22 (ii). **(ii)** Map of Sussex by John Luffman, 1803 (61 mm × 66 mm), no. 62(ii).

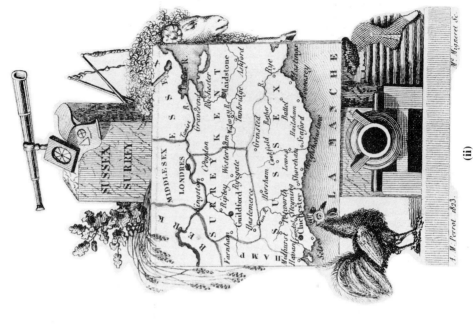

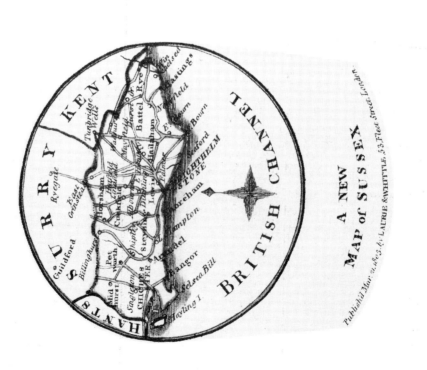

28. **(i)** Map of Sussex by Robert Laurie and James Whittle, 1803 (47 mm × 60 mm), no. 63. **(ii)** Map of Sussex and Surrey by A.M. Perrot, 1823 (68 mm × 108 mm), no. 86.

(i)

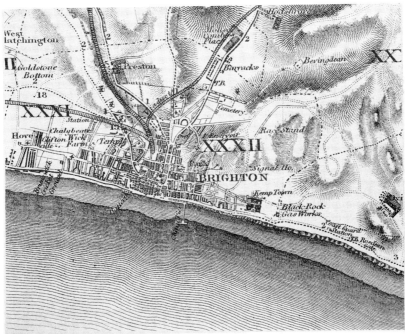

(ii)

29. The Brighton area from map of Sussex by Christopher and John Greenwood:
(i) 1825 (120 mm × 90 mm), no. 89(i): **(ii)** 1861 (122 mm × 95 mm), no. 89A,
which is a lithographic transfer from the same plate.

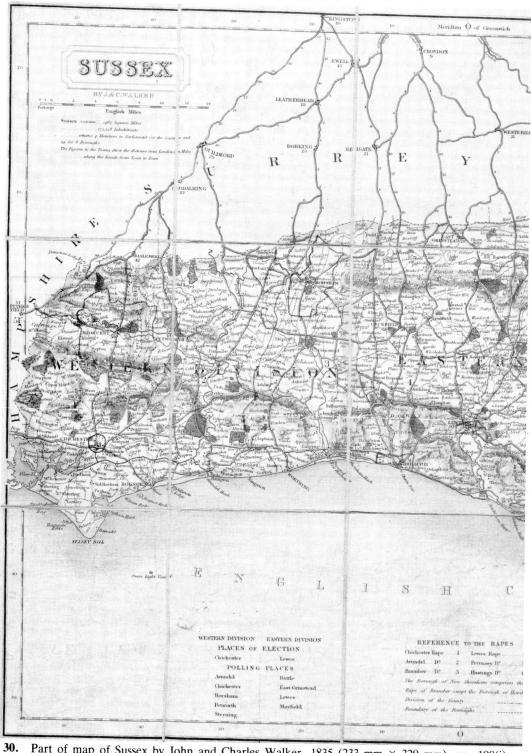

30. Part of map of Sussex by John and Charles Walker, 1835 (233 mm × 320 mm), no. 108(i).
Plates 31, 32 and 33 illustrate later editions of this map.

31. Part of map of Sussex by John and Charles Walker, 1852 (236 mm × 320 mm), no. 108(xv). Extensive alterations have been made to the plate since the first edition (**see plate 30**).

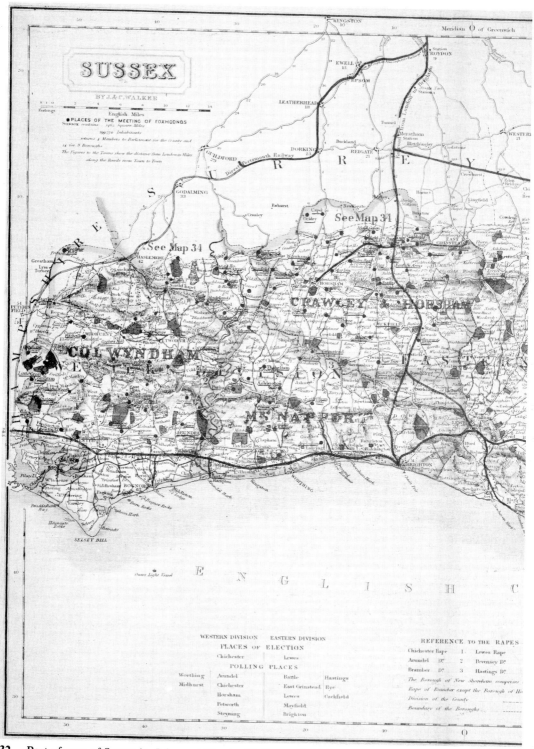

32. Part of map of Sussex by John and Charles Walker, c.1849 (233 mm × 318 mm), no. 108A(i). This lithographic transfer was taken from the engraved plate in state (xv) **(see plate 31)**, which was not the final state of the plate.

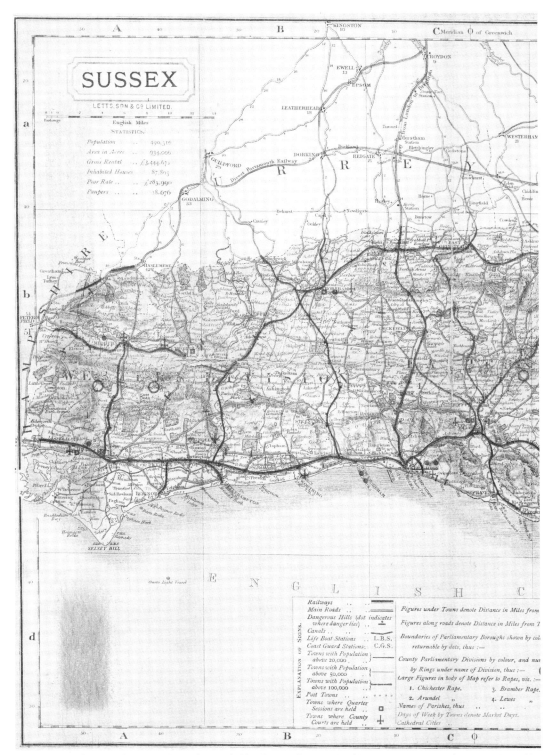

33. Part of map of Sussex by John and Charles Walker, 1884 (242 mm × 320 mm), no. 108I. This lithographic transfer as taken from the engraved plate in state (xxi). Some of the many changes compared with the map in its original state **(plate 30)** were made on the engraved plate, others on the lithographic stone.

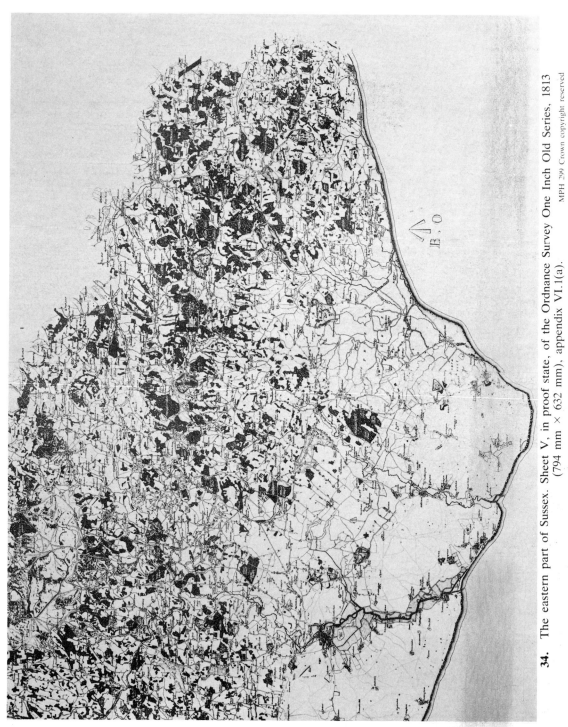

34. The eastern part of Sussex. Sheet V, in proof state, of the Ordnance Survey One Inch Old Series, 1813 (794 mm × 632 mm), appendix VI.1(a).

35. The Horsham area from James Edwards's *Companion from London to Brighthelmston*, 1799 (432 mm × 268 mm), appendix VII.3.

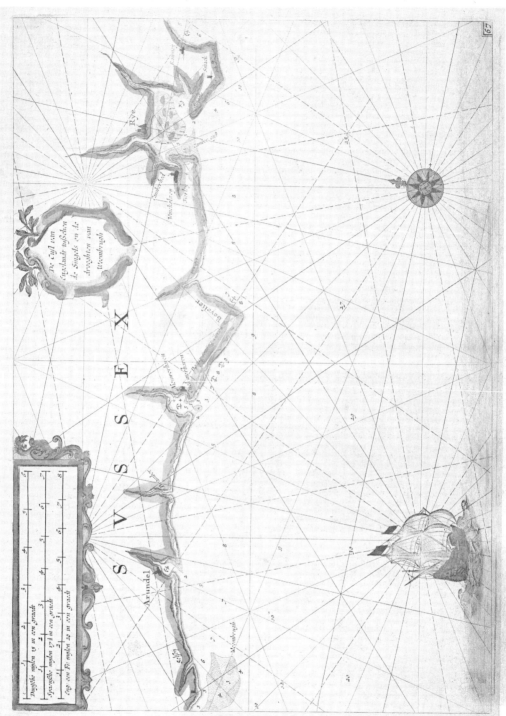

36. Chart showing the coast of Sussex by Jan Blaeu, 1625 (357 mm × 258 mm). appendix II.6.

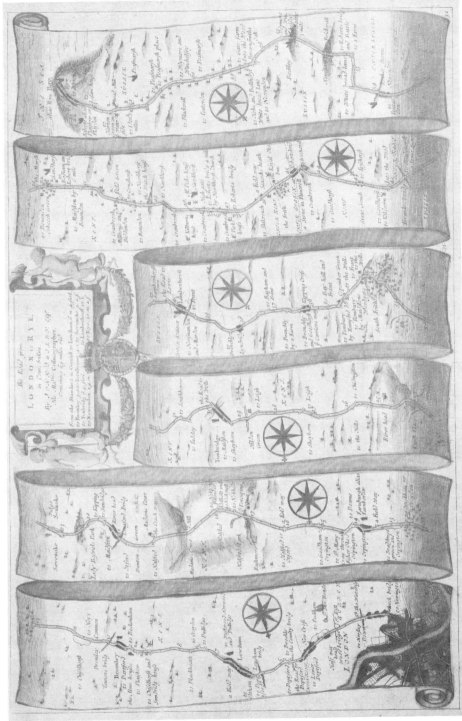

37. *The Road from LONDON to RYE* from John Ogilby's *Britannia*, 1675 (445 mm × 292 mm). appendix V.1.

38. The road from *Robooke* to Chichester from Emanuel Bowen's *Britannia Depicta*, 1720 (120 mm × 180 mm), appendix V.4(i).

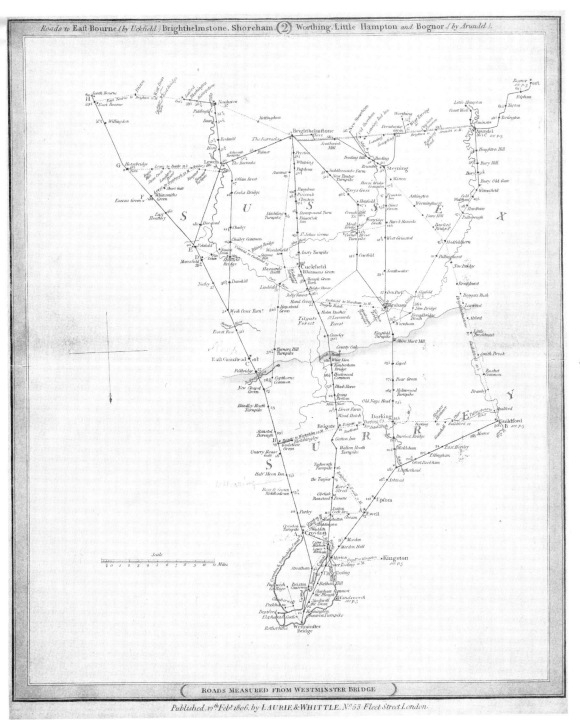

Published 12th Feby 1806, by LAURIE & WHITTLE, No 53 Fleet Street London.

39. The roads from London to the coast between Eastbourne and Bognor from *Laurie and Whittle's New Traveller's Companion*, 1806 (252 mm × 300 mm), appendix V.15(i). The coastline was added to the maps in state (ii).

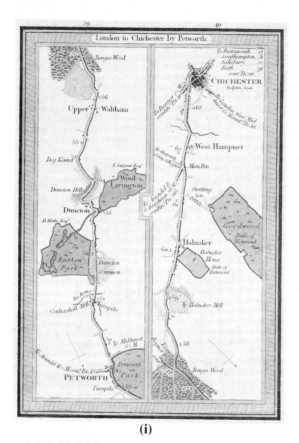

(i)

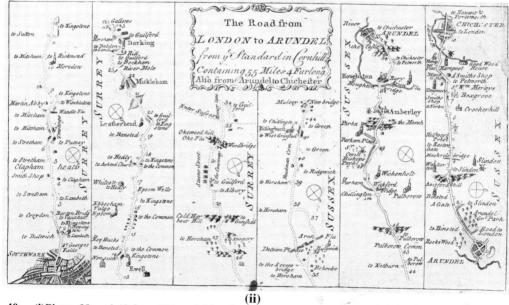

(ii)

40. **(i)**Plates 39 and 40 from Edward Mogg's *A Survey of the High Roads*, 1828 (142 mm × 207 mm), appendix V.16(iv), **(ii)** *The Road from LONDON to ARUNDEL* from an unidentified road-book (196 mm × 107 mm), appendix VIII.2.

III   MAPS OF SOUTH-EAST ENGLAND

Maps of south-east England are numerous. Although some, eg the geological maps, provide information about the county not found on other maps, their main importance lies in tracing the historical cartography of the area. The earlier maps and a selection from later publications are listed below.

1   GERARD MERCATOR   1595

Size: 448 mm × 347 mm   1:686,000

EDITIONS

(i) *Warwicum, Northhamtonia, Huntingdonia, Cantabrigia, Suffolcia, Oxonium, Buckinghamia, Bedfordia, Hartfordia, Essexia, Berceria, Middelsexia, Southhātonia, Surria, Cantiū & Southsexia* (Ec). *Miliaria Anglica magna* 22 = 64 mm. *Parva* 20 = 51 mm (De). Longitude 20' (2'); latitude 20' (2').

> *Atlas sive cosmographicae meditationes de fabrica mundi . . . Gerardo Mercatore Rumpelmundaño.*
> Duisburg, 1595.   BL
> The map appeared in Mercator atlases from 1595 to 1635.[1]

(ii) The title and cartouche re-engraved, *Warwicum Northamtonia Huntingdonia Cantabrigia Suffolcia Oxonium Buckinghamia Bedfordia Hardfordia Essexia Berceria Middelsexia Southantonia Surria Cantium et Southsexia* (Ec). *Sumptibus Henrici Hondy* added (Ee). Scales re-engraved, but wording (except *Milliaria* for *Miliaria*) and figures unchanged. Sea stippling erased.[2] Numerous minor alterations on the map, eg *Ernley* re-engraved (formerly in the sea).

> *Gerardi Mercatoris et I. Hondii atlas, or a geographicke description of the regions, countries and kingdoms of the world . . . Translated by Henry Hexham, quarter-maister to the regiment of Colonell Goring.*
> Amsterdam, Henry Hondius and John Johnson, 1636.   BL
> The map appeared in Mercator atlases published in 1638, 1639 and 1642,[3] and in an atlas published by Jacob de La Feuille after 1709.[4]

---

1   J. Keunig, 'The history of an atlas' *Imago Mundi* vol. 4 (1947), pp. 37–62; Whitaker, 1948, p. 200; Skelton, *County atlases,* 1970, p. 220.
2   Skelton, *County Atlases,* 1970 p. 222 states that the Mercator signature has also been erased, but no impression of the map in state (i) or (ii) *with* the Mercator signature has been found.
3   Whitaker, 1948, p. 200.
4   Cowling, 1959, addenda no. 173A; Le Gear, 1958, p. 208.

2 GERARD MERCATOR AND JODOCUS HONDIUS [1607]

Size: 169 mm × 127 mm (9 mm)   1:1,880,000

EDITION

Warwicum Northampton Huntingdon Cantabr. etc. (Ec). *Miliaria Anglica* 20 = 27 mm
(De). Longitude 1° (5'); latitude 1° (5').

> *Atlas minor Gerardi Mercatoris à I Hondio.*
> Arnhem, Jan Jansson [1607].   BL
> The map, with text on the back in Latin, German French and English, appeared in reissues of this atlas
> to 1637. Titles in the appropriate language (*ANGLETERRE, ANGLIAE VI TABULA* or *THE SIXT
> TABLE OF ENGLAND*), pages numbers (*87* or *91*) and printer's marks (*L2*) were added to the face
> of the maps in some issues.[5] Other editions of *Atlas minor* contained in no. 4 below.

3 SALOMON ROGIERS   1616

Size: 123 mm × 83 mm (6 mm)   1:3,240,000

Rogiers was probably the engraver; his signature appears on other maps in the
atlas.

Petrus Bertius (1565–1629) was born in Flanders. He was a professor of mathematics at Leyden, and in 1618 cosmographer to Louis XIII in Paris, where he died.

EDITION

Warwicum Northapton Hunting. etc. (Ec) *Miliaria Anglica* 30 = 17 mm (De).
Longitude 1° (6'), latitude 1° (6'). *148* (Ae OS). *TAB. VI. ANGLIAE,* IN QUA
WARWICUM &c. (Ca OS).

> *P. Bertii tabularum geographicarum . . .*
> Amsterdam, Jodocus Hondius, 1616.   BL
> Earlier editions of this atlas 1600 to 1613[6] do not contain this map. The map appeared in a reissue of
> the atlas in 1616, with French text and the title (Ca OS) altered to *TABLE VI D'ANGLETERRE EN
> LAQUELLE SONT WARWIC &c;* and in 1639 in *Gvili. Camdeni viri clarissimi Britannia* published by
> Blaeu with the title and page number erased.[7]

---

5 Whitaker, 1948, p. 201; Skelton, *County atlases,* 1970, p. 226–7.
6 Le Gear, 1958, p. 111 records Latin editions in 1600, 1602, 1605, 1606 and 1613, and a German edition
   in 1612. A Latin edition in 1620, a German edition in 1650, and French editions in 1617, 1618 and c.
   1640 are also noticed and may have contained this map.
7 Whitaker, 1948, nos. 32 and 75.

4   GERARD MERCATOR AND JODOCUS HONDIUS   1628

Size: 192 mm × 136 mm (6 mm)   1:1,550,000

EDITION

Warwicum, Northhamtonia, Hundingdonia, Cantabrigia, Suffolcia, Oxonium, Buckinghamia, Bedfordia, Hartfordia, Essexia, Berceria, Middelsexia, Southamtonia, Surria, Cātium, et Southsexia. (Ec). *Miliaria Anglica* 25 = 26 mm (Ec). Longitude 1° (5'), latitude 1° (5'). *ANGLIAE VI TABULA* (Ca OS). *79* (Ea OS).

Atlas minor Gerardi Mercatoris a I. Hondio.
Amsterdam, Jan Jansson, 1628.   BL
The map appeared in reissues of this atlas up to 1729, with text on the back in Latin, German, French and Dutch. The title (Ca OS) was altered to the appropriate language (eg *SIXIESME TABLE D'ANGELTERRE, DER SESTE CAERTE VAN ENGHELANDT*) and in some issues a page number was added.[8]

5   GERARD MERCATOR AND JODOCUS HONDIUS   1630

Size: 235 mm × 170 mm (9 mm)   1:1,300,000

EDITION

Warwicum, Northhamtonia, HUNTINGDONIA CANTABRIGIA, SUFFOLCIA, OXONIUM, BUCKINGHAMIA, BEDFORDIA Hartfordia Essexia BERCERI MIDELSEXIA, SOUTHHATONIA Surria, Cantium Southsexia (Ec). *Miliaria Anglica magna* 22 = 30 mm. *parva* 20 = 25 mm (below this title in same panel). *ANGLETERRE.* (Ca OS). *87* (Ea OS). Longitude 1° (2'), latitude 1° (2').

Gerardi Mercatoris atlas sive cosmographicae meditationes . . .
Amsterdam, Johan Cloppenburgh, 1630.   BL
The text on the back is in French. The map appeared in reissues of the atlas in 1632 (Latin), 1636 (French) and 1673 (plain back, published by Jansson).[9] In the 1632 edition the title (Ca OS) is *Angliae VI Tabula;* the 1673 edition has no heading. French editions, 1734 to 1738, are in the Library of Congress.[10]

8   Ibid., pp. 201–2.
9   Ibid, no. 53.
10 Cowling, 1959, addenda nos. 203A and 207A; Le Gear, 1958 pp. 219, 222.

6 WENCESLAUS HOLLAR   1644

Size: 510 mm × 278 mm (single-line border)   1:440,000

A re-engraved version of Saxton.

One of six sections, published for use by the parliamentary armies during the Civil War and known as the Quartermaster's Map. An unusual characteristic of this map is that it is etched (by use of acid), whereas line-engraving, using a graving tool to cut the metal plate, was the more popular technique.[11]

EDITIONS

(i) *A MAPPE OF KENT, SOVTHSEX, SVRREY, MID=dlesex, Barke, and Southampton Shire, & the Ile of Vight, part of Essex, & Wiltshire, etc.* (Ee). *English Myles* 20 = 85 mm (Ee, in same panel as the title).

Found only as a loose sheet.   (P)

(ii)   Compass added (Ce). Some place-names added, eg *marget bay. VIGTH* altered to *WIGTH* on the island.

The kingdome of England & principality of Wales exactly described . . . in six mappes portable for every mans pocket.
London, Thomas Jenner, 1644.   BL.RGS.AD

(iii)   In the title (Ee) *Vight* altered to *Wight. Denton* appeared as *Denion.*

The kingdome of England . . .
London, Thomas Jenner, 1644.   BL

(iv)   *Sold by Thomas Jenner at the South Entrance of the Royall Exchange in London* added (Ce, below compass). Roads added; in Sussex those from *LONDON* to *CHECHESTER* and from *LONDON* to *RYE* only.

The kingdome of England . . .
London, Thomas Jenner, 1671.   BOD

(v)   *Printed Coloured and* added above imprint (Ce); *Thomas Jenner* erased and replaced by *Iohn Garrett.*

---

11   Skelton, 1952, p. 4; Skelton, 1974, includes a full description of these maps.

The kingdome of England . . .
London, John Garrett, 1676.   BL.AD
The British Library copy (Maps C.7.b.15) is without title-page; Naval Historical Library copy (Vz 2/25) is disbound, but has title-page dated 1676.

(vi) Additional roads, represented by single and double lines, added. Some coast form lines erased in the Thames estuary and other rivers, and stippling to indicate sandbanks added. *Spitt head* added.

The kingdome of England . . .
London, John Garrett, [1688].   BL.AD
The date is from an Advertisement in the *Term Catalogue*. The map was reissued by 1752 by John Rocque, and again after Rocque's death, possibly as late as 1820. Although significant changes were made on other sheets, that containing Sussex seems to have remained unaltered, at least in the 1752 edition. Much of the physical detail, eg coastal form lines and trees, is very faint, giving the impression that the place-names, coastline and roads, but not other details, were retouched.

7 NICHOLAS SANSON   1654

Size: 463 mm × 350 mm (9 mm)   1:748,000

Nicholas Sanson (1600–67) was a pioneer of the French school of cartography. He had three sons, of whom two, Guillaume and Adrien, succeeded him. They in turn were succeeded by Alexis Hubert Jaillot (1632–1712). The map described below is an early example of the maps of south-east England which appeared in numerous continental atlases.

EDITION

ANCIENS ROYAUMES DE KENT, D'ESSEX, ET DE SUSSEX . . . Par le S'. SANSON . . . A PARIS . . . 1654 (Ed). *Mille Pas Geometriques* 30 = 63 mm *Milles d'Angleterre* 24 = 63 *Lieues Comunes de France* 12 = 63 mm (Ee). Longitude 10' (2½'); latitude 10' (2½').

Published in Sanson's first atlas in 1654, and in later Sanson atlases. It also appears in an atlas (NMM) dated 1658, but published later, with the title *Cartes générales de toutes parties du monde;* and in a Web edition of Saxton's atlas (BL).

8 JOHN SENEX   1746

Size: 1190 mm × 482 mm (2 mm)   1:201,000

Sussex is based on Budgen no. 24.

EDITION

A Map of the Counties of SURREY, KENT, SUSSEX, HAMPSHIRE and

BARKSHIRE with part of DORSET, WILTSHIRE &c with the Roads, Rivers, Sea-Coast &c, taken from the latest & best Maps extent, now published from y^e drawings of the late Iohn Senex F.R.S. 1746 (Aa to Ae OS). *A Scale of 15 Miles* = 130 mm (Ee). Longitude 10' (30"); latitude 10' (30"). Note commencing *Sold by M. Senex . . .* (Ee, below scale).

Issued in 1746 as a loose map.   (BL)

9 JOHN ANDREWS AND ANDREW DURY   1777

Sussex sheets based on Budgen no. 24, but with reference to Price no. 28 and to Overton no. 26.

The full map on twenty plates was first published between 1774 and 1777. The title is on plate *N°.1*. The Sussex plates, which are all dated 1777, are listed below, in order from top left to bottom right. The plate numbers were added from type.

EDITIONS

(i) *A MAP of the COUNTRY SIXTY FIVE MILES, ROUND LONDON; from ACTUAL SURVEYS, by John Andrews & Andrew Dury. Price 3L.3S. in Sheets. Now Drawing by Subscription a Map of England & Wales, on Forty one Sheets by John Andrews N°. 29, Long Acre.* (Ce, on plate *N°.1*; the first part in an oval frame, the second part in the border of the frame).

Plate *16* (Ea OS), 692 mm × 448 mm (12 mm). *London, Publish'd as the Act directs, June 10th 1777, by J. Stoke* (De in border). No engraver's signature or scale-bar.

Plate *15* (Ea OS), 653 mm × 468 mm (12 mm). *London, Publish'd as the Act directs June 10, 1777, by John Stoke* (Ce, in border). *Drawn & Engraved by J. Andrews* (Ee, OS). *Scale of English Miles 69½ to a Degree 5* = 109 mm (De, in border).

Plate *14* (Ea OS), 650 mm × 462 mm (12 mm). *London, Published as the Act directs 10 June 1777, by J. Stoke* (Ce, in border). *Drawn & Engraved by John Andrews* (Ae, in border). *Scale of English Miles 69½ to a Degree 5* = 109 mm (Be, in border).

Plate *20* (Ea, in border), 655 mm × 446 mm (12 mm). *London, Publish'd as the Act directs, June 10th. 1777. by John Stoke* (De, in border). *Drawn & Engrav'd by J. Andrews* (Ee OS). *Scale of English Statute Miles 69½ to a Degree 5* = 109 mm (Ce).

Plate *19* (Ea OS), 658 mm × 445 mm (12 mm). *London, Publish'd as the Act directs, April 12th 1777, by J. Stoke* (Be, in order).

Plate *18* (Ea OS) 650 mm × 444 mm (12 mm). *London, Publish'd as the Act directs June 10th. 1777, by J. Stoke.* (Ce, in border). *Drawn & Engrav'd by J. Andrews* (Ee, in border).

Plate *17* (Ea OS), 656 mm × 445 mm (12 mm). *London, Publish'd as the Act Directs June 10, 1777 by J. Stoke* (De OS). *Drawn & Engraved by J. Andrews* (Ee OS). Scale-bar 5 *Miles* = 109 mm (Be OS). This plate includes the dedication and the list of subscribers.

Issued as a set of maps, without title-page [1777].   RGS.GLC.WSRO
A set of these maps in a private collection has an additional page reading *Twenty sheets of a map, intended to consist of twenty four sheets, and to represent the county sixty-five miles round London, MDCCLXXVI.*

(ii) *Sold by John Andrews, No. 211, facing Air Street, Piccadilly.* added (below oval frame to title on plate *No.1*). No alterations to Sussex sheets.

Issued as a set of maps, 1791–3.   BL.GLC

(iii) *Now Drawing . . . Long Acre.* (in border of oval frame on plate *No. 1*) erased. Price altered to *4L,4s. John Andrews, No.211 . . .* (below oval frame) erased and replaced by *London Published Jan 22. 1807 by J. Stockdale Piccadilly.* The imprints amended to read *London, Published* [or *Publish'd*] *as the Act directs. Jany. 22. 1807. by J. Stockdale.*, except plate 19, which has *London, Publish'd as the Act directs, Jany. 22. 1807. by I. Stockdale.*

A map of the country, sixty-five miles round London . . .
London, John Stockdale, 1809.   BL.GL

(iv) Imprint (plate *No.1*, below oval frame) altered to *London Published Jan. 22. 1807 by T. McLean* or *T.M. Lean*, except plate 18, which has *J.* only (*Stockdale* erased).

Issued as a set of maps, without title-page, 1818.   GLC.BRIGHTON PL

10   MUTLOW[12]   1798

Size: (a) Eastern districts: 198 mm × 173 mm (6 mm)
       (b) Western districts: 198 mm × 173 mm (6 mm)   1:540,000

EDITION

(a) *THE EASTERN DISTRICTS OF THE SOUTHERN COUNTIES* (Ec). Compass (Da). (b) *THE WESTERN DISTRICTS OF THE SOUTHERN COUNTIES* (Ec). Compass (Ba). On both sections: *Mutlow Sc. Russell Court (*Ae OS). *Published July 1798, by G.G. & J. Robinson, Pater Noster Row, G. Nicol, Pall Mall, & J. Debret, Picadilly . . .* (Ce OS). Longitude 15' (5'), latitude 15' (5').

---

12 Hannas, 1972, states that the firm of T. Woodman and H. Mutlow took over the business of John Spilsbury, the inventor of jigsaw puzzles, in about 1771. Tooley, 1979, p. 457 refers to an I. Mutlow, engraver, 1794 to 1816.

The rural economy of the southern counties . . . by M^r. [William] *Marshall.*
London, G. Nicol, G.G. and J. Robinson, J. Debret, 1798.   BL.BRIGHTON PL
The work is in two volumes, one map in each. The maps cover the area from Salisbury to the Kent
coast.

11   THOMAS PENNANT[13]   1801

Size: 729 mm × 234 mm (no border)   1:320,000

EDITION

DOVER to the ISLE OF WIGHT (Ee, in oval frame). Sussex is in the centre of the
map. A few place-names are marked, eg *Horsham.*

> *A journey from London to the Isle of Wight, By Thomas Pennant, Esq.,* vol. 2.
> London, Edward Harding, 1801.   BL.WORTHING PL
> Volume 1 contains a map of London and north Kent.

12   M. PHILLIPS   1809

Size: 170 mm × 140 mm (single-line border)   1:1,370,000

EDITION

*Published as the Act directs PHILLIP'S Coasting Companion & Map of Roads to
Fashionable Watering Places. Bray sc Ship St^rt. Brighton.* (Aa, partly in circle sur-
mounted by fleur-de-lys). *Intended as a small sketch of the Grand Southern Tour. &
Map of Roads from London to all the fashionable Watering places between Margate &
Southampton delineating at one view the different Stages with number of miles charged
from one post Town to another* (Ae to Ee).

> *Attree's topography of Brighton: and, picture of the roads.*
> Brighton, H.R. Attree; London, Longman, Hurst and Co. 1809. BL.BRIGHTON PL
> A note preceding the map states 'there shortly will be published, price two guineas to subscribers, by
> the same correct delineator, Mr. Phillips, on an enlarged scale, another map of the same subjects as the
> preceeding . . . It is but an act of justice to observe, that Mr. Phillips has received letters of thanks from
> his Royal Highness the Commander-in-Chief; one of his Majesty's Principal Secretaries of State; the
> Master-General of Ordnance, &c for his descriptive survey of the coast'.

> *Brighton and its environs . . . by C. Walker.*
> London, Townsend, Powell and Co., 1809.   SAS

---

13   Malcolm, 1815; G. Walters, 'Two Welsh map collectors of the 18th century' *The Map Collector* no. 6
(1979). Pennant (1726–98) died before the work was published.

13 M. PHILLIPS   1809

Size: 140 mm × 110 mm (single-line border)   1:1,370,000

EDITION

A re-engraved version of the preceeding map. Part of *HAMPSHIRE* has been omitted,
and the borders moved inwards. The note (Ae to Ee) starts *Map of the Roads . . .*, the
first eleven words being omitted.

Attree's topography of Brighton . . .
Brighton, H.R. Attree; London, Longman, Hurst and Co. 1809.   P

14 J.R. JOBBINS   [1851]

Size: 600 mm × 329 mm (1 mm)   1:522,000

A lithographic transfer; probably from a drawing, not from an engraved plate. The
map may have been printed prior to the publication of the *Proceedings* in 1850–1.

EDITION

ANNO DOMINI 520 (Ca OS). *J.R. Jobbins; 3 Warwick C^t.* (Ee OS). *SCALE OF
MILES* 40 = 126 mm (Bc). Overprinted in yellow, blue and brown (roads).

Volume of proceedings of the Archaeological Institute at Salisbury 1849.
London, The Archaeological Institute [1851].   BL
The map illustrates a paper 'On the early English settlements in South Britain' by Edwin Guest. A map
of Sussex, based on this map, appears in Brandon, 1978, p. 140.
   A second and smaller (233 mm × 173 mm) version of this map (also produced by lithography) was
published in 1883 in *Origines Celticae* vol. 2, by Edwin Guest. The scale of the map is reduced to
1:1,340,000, and there are a number of differences, eg imprint (Ee OS) omitted, roads shown by
engraved double lines.

IV PERSPECTIVE VIEWS

1 WILLIAM HOLE   circa **1612**

Size: 333 mm × 252 mm (single-line border)   [1:420,000]

This is not exactly a perspective view, but fits best into this category. Hole engraved the title-page for *Poly-Olbion,* and he is assumed to have engraved these 'maps', which appear in it. He was born near Leeds, and was well-known for his portrait engravings, including one of Charles I. He also engraved a number of maps for the 1607 edition of Camden's *Britannia* (see catalogue no. 6).

EDITIONS

(i) *SVRREY* and *SVSSEX* are marked on the map, which covers the region between *Tames* and the Sussex coast. The map has little geographical value, but the coast and rivers are reasonably well delineated. Only three towns in Sussex are named. The name *SVSSEX* is grossly misplaced, as are the four forests and *Part of the Weald.* It must be assumed that these were intended primarily as decoration. Each feature is represented by an allegorical figure.

Poly-Olbion by Michael Drayton Esqr:
London, M. Lownes, I. Browne, I. Helme and I. Busbie, [1612].   BL.BRIGHTON PL

(ii) Page number *257* added (Da OS).

Poly-Olbion. or a chorographicall description of tracts, riuers, mountaines, forests, and other parts of this renowned isle of Great Britaine . . . digested in a poem by Michael Drayton, Esq. . .
London, Matthew Lownes, I. Browne, I. Helme and I. Busbie, 1613.
BL.BRIGHTON PL

A chorographicall description of all the tracts, rivers, movntains, forests, and other parts of this renowned isle of Great Britain . . . Digested into a poem by Michael Drayton. Esquire.
London, John Marriott, John Grismand and Thomas Dewe, 1622.   BL

The map in state (ii) was reproduced by the Spenser Society, Manchester, in 1890, in *Poly-Olbion; a chorographicall description of Great Britain. By Michael Drayton,* part 2.

2 GEORGE BICKHAM[1]

circa **1754**

Size: 139 mm × 227 mm (0.5 mm)

[1:1,220,000]

George Bickham (1684–1758) was author of *The Universal penman,* an outstanding work on the art of calligraphy. *The British Monarchy* was the joint work of Bickham and his son, also George. It was issued in parts, and the Sussex section must, therefore, have been issued for the first time between 1751 and 1754, when the complete work was published.

EDITIONS

(i) *A Map of SUSSEX, South from London. Humbly Inscrib'd to the R^t. Honble. ye Earl of Hertford Lord Lieutenant of the County* (Aa to Ea OS). Table of distances below map. *According to Act of Parliament 1751. by G. Bickham.* (Ee OS).   *before page 66* (Ea OS). Sussex is viewed from the North Downs; *KENT* and *SURREY* in the foreground, *ENGLISH CHANNEL* in the background. Eighteen towns and four other features are named in Sussex.

> *The British monarchy: or, a new chorographical description of all the dominions subject to the King of Great Britain . . .*
> London, G. Bickham, 1743 (actually a re-issue made not before 1754).   BL
> Earlier issues of the work, dated 1743, 1748 and 1749, do not contain 'maps'.

(ii) Title, signature and all inscriptions outside the border erased. *SUSSEX* added (Ca OS). Plate number *35* added (Ea OS). The size of the plate reduced.

> *A curious antique collection of birds-eye views of the several counties in England & Wales; . . .*
> London, Robert Laurie and James Whittle, 1796.   BL

---

1. D. Schrire 'Bickham's bird's-eye county views', *MCS* no. 27 (1966); D. Lyon 'A bird's-eye view of the Bickhams', *The Map Collector* no. 2 (1978).

V ROAD BOOKS

Road books fall into three categories: (i) those which contain county maps and are recorded in the catalogue, eg Bowen no. 23 and Cary's *Traveller's companion* nos. 51, 65 and 82; (ii) those which contain strip maps. These are listed below if there are individual plates which refer to Sussex roads; (iii) those which contain only written itineraries, sometimes with a general road map of the country, which are not catalogued.

The literature[1] is both inadequate and confusing: it does not differentiate between the three categories above, nor does it make clear which series of maps are from a given set of plates. The revision and updating of Fordham's work in this field is well overdue. He classified[2] road books in three periods: (i) 1577–1675, the period in which the old English or customary mile was used; (ii) 1675–1798, the period in which a large number of road books containing strip maps based on Ogilby's survey was published (nos. 1 to 9 below fall into this group); (iii) 1798–1850, the period in which the maps were based mainly on Cary's surveys, and an increasing number of road books were issued as county or general maps rather than strip maps. After about 1850 the market for the traditional road book was replaced by a demand for more general handbooks or tourist's guides, and by railway guides.

1 JOHN OGILBY   1675

John Ogilby[3] (1600–76) was born probably at Kirriemuir.[4] After a varied career as dancing master, theatre owner and translator of Homer and Virgil, he became, in the last decade of his life, a publisher of cartographic works. He is best known for his survey of the roads of England and Wales, the first systematic survey of British roads to be undertaken, and the first original survey work carried out in Sussex since Saxton and Norden, a century earlier. It was the publication of his *Britannia* which finally led to the adoption of the statute mile in place of the customary miles then in use. Although the statute mile had received official recognition as early as 1593, it did not become the legal mile for all purposes until 1824.[5]

Britannia, in the production of which Ogilby was assisted by his friends Robert Hooke and John Aubrey, was conceived as part of a much larger work which had to be abandoned.[6]

---

1 Fordham, 1924; also Chubb, 1927; Anderson, 1881, pp. 22–5.
2 Fordham, 1969, p. 23 et seq.
3 H.G. Fordham *The Library,* Sept. 1925; Skelton, *County atlases,* 1970, pp. 185–6; Harley, *John Ogilby,* 1970; Schuchard, 1973; Hyde, 1976, Van Eerde, 1976.
4 Ogilby's horoscope, cast c. 1653, includes 'Nov. 17, 1600, 4 A.M., Mr. Jo. Ogilby of Kellemeane, 10 myle north from Dundee.' Kirriemuir is about 15 statute miles north of Dundee. According to *The national gazetteer* of 1868 (see no. 128) it was 'vulgularly pronounced Killamuir'.
5 I.M. Evans, 'A cartographic evaluation of the old English mile', *GJ* vol. 141 (July 1975).
6 E.G.R. Taylor 'Robert Hooke and the cartographical projects of the late 17th century (1666–1696)', *GJ* vol. 90 (1937), p. 532.

After 1676 Ogilby's business was continued by William Morgan, his wife's grandson; his plates for the road maps eventually passed to Abel Swale and Robert Morden. After the 1698 re-issue of *Britannia*, and the death of Morden in 1703, the original plates disappeared. Twenty years later three redrawn versions (Gardner, Senex and Bowen, nos. 2–4 below), were published almost contemporaneously. Little or no effort was made to up-date Ogilby's work, although some of the information which was most likely to be erroneous. such as the names of landowners, was omitted. For example, *M*ʳ *Picks house* (twice) and *M*ʳ. *Kilburns house* appear near Hawkhurst on the map of the road to Rye in both Ogilby's and Gardner's versions, but are omitted by Senex and Bowen. Ogilby's work formed the basis of all road maps issued until the 1780s.

EDITIONS

(i)   Plate 4. *The Road from LONDON to ARVNDEL* . . . (London – Billingshurst – Amberley – Arundel, and on to Chichester). 440 mm × 320 mm (single line border).
    Plate 29. *The Road From LONDON to NEWHAVEN* . . . (London – East Grinstead – Chailey – Lewes – Newhaven – Brighton – New Shoreham. The general map in *Britannia* does not mark this road, but shows a direct road from London to Brighton via East Grinstead and on to Shoreham). 428 mm × 335 mm (single line border).
    Plate 30. *The Road from LONDON to PORTSMOUTH* . . . (a four mile section of road south of *Rake*). 435 mm × 330 mm (single line border).
    Plate 31. *The Road from LONDON to RYE* . . . (London – Lamberhurst – Flimwell – Newenden – Rye). 445 mm × 292 mm (single line border). `See plate 37.
    Plate 39. *The Road from LONDON to CHICHESTER* . . . (Guildford – North Chapel – Midhurst – Chichester). 438 mm × 320 mm (single line border).
    Plate 81. *The Road From OXFORD to CHICHESTER* . . . (the last 13 miles pass through Sussex). 428 mm × 352 mm (single line border).

Each plate is composed of six vertical strips, fashioned as a continuous scroll, and designed to read from bottom left to top right. Strips three and four are shorter than the others to allow space for the title panels (Ca). Plate 81, however, has seven strips, the middle three being shortened. The title panels include *By JOHN OGILBY Esq*ʳ. *His Ma*ᵗⁱᵉˢ. *Cosmographer.* On plates 29, 30 and 39 JOHN appears as IOHN; and on plates 29 and 81 *His* as *his*. Plate 29 has *Ric. Shortgrave Surveyor* at foot of title panel. There are no plate numbers.

Britannia, volume the first: or, an illustration of the kingdom of England and dominion of Wales: . . . By John Ogilby Esq; His Majesty's Cosmographer, and Master of His Majesty's Revels . . .
London, 'Printed by the Author,' 1675.   BL

(ii)   Plate 29, Shortgrave signature erased. Minor revisions have been made on all plates, eg on plate 4, *20'4* (at end of title panel), *Wardle Fluv, Arun Fluv* and *Fluv* (at top of scroll 3) have been added, and *Param Place* altered to *Parham Place;* on plate

29, *Sea* added at top of scroll 5; on plate 30, *Hampshire* altered to *Sussex* and *HAMP SH* added on scroll 5; on plate 31, *to Horsley* added (below *LONDON*); on plate 39 *to Southampto* and *to Rumsey* added to top of scroll 6, and *Enter* added at foot of scroll 2.

> *Britannia, volume the first:* . . .
> London, 'Printed for the Author', 1675.   BL

(iii)   Plate numbers added (Ee, on each plate). For reasons explained by Harley,[7] an additional plate number *55* is visible on plate 81. Some borders very indistinct.

> *Itinerarium Angliae: or, a book of roads, wherein are contain'd the principal road-ways of His Majesty's kingdom of England and dominion of Wales . . . by John Ogilby Esq.*
> London, 'Printed by the Author', 1675.   BL

> *Britannia, volume the first* . . .
> London, 'Printed by the Author, 1675.   BL

> *Britannia: or, the kingdom of England and dominion of Wales, actually survey'd with a geographical and historical description of the principal roads; explain'd by one hundred maps on copper plates . . . By John Ogilby, Esq; Cosmographer to King Charles the Second.*
> London, Abel Swall and Robert Morden, 1698.   BL.RGS

2   THOMAS GARDNER   1719

EDITION

Re-engraved versions of Ogilby's maps. The plate numbers (Ee OS) and titles correspond with Ogilby's except that *From* (on plates 29 and 81) is now *from*, and *ARVNDEL* (plate 4) is now *ARUNDEL*. The maps are on scrolls. Each title panel includes . . . *By THO: GARDNER* . . . Inscriptions as follows:

Plate

4	262 mm × 165 mm	*Humbly Inscrib'd to yᵉ Honourable Sir RICHARD FARRINGTON. Bart.* (Ce).
29	262 mm × 170 mm	*Humbly Inscrib'd to the Rt. Honourable SPENCER COMPTON, Esq., Speaker of the House of Commons.* (at end of title).
30	261 mm × 170 mm	*Humbly Inscrib'd to the Right Honourable THOMAS Lord ONSLOW* (at end of title).

---

7   Harley, *John Ogilby*, 1970, p. xxviii.

31	262 mm × 165 mm	*Humbly Inscrib'd to the Honourable JAMES BUTLER, Esq.* (at end of title).
39	264 mm × 165 mm	*Humbly Inscrib'd to the Rt. Honourable WILLIAM Lord POWLET* (at end of title).
81	262 mm × 177 mm	*Humbly Inscrib'd to the Honourable WILLIAM SLOPER, Esqr.* (at end of title).

The dimensions are taken from the scrolls (there is no border), but the engraving extends beyond the scrolls. On plate 30, for example, it extends to 273 mm horizontally.

A pocket-guide to the English traveller.
London, J. Tonson and J. Watts, 1719.   BL.RGS

3   JOHN SENEX   1719

EDITIONS

(i) Re-engraved versions of the Ogilby maps, with minor omissions. The plate numbers (Ee OS) and the titles are the same as Ogilby's except for *from* on plates 29 and 81, and *ARUNDEL* on plate 4 (see Gardner no. 2 above), *ROAD* in place of *Road* on plates 4, 29, 30, 31 and 39. The plate measurements are: plate 4, 192 mm × 155 mm; plate 29, 190 mm × 155 mm; plate 30, 190 mm × 155 mm; plate 31, 195 mm × 151 mm, plate 39 (later to become plate 40), 192 mm × 154 mm; plate 81 (later plate 89) 207 mm × 157 mm. Measurements are to the edges of the scrolls (there are no borders). References to Ogilby in the title panels are omitted. *I. Senex sculp^t.* on plates 4 and 29 (top of scroll 3) and on plate 31 (below title). There are minor differences by comparison with both Ogilby and Gardner, eg *Swanborough* (formerly *Swan Borough*) on plate 29; *Lavant R* (formerly *Lavant flu*) on plate 39.

An actual survey of all the principal roads of England and Wales.
London, J. Senex, 1719.   BL.GL
The work is in two parts.

(ii) Changes on plate 30, scroll 1. *Kingston Bridg, Black Bull, White Hart, Capt. Paggan's, Alms houses, Esq., Plumes, Royal Oak Inn, to Croydon, to Lambeth* (twice), *to Dulwich* and *to Deptford* added. *Caroon house* altered to *D^r. Cheny's Schole.*

An actual survey . . . The second edition.
London, M. Senex, [1742].   BL
The maps are printed on both sides of the paper. Part I is undated, Part II is dated 1742. Chubb[8] says that Sir H.G. Fordham's copy had 'The Third Edition' on the title-page of Part I.

---

8 Chubb, 1927, no. CXXXIX.

(iii) Plate numbers (Ee OS) erased, and new plate numbers added (Aa OS and Ea OS); plate *39* altered to *40* and *81* to *89*. On plate 4, to *Dover Pl. 18* (scroll 4), *see Pl. 40* (scroll 6) added; on plate 29, *Shoream* altered to *Shoreham* (in title panel); on plate 30, *e* added to *Kingston Bridge, to Midhurst & Chichester see Pl. 40* (scroll 3) and *see Pl. 89* (scroll 5) added; on plate 31, *Sevenoke 29* altered to *Sevenoke 23* (in title panel), *I. Senex sculp^t.* erased, note *N.B. . . . 2m½* added (below title panel), *I. Senex Sculp* added (above scroll 4), *to Tunbridge-Wells* (scroll 3) re-engraved *to Tunbridge Wells 5 miles, e* added to *Roberts Bridge* (twice) and to *Beauls Bridge* (scroll 5), engraving of a ship added (scroll 6); on plate 40, *e* added to *Leckford Bridge* (scroll 2), *see Pl. 89* (scroll 5) and *and Pool Pl. 52* (scroll 6) added, note commencing *Plate 89 shows . . .* added (Ce OS); on plate 39, *Pl. 14* and *Pl. 15* (scroll 1), *Pl. 10* and *to Hungerford Pl. 10* (scroll 3) *Pl. 25* (scroll 4), *Pl. 54* (scroll 5), *Pl. 30, Pl. 40* (twice) and *Pl. 4* (scroll 6) added.

> *The roads through England delineated . . . by John Senex F.R.S.*
> London, John Bowles and Son, 1757.   RGS

(iv) *I. Senex Sculp* erased (plate 31). *Horizontal distance 48 miles* (plate 4, scroll 5), *Distance in a straight line 50m* (plate 29, scroll 5), *Direct Horizontal distance 66 miles* (plate 30, scroll 6), *The Direct Horizontal distance of Rye from London is 51 miles* (plate 31, above scrolls 3 and 4), *Direct Horizontal distance 55 miles* (plate 40, scroll 3), and *Direct Horizontal distance 63 m* (plate 89, scroll 6) added.

> *The roads through England delineated . . . by John Senex F.R.S.*
> London, John Bowles and Son, 1757, 1759 and 1762.   BL;P⁹; BL.RGS.CUL

4 EMANUEL BOWEN   1720

Britannia Depicta (catalogue no. 23) contains road maps derived from Ogilby.

EDITIONS

(i) There are three strips (not scrolls) of varying length, on each plate (a few, including plate 217, have four strips); the vertical dimensions given below are those of the longest strip on each plate. Arms and extensive notes appear both inside and outside the borders. There are plate numbers (Aa OS, on left-hand plates; Ea OS, on right-hand plates), but they are sometimes trimmed off in binding.

Plate

10	89 mm × 147 mm	The Sussex section of *THE ROAD FROM LONDON TO ARUNDEL . . .* This title is on plate 8.

---

9 Deighton Bell catalogue 221, item 1130A.

69	100 mm × 166 mm ⎫	*THE ROAD FROM LONDON TO NEWHAVEN* . . .
70	100 mm × 160 mm ⎬	This title is on plate 68,
73	89 mm × 143 mm	Part of *THE ROAD FROM LONDON TO PORTSMOUTH* . . . This title is on plate 71.
76	91 mm × 152 mm	*THE ROAD FROM LONDON TO RYE.* This title is on plate 75.
96	90 mm × 151 mm ⎫	*THE ROAD FROM LONDON TO CHICHESTER*
97	90 mm × 143 mm ⎬	. . . This title is on plate 95.
217	100 mm × 149 mm	Part of *The Road from OXFORD to CHICHESTER.* This title is on plate 215.

For reproduction of plate 10 above, **see plate 38** in this catalogue.

Britannia depicta . . .
London, Thomas Bowles and Emanuel Bowen, 1720   BL
For details of later issues to 1753, see no. 23.

(ii)   Additions have been made in two categories. *The horizontal distance from London to Arundel is 48m* has been added on plate 10, and similar wording has been added on plates 70, 73, 76, 96 and 217. *See Pl. 95* has been added on plate 10, and similar references added on plates 73, 96, 97 and 217, sometimes with additional wording, eg *and Pool* on plate 97, and *Shews the Road from Chichester* . . . *& Oxford* on plate 96.

Britannia depicta . . .
London, Thomas Bowles, 1759.   BL

(iii)   On plate 10 *is an ancient* erased after *Arundel* and replaced by [*at* 55½]*is.* Similar alterations or additions have been made on all plates, eg [*at 30*] added on plate 69.

Britannia depicta . . .
London, Carington Bowles, 1764.   BL.CUL

5   JOHN SENEX   1759

EDITIONS

(i)   Re-engraved versions of Senex no. 3 above. Titles and wording on the maps are in French. One plate number on each plate (Ea OS, on even numbered plates; Aa OS, on odd numbered plates). There are six strips (not scrolls) on each plate, with a 1 mm margin between strips.

Plate

4	201 mm × 149 mm	*de Londres à Arundel* . . .
29	195 mm × 148 mm	*de Londres a Newhaven* . . .

30	207 mm × 152 mm	*de Londres à Portsmouth.*
31	193 mm × 144 mm	*de Londres a la Rye en Sussex.*
40	213 mm × 151 mm	*de Londres à Chichester . . .*
89	207 mm × 152 mm	*de Oxford à Chichester.*

Itinerarie de toutes les routes de l'Angleterre . . . par Senex . . . Bowles a ajouté en 1757 plusieurs nouvelles routes . . .
Paris, le Sᵣ. le Rouge Ing., 1759.

BL.RGS.W

The title is given in English on the same plate. Leeds University Library has two copies bound with Desnos's *Nouvel atlas d'Angleterre,* See Whitaker Collection, no. 247.

(ii) Titles and wording on maps re-engraved in English. Titles read:

Plate

4	*From LONDON to ARUNDEL, and CHICHESTER.*
29	*From LONDON to BRIGHTHELMSTONE, NEWHAVEN, and NEW SHOREHAM.*
30	*From LONDON to PORTSMOUTH.*
31	*From LONDON to RYE.*
40	*From LONDON to CHICHESTER . . .*
89	*From OXFORD to CHICHESTER.*

Published as the Act directs by R. Sayer and I. Bennett 16 Janʳʸ., 1775 (Janʸ. on plate 30) added (Ca OS on plates 4, 29, 31 and 40; Ce OS on plate 89; Ae OS on plate 30). Two plate numbers on each plate (Ae OS and Ea OS). The note at the top of strip 2 on plate 4 reads *Here the River Mole runs under Ground.* In state (i) it is *Ioy pres la Riviere Mole s'engoufre Coule sous Terre et sort pres de Letherhead.* On Senex no. 3 above it appears as *Near this Place the River Mole buries itself, and running under ground, rises again near Letherhead.* Clearly the French version was copied from the earlier Senex maps. How they came to be republished in England, and what justified the very extensive revisions required to the plates, remains unexplained.

Jeffery's itinerary.
London, R. Sayer and J. Bennett, 1775.

RGS

A copy in the British Library (maps 118.b.27) has the spurious title-page *The roads of England delineated.*

6 JOHN HINTON

1765–72

Based on Ogilby's maps.

EDITION

There are eight strips on each plate. Plate numbers (Ea OS).
    Plate II. 365 mm × 293 mm (1 mm). *The ROAD from LONDON to ARUNDEL*

(part of strip 1 and strips 2, 3 and 4), with an extension headed *ARUNDEL to CHICHESTER*.

> *The universal magazine of knowledge and pleasure.*
> London, John Hinton. Issue for Dec. 1765.   BL

Plate XI. 355 mm × 300 mm (1 mm). *A SURVEY of the ROAD from LONDON to NEWHAVEN* . . . (strips 7 and 8).

> *The universal magazine* . . .
> London, John Hinton. Issue for June, 1767.   (SAS)
> This map is missing from the British Library copy.

Plate XII. 365 mm × 305 mm (1 mm). *A SURVEY of the ROAD from LONDON to RYE* . . . and *A SURVEY of the ROAD from LONDON to CHICHESTER* . . . (strips 4 to 8).

> *The universal magazine* . . .
> London, John Hinton. Issue for August, 1767.   BL

Plate XXXIV. 345 mm × 289 mm (1 mm) *A SURVEY of the ROAD from OXFORD to CHICHESTER* . . . (part of strip 1 and strips 2, 3 and 4).

> *The universal magazine* . . .
> London, John Hinton. Issue for March 1772.   BL

7   D. HENRY AND R. CAVE   1765

Based on Ogilby's maps.

Nineteen maps in this series were published between 1765 and 1775; two refer to Sussex. They may have been engraved by Thomas Jefferys who died in 1771 (see no. 34). Jefferys engraved other maps for the *Gentleman's Magazine*.

EDITION

(a)   290 mm × 167 mm (2 mm). *A MAP of the ROADS from LONDON to DOVER, RYE, HITH, MARGATE, RAMSGATE and DEAL* (in panel 6 mm × 290 mm across top of map). *Gent. Mag. May 1765* (Ae OS). *N.B. These Roads are measured from the Royal Exchange* (De OS). The plate is divided into ten vertical strips.

> *Gentleman's magazine,* vol. 35.
> London, D. Henry and R. Cave, 1765.   BL

(b)   285 mm × 167 mm (2 mm). *A MAP of the ROADS from LONDON to*

PORTSMOUTH, CHICHESTER, SOUTHAMPTON, POOL, & from SOUTHAMPTON to WINCHESTER (in panel across top of map). *Gent: Mag.* (Ea OS). The plate is divided into ten vertical strips.

Gentleman's magazine, vol. 35.
London, D. Henry and R. Cave, 1765
This map is missing from the British Library copy.

8 THOMAS KITCHIN   1767

Re-engraved versions of Senex (no. 3 above). The equivalent Senex plate numbers and some minor differences by comparison with the Senex plates are given below. The maps are on scrolls with no outer borders.

EDITION

The titles are the same as on Senex (no. 3 above) except that the continuation wording has been changed, eg plate 5 (equivalent to Senex plate 4) reads *Containing from the Royal Exchange in London to* . . . whereas on Senex it reads *Containing from the head of Cornhill in London to* . . .; *Newhaven* (plate 28) is not in capitals. Plate numbers (Aa and Ea).

Plate

5	187 mm × 152 mm (Senex pl. 4)	*Ewell* (in title panel) formerly *Ewel.*
28	188 mm × 153 mm (Senex pl. 29)	*South Wick* (scroll 6), formerly *Week.*
30	189 mm × 151 mm (Senex pl. 30)	*Portsmouth Harbour* and *Gosport* added.
31	200 mm × 144 mm (Senex pl. 31)	Fourth scroll widened to 48 mm. and road from *Tunbride* to *Tunbridge Wells* added.
41	189 mm × 152 mm (Senex pl. 39)	*Azure R.* added (scroll 1).
91	201 mm × 154 mm (Senex pl. 81)	*Basingstoke* (in title panel) formerly *Basinstoke.*

Kitchin's post-chaise companion . . .
London, John Bowles, Carington Bowles and Robert Sayer, 1767. BL.RGS.CUL
Reissued 1770[10], and by Carington Bowles c. 1780 (BL)

10 Chubb, 1927, no. CXLII.

9 THOMAS KITCHIN   1771

Based on Ogilby maps.

EDITION

There are six strips (not scrolls) on each plate with no margins between strips. Each plate measures approximately 153 mm × 120 mm. Plate numbers (Ea OS). Titles (Ce OS).

Plate

3	*LONDON to Arundell.* (strips 5 and 6).
4	*LONDON to Arundel continued,* . . . (strips 1 to 3).
26	*LONDON to Newhaven,* . . . (strips 1 to 6).
29	*LONDON to Portsmouth.* (strips 1 to 6).
30	*LONDON to Rye,* . . . (strips 1 to 4).
39	*LONDON to CHICHESTER,* . . . (strips 1 to 6).
84	*OXFORD to CHICHESTER.* (strips 1 to 6).

Ogilby's survey improv'd: or Kitchin's new and instructive traveller's companion.
London, T. Kitchen 1771.   RGS

10 LOUIS CHARLES DESNOS   1773

Desnos published *L'indicateur fidèle, ou guide des voyageurs* (1764 to 1785), which contained road maps of France. The map of the north coast showed channel crossings and the routes from channel ports to London. The first edition showed only the road from London to *N.HAVEN*. On later editions a branch to *Brighthelmstone* and the road from *RYE* were added. There are no plates relating primarily to Sussex.

The work noticed below contains one map relating to Sussex.

EDITIONS

(i) 46 mm × 91 mm (1 mm). *Route de Londres a N.Haven* (Ea in panel). Plate number *81* (Ea OS).

Etrennes utiles et nécessaires . . . ou indicateur fidèle . . .
Paris, le S. Desnos, 1771 and 1773.   BL;RGS

(ii) Grave accent added to *à* in title. *LA MANCHE* added. *Tamise* re-engraved in larger letters.

Etrennes utiles . . .
Paris, le S. Desnos, 1774, 1775 and 1780.   RGS;RGS;RGS

11   CARINGTON BOWLES

The first series of road maps which were not copied from Ogilby. The extent and source of any original topographic content has not been determined.

EDITIONS

(i)   The maps are printed from plates which cover a two-page spread. Each page (half plate) is numbered (Aa OS on left hand pages; Ea OS on right hand pages), and is divided into three vertical strips. Each plate measures 148 mm × 122 mm (1 mm each side, 8 mm at top, 5 mm at bottom). *BOWLES's POST-CHAISE COMPANION* (Ac OS, sideways), *VOL. I* or *VOL. II* (Ae, in border). *London: Published 2 Jany. 1782* (Ec OS, sideways). The top border contains a short title, eg *OXFORD to Chichester* (plate 167/8), and road distances. Sussex features on half plates 7, 51, 52, 59, 60, 77, 78, 168, 191, 192.

> *Bowles's post-chaise companion; or traveller's directory through England and Wales . . . second edition.*
> London, Carington Bowles, 1782.   BL.RGS.CUL
> The first edition of this work has not been found. Volume I contains fifty plates numbered 1 to 100; volume 2 fifty plates numbered 101 to 200.

(ii)   Imprints (Ec OS) omitted.

> *Bowles's post-chaise companion; . . . third edition.*
> London, Bowles and Carver, [1790].   BRIGHTON PL

12   DANIEL PATERSON

EDITIONS

(i)   Two strips per plate, each strip being numbered (Aa and Ea, in border). Plates measure 85 mm × 145 mm (1 mm at sides, 8 mm at top and bottom). There is a 1 mm 'border' between the two strips. *Printed for the Proprietor CARINGTON BOWLES, LONDON, 3 Jan. 1785* (Ce OS on all plates). Sussex features on strips 14, 18, 19, 20 22, 23, 25, 26, 27 and 32.

> *Paterson's British itinerary . . . by Captn. Daniel Paterson, assistant to the Quarter-Master General . . .*
> London, Carington Bowles, 1785.   BL.RGS.GL
> Volume 1 contains 188 strips, 187 and 188 are blank; volume 2 172 strips, numbered 1 to 142 and 1 to 30.

(ii)   Imprint (Ce OS) erased and replaced by *Printed for the Proprietors BOWLES & CARVER, London 6 Jan. 1796* (Ce OS on all plates). Many minor alterations on the maps, eg on strip 23 *Brighthelmston* erased and replaced by *Brighton;* road distances *4* to *9* and *1* to *13* altered to *35* to *53; to Deal* erased and replaced by *to Seaford;* and many additions.

> *Paterson's British itinerary . . . the second edition, improved.*
> London, Bowles and Carver, 1796, 1803 and 1807.   BL.RGS.GL;RGS;RGS
> Volume I contains 340 strips, of which 187 to 198 are new and 199 to 340 from the original volume 2; volume 2 contains 30 of the original strips numbered 404 to 433, and new strips 434 to 448 or 449. Date in imprint (Ce OS) erased in 1803 and 1807 issues.

13   JOHN CARY   1790

The road-book described below contains forty plates measuring 124 mm × 185 mm (2 mm). There are two strips on each plate, each having a plate number (Ba OS and Da OS). Only strip 65 relates to Sussex.

EDITIONS

(i)   Strip measures 59 mm × 141 mm (2 mm). *65* (Ca OS of the strip). *Published by J. Cary July 1st. 1790* (Ce OS of the plate). The strip shows the road from London to *EAST GRINSTED*. Above the strip is a list of inns, which includes the *Dorset Arms* and *Crown* at *East Grinsted*. Points on the road from which gentleman's seats can be seen are indicated.

> *Cary's survey of the high roads from London to* [the twenty-six towns named include *East Grinsted*].
> London, J. Cary, 1790.   RGS

(ii)   Year in imprint (Ce OS) altered to *1799*.

> *Cary's survey of the high roads . . .*
> London, J. Cary, 1799.   RGS

(iii)   *Mr. Evelyn* erased and *Sr. G. Shuckburg Evelyn Bt.* added. Year in imprint (Ce OS) altered to *1801*.

> *Cary's survey of the high roads . . .*
> London, J. Cary, 1801.   RGS

(iv)   *Sr. G. Shuckburg Evelyn Bt.* erased and *Genl. Houston* added. Year in imprint (Ce OS) altered to *1810*.

> *Cary's survey of the high roads . . .*
> London, J. Cary, 1810.   RGS

14 JONES AND SMITH

1800

EDITION

Twenty-seven strip maps on twenty-seven plates, 86 mm × 124 mm, (1 mm top and sides, 7 mm at bottom), all relating to Sussex. Plate numbers (Ca, in border which is expanded in a semi-circle to accommodate them). *Jones and Smith sculp^t. Pentonville* on plate 1 (Ce OS); *Jones and Smith sculp. Pentonville* on plates 12, 15 and 25 (Ce OS). Notes and references to inns in bottom border.

> *Smith's actual survey of the roads from London to Brighthelmstone . . . Planned from a scale of one inch to a mile.*
> London, C. Smith, 1800.

BL.RGS.WORTHING PL

15 LAURIE AND WHITTLE

1806

In addition to the works listed below, Fordham[11] has recorded an edition for 1830. In his personal copy of his book (now at RGS), he has also noted editions for 1823 and 1832. None of these has been found. Plates 1, 2 and 3 of the twenty-four road maps relate to Sussex.

EDITIONS

(i) The titles and plate numbers are engraved across the top border. Imprint *Published, 12th. Feby. 1806, by LAURIE & WHITTLE, N°. 53 Fleet Street London* (Ce OS) on all plates. The coastlines are not marked.

Plate 1. 239 mm × 284 mm (8 mm). *Roads to ROCHESTER, CANTERBURY, Margate Ramsgate, Deal, Dover, (1)[12] Folkstone, Hythe, New Romney, Rye, Hastings, & Eastbourne (by Tunbridge). Scale 1 + 11 Miles = 38 mm* (De). *J. Bye sculp^t.* (Ee OS). Compass (Db).

Plate 2. 236 mm × 284 mm (8 mm). *Roads to East-Bourne, (by Uckfield) Brighthelmstone, Shoreham, (2) Worthing, Little Hampton and Bognor (by Arundel). Scale 1 + 11 Miles = 47 mm* (Bd). Compass (Ac). **See plate 39.**

Plate 3. 233 mm × 288 mm (8 mm). *Roads to Arundel, Bognor, (by Petworth) (3) Chichester, and Portsmouth. Scale of Miles 1 + 13 = 45 mm* (Ae). *B. Smith sc* (Ee OS). Compass (Bc).

> *Laurie and Whittle's new traveller's companion . . . by Nathl. Coltman.*
> London, Laurie and Whittle, 1806

BL.CUL

---

11 Fordham, 1924.
12 On the maps, these numerals (plate numbers) are enclosed by complete circles, not brackets.

(ii)   Coastlines added on all plates.
Plate 1. *I. OF SHEPPEY* added.
Plate 2. *West Tarring 57* and *Beachy Head* added.
Plate 3. *Swan* added. *Rise* erased and re-engraved below *Battersea*.

Laurie and Whittle's new traveller's companion . . . by Nathl. Coltman.
London, Laurie and Whittle, 1806.   BL.RGS.GL

(iii) Plate 1. *Shorncliff and Rye Canal* and *New Military Road* added. *Tunbridge,* in title, altered to *Tonbridge*. Place-names, new roads and references to adjoining plates added, eg road from *East Grinstead* to *Uckfield* and *to Lewes p. 2.*
Plate 2. A note *The New Road through Merstham saves Reigate Hill.* added (Ba). Single line, marking road from *Purley* to *Reigate,* added. Place-names, other new roads and references to adjoining plates added, eg *Church Cobham* and *Cobham p. 3.* The London to *Guildford* road is now shown by double lines.
Plate 3. *Godalming* to *CHICHESTER* road shown by double lines, ie as a *Mail Coach Road* (see preface to the work). *Cripple Crouch Hill, Chertsey* and other place-names, roads and refrences to adjoining plates added, eg *to Leatherhead p. 2* (twice).

Third edition, corrected to 1809, of Laurie and Whittle's new traveller's companion . . . by Nathl. Coltman.
London, Laurie and Whittle, 1806 (not issued before 1809).   CUL

Fourth edition, corrected to 1810, of Laurie and Whittle's new traveller's companion . . . by Nathl. Coltman
London, Laurie and Whittle, 1806 (not issued before 1810).   BL

Laurie and Whittle's new traveller's companion . . . The fifth edition.
London, Robert Laurie and James Whittle, 1810.   BL

(iv) Plate 1. The road from London to *Tonbridge, Frant, Flimwell* and *Hastings* is now shown by double lines.
Plate 2. The road from London to *Brighthelmstone,* via *Purley* and *Reigate* now shown by double lines.

Laurie and Whittle's new traveller's companion . . . the [fifth] [sixth] [seventh] edition.
London, Robert Laurie and James Whittle, 1810 (5th), 1811(6th), 1812 (6th) and 1813 (7th).   CUL;W;BL.CUL;W

Whittle and Laurie's new traveller's companion . . . the seventh edition.
London, James Whittle and Richard Holmes Laurie, 1813.   CUL

(v)   *A New Edition, 1815,* added on all three plates (Ce OS, below imprint).
Plate 2. Road from *Piecomb* to *Hand Cross* via *Hixted Place* and *Bolney* added. *& the New Road through Hixted, saves Clayton Hill, to Brighton* added to note (Bd).

Place-names added, eg *Balls Hut, Fair Mile Bottom, Amberley.*
    Plate 3. *to Steyning p. 2* added.

Whittle and Laurie's new traveller's companion . . . The [seventh] [eighth] edition . . .
London, James Whittle and Richard Holmes Laurie, 1814 and 1817.

BL.CUL.GL;CUL

(vi) Plate 1. Date in *A New Edition, 1815* (Ce OS) altered to *1819*. Place-names etc.
added, eg *North Foreland Light.*
    Plate 2. Date in *A New Edition, 1815* (Ce OS) altered to *1818*. The note (Bd)
expanded to read *The New Road through Merstham, saves Reigate Hill. the New Road
through Bolney, & Hixted saves Clayton Hill, & the New Road through Worth, is nearst
by 1½ Mile, to Brighton.*

Whittle and Laurie's new traveller's companion . . . The eighth edition . . .
London, James Whittle and Richard Holmes Laurie, 1818. RGS

(vii) Imprint (Ce OS) erased and re-engraved *London: Published by R.H. LAURIE,
No. 53, Fleet Street.* on all plates.
    Plate 1. *A New Edition, 1819* erased. *Packet sails every Mon. Tu. Th. & Fri. for
Calais, distance 25½ Miles* added (at *Dover*). *J. Bye Sculpt.* erased.
    Plate 2. *A New Edition, 1818* erased.
    Plate 3. *A New Edition, 1815* erased.

Laurie's new traveller's companion . . . ninth edition.
London, R.H. Laurie, 1824. RGS

(viii) Plate 2. *Balsdean* and road from *Lewes* to *Rottingdean* added. *Hixted* altered to
Hickstead in note (Bd) and *Hixted Place* to *Hickstead* on map. *4½* added.
    Plate 3. *Selsea Bill, Stansted Pa* and *Idsworth Pa.* added.

Laurie's new traveller's companion . . . An improved edition.
London, R.H. Laurie, 1828. CUL

(ix) Plate 1. *The Steam Packet leaves Margate for Ostend, every Wes. & Sat.* added (at
Margate).

Laurie's new traveller's companion . . . An improved edition.
London, R.H. Laurie, 1834. RGS

(x) Plate 1. Key comprising *Denotes where Post Horses may be had, Do Parks* and
Mail Coach Roads added (De, below scale).
    Plates 2 and 3. Key to *Post Horses* and *Mail Coach Roads* only added (Ee).

Laurie's new traveller's companion . . .
London, R.H. Laurie, 1836. BL

(xi) Plate 1. References to Packet boats erased at *Dover* and *Margate*. *Railways* added to key; railways on map include *London and Dover Rail road*. *To Brighton see p. 2* and road added.

Plate 2. Key to *Railways* added (Bd, below scale); railways added include *Brighton Railroad*.

Plate 3. Railways added include *London & Southampton Railroad*.

Laurie's new traveller's companion.
London, R.H. Laurie, 1846.   CUL.(SAS)

16   EDWARD MOGG   1808

EDITIONS

(i)   Two strips on each of the plates, 126 mm × 187 mm (8 mm). Strips numbered (Ba OS and Da OS, on each plate). Roads named (Ca, in border). Strips 7, 8, 30, 31, 32 and 36 to 39 refer to Sussex. *Published by E. Mogg, June 18, 1808* (Ce OS, on plates 35/6 and 37/8).

A survey of the roads from London to Brighton, Southampton, Portsmouth, Hastings, Tunbridge Wells, Margate, Ramsgate & Dover . . . by Edward Mogg.
London, Edward Mogg, 1808.   BL.GL.RGS
The work contains 56 strips on 28 plates. The imprint (Ce OS) appears on other plates; and in the form *Printed and Published by E. Mogg, 14 Little Newport Street* on one plate.

(ii)   The work has been expanded and the strips renumbered. Those featuring Sussex, with the original strip numbers (where applicable) in brackets, are 20 (30), 21/2 (31/2), 29/30 (7/8), 34 to 44 (–), 48 to 51 (36 to 39), 56 to 60 (–) and 64 to 67 (–). The imprints (Ce OS) carry various dates from June 1st 1814 to Feb.y 18th 1815, and appear on nearly all plates up to strips to 129/30. *No. 51 Charing Cross* is added on plates dated December 1814 and later. Substantial additions have been made on all plates, eg on strip 20 (formerly 30) *To Ticehurst 2M. Down Wood, Sussex* and *Kent* (in three places), *Shingley Wood, To Maidstone 17 M. Kiln Down, Lamberhurst Down*, road distances *18M.11½M, 3M. 16M, 3M* and *15M* and three park symbols.

A survey of the high roads of England & Wales . . . By Edward Mogg . . . To be continued monthly till the whole is completed.
London, Edward Mogg.   BL
Probably issued in 1814–15. The work contains 162 strips on 81 plates.

(iii)   The work has again been expanded. Of the new strips, numbers 215 to 219 feature Sussex. Additions have been made on some strips eg on strip 39 *John [Biddulph]* added; on strip 40, four road directions re-engraved above *CHICHESTER, To Bognor 7½M. contin.d Pa.41* re-engraved lower down, *Swan* re-engraved on same

373

line as *Dolphin. To London thro' Midhurst 62M. con^d. Pa.36.* added. *To Arundel & Brighton P.213* erased, *To Arundel 8M. con^d. Pa.213* altered to *To Arundel 8 & Brighton 28M. contin^d. PA.216* and the centre margin interrupted; on strip 48, *Heaverswood F^m.* and *Lodgers F^m,* added, a new direct road added. *Wolvers Farm* and *Irons Farm* each re-engraved on two lines, *Dowson Esqr.* added.

Survey of the high roads of England and Wales . . . Part the First . . . Sussex [with eight other counties].
London, Edward Mogg, 1817.

BL.CUL.GL

The work has an additional title-page, dated 1816, and contains 223 strips on 112 plates.

(iv) Imprints (Ce OS) erased. Minor changes on many strips, eg on strip 20, the county boundary with the names *Sussex* and *Kent* moved from *Flimwell* to *Ticehurst, To Cranbrook* added; on strip 39 *J. Sargent Esqr.* and *John Biddulph Esqr.* erased and *I. Sargent Esqr.* and *D. Blake Esqr.* added; on strip 36. *Pa.213* and *Pa.212* altered in each case to *Pa.216, Lord Selsey* altered to *Dow. Lady Selsey;* on strip 217 *Admi^l. Montagu* erased and replaced by *Sir W. Houston.* **See plate 40(i).**

A survey of the high roads . . . vol. I.
London, Edward Mogg 1828.

RGS

The work has, in addition, the title-page from the 1817 edition.

17 CHARLES SMITH   1826

EDITION

Three strips are engraved on each plate. The plates measure 93 mm × 153 mm (1 mm). The strip number and the name of a relevant town are engraved above each strip. The following relate to Sussex:

1 to 6	London to Brighton (by various routes), New Shoreham, Worthing and Hastings.
8	Tenterden to Rye.
11, 12	London to Petworth, Arundel and Chichester.

Smith's new pocket companion to the roads of England and Wales and part of Scotland . . .
London, Charles Smith, 1826 and 1827.

BL.CUL;CUL.GL.RGS

The title-page is missing from the GL copy. The work comprises 126 strips on 42 plates. *Gardner sc* appears (Ee OS) on alternate plates from strip 78 to strip 108. In the 1827 issue of the work, *Pickett sc* has been added on alternate plates from strip 1 to strip 72, and on the plates comprising strips 112/4 and 118/20.

18 LETTS AND SON   circa **1834**

The maps described below are advertised on the back cover as no. 32 in a series of
thirty-three small road atlases containing strip maps of specific roads. They were
published by Letts and Son, 95 Royal Exchange; Simpkin and Marshall, Paternoster
Row; and Mark Bimgley of Bell Court, Walbrook. None of the others has been found,
but the following would have related to Sussex:

   No. 25   *Hastings and Tunbridge Wells from London.*
      26   *Brighton from London, by Croydon.*
      27   *Southern Coast from Southampton to Margate.*

   The text of no. 32 included 'Coach list for Brighton corrected to April 1834'. It
gave the population of that town as *40,634*, which is the figure in the 1831 Census. No
mention is made of railways, and it therefore seems probable that the series was
published in the mid-1830s.

EDITION

Eleven plates, 63 mm × 99 mm (1 mm), of which the first eight delineate the road from
London to Brighton, and the other three the roads from Dieppe to Paris and Havre.

> *The British roadster or stage coach companion, no. 32, being a map and description
> of the road from London to Paris, by Brighton and Dieppe.*
> London, Letts and Son, Simpkin and Marshall and Mark Bimgley [1834].   BL

19 MASON AND PAYNE   circa **1888**

EDITION

Ten plates, 153 mm × 77 mm. Plate numbers (Ea OS). Titles (Ca OS), eg plate 1 has
the title *SOUTH LONDON*. Plates 1 to 9 delineate the road from London to Brighton;
plate 10 has the title *REIGATE & DORKING* and shows the side roads.

> *Mason & Payne's Ordnance map of the roads between London & Brighton.*
> London, Mason and Payne [1888].   BL

20 S.L. JOHNSON   circa **1893**

Size: 276 mm × 422 mm (2 mm)

EDITION

*S.L. Johnson's NEW TOURIST & CYCLISTS ROAD MAP TO & FROM LONDON,
CROYDON, EPSOM, REDHILL, REIGATE, TUNBRIDGE WELLS,
BRIGHTON, HASTINGS, LEWES AND EASTBOURNE* (Cb). *SCALE FROM*

THIS LINE SOUTHWARDS 5 MILES TO 1 INCH (Cb, below title). *DESIGNED BY S.L. JOHNSON, EASTBOURNE* (Be). There are six inset town plans.[13]

Sold about 1893 as a folding map.
London, Simpkin, Marshall, Hamilton, Kent and Co.   (BL)

21 GALL AND INGLIS   circa **1899**

Size: 90 mm × 635 mm (1 mm)

EDITION

Gall & Inglis, Edinburgh (Ee OS). Above the map is a section showing heights along the whole route.

Sold about 1899 as a folding map with printed title on cover. *The 'Brighton Road' map by H.R.G. Inglis.*
London, Gall and Inglis.   (BL)
This is no. 3 in the series. On the back is printed a similar map of the road from London to Portsmouth.

---

13 Brighton, Eastbourne, Croydon, Tunbridge Wells, Lewes and Hastings.

VI ORDNANCE SURVEY MAPS[1]

1 ONE-INCH SCALE

(a) OLD SERIES or *First Edition*

Most of Sussex is covered by sheet V (east Sussex from *Rottingdean* to *WINCHELSEA*) and sheet IX (west Sussex from *E. Wittering* to *Kemp Town*). Four other sheets cover small sections of the county: sheet XI (the western end); sheets VIII and VI (the north boundary from *Rudgwick* to *Lamberhurst* in Kent); and sheet IV (the eastern end, including *Rye*).

East Sussex was surveyed between 1793 and 1796, and the survey of the whole county was completed in the early 1800s. Sheets V and IX were drawn by Thomas Yeakell junior, and were *Engraved . . . by Benjn. Baker & Assistants. The Writing by Eben^r. Bourne.* Each sheet measures 880 mm × 582 mm (17 mm), but the earliest editions did not have borders. When added, the bottom borders on both sheets V and IX were interrupted, *Beachy Head* extending 28 mm, and *Selsey Bill* 45 mm, below the outer line of the border.

The Sussex sheets were published as follows: sheet XI in 1810, sheets V and IX in 1813, sheets IV and VIII in 1816 and sheet VI in 1819. *Ordnance Survey of Great Britain. Part the 5th, containing nearly the whole of Sussex . . .* was published about 1816, and comprised sheets IV, V, IX, X and XI.

Electrotype reproductions from the original plates were introduced about 1850, and the plates continued in use until about 1890, although the Sussex sheets of the *New Series* had been published between 1876 and 1882.

Substantial revisions were carried out during the life of the plates, in particular the addition of railways. Electrotype printing facilitated the production of duplicate plates, which reduced wear on the originals. These electrotypes were also used for special series of maps, such as the geological survey. The boundaries of geological formations were engraved on the duplicate plates; a key to the hand colouring was added in the vertical margins, and the date of publication in the bottom margin of each sheet. The Sussex sheets first appeared between 1862 and 1868 with the heading *GEOLOGICAL SURVEY OF GREAT BRITAIN.* The main sheets (V and IX) were both published in 1864. The 'Drift' edition of the Sussex sheets was published between 1887 and 1893.

Other electrotype productions with the title *INDEX TO TITHE SURVEY* were published in the early 1850s, the boundaries of parishes being added as dotted lines to the duplicate plates.

A publishing history of the plates will be found in Harley's notes to the *Reprint of the first edition of one-inch Ordnance Survey of England and Wales.*[2] Harley and O'Donoghue[3] list the early states of sheets V and VI in detail. This work also shows the

---

1 Harley, 1975; Seymour, 1980.
2 Harley, Newton Abbot, 1969, sheets 87 and 88.
3 Harley and O'Donoghue, 1975.

arrangement of the Sussex sheets (fig. 4), and reproduces sheets V and VI in early states. Impressions of sheet V have been found in two earlier states that those listed by Harley and O'Donoghue: (i) a proof impression (PRO MPH 299, **see plate 34**), which omits *Cuckmare River* and *R. Ouse*, hill hachures, those place-names which were later added in the sea (eg *LANGLEY POINT, Meridian of Greenwich*), inscriptions above the top neatline, and all engraving lying east of a line to the right of *Hastings, Lit. Maxfields, Horns Cross* (By the *X* in *SUSSEX*), *Bellhurst* (north-east of *Etchingham*) and *Riverhall* (north-east of *Rotherfield*); (ii) with only *Cuckmare River* and *R. Ouse* omitted. (BL maps 148.e.27, and WSRO PM 313). Equivalent proof impressions of sheet IX have not been found.[4]

The introduction to Harley and O'Donoghue gives an excellent and comprehensive history of the early years of the Ordnance Survey, and includes many valuable references. A reproduction of sheet IX and other Sussex sheets will be included in subsequent volumes.

(b)   NEW SERIES or *Second Edition*

Maps in this new series were issued as 'quarter sheets', ie they were approximately one quarter of the size of the *First Edition* sheets. The actual measurements were 460 mm × 304 mm (17 mm). They were numbered consecutively from 1 to 360, starting in the north of England. Sussex was re-surveyed for this series between 1860 and 1875, and the sheets were published between 1876 and 1882.

A national revision was undertaken again between 1893 and 1898, Sussex being covered in 1893–4 and the revised Sussex sheets were issued in 1895–6. (This issue is sometimes known as the *Third Edition*; but it is more correct to regard it as a revised version of the *Second Edition*, since the same plates were used as a basis. The revised sheets were probably printed from new plates made from heavily revised electrotype reproductions of the original plates).

The publication dates of the Sussex sheets were as follows:

Sheet number	Survey	Publication (Second Edition)	Revision	Publication (Second Edition revised)
300	1868–72	1876	1893	1895
301	1868–74	1880	1893	1896
302	1869–75	1882	1893–94	1896
303	1866–74	1881	1893–94	1896
304	1868–72	1879	1893	1896
316	1855–73	1876	1893–94	1895
317	1872–75	1881	1893–94	1895
318	1872–75	1881	1893–94	1895
319	1872–74	1880	1894	1895

---

4   James Dallaway expressed considerable indignation at having been supplied by Faden with a 'false' impression of sheet IX, probably a proof, which modern collectors would now be delighted to find. See F.W. Steer, 'Memoir and letters of James Dallaway, 1763–1835', *SAC* vol. 103 (1965), p. 27.

320	1871–73	1879	1893	1895
321	1870–72	1880	1893	1895
331	1856–66	1876	1893–94	1895
332	1860–75	1881	1894	1895
333	1872–76	1881	1893	1895
334	1860–74	1880	1894	1895

The survey dates are taken from figure 2 in *The historian's guide to Ordnance Survey Maps.*[5] The original publication dates (of the *Second Edition*) appear on the maps. The maps are contoured but do not have hill hachures. The sheets were subject to corrections between the date of publication and the 1893–4 revision. An amount of sometimes confusing information appears below the bottom border of each sheet, and the actual date of publication is not easily determined. For example, one impression of sheet 320 has these inscriptions: *Engraved at the ORDNANCE SURVEY OFFICE Southampton — under the direction of Captain Burke, R.E. The Outline by F. Kohler, the Writing by J. Grandison, the Ornament by H. Bennett. Published by Colonel A.C. Cooke, C.B.R.E. Director General. August 1879* (Ee OS), and *Printed from an Electrotype taken in 1886. Parish boundaries corrected to 1886* (Ae OS).[6]

In addition to these 'outline' versions, both the *Second Edition* and the *Second Edition revised* were published 'with hills' ie with hachures added.

Some *Second Edition* sheets 'with hills' carry the same publication dates as the outline version; others have the date amended, eg sheet 301 has *1892* in place of *1880*. Even where the publication date has not been amended, there are usually additional inscriptions which point to a later date of publication. These inscriptions take three forms: *Parish boundaries corrected to* [date], *Railways inserted to* [date], and *Printed from an Electrotype taken in* [date]. Most of the Sussex *Second Edition* sheets 'with hills' were published between 1888 and 1892; but some may have been issued earlier. Sheet 333, for example, has *Hills by W.H. Conway*, a publication date *1881* (as for the outline version), and *Printed from an Electrotype taken in 1881*. There is no later inscription; but it would be wrong to assume that the sheet was available 'with hills' by 1881.

Most of the Sussex sheets of the *Second Edition revised* 'with hills' have inscriptions corresponding precisely with the equivalent outline sheets. Five sheets (318, 319, 320, 333, 334), however, have *Boundaries revised to December 1898* added. All sheets were received by the British Museum in 1899 or 1900; it seems probable that none was issued before 1899. The railway lines, cross-hatched in the outline version, are diced (alternate spaces blacked in) on the hachured version.

All the above editions are in black and white. There followed a coloured printing, and a printing with hachured relief shaded in brown. These versions also embodied minor corrections.

5   Harley, *The historian's guide,* 1964.
6   In addition to papers already cited, problems of dating are referred to in Mumford, 1968, and in Mumford and Clark, 1968.

(c) THIRD EDITION

This was published between 1901 and 1913, based on surveys commencing in 1901. Sussex was re-surveyed in 1901–3, and the sheets, which maintain the same sheet-lines and numbers as the *Second Edition*, were published in 1903 or soon afterwards.

2 TWENTY-FIVE AND SIX INCH SCALES

(a) SURVEY

The survey of Sussex on a twenty-five inch scale (actually one mile: 25.34 inches or 1:2500) was undertaken between 1869 and 1875. It was revised in 1895–8, and again in 1907–10. The date of survey, which formed the basis for both the six inch and twenty-five inch series of maps, is printed on each sheet.

(b) SIX INCH SCALE

The six inch sheets (nominally 36" × 24" or 914 mm × 610 mm and covering an area 6 miles × 4 miles) were numbered county by county. The Sussex sheets are numbered *I* to *LXXXIII* (see index maps, nos. 138C and D (1885), 138E (1900) and 146A (1888) in the catalogue), and were published between 1877 and 1880. Each sheet has *SUSSEX* (Aa OS) and the sheet number in the form *Sheet XL* (Ea OS). When first published, the area outside the county boundary was left blank; the Sussex sheets taken together would, therefore, comprise a multi-sheet map of the county. On later issues the detail of adjacent counties was added, and the title and number appeared (Ea OS) in the form *Sussex --- Sheet --- VII Kent. Part of Sheets LX.LXI. & LXIX.*

Quarter-sheet (18" × 12" or 457 mm × 305 mm) versions of the six inch maps were published after 1881; they are distinguished by the six inch Roman numeral of the full sheet followed by *N.W., N.E., S.W.* or *S.E.*; but full sheets of the first series continued to be issued until at least 1898, in spite of the fact that maps of the six inch *SECOND SERIES* (in quarter sheets only) were then available.

The second series of six inch maps was published in 1898–1900, based on the 1895–8 revision of the original survey, see index map no. 154A (1899). These were issued only as quarter sheets (18" × 12" or 457 mm × 305 mm). Each sheet has the county and sheet number in the form *SUSSEX [EAST] SHEET VII.S.W.* (Ea OS), and *SECOND SERIES*, followed by the year of publication (Ca OS). The maps were printed by zincography from photographic reductions from the twenty-five inch drawings. Detail not required for the six inch maps was drawn in cobalt, to which the camera was blind. Quarter-sheets were introduced because the camera was not capable of handling a larger size until some time after 1893.[7] There was no sheet VIII in this series.

New drawings were again made for the third series published in 1911–14.

7 Winterbotham, 1934, p. 21.

(c) TWENTY-FIVE INCH SCALE

Twenty-five inch maps of Sussex were published before the six inch series, and first appeared in 1872–7. Sixteen twenty-five inch sheets (38" × 25.3") cover the same area as each six inch full sheet. Each twenty-five inch sheet covers an area of 1½ miles × 1 mile. The sheets are identified by the appropriate Roman numeral from the six inch sheet, followed by a number, *1* to *16*, reading from top left to bottom right of the six inch sheet. Sussex was covered by 1081 such sheets.

The maps were originally issued as 'parish' maps, with the name(s) of the parish, or group of parishes, in capitals (Aa OS). All detail outside the parish boundaries was omitted. Some sheet numbers are, therefore, found in more than one form; sheet *XL.15*, for example. The British Library has an impression of this sheet with *BARCOMBE PARISH* (Aa OS), *C⁰. SUSSEX (Eastern Division) Sheet XL.15* (Ea OS), *Surveyed in 1873 by Capt. A. Hill R.E. Levelled by Lieut. W. Wynne R.E. . . . Zincographed under the Superintendence of L*ᵗ. *Col. Parsons R.E. F.R.S. at the ORDNANCE SURVEY OFFICE, SOUTHAMPTON. Major General Sir Henry James, R.E. F.R.S. &c. Director. Price 2s/6d* (Ce OS). The right half of the sheet is blank. It was received at the British Museum in 1877. The compiler has seen another impression of sheet *XL.15*, which has *ISFIELD, RINGMER, & LITTLE HORSTED PARISHES* (Aa OS). *C⁰. SUSSEX (Eastern Division) Sheet XL.15* (Ea OS). *Surveyed in 1875 by Lieut. H.R.G. Georges R.E. Levelled by Lieut. W. Wynne R.E. . . . Zincographed under the Superintendence of L*ᵗ. *Col. Parsons R.E. F.R.S. at the ORDNANCE SURVEY OFFICE, SOUTHAMPTON, Major General J. Camerson, R.E. C.B. F.R.S. Director General. Price 2s/6d.* (Ce OS). The embossed stamp (Ca OS) appears to carry the date *Nov 1873*. On this impression the left side of the sheet is blank. On a third and later impression of the same sheet (BL) the title reads *BARCOMBE, ISFIELD, RINGMER & LITTLE HORSTED PARISHES* (Aa OS); *Surveyed in 1873, 1874 & 1875* has been added (Ae OS), and in the imprint (Ce OS) the date is *1880* and the price is *4s*. There is now no blank area, and the date indicates that the issuing of 'parish' maps lasted only a few years. The 1880 version was produced from the same drawing as the 'parish' versions; but much of the detail — place-names and trees in particular — is differently located, an indication that some of the information was added on the 'stone'.

A new twenty-five inch series was published in 1897–9 from entirely new drawings based on the 1895–8 revision. Each sheet has *SECOND EDITION* followed by the year of publication (Ca OS). They differ from the earlier series in that the buildings are shaded diagonally (formerly marked in outline only), tree symbols have been added by 'stamping' so that the design repeats itself, and fields have been renumbered and acreages added.

New drawings were again made for the third series published in 1909–12.

3   TOWN PLANS

Town Plans on a scale of 1:500 were published by the Ordnance Survey for the following Sussex towns:

	Date of Survey	Date of Publication	Number of Sheets
Brighton	1873–5	1878	55
Chichester	1874	1876	16
Eastbourne	1874	1877	20
Hastings	1872	1876	38
Horsham	1874–5	1877	8
Lewes	1872–3	1875	14
Petworth	1872	1874	6
Rye	1871–2	1874	5
Worthing	1875	1879	17

4 TRIGONOMETRICAL SURVEY

A diagram entitled *TRIANGLES for the SURVEY of the COUNTY of SUSSEX* (Ae) and *Plate VIII* (Ea OS) appears in *An Account the trigonometrical survey . . . by Lt. Col. William Mudge and Capt. Thomas Colby. Vol. III* published by W. Faden in 1811. This is not a map, but shows the locations in the county of the main trigono-metrical stations. *Plate XXII* from volume I of the same work (1799) is a similar diagram for Kent and part of east Sussex.

VII MAPS OF PART OF THE COUNTY

1 MAPS OF A SINGLE DIVISION

Such maps, which were published as a complementary pair, are included in the main catalogue (see no. 104). Two maps of east Sussex have been found without companion maps of the western division, but it is very probable that other maps of each division were issued prior to 1900.

(a) DAY AND HAGHE   1837

Size: 176 mm × 112 mm (1 mm)   1:420,000

EAST SUSSEX POLLING DISTRICTS (Ea). *Day & Haghe lith^{rs}. to the Queen 17 Gate S^t.* (Ae OS). *Pub^d. for Baxter's Edition of the Poll. 1837.* (Ce OS).

> *East Sussex 1837. List of the registered electors, with the votes of such as actually polled . . . on the eleventh day of September, 1837 . . . with a map of the polling places in east Sussex.*
> Lewes, Baxter and Son, 1837.   P

(b) FARNCOMBE AND COMPANY   1896

Size: 384 mm × 295 mm (2 mm)   1:265,000

COUNTY OF EAST SUSSEX. RURAL AND URBAN DISTRICTS. ALSO PARISHES. August 1896 (Ca). *SCALE FOUR MILES TO AN INCH* (Ac). *FARNCOMBE & Co. LITHO. LEWES* (Ee). Overprinted in red.

> Found only as a loose map.   (ESRO)

2 GUIDE BOOKS

A large number of tourist guides were published during the latter half of the nineteenth century by A. and C. Black, Ward Lock and Co., John Heywood and others. Some, such as the *D.B. Friend's handy guide to Brighton*, which was published in August 1886, were produced by local book-sellers. Sussex, because of its south coast watering places, is particularly rich in such guides, and many contained maps covering a considerable area of the county. For example, *A pictorial and descriptive guide to Eastbourne*, from Ward Lock and Co. (second edition, 1900) contained a map by George Philip and Son entitled *SUSSEX COAST WORTHING TO RYE.*

3 JAMES E. EDWARDS

Edwards was a surveyor, publisher and engraver, of Betchworth in Surrey, later of Belvidere Place, Southwark (1799), Lee Place, Old Brompton (1816) and of Cromwell's Lane, Kensington (1817).

He is best remembered for *A Companion from London to Brighthelmston,* which was published in parts commencing in or before 1796. Work on the survey had started in 1787, and, it was claimed, took twenty years to complete. Sir Joseph Banks, President of the Royal Society, was named as 'original promoter' of the scheme. Most bound copies contain nine maps of the route, dated 1787 to 1800. These can be identified by plate numbers (Ea OS) in the form *T.P.* followed by the number in Roman numerals (**see plate 35**). In addition, there was *AN Illustration PLAN to PART, 1ST.* dated 1789, and town plans of Steyning (1793) and New Shoreham (1798). Some copies contain a plan of Lewes (1799), and the advertisement indicates that a plan of Brighton was also projected.

The work was republished in parts with the title *Edwards's topographical surveys through Surrey, Sussex, and Kent . . .* commencing in 1817. According to the advertisement, 'an original Survey . . . was, after Twenty Years Labour, and nearly Two Thousand Pounds Expense, in completing, unfortunately destroyed by the great Fire which happened at the Printer's,[1] Bolt-court, Fleet-Street, in November, 1807, and nothing recovered from the loss.' The maps appear to have been printed from the original plates, which had been considerably revised. They were dated 1817 to 1820.

Copies of the work with maps dated from 1787 to 1800 and from 1817 to 1820 are at the GUILDHALL LIBRARY.

He also published *EDWARDS'S GENERAL MAP of 1400 Square Miles. SCALE of Ten Statute MILES* 1 + 9 = 87 mm. The size is 581 mm × 268 mm (6 mm). It covers central Sussex from *Worthing* to *EASTBOURN* and north as far as *LONDON.* Impressions have been found with the imprint (Ce OS) dated *1800* (BL.ESRO), *1816* (GL.ESCL.SAS), and *1817* (ESRO.WORTHING PL).

4 MAPS OF RAPES

The following maps appear in sections of Dallaway's *A history of the western division of the county of Sussex.*

(a) *THE RAPE OF CHICHESTER 1815.* (Aa). 480 mm × 286 mm (3 mm). Compass (Ea). Arms (Ae). North is to the left.

---

1 T. Bensley, 8 Bolt Court. Another fire at the same premises, then Bensley and Son, in 1819, destroyed remaining copies of Dallaway's *A history of the western division of the county of Sussex* (See appendix VII.4). No. 8 Bolt Court was the residence of Dr. Johnson from 1776. He died there in 1784, see *SAC* vol. 103 (1965), p. 30, n.1.

A history of the western division of the county of Sussex . . . vol. 1.
London, T. Bensley, 1815.   CUL.BRIGHTON PL.WSCL
Loose impressions of this map (WSRO, WORTHING PL) have *Neele & Co., sc 342 Strand* (Ec OS).

(b) *THE RAPE OF CHICHESTER 1819.* (Ea). 282 mm × 485 mm (3 mm). *T. Starling sculp^t.* (Ee OS). *British Statute Miles. 1 + 4 = 72 mm* (Ee). Compass (Ee, behind scale).

A history of the western division of the county of Sussex . . . vol. 1.
London, T. Bensley, 1815.   BL.ESCL.WSCL
This section of the work covers the city and rape of Chichester. Some copies (eg SAS) do not contain the map, and the discrepancy in dates makes it probable that this version of the map was added at the time volume 2 was published.

(c) *THE RAPE OF ARUNDEL 1819.* (Aa). 284 mm × 440 mm (2 mm). *Froggett sculp^t.* (Ee). *SCALE OF STATUTE MILES 1 + 4 = 72 mm* (Ee). Compass (Ed).

A history of the western division of the county of Sussex including the rapes of Arundel and Bramber. By James Dallaway M.B.F.A.S., vol. 2, part 1.
London, Bensley and Son, 1819.   BL.ESCL.WSCL

The parochial topography of the rape of Arundel . . . by James Dallaway . . . A new edition by Edmund Cartwright. vol. 2, part 1.
London, John Bowyer Nichols and Son, 1832.   BL.SAS.WORTHING PL

(d) *Plan of the RAPE OF BRAMBER in the county of SUSSEX surveyed in 1824. B.R. Davies sculp^t. London, 1830* (Aa). 393 mm × 710 mm (10 mm). *SCALE OF STATUTE MILES 1 + 6 = 150 mm* (Ee). Longitude 5' (1'), latitude 5' (1'). Compass (Ac). *Explanation* (Ae).

The parochial topography of the rape of Bramber . . . by Edmund Cartwright. vol. 2, part 1.
London, J.B. Nichols and Son, 1830.   BL.SAS.WORTHING PL
This work also contains Mantell no. 84.

(e) *GEOLOGICAL MAP OF RAPE OF BRAMBER BY GIDEON MANTELL ESQ. F.R.S. &c.* (Ce). 197 mm × 352 mm (6 mm). *Scale of Statute Miles 1 + 6 = 75 mm* (Ee). Longitude 5' (1'), latitude 5' (1').

The parochial topography of the rape of Bramber . . . by Edmund Carwright. vol. 2, part 2.
London, J.B. Nichols and Son, 1830.   BL.SAS.WORTHING PL

385

VIII UNTRACED AND UNIDENTIFIED MAPS

1 PORCELAIN PLATE

Maps of three counties — Hertfordshire, Oxfordshire and Somerset — have been found on nine inch porcelain plates. The maps are transfer-printed, and occupy a circular area of about six inches diameter. They are attractively decorated and coloured, and are thought to have been made in Staffordshire about 1830. It is probable that the set included a map of Sussex (see Hodson, 1974, no. 92a).

2 *The Road from LONDON to ARUNDEL.* see plate 40(ii).

It is probable that this strip map was one of a series, but no road-book or other work in which it appeared has been identified. It measures 197 mm × 107 mm, and is printed on laid paper, without watermark. It is based on Ogilby (appendix V.1(ii), 1675), and is on plain strips, not scrolls. The first known work to omit scrolls was Bowen's *Britannia depicta* (appendix V.4, 1720), but that work incorporated differences from Ogilby which are not on this map, eg Bowen has added *Gallows* (strip 1) and omits *S^r. W^m. Morleys* (strip 6). This map may be later than 1720 — it marks *Vauxhall* (strip 1), as opposed to *Foxhall* on both Ogilby and Bowen — but, if so, it was clearly copied from Ogilby, and not from Bowen.

3 HISTORY OF SUSSEX, 1708

G. Slade Butler's 'Topographia Sussexiana' (*SAC* vol. 15, 1863, p. 217) includes 'History of the County of Sussex, and the Towns and Villages therein situated, account of the Monasteries, Church History, the Martyrs of the County, etc., with an Old Map, 4to. 1708.' The map has not been traced, but the reference may be to a work containing Morden (catalogue, no. 21; see note under *Magna Britannia*, 1738).

4 DISTRICT BLUE BOOK

The copy of *W.T. Pike's District Blue Book. Eastern or Rye Parliamentary Division of Sussex 1885–6,* at the GUILDHALL LIBRARY does not contain a map. A copy at another library, now lost, contained a map with the title *Eastern or Rye Parliamentary Division of Sussex (from the Ordnance Survey) Scale 5 m = 5".* Published by *W.T. Pike, 62 Queens Road, Hastings,* and bore the signature *G.W. Bacon's Geographical Establishment, 127 Strand, London* (Ce OS). There was an advertisement which implied that this map covered the whole Eastern Division. The map(s) may well have been lithographic transfers from the same plates as no. 121M or N.

IX SUMMARY OF NORDEN'S KNOWN WORK ON ENGLISH COUNTY MAPS

This summary updates and expands an earlier account by R.A. Skelton (1952, p. 53). Unless otherwise stated, the maps mentioned may be found at the British Library and/or the Royal Geographical Society. The maps of Surrey, Sussex and Hampshire were reproduced by The Royal Geographical Society in *English county maps,* 1932.

NORTHAMPTONSHIRE

The description and map, 166 mm × 141 mm (7 mm),[1] in manuscript and entitled *Specvlvm Northamptoniae,* was sent to Lord Burghley in 1591. The manuscript was lost until 1938, when it was discovered at the Bibliothèque Nationale in Paris. It has never been printed, but there is a photocopy at the British Library.

Another version of both text and map was probably executed by Norden in 1610.[2] The description only was printed in 1720. The existence of this later version of the map is only known from reference to it in the 1720 text.

MIDDLESEX

The description and map were completed in 1592. The work, entitled *Specvlvm Britanniae. The first parte,* was printed and published in 1593 at Norden's own expense. The map was engraved by van den Keere, and measured 195 mm × 157 mm (6 mm).

An abridged version of the text and the map were included in *A chorographicall discription . . .,* which was sent to the Queen in 1595. Although a printed impression of the map would then have been available, it is probable that a manuscript version, by Norden himself, would have been included in this collection.

The text and map, 197 mm × 163 mm (5 mm) were reprinted, with Hertfordshire, in 1723 under the title *Speculum Britanniae: An historical and chorographical description of Middlesex and Hartfordshire.* This work also included *Nordens Preparative to his Speculum Britanniae,* originally published in 1596. The maps were engraved by Senex.

SURREY

A reference in Rawlinson[3] implied the existence of a description of this county in manuscript, which is now lost. A Norden map of the county, 382 mm × 306 mm (11

---

1 Dimensions from photocopy at British Library.
2 Rawlinson, 1720, p. 162 and Gough, 1780 vol. 2, p. 37; but Whitaker has observed that the description refers to Queen Elizabeth as if she were still alive (Whitaker, 1948, p. xii).
3 Rawlinson, 1720, p. 228, and Gough, 1780 vol. 2, p. 261.

mm), engraved by Charles Whitwell, was published in 1594 with the help of Robert Nicholson and William Waad. A manuscript version of the description is included in *A chorographicall discription* . . . (1595), but the map is missing. The map was reissued, with numerous alterations to the plate, perhaps about 1604.[4]

ESSEX

The description and map were completed in 1594, and four manuscript versions are known to have survived:[5]
   (i) At Essex Record Office. 255 mm × 198 mm (5 mm). Probably the earliest version. The map was reproduced by the Essex Record Office and Royal Geographical Society jointly in 1957.
  (ii) *Essex described.* Lord Burghley's copy, now at Hatfield House, 420 mm × 328 mm (7 mm). The text and map, engraved by J. Basire, were published by the Camden Society in 1840. A lithographic reproduction of the map by Maclure and Co. was published in *The Essex naturalist* for February 1887.
 (iii) *An Exact Discription of Essex* . . . *1594.* The Earl of Essex's copy, at British Library (Add. MSS 33769). Map 481 mm × 376 mm (5 mm bottom and sides, 10 mm top).
  (iv) The Queen's copy in *A chorogaphicall discription* . . ., 485 mm × 377 mm (12 mm). The text in this version is abridged. The map is dated 1594.

HAMPSHIRE

A description and map, 519 mm[6] × 380 mm (9 mm), in manuscript formed part of *A chorographicall discription* . . ., (1595). The map was engraved and published about 1595–6, but no impression in the original state has survived. About 1642 Stent republished the map, 400 mm × 334 mm (11 mm), from the original plate, but with alterations. It was later published by John Overton, who had acquired the plate in 1663.

SUSSEX

The map (catalogue no. 3) was published in 1595. A description and map in manuscript formed part of *A chorographicall discription* . . . (1595), but the map is missing, and of the text only one page of index remains. A copy of the complete text made between 1656 and 1670, probably for Sir Christopher Hatton, survives in the Northamptonshire Record Office. It has never been printed, but has been described by Farrant.[7]

---

4 Sharp, 1929, p. 14.
5 F.G. Emmison and R.A. Skelton, 'The description of Essex by John Norden, 1594', in *GJ* vol. 123 part 1 (March 1957). Rawlinson, 1720, p. 47 refers to a survey of the county by Norden in the library of Sir Edward Turner.
6 The map of *HASHIRE* itself is only 412 mm × 380 mm. A column (107 mm × 380 mm) on the right contains maps of *Weyght, Jarsay* and *Garnesay.*
7 *SAC* vol. 116 (1978).

HERTFORDSHIRE

The description and map were completed in 1597, and printed as *Specvli Britanniae pars . . .* at Norden's expense in 1598; the map, 236 mm × 189 mm (4 mm), engraved by Kip. The text and map were reprinted in 1723, the map having been re-engraved by Senex. See Hodson, 1974 nos. 3 and 26, for full descriptions of the maps.

CORNWALL

Norden surveyed the county between 1597 and 1601. The text and map, 370 mm × 260 mm (7 mm),[8] were completed about 1604, or perhaps rewritten about then from an earlier version, before being presented to James I. About 1680 a copy was made of the original text. In 1728 the map was engraved by John Pine and published by Christopher Bateman. In addition to the map of Cornwall there were maps of the nine hundreds. The original text[9] now contains impressions of the printed maps (1728), whereas the c. 1680 copy of the text[10] contains the original manuscript maps. Ravenhill has published[11] a fascinating account of the steps by which the provenance of the text and maps was pieced together.

KENT

According to Gough,[12] 'Norden made a survey of this county, still in MS'. This is now lost, but the map of Kent in Camden's *Britannia*, 1607 (see catalogue no. 6) is signed *Iohannes Norden deliniauit*, and presumably was derived from the manuscript mentioned by Gough. There is also evidence that Norden prepared a description of Kent. In 1666 Sylvanus Morgan announced[13] that he could procure several pieces of Norden's *Speculum Britanniae*, viz. 'Kent, Essex, Surrey, Sussex, Hampshire, the Isles of Whight, Gersey and Garnsy'. It will be seen that this is the same list as appeared in *A chorographicall discription . . .* (1595), except that Kent has replaced Middlesex, the only county in the list to have been printed by 1666.

NORFOLK

An anonymous description of the county, written between 1598 and 1610, has been attributed to Norden;[14] but the evidence is weak, and there is no map.

---

8 Measured from facsimile reproduction in *Specvli Britanniae pars. A topographicall & historical description of Cornwall*, see Ravenhill, 1972
9 BL. Harl MS 6252.
10 Trinity College Library, Cambridge.
11 Ravenhill, 1972, pp. 3–10.
12 Gough, 1780, vol. 1, p. 441.
13 *Armilogia sive ars chromocritica.*
14 Hood, 1938, p. 27.

SUFFOLK

Gough[15] states that Speed's map of this county was derived from one by Norden. The statement is unsupported, and the map in *Britannia* (1607) is signed *Auctore Christopher Saxton*. Had a Norden map been available at that date, it would probably have been used.

CAMDEN'S *BRITANNIA*, 1607 (see catalogue no. 6).

Of the fifty-seven maps in this work, forty-one are derived from Saxton, six from Norden and one from Owen; the other nine do not name a cartographer. The Saxton and Owen maps are signed either *Descripsit* or *Auctore*. Three of the Norden maps (Hampshire, Hertfordshire and Middlesex) are signed *Descripsit;* the other three (Surrey, Sussex and Kent) are signed *Deliniauit*. The distinction may be intentional. The first three were probably derived from Norden's earlier maps; the other three were perhaps redrawn by Norden himself for the engraver.

X DATING OF MAPS

The only certain way to fix the date of issue of a map is to establish the date of issue of the atlas or book in which it was published; it must be remembered that many atlases and books bear dates earlier than the actual date of publication. When an atlas was first issued, extra quantities of the text, perhaps including the title-page, were sometimes run off so that the moveable type could be dispersed and reused. The maps, however, were printed from copper plates as and when required, and sometimes amended. They would then be bound with the text, which might still bear the original publication date. Even a dated map may not have been issued until some years after the date appearing on it. A number of helpful indications[1] as to the date of issue are discussed below, but all are inconclusive, and any date in brackets in the catalogue must be accepted with reservation.

(i) RAILWAYS (See **KEY TO RAILWAYS** – appendix XI)

Railways are a useful indication of issue date — after 1840, as far as Sussex is concerned. An analysis of a typical map which emphasises railways (Hall no. 96) shows that up to 1850 new lines were added on the map as soon as authorised, and in this connection it must be born in mind that some lines were originally authorised earlier than the date given in appendix XI. For example, no. 16 (the line from Three Bridges to East Grinstead) was first authorised in 1846, but the project was not pursued. A new Act for the line was passed in 1853, and the line opened in 1855. After 1850, Hall's policy seems to have changed, and he did not add new lines on his map until they were in use.

The dates on which stations were opened, closed or named can also be helpful, and these are listed by Clark.[2]

(ii) ROADS

Early county maps, prior to the publication of Ogilby's *Britannia* in 1675 (appendix V, 1), did not generally mark roads.[3] Perhaps they were not of great significance when travel was mainly on horseback and there was always a track of some sort between one town and the next. They did, however, show an appreciation of the importance of river crossings to the traveller and to the military. Saxton pinpoints thirteen bridges in Sussex (five on the Arun, two on the Adur, one each on the Ouse, Cuckmere and

---

1 Verner, 1965, reviews the methodology.
2 Clark, 1964.
3 The first county map to mark roads was Norden's Middlesex (1593). Roads were shown on some of Norden's other large maps, eg Surrey (1594); on Symonson's map of Kent (1596) and on William Smith's maps (1602–3).

Brede, and three on the eastern Rother). Nevertheless, he omits many important bridges, for example Houghton Bridge[4] south of Amberley. The first map of Sussex to indicate roads was Morden's playing card map (no. 17, 1676).

A check list of turnpike Acts affecting Sussex (1710[5] to 1840), compiled by G.D. Johnston, is available at the SAS library, and extracts will be found in a paper by Ivan Margery.[6] Horsfield[7] lists turnpike trusts as at 1835, and Armstrong[8] provides a useful map. See also Day and Son no. 118 for the position in 1852.

The first turnpike roads to involve Sussex — Sevenoaks to Tunbridge Wells (1710), and London to East Grinstead (1717) — hardly touch the county, and were not added on any Sussex map. The first routes of significance to the county were the Hindhead/Midhurst/Chichester road (1749) and the Flimwell/Hastings road (1753). Thereafter new Acts were frequent, almost annual, events; but they were ignored by cartographers before Cary. *Cary's new and correct English atlas*, 1787 and 1793 (catalogue no. 49), *Britannia*, 1789 and 1806 (no. 50), and *Traveller's companion*, 1789 to 1828 (nos. 51, 65 and 82) add and upgrade a number of roads from one edition to the next; but only a few of these changes can be related to turnpike Acts. For example, the 1806 edition of the *Traveller's companion* (no. 65) adds the road from Eastbourne to Alciston with branch to Hailsham, which had been turnpiked in 1792; and the 1828 edition is the first to mark the Crawley to Horsham direct road, which had been turnpiked in 1823. In general, the upgrading of roads on Cary's maps seems to reflect the status of the road rather than the passing of turnpike Acts. Johnson, in a detailed study of the roads from Arundel,[9] refers to Cary's maps, but not particularly his county maps, and concludes 'Cary's maps are clearly inaccurate'.

Smith's *New English atlas* of 1808, no. 60(v), was the first Sussex map to include *Turnpike Roads* in the 'Explanation', and, from then on, there was a better correlation between the turnpike Acts and the maps. The 1818 edition of the *New English atlas* added the Piecombe/Bolney/Staplefield road, turnpiked in 1808, and the Amberley/Yapton (Slindon) road, turnpiked in 1812. Nevertheless, turnpike Acts are neither very helpful nor reliable as a means of dating maps.

The *New Brighton Road* first appears in Cary's *New English atlas,* no. 61 (v), and in his *New and correct English atlas,* no. 68 (iii), both published in 1818. This refers to the Cuckfield/Balcombe/Worth road, as opposed to the earlier routes through Crawley and through Lindfield.

(iii)   CANALS AND NAVIGATIONS[10]

a)   Western Rother.   An Act of 1791 covered the navigation of this river from

4   *SAC* vol. 17, p. 215.
5   I am indebted to John Farrant for reference to an earlier Act covering the road from Reigate to Crawley (1697). See also Brandon, 1974, pp. 178–81.
6   *SNQ* vol. 13, p. 49.
7   Horsfield, 1835, vol. 1, p. 97.
8   Armstrong, 1974, pp. 132–3.
9   *SNQ* vol. 17, p. 58.
10   Hadfield, 1969, gives key dates in tabular form.

Midhurst to its junction with the Arun. Work was completed, including the branch to Petworth, by 1795. Gardner, Yeakell and Gream no. 57 (i), 1795, marked two minor cuts near Selham and a canal to Haslingbourne. It also showed the cut joining the Rother directly to the Arun just below Stopham bridge. *Canal* has been added on edition (ii).

b) Arun. The navigation through Hardham tunnel and then rejoining the river below Greatham bridge was authorised in 1785[11] and completed by 1790. It is shown by Gardner, Yeakell and Gream in 1795. *Canal* was added on edition (ii).

The Wey and Arun canal was authorised in 1813 and first appears on no. 57 (v). Gream no. 58 (ii), refers to it as the *Surrey and Sussex* canal. The canal was abandoned in 1868. An attractive plan of the Rother and Arun navigations, engraved by Neele, will be found in the 1808 and 1813 editions of Young's *General view of the agriculture . . .* (see no. 55).

c) Royal Military Canal. This runs from Pett to near Hythe in Kent. It was designed as a military defence work, started in 1804 and completed in 1806. Parts of it appear on Coltman no. 59(ii), 1807, and on Gardner, Yeakell and Gream no. 57(v), 1815.

d) The Arun and Portsmouth canal. Authorised in 1817 and opened in 1822–3. *Intended Arun and Portsmouth Canal* appears on Gardner, Yeakell and Gream no. 57 (vi), 1820, and on Gream no. 58(ii), 1819.

e) Ouse.[12] The first edition of Gardner, Yeakell and Gream no. 57(i), 1795, marks three sections of 'canal' or navigations between Lindfield and Sheffield Bridge, one section marked *Lock* at Buckham, four sections between Isfield and Lewes, and two sections between Lewes and Newhaven. These navigations were undertaken about 1790. The waterway above Lewes fell into disuse by about 1868. On the third edition of no. 57, four additional cuts appear between Lewes and Newhaven, and *Proposed Canal* from Laughton to Hellingly has been added. There is also an unlabelled section of the proposed canal from the Glynd River to Ripe. These proposed canals were never constructed. On the 1818 edition the main canal has been extended from Lindfield to Rye Bridge, south of Ardingly. This section was opened in 1812 and closed in 1861.

(iv) PIERS, ETC.

These are conspicuous features on later maps.

Bognor pier was built in 1864.

Brighton Chain Pier was started in 1822 and completed the following year. After severe damage it was re-opened in 1836 and finally destroyed in 1896. The West Pier opened in 1866, and the Palace Pier in 1899. The gas works at Black Rock were built in

---

11 *SNQ* vol. 13, p. 272.
12 D.F. Gibbs and J.H. Farrant, 'The upper Ouse navigation, 1790–1800', in *Sussex Industrial History* no. 1 (1970–1); Farrant, 'Civil engineering in Sussex around 1800, and the career of Cater Rand', ibid. no. 6 (1973–4); and 'The Lower Ouse Navigation', *Sussex Industrial Archaeology Society Newsletter* nos. 3 (June 1974) and 4 (October 1974).

1818; the Aquarium was opened in 1872, and the electric railway in 1896.

Eastbourne pier was commenced in 1865, opened in 1870. After major damage, it was rebuilt and re-opened in 1877.

Hastings pier was opened in 1872; St. Leonards pier in 1891.

Pagham harbour wall, closing off the inlet, was built in 1876.

Shoreham harbour. The new (west) entrance, about a half mile west of Southwick, was dredged in 1762, but it quickly silted up, moved steadily eastwards and was hardly navigable. In 1818 the west entrance was re-opened, and this time it was protected by properly constructed piers, which were successful in preventing the eastward drift.[13] The suspension bridge over the Adur was opened in 1833.

Worthing pier was opened in 1862.

(v) PLACE—NAMES

The spelling[14] can give an indication as to date.

Brighton, the abbreviated form, is said by Lower to have been used in the time of Charles II, and to have been generally accepted from about 1760.[15] Mawer and Stenton,[16] however, suggest that it only came into common use at the start of the nineteenth century. The first map to use the modern form was Hall no. 77 in 1820.

Eastbourne is marked on early maps as *Borne* or as *Eborn*. Budgen seems to have introduced *E.bourne* and *S.bourne*, together with *Medes* and *Seahouses*, in 1723. About 1880 we get *Eastbourne (Old Town)* together with *Eastbourne (New Town* is sometimes added) and *Southbourne* or *Sth. Bourne*. Later issues of the Ordnance Survey one inch New Series, sheet 334, mark *EASTBOURNE* only.

Newhaven was used as the name for the port of Meeching as early as 1586, but Budgen's map in 1723 was the first to drop Meeching altogether in favour of *Newhaven*.

Selsey, Celsey or *Chelsey* appear on early maps. Yeakell and Gardner introduce the etymologically incorrect form *Selsea* in 1778 (catalogue no. 47), but it was not used by later cartographers or on their own 1795 map (no. 57), until reintroduced by Gream (no. 58) and Coltman (no. 59) in 1799. *Selsea* was then used by a number of map-makers, including Greenwood. Lower[17] uses both forms. The Ordnance Survey one inch Old Series uses *Selsea*. The New Series adopts the more correct *Selsey;* but both forms were in use until at least 1900.

St Leonards as we know it was laid out in 1870, but as a locality 'juxta Hasting' it appeared in the late thirteenth century. Greenwood, no. 93(v), used the name in 1834 in place of *St. Mary Magdalen*.

13   *SAC* vol. 88, pp. 42–50.
14   Harley, 1971. This paper deals with the toponymy before the advent of the Ordnance Survey.
15   Lower, *Compendious history*, 1870, p. 81. R. Coates 'Studies and observations on Sussex place-names' *SAC* vol. 118 (1980) p. 316 records the use of the abbreviated form in 1686.
16   Mawer and Stenton, 1929, p. 291.
17   Lower, 1931, p. 219.

Worthing is spelt without the *h* on early maps. Morden introduced the *h* in the 1722 edition of *Britannia.*

The spelling of place-names on maps is often a better guide to contemporary pronunciation than that derived from more formal sources such as legal documents and official returns, because surveyors and cartographers (to the extent that they included original information in their work at all) usually obtained it orally from local sources. This point was noted by Blaauw as early as 1848.[18] Hyde[19] records an amusing example of the danger of relying on oral information; *South Island Place,* on the Greenwood map of London published in 1827, is corrected in later editions to *South Highland Place.*

A full analysis of the spelling of Sussex place-names on maps is outside the scope of this appendix, but the various spellings of *Bodiam* on Sussex maps are given as a random example, and perhaps as a guide to local pronunciation: *Bodiham* (Saxton, 1575), *Bodgihim* (Norden, 1595), *Bodgihem* (Norden, 1607), but *Bodiam* in Camden's text (1610), *Bodgiham* (Speed, 1611 and derivations to about 1720, except for Blaeu who spells it *Bodigham*), *Bodyham* (Budgen 1723, to about 1800), *Bodiham* (Smith, 1801, to about 1868; although some cartographers in this period adhere to the earlier form — *Bodyham*), amd *Bodiam* (the modern spelling, first used by Hughes 1868). The dialect form *Bodgem*, recorded in 1887 by Sawyer[20] (see no. 142), would seem, therefore, to have been a nineteenth century invention. Sawyer made good use of maps, but he would have benefited from an accurate bibliography. His list of authorities included Jenner's *A book of the names* . . ., see no. 11(i); 'Lea's map of 1576' — presumably a Saxton/Lea map no. 1(v)(vi) or (vii), although none carried that date; and Norden's map of 1646, a reference to Speed, no. 7(ii). In a subsequent paper,[21] Sawyer refers to Norden no. 6, and to later maps on which market towns are designated.

(vi)   PARLIAMENTARY REPRESENTATION

Parliamentary representation is indicated on early maps by asterisks, eg on Morden no. 21. Later maps often give fuller information in the form of a note, eg Davies no. 121.

Originally there was no formal distinction between the two halves of the county. The first official recognition came in 1504–5, when an Act allowed the county justices to sit alternately at Chichester and Lewes. The effect of this move went beyond the administration of justice. The justices had other functions, and it became the custom to treat the three western rapes and the three eastern rapes as separate areas for, for example, the raising of rates. This long established custom did not receive statutory recognition until 1864.

18   H.W. Blaauw 'Subsidy roll of the rape of Lewes in 1296', *SAC* vol. 2 (1849), p. 293n.
19   Hyde, 1975, p. 1. See also Raistrick, 1969, p. 17.
20   F.E. Sawyer, 'Glossary of Sussex dialected place-nomenclature', *SAC* vol. 35 (1887), p. 168. A further list in Lower, 1854, p. 270.
21   F.E. Sawyer 'Sussex markets and fairs', *SAC* vol. 36 (1888), p. 184.

In 1832 two separate Divisions were created for parliamentary representation.

The County of Sussex Act of 1865 (which re-enacted the 1864 Act) formalised the two Divisions for various purposes, eg rating, expenditure, constabulary; but Sussex remained one county for other purposes, eg militia.[22]

Separate administrative counties were set up by the Local Government Act of 1888, after which the use of capitals for *East* and *West Sussex* seems appropriate. But Sussex remained one county, with one Lord Lieutenant, one Sheriff and one Assizes until 1974.

With minor exceptions Sussex returned twenty-eight members to Parliament up to the 1832 Reform Act: two for the county; two each for the nine towns (Arundel, Bramber, Chichester, East Grinstead, Horsham, Lewes, Midhurst, New Shoreham, Steyning); and two for each of the four Cinque ports[23] (Hastings, Rye, Seaford and Winchelsea). Steyning was combined with Bramber until 1460, and Seaford was disenfranchised between 1490 and 1640.

The 1832 Act reduced the representation to eighteen, two each for Eastern Division, Western Division, Brighton, Chichester, Lewes, New Shoreham and Hastings; one each for Arundel, Horsham, Midhurst and Rye. Bramber, East Grinstead, Steyning, Seaford and Winchelsea were disenfranchised.

In 1868 the number of members was further reduced to fifteen: two each for the two Divisions, and for Brighton, New Shoreham and Hastings; one each for Chichester, Horsham, Lewes, Midhurst and Rye. Arundel was disenfranchsed.

Under the 1885 Act the county was divided into six rural divisions — Horsham, Chichester, East Grinstead, Lewes, Eastbourne and Rye — each returning one member. In addition Brighton returned two members and Hastings one member, a total of nine for the county.

[In 1979 East and West Sussex returned fourteen members — just half the pre-1832 representation].

(vii) THE COUNTY BOUNDARY

The following changes, which are sometimes reflected on maps, have been traced. In 1844 Ambersham was transferred from Hampshire.[24] In 1894–5 Broomhill was transferred from Kent to Sussex, and parts of Frant and Lamberhurst were ceded to Kent.[25]

Part of Shoyswell hundred, including Dale Hill Farm, was excluded from the county by Gardner, Yeakell and Gream (no. 57(vi) 1820) and by Gream (no. 58(ii)

---

22 *SNQ* vol. 13 (1950), p. 14.
23 *Magna Britannia* (see Morden no. 21) has a triangular table of distances at the end of the Sussex section, which includes 'Sussex sends XX Members to Parliament', ie excluding the Cinque Ports.
24 Under the County Boundaries Act (7 and 8 Victoria, c.61). The map attached to Mawer and Stenton, 1929, gives the date as 1832, and *VCH* vol. 1, p. 536 gives it as 1834. The transfer for some purposes must have occurred prior to 1844.
25 *VCH*. vol. 1.

1819); but no authority for this adjustment has been found, and it was not made on the Ordnance Survey one inch maps.

(viii)   POPULATION

The first decennial census was held in 1801, and from then onwards the figures (tabulated below) were included on many maps and in the text of topgraphical works containing county maps; but there is room for flexibility even in the interpretation of the official figures. The 1801 population is usually reported as 159,311, being the total for Sussex in the *Abstract*; but Horsfield[26] reduces it to 159,303 by excluding eight persons returned as 'in gaol'. Black's guides (see catalogue no. 121) give 159,471, which is the adjusted population figure for 1801 in the 1871 and later *Abstracts;* such adjustments may reflect minor boundary changes. Another source of discrepancy is illustrated by the 1901 *Abstract*, which reports the population as 605,202 for the *Geographical County*, 602,255 for the two administrative counties and county boroughs, and 605,785 for the registration area.

Year	Population	Year	Population	Year	Population
1801	159,311	1841	300,108	1881	490,505
1811	190,083	1851	336,844	1891	550,442
1821	233,019	1861	363,735	1901	605,202
1831	272,340	1871	417,456	1981	[1,311,130]

The new description and state of England published in 1701 (see no. 21) gave the population of Sussex as 129,240.

(ix)   AREA

Bowes no. 2 gave the area of Sussex as 900 square miles. These playing cards seem to have contained the first assessment of the sizes of the English counties. Bowes was probably using the ten-furlong mile, so his figure is equivalent to just over 1,400 square statute miles, a surprisingly accurate assessment, probably made from Saxton's map *Anglia;* the true area was about 1,460 square miles.

Over a hundred years later Morden's *The new description and state of England*, 1701 (no. 21), gave an area of 1,140,000 acres — equivalent to 1,785 square miles of eight furlongs, 1407 square miles of nine furlongs and 1,000 square miles of ten furlongs. The same figure appeared in other works of the period, eg *Britannia Depicta*, 1720 (no. 23). About 1729 Thomas Templeman published *A new survey of the globe*, in which he recorded areas and other geographical facts, said to have been measured from

26   Horsfield, 1835, vol. 2, p. 87.

Moll's[27] maps and from the Senex twenty-eight inch diameter globe. He gave the area of Sussex as 1,416 square miles; but pointed out that this was based on taking 60 miles as an equivalent to one degree, whereas the true equivalent was 69½ miles to one degree. He added that his figures should be increased in the ratio 60^2 to $69½^2$. There is clearly some confusion in his reasoning, since this adjustment would increase the area to about 1,900 square miles. Templeman's measurement of 1,416 square miles was accepted until the end of the century, and appeared on Walker no. 32 (1746), Bowen no. 45 (1767), and other maps.

In 1793 Arthur Young wrote[28] 'It contains, according to the Mensuration in Templeman's Tables, 1,416 square miles, and 1,140,000 acres'. The latter figure does not come from Templeman, but from Morden (1701) or some earlier source; and the juxtaposition is curious as it postulated a nine-furlong mile, whereas the eight-furlong mile had become well established since the publication of Ogilby's *Britannia* in 1675. Young then quoted another assessment of 908,952 acres, and the figure of 935,040 from the Poor Returns. He also made what appears to be his own calculation as 933,360 acres.

Dix's map no. 75 (1818) gave 953,360 acres. *The new British traveller,* 1819 (see no. 74), reproduced the various acreages given by Young. Lower[29] in 1831 somewhat surprisingly again gave 1,416 square miles and 1,140,000 acres. He also quoted Camden's figure of 7,000 hides for the kingdom of the south Saxons, which cannot be related to any modern calculation. Tymms's *The family topographer,* 1832 (see no. 100) gave 1520 square miles and 933,360 acres (Young's assessment); but Tymms's calculations were inconsistent, 933,360 acres being equivalent to 1,460 square miles. Cobbett, 1832 (see no. 101) gave 1,463 square miles and 936,320 acres; the latter figure being the same in Gorton's *Topographical dictionary,* 1831 (no. 96) and in *The parliamentary gazetteer,* 1840 (no. 102) which added 'according to Arrowsmith's map of 1815/16, which was principally founded on the Ordnance Survey'. Horsfield[30] yet again reproduced in 1835, the various computations offered in Young in 1793.

The *Enumeration Abstract* for 1831, published in 1833, was the first to include areas (p. xxii), compiled by Mr. John Rickman. The preface stated: 'The present Abstract attempts to give the AREA of every parish in England; for which purpose those County Maps which profess to mark the limits of each Parish were sedulously corrected whenever error or defect was discoverable; not less than 3,000 letters of local enquiry (inclosing explanatory Tracings) having been dispatched for this purpose.* After correction thus obtained the Area of each Parish was computed by means of Glass plates marked in squares of 40 Acres; and although reliance for any accurate purpose would be misplaced on the Result thus obtained, it may be deemed usually correct within one-tenth part, seldom erroneous beyond one-fifth part'. The asterisk

27 Presumably *Atlas geographus* (see no. 21) published from 1708, and *A new description,* 1724 (see no. 24). A note on the title-page of some issues of Templeman's work stated that the tables were designed to be bound with Moll's *Atlas minor* (1729).
28 Young, 1793 (see no. 55).
29 Lower, 1831 (see no. 98).
30 Horsfield, 1835.

referred to a footnote which read: 'The boundaries of Borough-Towns as ascertained for the purpose of the Reform of Parliament Act,[31] have afforded means (in many instances) or correcting former Maps as to Parish-boundaries: in some instances (on the contrary) they have created confusion or false inference: The Parishes adjacent to the Borough of Lewes are inaccurately stated from this cause.' Greenwood no. 89, the first map of Sussex to mark parish boundaries, had been published in 1825.

The Sussex section of the 1831 *Abstract* gave the area of the county as 907,920 acres, but added the following note: 'The Area of the County of Sussex is 1,466 square statute miles, and consequently 938,240 acres, while the area here assigned to the several parishes, amounts to no more than 907,920 acres; but no attempt to reconcile this apparent discrepancy has been deemed allowable.' The source of the 1466 square mile measurement is not given.

In the 1871 *Abstract* the area was amended to 934,006 acres; by 1891 it was 933,269 for the *Ancient County*, and 932,733 for the *Administrative County*. The difference is accounted for by the part of Frant administered by Kent.

The 1901 *Abstract* included an excellent map of the various administrative divisions on a scale of four miles to one inch, *Heliozincographed at the Ordnance Survey Office, Southampton 1902*. In the text the areas were given as 933,887 acres for the ancient or geographical county, 932,409 acres for the administrative counties of East and West Sussex plus the county boroughs of Brighton and Hastings, and 938,630 acres for the registration area.

(x) RELIEF

The representation of relief on a flat surface has always troubled cartographers. Most books about maps[32] contain a chapter on the subject, and it is still much discussed.[33] Many maps make no attempt to show relief, and a study of the various methods is, therefore, of limited value in dating maps.

Early cartographers of the counties, from Saxton onwards, showed hills in perspective, sometimes shaded on one side. These are usually diagramatic, making no attempt to identify specific hills, to represent the actual height above sea level, or to indicate the steepness of the slopes. This 'molehill' method was gradually replaced during the eighteenth century by various forms of hachuring, but it continued in use at least until 1790, when it was used by Lodge (no. 52).

Budgen no. 24 used in 1723 an elementary form of hachuring[34] in conjunction with molehills. The first 'series' map to use this combination was Bowen's *Large English atlas* 1749 (no. 35). To be effective, hachuring requires great skill and artistry on the

---

31 Presumably a reference to the Dawson maps (no. 99).
32 Jervis, 1936, for example; also H.G. Lyons, 'Relief in cartography', *GJ* vol. 43. (1914), pp. 233 et seq., and 395 et seq.
33 See papers in *Cartographic Journal* for June 1964, December 1967, June 1969 and June 1975.
34 True hachuring assumes the light to fall vertically from above; see Wallis, 1976.

part of the engraver. It was used without molehills on Yeakell and Gardner's map in 1778 (no. 47), but the shading obscures the other detail in many places. Cary did much to improve the technique which he employed on the maps he prepared for the 1789 edition of Camden's *Britannia*.

Contours were introduced on Sussex maps by the Ordnance Survey for the Second Edition of the one inch sheets, starting in 1876 (appendix VI.1.b, and no. 143), and for the six inch sheets starting in 1877 (appendix VI.2); but hachuring continued in use, and has never been wholly abandoned. About 1880, Bartholomews introduced to this country the 'contoured coloured' maps so familiar to users of school atlases. No. 153 is an example of this advance in the basic contour technique.

Another method, 'spot heights',[35] was not much used on county maps. Examples can be found on Hughes no. 128 (1868), Stanford no. 139 (1885), and Boothby no. 149 (1893).

(xi) WATERMARKS

Occasionally watermarks can provide important evidence, for example no. 1(iv). For further information the reader is referred to papers by Heawood[36] and Clarke.[37] Heawood's 1924 work is reproduced in full by Lister.[38] The watermark on some later papers (eg Whatman paper used for Cary no. 61) included the date, which at least establishes the earliest date of issue.

Laid paper has parallel lines, which resemble watermarks, at intervals of just over one inch. These lines are caused by wires in the mould, and indicate that the paper was made before 1759, although it may not have been used until some time later.

(xii) ORDNANCE SURVEY ONE INCH OLD SERIES (appendix VI.1.a)

Dating these sheets presents special problems, which have been studied in depth by Mumford and Clarke.[39]

(xiii) IMPRINTS AND ADRESSES

The form of publisher's imprint and the address from which he operated at the time, can provide useful evidence, see Langley no. 73(iii). The main sources of this infor-

---

35   A.A. Horner, 'Some examples of the representation of height data on Irish maps before 1750', *Irish Geography* vol. 7 (1974), deals with the origins of this method.
36   Heawood, 1924 and 1931. Also B. Akers, 'History of Watermarks', *The map collector* no. 6 (March 1979).
37   R.V. Clarke, 'The use of watermarks in dating old series one inch Ordnance Survey maps', *CJ* December 1969.
38   Lister, 1965.
39   Mumford, 1968; Mumford and Clark, 1968.

mation are Plomer, 1907, 1922 and 1932; Chubb, 1927; Skelton, 1970 (pp. 231–50); Hannas, 1972; Tyacke, 1973 and 1978; Hyde, 1975 (general introduction); Tooley, 1979; and trade directories.[40] In other cases appropriate dates can be established by searching catalogues for other maps bearing the same imprint or address, or by reference to published histories of the leading publishing houses.

(xiv) HISTORY AND HERALDRY

References on the map, or in the text of a work, to historical events will provide positive evidence as to the earliest date of printing. Miller's *New miniature atlas* (no. 81) is a good example. It is undated, and was assigned to 1810 by Chubb.[41] This date was adopted by subsequent bibliographers until Harvey,[42] who observed that the catalogue at the back of the atlas refers, on page 4, to 'his present Majesty, George IV.' He, therefore, amended the date to c. 1821.

Contemporary heraldry, or the dedication of the map to a living person, is often helpful, see Budgen no. 24, note 32.

(xv) RECORDS OF THE STATIONERS COMPANY, TERM CATALOGUES, ADVERTISEMENTS

Records of the Court of the Stationers Company 1602 to 1640, edited by W.A. Jackson, was published in 1957; *A transcript of the register of the Worshipful Company of Stationers 1640–1708* was published in three volumes in 1913. These works contain useful information relating to book-sellers, apprentices, etc.

The Term catalogues, 1668–1708 by Edward Arber was published in three volumes 1903, 1905 and 1906. These contain an invaluable record of books and maps printed in London during that period, see for example Redmayne no. 16.

Book-seller's advertisements figure prominently (together with those for patent medicines) in newspapers from the end of the seventeenth century[43] until at least the end of the eighteenth century. Although the search for such advertisements in both national and local papers can be somewhat laborious, they can provide essential information not available elsewhere. *London map-sellers 1660–1720* by Sarah Tyacke (Tring 1978) lists advertisements in the *London Gazette* between 1668 and 1719.

40 See Norton, 1950.
41 Chubb, 1927, no. 340.
42 Harvey, 1959, no. 74.
43 Tyacke, 1978.

XI KEY TO RAILWAYS[1]

See map on page 404. Railways in Sussex numbered 1 to 44; selected lines wholly outside the county lettered A to W.

Line[2]			Date of act[3]	Date opened
1	LBSCR	Brighton–Shoreham	[1837]	1840
2	LBSCR	Croydon–Brighton	1837	1841
A	SER	Redhill–Tonbridge–Headcorn–Ashford	1839–40	1842
B	SER	Maidstone Road (Paddock Wood)–Maidstone	1844	1844
3	LBSCR	Shoreham–Worthing	1844	1845
C	SER	Tonbridge–Tunbridge Wells	1845	1845
D	LSWR	Woking–Guildford	–	1845
4	LBSCR	Chichester–Worthing	1844	1846
5	LBSCR	Brighton–Lewes–St Leonards	1844	1846
6	LBSCR	Southerham Junction (Lewes)–Newhaven	1846	1847
7	LBSCR	Chichester–Havant	–	1847
8	LBSCR	Keymer Junction–Lewes	1845	1847
9	LBSCR	Three Bridges–Horsham	1846	1848
10	LBSCR	Polegate–Eastbourne	1846	1849
11	LBSCR	Polegate–Hailsham	1846	1849
E	LSWR/SER	Guildford–Shalford–Dorking	1847	1849
F	SER	Redhill–Dorking	1847	1849
12	SER	Tunbridge Wells–Robertsbridge	1846	1851
13	SER	Hastings–Ashford	1845	1851
14	SER	Robertsbridge–Battle–Bopeep Junction–Hastings	1846	1851–2
15	SER	Rye–Rye Harbour	1846	1854
16	LBSCR	Three Bridges–East Grinstead	1853	1855
G	SER	Purley–Caterham	1854	1856
H	SER	Strood–Maidstone	1853	1856
17	LBSCR	Lewes–Uckfield	1857	1858

1 Compiled from Clark, 1964. For other works on Sussex railways, see Farrant, 1977, p. 31.

2 LBSCR   London, Brighton and South Coast Railway (formed in 1846 by amalgamation of the London and Brighton and the London and Croydon companies). See Ellis, 1960.

   SER   South Eastern Railway.
   LSWR   London and South Western Railway
   LCDR   London, Chatham and Dover Railway
   RVR   Rother Valley Railway
   K&ESR   Kent and East Sussex Railway (formerly RVR)
   SE&CR   South Eastern and Chatham Railway.

3 Date of Act refers to the date of the main authorising Act or to the formation of the original construction company. There were numerous amalgamations, take-overs and changes of name, particularly in the early years; the companies listed above were the main operating companies during the period 1840 to 1900.

Line			Date of act	Date opened
18	LBSCR	Horsham–Petworth	1857	1859
19	LSWR	Godalming–Petersfield–Havant	1847–53	1859
20	LBSCR	Itchingfield Junction–Partridge Green–Shoreham	[1858]	1861
J	LCDR	Swanley–Sevenoaks	–	1862
21	LBSCR	Hardham Junction (Pulborough)–Ford	1860	1863
22	LBSCR	Ford–Littlehampton	1860	1863
23	LBSCR	Barnham Junction–Bognor	1853–61	1864
24	LWSR	Petersfield–Midhurst	–	1864
25	LBSCR	Newhaven–Seaford	–	1864
K	LSWR	Woking–Brookwood	–	1864
L	LBSCR	Sutton–Epsom Downs	1862	1865
26	LBSCR	South Fork–Itchingfield Junction	1860	1865
27	LBSCR	Petworth–Midhurst	1862	1866
28	LBSCR	East Grinstead–Groombridge–Tunbridge Wells	1862	1866
29	LBSCR	Leatherhead–Dorking–Horsham	1863	1867
M	SER	Chislehurst–Sevenoaks–Tonbridge	1859	1868
30	LBSCR	Groombridge–Uckfield	1861	1868
31	LBSCR	Kemptown branch	1864	1869
32	LBSCR	Stone Cross (Eastbourne) spur	1870	1871
N	LCDR	Otford–Maidstone	–	1874
33	LBSCR	Preston Park–Hove spur	–	1879
34	LBSCR	Hailsham–Heathfield–Redgate Mill Junction (Eridge)	1873	1880
35	LBSCR	Midhurst–Chichester	1876	1881
P	SER	Dunton Green–Westerham	–	1881
36	LBSCR	East Grinstead–Culver Junction (Barcombe)	1877	1882
37	LBSCR	Haywards Heath–Horsted Keynes	1877	1883
38	LBSCR	Croydon–Oxted–East Grinstead	1878	1884
R	LCDR	Maidstone–Ashford	1880	1884
S	LSWR	Guildford–Leatherhead	–	1885
39	LBSCR	Newhaven Quay extension	–	1886
40	LBSCR	Littlehampton direct line	–	1887
41	LBSCR	Dyke railway	1877–85	1887
42	LBSCR	Oxted–Ashurst Junction (Groombridge)	1881	1888
T	SER	Paddock Wood–Goudhurst	1879	1892
U	SER	Goudhurst–Hawkhurst	1882	1893
V	SER	Purley–Walton	1893	1897
43	RVR	Robertsbridge–Tenterden	1896	1900
44	SE&CR	Bexhill–Crowhurst	1898	1902
W	K&ESR	Headcorn–Tenterden	1895	1905

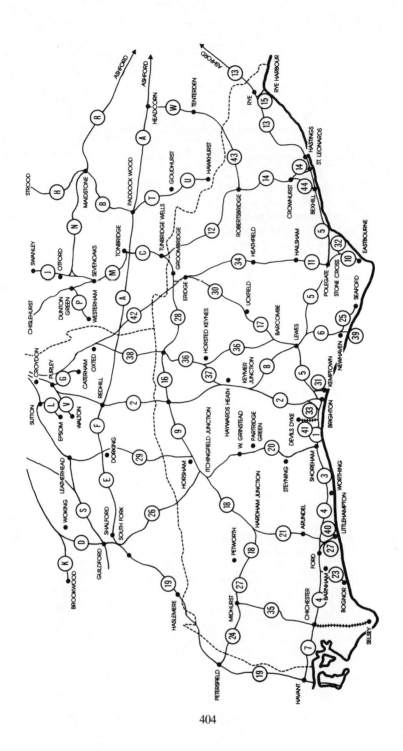

The following lines in Sussex were authorised but not built; they sometimes appear on Sussex maps:

Chichester–Bognor	1853
Chichester–Midhurst–Haslemere	1864
Uckfield–Hailsham	1864
West Grinstead–Haywards Heath	1864
Hardham Junction–Steyning	1867
Brighton–Rottingdean–Newhaven direct	1886
Eastbourne–Seaford–Newhaven	1889
Bexhill–Rotherfield	1899

XII BIBLIOGRAPHIES

1 COUNTY CARTOBIBLIOGRAPHIES

Year of publication	County	Compiler	Terminal date	Method (see p. xxii)
1901–7	*Hertfordshire	Fordham	1900	A
1908	Cambridgeshire	Fordham	1900	B
1911	Wiltshire	Chubb	1885	A
1913	Gloucestershire	Chubb	1911	A
1914	Somersetshire	Chubb	1914	A
1918	Cumberland and Westmoreland	Curwen	[1850]	A
1928	Norfolk	Chubb	1916	A
1933	Yorkshire	Whitaker	1900	A
1938	Lancashire	Whitaker	1900	A
1942	Cheshire	Whitaker	1900	A
1948	Northamptonshire	Whitaker	1900	A
1949	Northumberland	Whitaker	1900	A
1950	†Buckinghamshire	Price	1800	B/A
1959	Shropshire	Cowling	1900	A
1959	Warwickshire	Harvey	1900	B
1974	Hertfordshire	Hodson	1900	B
1977	Radnorshire	Lewis	1900	A

* In *Transactions of the Hertfordshire Natural History Society*. Reissued with supplement, 1914.

† In *Records of Buckinghamshire,* 1948–50. Reproduced by G. Wyatt in *Maps of Buckinghamshire*. Buckingham, 1978.

In addition to the above, descriptive lists are available for Cardiganshire, Cornwall, Durham, Essex, Leicestershire, Merioneth, Nottinghamshire, Staffordshire and Surrey (see Hyde, 1972; Harley, 1972, pp. 77–85; Harvey, 1959, pp. 254–5).

2 WORKS CITED

Additional references will be found in Tooley, 1949; Harvey, 1959; Lister, 1965; Harley 1972. Skelton, *County atlases,* 1970 and Shirley, 1980 include references to the literature on individual cartographers.

References to further papers published in periodicals are included in the footnotes. Periodicals are included in the list of abbreviations (page xxxvii).

Albery, W. *A parliamentary history of the ancient borough of Horsham*. London, 1927.
Anderson, J.P. *The book of British topography*. London, 1881; Amsterdam 1966.
Andrews, A. *The history of British journalism*. London, 1859.

Armstrong, J.R. *A history of Sussex*. London & Chichester, 1974.

Bagrow, L. *History of cartography*. London, 1964.

Barrett-Lennard, T. *An account of the families of Lennard and Barrett*. 1908.

Boase, F. *Modern English biography*. London, 1965.

Brandon, P.F. *The Sussex landscape*. London, 1974.

Brandon, P.F. ed. *The South Saxons*. Chichester, 1978.

Butler, D.T. *The town plans of Chichester 1595–1898*. Chichester, 1972.

Butler, G.S. 'Topographia Sussexiana', *SAC* vols 15–18 (1866–9).

Campbell, E.M.J. 'The beginnings of the characteristic sheet to English maps', *GJ* vol. 127 (1962).

Chubb, T. *The printed maps in the atlases of Great Britain and Ireland*. London, 1927, 1966, 1979.

Clark, R.H. *A Southern Region record, 1803–1965*. Lingfield, 1964.

Coldwell, J.F. 'Sussex in maps', *Sussex Life* vol. 10 (1973), nos 2 and 3.

Copley, G.J., ed. *Camden's Britannia. Surrey and Sussex*. London, 1977.

Courtney-Lewes, C.T. *George Baxter: his life and work*. London, 1908.

Cowling, G.C. *A descriptive list of the printed maps of Shropshire*. Shrewsbury, 1959.

Cowton, R. *Memoirs of the British Museum*. London, 1872.

Cox, H., and Chandler, J.E. *The house of Longman*. London, 1924.

Crone, G.R. *Royal Geographical Society reproductions of early maps VII*. London, 1961.

Crone, G.R. *Maps and their makers*. London, 1962; Folkstone, 1978.

Curwen, E.C. ed. *The journal of Gideon Mantell*. London, 1940.

Daly Briscoe, A. *A Tudor worthy*. Ipswich, 1979.

Daniell, W.V., and Nield, F.J. *Manual of British topography*. London, 1909.

Darlington, I., and Howgego, J. *Printed maps of London*, c. 1553–1850. London, 1964; Folkstone, 1978.

Davies, A.G. 'William Smith's geological atlas and the later history of the plates', *Journal of the Society for the Bibliography of Natural History*. vol. 2, pt. 9. 1952.

Dawson, L.S. *Memoirs of hydrography*. Eastbourne, 1885.

Day, A. *The Admiralty hydrographic service, 1795–1919*. London, 1967.

Dickins, K.W. *A catalogue of manuscript maps in the custody of the Sussex Archaeological Society*. Lewes, 1981.

Eden, P., ed. *Dictionary of land surveyors . . . 1550–1850*. Folkstone, 1975–9, 3 pts and supp.

Eeles, H.S. *Frant, a parish history*. Tunbridge Wells, 1947.

Ellis, C.H. *The London, Brighton and South Coast railway*. London, 1960.

Evans, I.M. 'A cartographic evaluation of the old English mile', *GJ* vol. 141 (1975), p. 259.

Evans, I.M., and Lawrence, H. *Christopher Saxton, Elizabethan map-maker*. Wakefield & London, 1979.

Farrant, J.H. *Sussex directories, 1784–1940*. Rustington, 1969; 1975*.

Farrant, J.H. *Sussex in the 18th and 19th centuries. A bibliography*. Brighton, 1977.

Fordham, H.G. *Cambridgeshire maps*. Cambridge, 1908.

Fordham, H.G. *Hertfordshire maps*, with supplement. Hertford, 1914.

Fordham, H.G. *Studies in cartobibliography*. Oxford 1914; London, 1969.

Fordham, H.G. *The road-books and itineraries of Great Britain. 1570–1850.*

Cambridge, 1924.

Fordham, H.G. *John Cary, engraver, map, chart and print-seller and globe-maker.* Cambridge, 1925; Folkestone, 1976.

Fordham, H.G. *Christopher Saxton of Dunningley.* Leeds, 1928.

Gardiner, L. *Bartholomew 150 years.* Edinburgh, 1976.

Gardiner, R.A. 'Some lesser men', in Wallis and Tyacke, London, 1973.

Gerard, E. 'Notes on some early printed maps of Sussex and their makers', *Library* 3rd ser. vol. 6 (1913)*.

Gerard, E. 'Early Sussex maps', *SCM* vol. 2 (1928), pp. 146, 212*.

Gohm, D.C. *Maps and prints.* London, 1969.

Gough, R. *Anecdotes of British topography.* London, 1768.

Gough, R. *British topography.* London, 1780.

Greenwood, J. *The posts of Sussex. The Chichester branch 1250–1840.* Reigate, 1973*.

Hadfield, C. *The canals of south and south-east England.* Newton Abbot, 1969.

Hannas, L. *The English jigsaw puzzle, 1760–1890.* London, 1972.

Hare, A.J.C. *The story of my life.* London, 1896.

Harley, J.B. *Christopher Greenwood, county map-maker.* Worcester, 1962.

Harley, J.B. 'The Society of Arts and the survey of English counties', *Journal of the Royal Society of Arts,* March 1964.

Harley, J.B. *The historian's guide to Ordnance Survey maps.* London, 1964.

Harley, J.B. 'The remapping of England, 1750–1800', *Imago Mundi* vol. 19 (1965).

Harley, J.B. 'The bankruptcy of Thomas Jefferys', *Imago Mundi* vol. 20 (1966).

Harley, J.B. 'The evaluation of early maps', *Imago Mundi* vol. 22 (1968).

Harley, J.B. 'Error and revision in early Ordnance Survey maps', *CJ* Dec. 1968.

Harley, J.B. *Reprint of the first edition of the one inch Ordnance Survey of England and Wales.* Newton Abbot, 1969.

Harley, J.B. Introduction to *John Ogilby Britannia.* Amsterdam, 1970.

Harley, J.B. ed. *Britannia depicta or Ogilby improved.* Newcastle-upon-Tyne, 1970.

Harley, J.B. 'Place-names on early Ordnance Survey maps', *CJ* Dec. 1971.

Harley, J.B. *Maps for the local historian.* London, 1972.

Harley, J.B. *Ordnance Survey maps.* Southampton, 1975.

Harley, J.B. and Hodson, D. Introduction to *The Royal English atlas.* Newton Abbot, 1971.

Harley, J.B., and O'Donoghue, Y. *The old series Ordnance Survey maps of England and Wales.* Lympne, vol. 1 1975, vol. 2 1977.

Harvey, P.D.A., and Thorpe, H. *The printed maps of Warwickshire.* Warwick, 1959 (cited as Harvey, 1959).

Heawood, E. 'The use of watermarks in dating old maps and documents', *GJ* vol. 63 (1924).

Heawood, E. 'Papers used in England after 1600', *Transactions of the Bibliographical Society* Dec. 1930 and March 1931.

Hind, A.M. *Engraving in England in the sixteenth and seventeenth centuries. Part 1, The Tudor period.* Cambridge, 1952.

Hodson, D. *The printed maps of Hertfordshire, 1577–1900.* Folkestone, 1974.

Hodson, D. *Maps of Portsmouth before 1801.* Portsmouth, 1978.

Holman, G. *Some Lewes men of note.* Lewes, 1905, 1927.

Hood, C.M. ed. *The chorography of Norfolk.* Norwich, 1938.

Horsfield, T.W. *History of Lewes.* Lewes, 1824.

Horsfield, T.W. *The history, antiquities and topography of the county of Sussex.* Lewes, 1835; Dorking 1974.

Howse, D., and Sandeson, M. *The sea chart.* Newton Abbot, 1973.

Hyde, R. 'What future for cartobibliography?', *New Library World,* May 1972.

Hyde, R. *Printed maps of Victorian London 1851–1900.* Folkestone, 1975.

Hyde, R., ed. *The Ogilby and Morgan survey of the City of London.* Lympne, 1976.

Jervis, W.W. *The World in maps,* London, 1936.

Kain, R.J.P. 'R.E. Dawson's proposals in 1836 for a cadastral survey of England and Wales', *CJ* Dec. 1975.

Koeman, C. *The history of Lucas Janszoon Waghenaer and his Spieghel der zeeraerdt.* Lausanne, 1964.

Koeman, C. *Atlantes Neerlandici,* vol. 4. Amsterdam, 1970.

Laxton, P. 'The geodetic and topographical evaluation of English county maps, 1740–1840', *CJ* June 1976.

Lee, R.J. *English county maps.* London, 1955, (Library Association pamphlet no. 13).

Le Gear, C.E. *A list of geographical atlases in the Library of Congress,* vol. 5, 1958.

Lewis, M.G. *The printed maps of Radnorshire.* Aberystwyth, 1977.

Lister, R. *How to identify old maps and globes.* London, 1965.

Lower, M.A. *Sussex.* Lewes, 1831.

Lower, M.A. *Contributions to literature.* London, 1854.

Lower, M.A. *Worthies of Sussex.* Lewes, 1865.

Lower, M.A. *A compendious history of Sussex.* Lewes, 1870.

Lower, M.A. *A Survey of the coast of Sussex made in 1587.* Lewes, 1870.

Lynam, E. *British maps and mapmakers.* London, 1944.

Lynam, E. 'English maps and map-makers of the 16th century', *GJ* vol. 116 (1950).

Lynam, E. *The map-maker's art.* London, 1953.

Malcolm, J.P. *Lives of the topographers and antiquaries.* London, 1815.

Mann, S. *Collecting playing cards.* London, 1966.

Mann, S., and Kingsley, D. 'Playing cards depicting maps of the British Isles and of English and Welsh counties', *MCS* no. 87, 1972.

Manning, R.B. *Religion and society in Elizabethan Sussex.* Leicester, 1969.

Map Collector   Published quarterly from December 1977.

Mawer, A., and Stenton, F.M. *The place-names of Sussex.* 2 vols, Cambridge, 1929 and 1930.

Maxted, I. *The London book trades 1775–1800.* Folkestone, 1977.

McGechan, A., and Verner, C. 'Maps in the parliamentary papers by the Arrowsmiths', *MCS* nos 88 and 89, 1973.

McKerrow, R.B. *A dictionary of printers and booksellers, 1557–1640.* London, 1910*.

Mullins, E.L.C. *A guide to the historical and archaeological publications of societies in England and Wales, 1901–1933.* London, 1968*.

Mumford, I. 'Engraved Ordnance Survey one inch maps — the problem of dating', *CJ* June 1968.

Mumford, I., and Clark, P.K. 'Engraved Ordnance Survey one inch maps: the methodology of dating', *CJ* Dec. 1968.

Nichols, J. *Literary anecdotes of the eighteenth century*. London, 1812–5.

Nichols, J. and J.B. *Illustrations to the literary history of the eighteenth century*. London, 1817–58.

Norton, J.E. *Guide to national and provincial directories*. London 1950.

Nowell-Smith, S. *The house of Cassell*. London, 1958.

O'Byrne, W.R. *A naval biographical dictionary*. London, 1849.

Palmer, G.H. *The early history of the Palmer family*. 1918.

Philip, G. *The story of the house of Philip*. London, 1934.

Phillips, P.L. *A list of geographical atlases in the Library of Congress*. 4 vols. Washington, 1909–20.

Plomer, H.R. *A dictionary of booksellers and printers,* [1641–1775]. 3 vols. London, 1907–32.

Pocklington, G.R. *The story of W.H. Smith and Son*. London, 1921.

Quérand, J.M. *La France littéraire*. Paris, 1827.

Raistrick, A. *Yorkshire maps and map-makers*. Clapham via Lancaster, 1969.

Ravenhill, W. *John Norden's manuscript maps of Cornwall and its nine hundreds*. Exeter, 1972.

Rawlinson, R. *The English topographer*. London, 1720.

Rawnsley, J.E. *Antique maps of Yorkshire and their makers*. 1970.

Ray, J.E. *Notes on local maps and mapmaking*. Hastings, 1936.

Rivington, S. *The publishing family of Rivington*. London 1919.

Robinson, A.H.W. *Marine cartography in Britain*. Leicester, 1962.

Rodger, E.M. *The large-scale county maps of the British Isles*. Oxford, 1972.

Rostenberg, L. *English publishers in the graphic arts, 1599–1700*. New York, 1963.

Schilder, G. and Welu, J. *The world map of 1611 by Pieter van den Keere*. Amsterdam, 1980.

Schuchard, M. *John Ogilby, 1600–1675*. Hamburg, 1973.

Seymour, W.A. ed. *A history of the Ordnance Survey*. Folkestone, 1980.

Sharp, H.A. *An historical catalogue of Surrey maps*. Croydon, 1929.

Sheppard, T. *William Smith: his maps and memoirs*. Hull, 1920.

Shirley, R.W. *Early printed maps of the British isles, MCS* 1972–4; London, 1980.

Skelton, R.A. *Decorative printed maps*. London, 1952.

Skelton, R.A. 'Landmarks in British cartography. III. The origins of the Ordnance Survey', *GJ* vol. 128, 1962.

Skelton, R.A. *County atlases of the British Isles 1579–1703*. London, 1970.

Skelton, R.A., ed. *Two hundred and fifty years of map-making in the county of Sussex*. Lympne, 1970.

Skelton, R.A. 'Saxton's survey of England and Wales', *Imago Mundi* supplement, 1974.

Smail, H.C.P. *The Worthing map story*. Worthing, 1949.

Spokes, S. *Gideon Algernon Mantell*. London, 1927.

Stanford, E. *The Ordnance Survey from a business point of view*. London, 1891.

Steer, F.W. *A catalogue of Sussex estate maps and tithe award maps*. Lewes, 1962. (SRS vol. 61).

Steer, F.W. *A catalogue of Sussex maps*. Lewes 1968. (SRS vol. 66).

Stevenson, E.L. *Willem Janszoon Blaeu*. New York, 1914.

Taylor, E.R.G. *Tudor geography, 1485–1583*. London, 1930.

Taylor, E.R.G. *The haven-finding art.* London, 1956.

Thorpe, H. See Harvey, P.D.A. and Thorpe H.

Timperley, C.H. *Encyclopaedia of literary and typographical anecdote.* London, 1842.

Tooley, R.V. *Maps and map-makers.* London, 1949; 1970.

Tooley, R.V. *Dictionary of mapmakers.* Tring, 1979.

Twyman, M. *Lithography 1800–1850.* London, 1970.

Tyacke, S. 'Map-sellers and the London map trade *c.* 1650–1710', in Wallis and Tyacke, 1973.

Tyacke, S. *London map-sellers 1660–1720.* Tring, 1978.

Tyacke, S. and Huddy J. *Christopher Saxton and Tudor map-making.* London, 1980.

Upcott, W. *A bibliographical account of the principal works relating to English topography.* London, 1818*.

Van Eerde, K.S. *Wenceslaus Hollar and his time.* Charlottesville, 1970.

Van Eerde, K.S. *John Ogilby and the taste of his times.* Folkestone, 1976.

Varley, J. 'John Rocque — engraver, surveyor and map-seller', *Imago Mundi* vol. 5 (1948).

Verner, C. 'The identification and designation of variants in the study of early printed maps', *Imago Mundi* vol. 19 (1965).

Verner, C. 'Engraved title plates for the folio atlases of John Seller', in Wallis and Tyacke, 1973.

Wace, A.A. *The Story of Wadhurst.* Tunbridge Wells, [1923].

Wallis, H. ed. *Atlas of the British Isles by Pieter van den Keere, c. 1605,* Lympne, 1972.

Wallis, H. ed. *Map making to 1900.* London, 1976.

Wallis, H. and Tyacke S., ed. *My head is a map.* London, 1973.

Walters, G. 'Engraved maps from English topographies, 1660–1825', *CJ* Dec. 1970.

Whitaker, H. *The Harold Whitaker collection.* Leeds, 1947.

Whitaker, H. *The printed maps of Northamptonshire.* Northampton, 1948.

Whorlow, H. *The Provincial Newspaper Society, 1836–1886.* London, 1886.

Wiles, R.M. *Serial publication in England before 1750.* Cambridge, 1957.

Wilson, E. *The story of the blue black chart.* London, [1937].

Winterbotham, H. St. L. *The national plans.* London, 1934.

Woodward, D. ed. *Five centuries of map printing.* Chicago & London, 1975.

Young, A. *General view of the agriculture of Sussex.* London, 1793; 1813; Newton Abbot, 1970.

* Reference works used in compilation of the catalogue, but not cited.

PRINTED MAPS
OF
SUSSEX

INDEX

Index

1. Numbers in **bold** type refer to Entry numbers in the catalogue or in appendixes I to VIII, and are followed, where appropriate, by a letter (a lithographic transfer) and/or a Roman numeral (the edition number). This form of reference is used for

   a. the names of persons and bodies under which maps have been catalogued. This is indicated by the addition of an asterisk, and, since the name usually recurs throughout the entry, reference to specific lithographic transfers or editions is omitted.

   b. references to persons, places, atlases (and other works) and subjects which occur in the 'Editions' section of each entry. The number of the relevant transfer(s) or edition(s) is given.

2. Numbers not in bold type refer to page numbers, and are used for other entries. The addition of *n* to the number indicates that the reference will be found in the footnotes.

3. Works listed in Bibliography (appendix XII) are indexed under the author's name, followed by abbreviated title and the date(s) of publication.

4. Place-names are only included in the index in special circumstances, eg where there is an insert plan or view of the town on a map.

5. Selected subjects, eg boundaries, longitude, are included in the index.

Abel Heywood and Son, 284
Abel Heywood's tourist guides, 284
Abergavenny, Lord, 175
Abridgement of Camden's Britañia, **9**
Abstract, see *Enumeration abstract*
Account of the trigonometrical survey, **App VI.4**
Accounts and papers, **99(i)(ii), 118, 138B**
Actual survey of all the principal roads, **App V.3(i)(ii)**
Adams, Hamilton and Co., **125B**
Adams, John, xviii
Adams (Adamo), Robert, **App II.4,*** xxxiiin, 12
Addison, J., **150***
Agas, Ralph, *A preparative to platting of landes* (1596), xi
Agreeable historian, 32
Agrippa, Henricus Cornelius, *De incertitudine et vanitate scientiarum* (1530), ix
Aikin, John, **53**, 102, 137
Aikin, Lucy, 102
Akers, B., 400n
Albery, W., *Parliamentary history of . . . Horsham* (1927), 60n, 63n, 406
Albiny, William of, **35(iii)**
Alfred, King, 7n
Algemeene oefenschoole, **39**
All the shires of England and Wales, **1(v)(vi)**
Allard, Karel (Carolus), **13(i)**, 33
Allen, G.S., 104
Allen, George, **59(i)(ii), 150**, 114, 328
Amey, M., 74

Anciens royaumes de Kent . . ., **App III.7**
Ancient deaneries in the diocese of Chichester, 227
Anderson, J.P., *British topography* (1881, 1966), 245n, 281n, 358n, 406
Andrews, A., *History of British journalism* (1859), 176n, 406
Andrews, John, **App III.9***
Andrews, Peter, 84
Angleterre, ou description historique, 86
Anglia (Saxton), 397, see Derivatives
Anglia contracta, **19(i)**, 46, 49
Angliae Regni, **3**, plate 3
Ansted, D.T., **132**, 299
Antiquities of England and Wales, **19(ii)**, 47
Antiquities of England and Wales displayed, **36(ii)**
Apian, Peter, xi, 4n
Apian, Philip, 4, 4n
Arber, Edward, 401
Archaeologia Cantiana, 28n
Archaeological Institute, **App III.14**
Archaeological map of Sussex, **141**
Archaeological maps, **141, App III.14**, xx (See Roy)
Archaeological review, 7n
Archer, Joshua, **106*, 111*, 114*, 119***, 239
Areas, **138C and D**, 397, 398
Armada, xxxiiin, 340, 341, 341n
Armilogia sive ars chromocritica, 389n
Armstrong, Andrew, **35(ix)(x)**
Armstrong, J.R., *History of Sussex* (1974), 392, 392n, 407

414

Arnold family, 278
Arnold, F.H., **125B**, 278
Arrowsmith family, 120, 227
Arrowsmith, Samuel, **109***, 114, 398
Arundel, **75(i)**, **103, 110, App VII.4(c), App VIII.2,** 97n, 203, 337, 392, 396, plate 40(ii)
Ashburnham, John, 47
Ashley, Anthony, **App II.3**
Aspley, William, **6(iii)**
Atlas Anglicanus, **13(i)**, **45(i)(ii)**, xviii, 46
Atlas anglois, **1(vii)**, **13(ii)**
Atlas Britannique, **44**
Atlas classica, 134
Atlas, comprising maps of the several counties, **97(v)**
Atlas contracta, xviii
Atlas contractus, 33
Atlas geographicus, **21(ii)**
Atlas geographus, 51, 398n
Atlas major, **13(i)**
Atlas minimus, **38**
Atlas minor (Moll), 398n
Atlas minor Gerardi Mercatoria à I Hondio, **App III.2** and **4**
Atlas nouveau, **26**
Atlas of England, **64**
Atlas of England and Wales (Collins), **134B**
Atlas of Great Britain and Ireland, **52(ii)**
Atlas of the British islands, **67(i)**
Atlas of the counties of England, **93(i)–(vi)**
Atlas of the English counties, **94(i)–(iii)**, 171
Atlas sive cosmographicae, **App III.1**
Atlas to the topographical dictionaries, **97(v)–(vi)**
Atlas to the topographical dictionary, **97(v)–(vi)**
Atmospheric railway, Epsom and Croydon, **108(xi)**
Atree, H.R., **App III.12** and **13**, 105
Atree's topography of Brighton, **App III.12** and **13**, 105
Aubrey, Elizabeth, 60
Aubrey, John, 60, 358
Avery, Jos., 57, 91
Aylward, J., 245
Azores (Asores), **App II.8**

Bacon, George P., **125**, **125A**, 277
Bacon, George Washington, **121K–M** and **O**, 246
Bacon, G.W. and Co., **121E–H** and **O–Q**, **145A,** 246
Bacon, John, **109**
Bacon, Richard M., 277
Bacon's county atlas, **121E**
Bacon's county guide and map, **121N**
Bacon's county map and guide, **121Q**
Bacon's Geographical Establishment, **121N, App VIII.4**
Bacon's [illustrated] map of Sussex, **121E** and **Q**
Bacon's Map Establishment, **121G**

Bacon's new county guide, **121L(ii)**
Bacon's new large-scale atlas of London, **121O(iii)**
Bacon's new pocket map, **121F**
Bacon's new quarto county atlas, **121G**
Bacon's new tourist map, **121E** and **H**, **145A**
Bacon's tourist map, **121H**
Badeslade, Thomas, **29***
Bagrow, Leo., *History of cartography* (1964), 4n, 407
Baines, A., **124M**
Baker, Benjamin, **56***, **App VI.1(a)**
Baker, J.N.L., 64n
Bakewell and Parker, **43(i)**
Bakewell, Robert, 166
Bakewell, Thomas, **14(vii)**, 36
Baldwin, Cradock and Joy, **66(i)(ii)**, **85**, 134, 168
Baldwin, R., **36(i)**, 80
Ballard, A., 6n
Banks, Joseph, **App VII.3**
Barber Institute, **123H**
Barclay, James, **110(iv)(vi)** and **(vii)**, **114(ii)**
Barclay's universal English dictionary, **110(v)**
Barfoot, Peter, 188
Barnes, Malcolm, 328n
Barrett-Lennard, T., *Account of the families of . . .* (1908), 36n, 407
Bartholomew family, 259
Bartholomew, John, **122***, **123***, **124***, **129***, **131***, **144***, **153***, xxvii, 400, see Derivatives
Bartholomew, J. and Son, **124A**
Bartholomew's pocket atlas of Ireland, 203
Basire, J., 388
Bassett, Thomas, **7(vi)**, **8(iii)**, 21, 44
Bateman, Christopher, 389
Battle Abbey, **103**, **121E**, 245
Baxter and Son, **App VII.1(a)**
Baxter family, 175–7, 175n
Baxter, George, 177
Baxter, John, **104(i)–(iv)**, 175, 175n, 177, 209, 212, 243
Baxter, William Edwin, **89A**, 175–7, 175n, 339
Baxter, Wynne Edwin, 176, 340
Baxter's library of agriculture, 175
B.C.B., **155***
Beacons, 5
Beal, John and Son, **140***, **145B**
Beale, Robert, *A treatise of the office of a Councellor* (1592), xiv
Beauties of England and Wales, **74**, 134, 135, 154
Becker, Francis P., 239
Becker, F.P. and Co., **116***
Becker's patent process, 239
Beckett, Arthur, 58
Bedfordshire, **App III.1–5**
Beighton, Henry, 58n 61
Belch, see Langley & Belch

416

Butters, R., **52(i), 64***
Bye, J., **App V.15(i)** and **(vii)**

Cadell, T., **109**
Calendar of King's College, 281n
Cambridgeshire, **App III.1(i)(ii)–5,** xxii, 406
Camden (Cambden, Camdenus), William (Guilielmus, **5, 6(i), 9, 13(i), 19(i), 20(i)(ii), 21(ii), 50(i),** 17, 17n, 18, 18n, 30, 33, 39, 48, 50n, 51, 98, 99, 100, 356, 389, 390, 398, 400
Camden's Britannia abridg'd, **19(i),** 18n
Camden's Britannia epitomised, **100(i)**
Camden's Britannia, newly translated, **20(i),** 50
Camden's Britannia. Surrey and Sussex (Copley, 1977), 17n
Camden Society, 388
Cameron, J., **App VI.2(c)**
Campbell, E.M.J., *Beginnings of the characteristic sheet* (1962), 14n, 407
Campion (of Horsham), 108
Canals and navigations, 392, 393
Capper, Benjamin Pitts, **67(i)–(iii)**
Cardiganshire, 97
Carnan, Thomas, **38,** 82
Carnan, William, 82
Carpenter, Elizabeth, 58
Cartes générales de toutes parties du monde, **App III.7**
Cartographic Journal (CJ), 59n, 92n, 134n, 147n, 245n, 399n, 400n
Cartwright, Edmund, **84(ii), App VII.4(c)–(e),** 167
Carver, see Bowles and Carver
Cary, George, 97
Cary, George and John [G. & J., J. & G.], **61(viii)** and **(x), 82*, App II.9** (ii), 97
Cary, John, **49*, 50*, 51*, 61*, 65*, 68*, 145*, App II.9*, App V.13*,** xxv, xxvi, xxxiiin, 18, 116, 203, 227, 259, 338, 345, 358, 392, 400, plates 20, 21, 24, 25, see Derivatives
Caryll family, **148**
Cary's improved map of England and Wales, 319
Cary's new and correct English atlas, **49(i)–(v), 68(i)–(v),** 120n, 392
Cary's new English atlas, **61(i)–(v)(vii)–(ix)** and **(xi),** xxiii
Cary's new itinerary, **App II.9,** 98, 101, 120
Cary's new map [of the county] of Sussex, **61(viii)** and **(x)**
Cary's survey of the high roads, **App V.13(i)–(iv)**
Cary's travellers companion, **51(i)–(iv), 65(i)–(vii), 82(i)(ii), App II.9(i),** 101, 358, 392
Cassell and Co., 216, 246
Cassell, John, 246
Cassell, Petter and Galpin, **121B–D, 132,** 246
Cassell's British atlas, **121D**
Cassell's complete atlas, **121C**

Cassell's county geographies, **132**
Cassell's county maps, **121B**
Cassell's folio county atlas, **121B**
Cassell's illustrated family paper, **121D**
Cassell's topographical guides, **121D**
Catalogue of the maps and plans accumulated by the late William Figg, 178n
Cave, R., **App V.7***
Cecil, see Burghley
Chambers, George F., **135B**
Chambers handy guide, 303
Chandler, J.E., see Cox, H.
Chandler, Richard, **21(ii)**
Chapman and Hall, **96(i)–(xi), 96A–E**
Characteristic sheet, see Key
Charles I, **1(iii),** 356
Charles II, 21, 36, 314, 394
Charles, King, **App V.1(iii)**
Charterhouse, London, x
Charters of the Cinque Ports, 60
Cheffins, C.F. and Son **115F**
Cheshire, xviii, 49n, 150n, 406
Chertsey Abbey, x
Chichester [Cathedral], **3, 7(i), 24(i), 26, 35(i), 41, 43(i), 89, 90(i), 93(i)(vi), 110, 121E, 136A, 137, 146A, App VI.3, App VII.4(a)(b),** xvii, xxxii, 13, 14, 68, 81, 93, 94, 227, 278, 395, 396, plates 19, 38
Chichester diocese, **109, 111, 126, 127,** xxvii, 7, 7n
Chilcot, Mrs. **28(i)**
Children's Friend, **130**
Chiswell, Richard, **7(vi), 8(iii),** 21, 44, 64
Chorographia Britanniae, **29(i)–(iii)**
Chorographicall description of all the tracts . . ., **App IV.1(ii)**
Chorographicall discription of the seuerall shires and islands of Middlesex . . ., 14, 387, 388, 389
Christ Church Priory, x
Christian G., 175n, 176
Chronica Maiora, x
Chronometer, 4, 58
Chubb, T., *Atlases of Great Britain* (1927–1979), **6(iii), 31(i), 38, App V.3(ii),** xxv, 19n, 26n, 33, 39n, 48, 50, 50n, 55n, 71n, 75n, 80, 80n, 83, 88n, 104n, 139n, 145n, 154n, 158n, 163n, 231n, 281n, 358n, 351; 351n, 366n, 401, 401n, 407
Churchill, Awnsham and John, **20(i)(ii),** 48, 50
Cinque ports, 60, 309, 396
Cinquiéme volume de la geographie Blaviane, **12(ii)**
Clark, **28(i),** see also Darton and Clark
Clark, J., **29(iii)**
Clark, P.K. see Mumford, I., *O.S. maps, methodology of dating* (1968)
Clark, R.H., *Southern Region record* (1964), 391, 391n, 402n, 407
Clark, Sam, 106
Clarke, B., **72B(ii)**

Clarke R.V., 400, 400n
Clifford, J., 59n
Climatological map, **147B(iv)**
Cloppenburgh, Johan, **App III.5**
Close, C., 6n, 43n
Cluer, J., 8
Coast (coastline of Sussex), **88D, 103, 104, 120A, 129B** and **E, 131I, App II,** xii, xxx, 3, 5, 6, 6n, 14, 47, 57, 70, 279, plates 36, 39
Coates, R., 394n
Cobbett, William, **101***, 167, 398
Cockerill, Thomas, **21(i)**
Colby, Thomas, **App VI.4,** 206
Coldbrand, James, **App I.2***
Colbrand, Letitia, 27
Colbrand, Thomas, 27
Coldwell, J.F., *Sussex in maps* (1973), 6n, 407
Cole, G., **66***, see Derivatives
Cole, William, **88(i),** 170, 171
Collingridge, W.H., **72E(i),** 147
Collins British coasting pilot, 57
Collins' county geographies, **134A**
Collins, Greenvile, 46, 47, 49
Collins, Henry George, **66A, 72A–B, 95A, 119A,** 134, 147, 244, 245
Collins' indestructable atlas, 244
Collins' one shilling atlas, 244
Collins' pocket ordnance railway atlas, **119A**
Collins' railway & pedestrian atlas, **66B**
Collins' railway & telegraphic map, 171
Collins' railway map, **88A**
Collins' series of atlases, **134B**
Collins' Sussex with its railways, **72B(ii)**
Collins, William, 302
Collins, William, Sons and Co., **134A–B,** 302
Coltman, Nathaniel, **59*, App V.15(i)–(iii),** 393, 394, see Derivatives
Combridge, J.H., 278n
Commercial and library atlas, **121P**
Companion from London to Brighthelmston, **App VII.3,** plate 35
Compass, xxxi
Compass traverse, xviii, 4, 5
Compendious history of Sussex, **125A**
Compendium of the history of the home circuit, **100(i)**
Compleat history of Sussex, **21(ii)**
Complete and universal English dictionary, **110(iv)** and **(vi)–(viii)**
Complete atlas of the English counties, **75(i)**
Complete county atlas of England and Wales, **88 (iii)(iv)**
Complete historical descriptions . . . of the antiquities of England and Wales, **36(iii)**
Comprehensive gazetteer, **151A**
Compton, Elizabeth, 61

Compton, Spencer, **24(i), App V.2,** 59, 61
Conder, Thomas, **48***
Contours, see Heights
Conventional signs, see Key
Conway, Robert, **48(i)**
Conway, W.H., **App VI.1(b)**
Cook, Andrew, 202n
Cooke, A.C., **App VI.1(b)**
Cooke, Charles, **69***
Cooke, George Alexander, **69(i)(ii)**
Cooke, John, 142
Cooke's topographical library, **69(ii)**
Coombes, A.J., 266n, 288n
Cooper, H., **67***
Cooper, John, 58
Cooper, M., **30**
Coote, J., **31(vi)**
Copley, G.J. *Camden's Britannia* (1977), 17n, 407
Cornwall, **27,** xviii, 5, 14, 55, 389, 389n, 406
Cosmographical Glasse, ix, ixn, 4
Cosmographicus liber (1533), xi
Cosmography and geography, **14(iv)**
Cotton, Robert, xii
Counties of England, **75(ii)**
County geographies by D.T. Ansted, **132**
County journal: or, the craftsman, 68
Courtney-Lewis, C.T., *George Baxter* (1908), 177n, 407
Covens, J., **26**
Covert, John, 12
Covert, Richard, 6, 12
Covert, Waltar, **App II.2*,** xii, 12, 176, 178, 336
Cowie, George and Co., **74**
Cowley, John, **30***
Cowling, G.C., *Maps of Shropshire* (1959), 44n, 171, 171n, 347n, 349n, 407
Cowton, R., *Memoirs of British Museum* (1872), 281, 281n, 407
Cox, H., **16(i)**
Cox, H. and Chandler, J.E., *House of Longman* (1924), 167n, 407
Cox, T., **21(ii),** 51
Cox, Thomas, **21(ii),** 51
Cradock, Charles & Co., 134
Cradock, see Baldwin, Cradock and Joy
Crawford (of Brighton), 108
Creighton, R., **97*, 107*,** 303
Croft-Murray, Edward, xn
Crofts, P., 178
Crone, G.R., *Maps and their makers* (1962, 1978), 4, 4n, 407
Crone, G.R., *RGS reproductions* (1961), 3n, 336, 336n, 407
Crooke, Andrew, **6(iii)**
Crosby, Benjamin, 168
Crosby's complete pocket gazetteer, **85**

419

Ellis, C.H., *L.B. and S.C. Railway* (1960), 402, 407
Ellis, G., **70(iv)**
Ellis, John, 88, 88n
Ellis, Joseph, **44***, see Derivatives
Ellis, Thomas J., 88
Ellis, W.S., 60n
Ellis's English atlas, **44**, **70(iv)**, 112
Ellis's new and correct atlas, **70(iv)**
Elmham, Thomas, xi
Emery, F., 50n
Emmison, F.G., 388n
Emslie, John, **117***
Emslie, J.P., 240
Encyclopedia Britannica, **144A** and **C**, 259, 317
Encyclopedia Londinensis, **91**
England: an intended guyde, 14, 27
England delineated, **53**
England depicted in a series . . ., **72B**
England displayed, **31(vi)**
England exactly described, **14(iv)–(vii)**
England fully described, **7(vi)–(viii)**, **18**
England illustrated, **42**
England, Wales and Ireland: their severall counties, **8(i)**
England, Wales, Scotland and Ireland described, **8(ii)(iii)**
English atlas, **72(i)(ii)**, xviii, 9n
English atlas, or a complete set, **7(ix)**
English atlas or a concise view, **34(iv)**
English atlas: or, a set of maps, **43(iii)**
English counties by [By] Sidney Hall, **96B**
English counties delineated, **110(i)–(iii)**
English County Maps (RGS), 387
English pilot, **App II.7**, 338
English topography (Nightingale), **66(i)(ii)**, 134
English topography: or, a series of descriptions of the several counties, **61(i)(ii)**
English traveller, **31(i)**
Enumeration abstract, 397, 398, 399
Essex (County), **App III.1(i)(ii)** and **2–7**, xvi, 14, 15, 66, 388, 388n, 406
Essex described, 388
Essex, Earl of, 14, 388
Essex naturalist, 388
Essex Record Office, 388
Etrennes utiles, **App V.10(i)(ii)**
Evans, David Wynne, **48(i)**
Evans, I.M., *The old English mile* (1975), 358n, 407
Evans, I.M., and Lawrence, H., *Christopher Saxton* (1979), xv, 3n, 4n, 7n, 9n, 407
Evans, T., **31(vi)**
Exact description of Essex, 388
Excursions from London to Brighton, 211
Excursions in the county of Sussex, **80**
Excursions through Sussex, **80**
Expeditionis Hispanorum, **App II.4**

Explanation, see Key
Exshaw, S. and I., **36(ii)**
Eyles, V.A., 122n
Eyre and Spottiswoode, **138A**
Eyre Brothers, **131F**
Eyre's shilling county guide, **131F**

Faden, William, **57(i)(ii)(vi)** and **(vii)**, **58(i)–(iii)**, **82(i)**, **App II.10**, **App VI.4**, xx, 93, 108, 112, 114, 227, 378n
Fairclough, Roger, xxvi
Family paper, 246
Family topographer, **100(i)(ii)**, 398
Farncombe and Co., **App VII.1(b)**
Farrant, J.H., xxvi, 13n, 14n, 59n, 110n, 120n, 203n, 337n, 388, 392n, 393n
Farrant, J.H., *Sussex directories* (1975), 407
Farrant, J.H., *Sussex in the 18th and 19th cent.* (1977), 402n, 407
Farrington, Richard, **App V.2**
Fathers, Betty, xxvi
Faunthorpe, J.P., **131A**
Fermor, Henry, 63n
Feuille, Jacob de la, **App III.1**
Fifty six new and accurate maps, **21(i)**
Figg family, 177–8
Figg, William, **89(viii)**, **89A**, 177–8, 178n
Fisher, Henry, 239
Fisher, Robert, 239
Fisher, Son and Co., **116**, 239
Fisher, William, 68
Fisher's county atlas, **116**
Fitzherbert, John, xi
Fitzroy, Ann, 36
Flambeav de la navigation, **App II.5** and **7**
Fletcher, Henry, 60
Flora of Sussex, **125B**
Flower, R., 336n
Folio Fine Art Ltd., **45(iv)**
Foot, Thomas, **57(ii)**, 108
Fordham, H.G., **App V.3(ii)**, xxii, 345n, 358n, 361
Fordham, H.G., *Cambridgeshire maps* (1908), 406, 407
Fordham, H.G., *Christopher Saxton* (1928), 3n, 408
Fordham, H.G., *Hertfordshire maps* (1914), 55n, 174, 175n, 209n, 210n, 211n, 257n, 407
Fordham, H.G., *John Cary* (1925, 1976), 97n, 98, 98n, 408
Fordham, H.G., *Road-Books* (1924), 358, 358n, 370, 370n, 407
Fordham, H.G., *Studies in cartobibliography* (1914, 1969), 49, 49n, 97, 97n, 202n, 358n, 407
Fossils of the South Downs, **84(i)**
Fox-hunting maps, **108A–E**, **G** and **H**, **140**, **145B**, 215
Francis, William F., **126**, **127**

423

426

Mortier, Peter, 33
Mortlock, Henry, **16(i)**
Moule, Thomas, **110(i)**, 167, 228
Mount, Richard, 47, 58, 68
Mount, William, **28(ii)**, 57
Mudge, William, **App VI.4**, 108, 112
Mullins, E.L.C. *Guide to historical . . . publications* (1968), 409
Multilingual dictionary of technical terms in cartography (MDTT), xxxn, 8n, 140n
Mumford, I., 147n
Mumford, I., *O.S., 1"maps — problem of dating* (1968), 379n, 400, 400n, 409
Mumford, I. and Clark, P.K., *O.S. 1" maps: methodology of dating* (1968), 379n, 400, 400n, 409
Murray, John, **108F(ii)**, 166, 215, 216, 324
Murray, John, R.N., 338
Murray, T.L., **94***,
Mutlow, [H.], **App III.10***, 353n
Musters, 336, 336n

National gazetteer, **128A–C**, 358n
National Library of Wales, 11n
National Map Co., **121I**
Natural history of England, **37**, 81
Naylor, 'Counceller', 36n, 328
Naylor, Francis Hare, 36n
Neele[s], [and Co.], **84(i)**, **App VII.4(a)**, 59
Neele, James, 104, 105n
Neele, Josiah, 104, 105n, 175
Neele, Samual John, **55***, **74***, 393, see Derivatives
Neele, Samuel John and Son, 79*
Neely, see Sherwood, Neely and Jones
New and accurate description of all the direct and principal cross roads, **App II.10**, 98
New and accurate maps of the counties of England, **38**
New and complete abridgement . . . in the antiquities of England and Wales, **36(ii)**
New and complete English traveller, **48(ii)**
New and comprehensive gazetteer, **102(i)**, 98
New and correct English atlas, see Cary
New and improved county atlas, **70(ii)**
New and improved English atlas, **56(ii)(iii)**
New atlas of England and Wales, **88(iii)**
New British atlas, **50(ii)**, **72(iii)–(v)**, **72A**, **96(ii)(iii)**
New British traveller, **48(i)(ii)**, **74**, 398, 398n
New county atlas, **96(vii)**, **128C**
New description and state of England, **21(i)**, 397
New description of England and Wales, **25(i)(ii)**
New English atlas, **44**, **87**, xxiii, 49, 120n, 392, see also *Smith's new English atlas*
New general atlas of the world, 60n
New geological atlas of England and Wales, **61(vi)**, 120

New large scale atlas of the British Isles, **121O**
New large scale Ordnance atlas, **121K–M**
New large scale Ordnance map, **121M**
New Library World, xxii
New London magazine, 231
New map of Sussex, **108(viii)**
New map of the counties of Surrey and Sussex (Laurie and Whittle), 114
New miniature atlas, see Miller
New monthly magazine, 154
New Ordnance atlas of Brighton, **121I**
New parliamentary and county atlas, **128D**
New pocket atlas, **62(i)(ii)**
New reduced Ordnance Survey map, **153A**
New set of diocesan maps, **126**, **127**
New Shoreham, **App VII.3**, 396
New survey of the globe, 397
New travelling atlas, **95(i)(ii)**
New Universal magazine, 84
Newbery, Francis, 82, 345
Newbery, John, **38**, 82
Newhaven, **123L**, 337, 394
Newman, H., **19(i)**
Nicol, G., **App III.10**
Nichols, 94
Nichols and Son, **104(ii)–(iv)**
Nichols, J., **55**, 105
Nichols, John, 208
Nichols, John, *Literary anecdotes* (1812–5), 55n, 59n, 60n, 102n, 410
Nichols, J. & J.B., *Illustrations to the literary history of 18th cent.* (1817–58), 100n, 102n, 105, 137n, 142n, 188n, 410
Nichols, John Bowyer, 105
Nichols, John Bowyer and Son, **84(ii)**, **100***, **App VII.4(c)–(e)**
Nichols, John G., 208
Nicholson, John, **21(i)(ii)**
Nicholson, Robert, 388
Nield, F.J., see Daniell, W.V.
Nieuwen atlas, **13(i)**
Nightingale, Joseph, **66(ii)**, 100, 134, 154
Nine new and accurate maps of the southern counties, **27**
Noe, B., xxxiiin
Norden, John (Johẽs, Jo'annes, Johannes), **3***, **6***, **7(ii)**, **App IX**, xi, xii, xv, xvi, xvin, xvii, xxv, xxxiiin, 4, 5, 6, 7, 18, 20, 27, 43, 388n, 391n, 395, frontispiece, see Derivatives
Norden's Preparative to his Speculum Britanniae, xvi, 387
Norfolk, 69n, 120, 156, 170n, 389, 406
Norfolk archaeology, 69n
Norie and Wilson, 68n
Norman, **24(i)**, 61
North Briton, 188

431

84(ii), **App VII.4(d)**
Parry, John D., **103**, 211
Parson, Lt. Col., **App VI.2(c)**
Parsons, E.J.S., xn
Parsons, F.G., 177
Partridge, S.W. and Co., **130***,
Pask, Joseph, **17(iii)**
Pass, J., **91***, see Derivatives
Passage of the hurricane . . . at Bexhill, 58
Past and present, **142A**
Paterson, Daniel, **App II.10***, and **11***, **App V.12***,
98, 338
Paterson's British itinerary, **App V.12(i)(ii)**
Paterson's roads, **App II.10** and **11**, 82, 345n
Patronymica Britannica, 205
Payne, see Mason and Payne
Payne, H.A., **142A**
Payne, M., 74
Payne, T. and Son, **50(i)**
Payne, Thomas, 100
P. Bertii tabularum geographicarum, **App III.3**
Peadle, 93
Pearce, W., 92, plate 23(i)
Pearson's 'Athletic Record', **124O**
Pelham, R.A., 99n
Pelham, Thomas, **47**
Pembrokeshire, xiv, xv
Penn, Mrs., **28(i)**
Pennant, Thomas, **App III.11***
Penrose annual, xiin
Pepys, Samuel, 37
Percy, Henry, 16
Perrot, A.M., **86***, plate 28(ii)
Perspective views, **App IV**, x, xi, xvii
Petter, see Cassell, Petter and Galpin
Petworth, **App VI.3**, 16
Phelps, Joseph, **73(i)–(iii)**, 153
Philip, George, **88D**, 147
Philip, George, *Story of the house of Philip* (1934),
147n, 410
Philip, George and Son, **72E(ii)**, **124A–L and O–R**,
131A, C–E, G–K, M and N, App VIII.2, 147,
215, 245, 281
Philip, John, 147
Philip, Robert, 147
Philip, Son and Nephew, **131N**, 147
Philips atlas of the counties of England, **124B–E,
H, I, K and R**
Philips' county atlas, **72E(ii)**
Philips' cyclists' map, **124J, P and Q**
Philips' educational series, **131A**
Philip's handy atlas, **131C–E, G–K, M and N**
Philip's new series . . . of county maps, **124A, E(ii),
G, H and K(ii)**
Philips popular series of county maps, **72F**
Phillips, J.C., 240n

Phillips, M., **App III.12*** and **13***
Phillips, P.L., *Atlases in the Library of Congress*
(1909–20), 89, 103n
Phillips, Richard, **55, 67(i)–(iii)**, 137
Photozincography, xxviii, xxix, 308, 309, 322, 380,
381
Pickett [A.J. or J.], **83*, App V.17**, xxvii, 116
Pictorial and descriptive guide to Eastbourne, **App
VII.2**
Pictorial and descriptive guide to Hastings, **88C, D**
Pictorial world, **124F**
Picture of England, **64**
Piers, **110**, 393, 394
Piggott, S., 18n, 50n
Pigot and Co., **90(i)–(v), 113A**
Pigot and Co's. British atlas, **90(i)–(v)**
*Pigot and Co's. London & provincial new commer-
cial directory*, **90(i)**
*Pigot and Co's national London and provincial
commercial directory*, **90(iii)**
Pigot and Co's. pocket atlas, 231
*Pigot and Co's. royal national and commercial
directory*, **90(iv)(v)**, 59n
*Pigot and Co's royal national, commercial, and
street directory*, **90(v)**
Pigot [James] and Slater [Isaac], **90(v), 113***
Pigot, James and Son, **90***, see Derivatives
Pike, W.T., **143A(i), App VIII.4**, 315
Pike's district blue book, **App VIII.4**
Pine, Charles, 68
Pine, John, **App II.4**, 341n, 389
Pinnock and Maunder, **79(i)**
Pinnock, William, **106**, 160, 171
Pinnock's county histories, **79(i)(ii)**
*Pinnock's history of topography of England and
Wales*, **79(ii)**
Piper, see Sherwood, Gilbert and Piper
Pitt, Moses, xviii, 9n
Place-names, spelling of, 15, 20, 49, 278, 394, 395
Plan of railway between London and Brighton, 319
Plane table, ix, x, xi, 4
Plans of the cities and boroughs of England, **99(ii)**
Plantin, Christoffel, **App II.1**
Plates, maps on, **App VIII.1**
Playing-card maps, **2, 4, 16, 17, 22**, plates 6, 27(i)
Plomer, H.R., *Dictionary of book-sellers* (1907–32),
80n, 401, 410
Pocket atlas and guide to London, 203
Pocket atlas of Ireland, 203
Pocket book of all the counties, **17(iii)**
Pocket county maps, **96(i)**
Pocket guide to the English traveller, **App V.2**
Pocket map of London, 67n
Pocket topography and gazetteer of England, **113A**
Pocket tourist & English atlas, **87**
Pocklington, G.R., *Story of W.H. Smith* (1921),

284n, 410
Pocock, 243
Political magazine, **52(i)**
Poll book, 383
Pollard, A.W., 13n
Poly-Oblion, **App IV.1,** xvii, 17, 356
Pope, Alexander, 59, 70
Population, 397
Portable atlas of England and Wales, **117A**
Porter, R.H., **131L**
Portolan charts, 338
Post horses, **App V.15(x)**
Post Office directory, **115A–K**
Post Office map, **115A, 133A**
Powlet, William, Lord, **App V.2**
Practical guide to health and longevity, 246
Preswich, Professor, 283
Price, Charles, **28*,** 8, 46, plate 16
Price, Owen, **31(vi)**
Priestley, Joseph, 103, 137
Prima Europe tabula, xii
Prince of Wales, **57(ii)** and **(vi), 58(i)(ii),** 11n. 85
Prince Regent, **58(ii)**
Pringle, George, 174
Printed maps in the atlases of Great Britain and Ireland, see Chubb (1927)
Printed maps of Hertfordshire 1577–1900, see Hodson, 1974
Prior, John, xviii
Proceedings of the archaeological institute, **App III.14**
Proceedings of the British academy, 18n, 50n, 336n
Proceedings of the geological society, 281n, 284n
Proceedings of the royal geographical society, 313n
Proceedings of the royal society of medicine, 166n
Prospect of the most famous parts of the world, **8(ii)**
Provincial newspapers Society, 176, 277
Ptolemy, ix, xii, 15n, 76
Public record office, maps and plans in, xi
Publick Register, 70
Punch, 284

'Quartermaster's map', **App III.6,** 28, 37
Quérard, J.M., *La France littéraire* (1827), 169n, 410

Railway and road map of England and Wales (Stanford), see Derivatives
Railways, **App XI,** xxv, xxviii, xxxi, 175, 179, 391, 404
Railway maps, **61A–K, 68A–D, 88A, 155,** 259, 262, 319
Raistrick, A., *Yorkshire maps* (1969), 49n, 74n, 395n, 410
Ralegh, Walter, 16
Ramage, J., **123C–D**
Ramble, Reuben, **81A**

Rambles in the vicinity of Brighton, **76(i)(ii)**
Rand, Cator, 393n
Rapes, maps of, **App VII.4,** see also Boundaries
Ravenhill, W., *Norden's manuscript maps of Cornwall* (1972), 4, 4n, 13n, 389, 389n, 410
Rawlinson, R., *English topographer* (1720), 39, 39n, 387, 387n, 388n, 410
Rawnsley, J.E., *Maps of Yorkshire* (1970), 88n, 410
Ray, J.E., *Notes on local maps* (1936), 15n, 20n, 410
Rea, Roger, (elder and younger), **7(iv), 8(ii)(iii),** 21
Read, Conyers, xiv
Read, Thomas, **31***
Reading Mercury and Oxford gazette, 82
Ready guide and tourists' handbook, **88B**
Recommendations for bibliographical references to maps and charts, xxixn
Records of Buckinghamshire, 406
Records of the court of the stationers company, 401
Redistribution of Seats Act, 1885, **138B**
Redmayne, William, **16*,** 401, plate 6(iii)
Reduced Ordnance Survey round Brighton, 319
Rees, see Longman . . .
Reeves, see Hoare and Reeves
Reid, W.H., **78*,** see Derivatives
Relfe, Lupton, **84(i),** 166
Relief, **App VI.1(b),** 339, 400, see also Heights
Renshaw, **35(i)**
Reports from commissioners, **109, 138A, 146D**
Reprint of the first edition of the one inch Ordnance Survey, **App VI.1(a)**
Reproductions, xxxiii, xxxiiin
Reuben Ramble's travels, **81A**
Reynolds, James [and Sons], **117(i)–(iii), 117A–D,** 240
Reynolds, (Reynoldus), Nicholas (Nicolaus), 339, 340
Reynolds's geological atlas, **117(iii), 117A–D**
Reynolds's travelling atlas, **117(i)(ii)**
Richards, Philip, see Phillips, Richard
Richardson, Samuel, 60
Richmond, Duke of, see Lennox
Richmond, G., 319
Rickman, John, 398
Ridgway, Lucy, 177
Ripper, Jack the, 176
Rivers, **125, 125B,** xxx, 5
Rivington, Alexander, 64
Rivington, C., **25(i)(ii),** 21, 64
Rivington family, 64
Rivington, J.F. and C., **109,** 60
Rivington, John, 177
Rivington, S., *The publishing family of Rivington* (1919), 64n, 410
Road traverse, see Compass traverse
Road books, **112, App V., App VIII.2,** xviii
Roads, **1(vi), 118,** xvi, xxv, 43, 97, 97n, 98, 112, 178,

437

Wayland, H. and V., 53n, 54n
Wayland, Virginia, 41n
Web, William, **1(iii)**, **App III.7**, 7
Webb, **24(i)**, 61
Weekly dispatch [atlas], **121A**, 246
Weekly journal or Saturday's post, 61
Weinreb and Douwma, 76n, 78n
Weire, 93
Weller, Edward, **121B**, **124B and E**, **134***
Weller, F.S., **151***
Welu, J., see Schilder, G.
West, J., **141***
West-Grinstead et les Caryll, **148**
Weston, May, 314
Whiston, **35(i)**
Whitaker collection, **73(i)**, **App V.5(i)**, 11n
Whitaker, H., xxii, 11n
Whitaker, H., *Harold Whitaker collection* (1947), 155n, 171n, 411
Whitaker, H., *Maps of Northamptonshire* (1948), **72B**, **83(iv)**, **86**, xxxvii, 9n, 145n, 150n, 165n, 170n, 171n, 172n, 228n, 347n, 348n, 349n, 387n, 411
Whitaker, H., *Maps of Northumberland* (1949), xxxvii, 11n
Whitaker, Richard, **6(iii)**
Whitchurch, 93
White, M., 202
Whitridge, H., 74
Whittaker, G. and Co., **79(ii)**
Whittaker, G. and W.B., **67(iii)**, **79(ii)**
Whittaker, George B., **67(iii)**, **79(ii)**, 137, 160
Whittle and Laurie's new traveller's companion, **App V.15(iv)–(vi)**
Whittle, James, 106
Whittle, [James] and Laurie, [R.H.], **56(ii)(iii)**, **App V.15(iv)–(vi)**, see also Laurie and Whittle
Whitwell, Charles, 388
Whorlow, H., *Provincial newspaper society* (1886), 176n, 277n, 411
Who was who 1916–1928, 176n
W.H. Smith & Son's [Series of] reduced Ordnance map[s], **129B**, **E and K**
Wight (Weighte), see Isle of Wight
Wigstead, see Hooper and Wigstead, Hookham and Wigstead
Wild, J., 92
Wild, Joseph, **19(i)**
Wiles, R.M., *Serial publication . . .* (1957), 51, 70n, 73n, 411
Wilford, J., **25(ii)**
Wilkes, John, **91**, 188

Wilkinson, Robert, **35(ix)–(xi)**, **43(ii)(iii)**, 55, 134
Willdey, George, **1(viii)(ix)**, 7, 11n, 67
Willdey, Thomas, 11n
William, I., 7, 7n
Wilson, E., *The blue black chart* (1937), 68n, 411
Wiltshire, **27**, **61(vii)**, **App III.6(i) and 8**, 120, 406
Winchelsea, **35(i)**, 396
Winterbotham, H. St. L., *The national plans* (1934), 380n, 411
Witham and Maldon, **80**
Wolfe, Reynor, 3
Wolff, H., **142**
Wood, Anthony à, 39
Woodman, T., 353n
Woodward, B.B., **110(vii)**
Woodward, D., *Five centuries of map printing* (1975), 243n, 411
Woodward, H.B., 240
Worcestershire, 65n
Worthies of Sussex, see Lower, M.A. (1865)
Worthing, **App VI.3**, xxivn, xxxii, 284, 394, 395
Wright, see Houlston and Wright
Wright and Son, **103**, 211
Wright, C., **76(i)**
Wright, Charles, 211
Wright, Edward, 15
Wright, Henry, 283
Wright, John, **15**
Wyatt, G., *Maps of Buckinghamshire*, 406
W.T. Pike's district blue book, **App VIII.4**
Wyche, Peter, 54n
Wyld, James I., **57(vii)**, **58(ii)(iii)**, **70A**, **82(i)**, **92**, **108I**, 109, 112, 205n
Wyld, James II, 112
Wyld's atlas of English counties, **70A**
Wynne, Margaret, 176
Wynne, W., **App VI.2(c)**

Yeakell, Thomas (elder), **47***, **57***, xix, xx, xxv, xxxiiin, 49, 57, 393, 394, 396, 400, plates 19, 22, 23(ii)(iii), see Derivatives
Yeakell, Thomas (younger), **App VI.1(a)**, 93, 108
Yelverton, see Longville
York, Duke of, **42**, 37
Yorkshire, **83(iv)**, x, 11n, 49n, 74, 150n, 174, 215, 406
Young, Arthur, **55**, 105
Young, Arthur, *Agriculture of Sussex* (1793, 1970), **55**, 393, 398, 398n, 411
Youngman, P., **80**

Zirizaeus, Regnerus Vitellius, **5**